Physics of Semiconductor
Laser Devices

Physics of Semiconductor Laser Devices

G. H. B. Thompson

Standard Telecommunication Laboratories Limited, Harlow, Essex

A Wiley–Interscience Publication

JOHN WILEY & SONS

Chichester · New York · Brisbane · Toronto

British Library Cataloguing in Publication Data:

Thompson, G. H. B.
  Physics of semiconductor laser devices.
  1. Semiconductor lasers
  I. Title
  535.5'8   TA1700   79-41217

  ISBN 0 471 27685 5

Typeset by Preface Ltd, Salisbury, Wilts
Printed and bound in Great Britain
at The Pitman Press, Bath

Contents

Preface

In the fifteen or so years since its invention the semiconductor injection laser has evolved almost beyond recognition. From the original rather crude component based on a simple p–n junction it has grown and diversified into a whole range of sophisticated opto-electronic devices specifically designed for a variety of potentially important applications. The considerable amount of research that has been necessary to reach this position has also contributed greatly to the more general understanding of opto-electronic processes in semi-conductors and has generated much fruitful inter-disciplinary cross fertilization.

Recent years have seen a spate of new ideas in the semiconductor laser field and much re-assessment of older concepts. However, the flood now seems to be passing its peak. Although there is still no diminution in the rate at which new literature appears, one senses a change in emphasis. The present papers are directed mainly to describing the improved technological realization of known ideas rather than to putting forward new fundamental concepts. A period of consolidation and exploitation seems to be at hand. The semiconductor laser is now poised and ready for wide practical application in a number of fields, such as optical fibre communication, military systems, information read-out and printing. The near future should predominantly see a refinement of existing devices rather than a diversification, and the present seems a suitable time for making a critical survey of the more fundamental aspects of the subject.

This book deals specifically with the physics of the semiconductor laser. The basic phenomena that control the operation of the device are analysed and described in considerable detail. The treatment has been keyed particularly to fundamental concepts and kept general in order to avoid being overtaken by events. In the places where the mathematical formalism becomes cumbersome, and analytic methods fail, approximate methods have been employed in preference to computer simulation in order to give a broader picture and a better understanding. Curves have been used freely for presenting the information, frequently in normalized form for wider applicability. The range of phenomena in a semiconductor laser involve a number of scientific disciplines. To cater for the reader who is not already a specialist in all of these I have endeavoured, in the chapters on fundamental behaviour, to provide in a readable form the minimum background that is needed to understand the more specialized part of the text.

The plan of the book is as follows. The first part deals with fundamental principles. After an introduction in Chapter 1, Chapter 2 gives a full account of light emission in semiconductors. This starts with the Einstein emission/absorption relations, applied specifically to semiconductors, and with electron transition probabilities and leads up to an analysis of threshold current, incremental efficiency, and the spectral mode distribution in lasers. Chapter 3 deals with carrier injection processes at semiconductor heterojunctions and with the effect of temperature on carrier confinement. Chapter 4 deals with the processes by which light is confined within the very small dimensions of the semiconductor laser chip. Deliberate dielectric light-guides are provided for this purpose within the semiconductor and advantage is also taken of 'waveguiding by gain'. The principles of the dielectric light-guide are introduced briefly for the non-specialist using both ray and wave treatments and the results are applied generally to all types of heterostructure light-guide. More particular attention is applied to the alternative process of gain-guiding. This process, which is largely specific to semiconductor lasers and is seldom treated elsewhere, is analysed in considerable detail. The waveguide theory is also applied in treating the transverse modes of the laser resonator.

The second part of the book deals with specific characteristics of semiconductor lasers. The main topics comprise: the properties of the various broad contact heterostructure lasers in Chapter 5; a comprehensive discussion of 'stripe lasers' and their mode of operation in Chapter 6; dynamic characteristics of lasers in Chapter 7, including modulation, delay, stability, and noise; and distributed-feedback and distributed-Bragg-reflecting lasers in Chapter 8. In all these chapters the bulk of the examples refer to GaAs/(GaAl)As lasers because only these devices are at present sufficiently well characterized to give a good illustration of the general principles. The main subject matter, however, is much more general.

In order to provide a setting for the more analytical material in the rest of the book, Chapter 1 gives a general review of the whole contemporary field of semiconductor lasers and the associated technology. Not only are the different laser types and materials described but also their fabrication processes and the factors that control operating life. The possible future role of the semiconductor laser in integrated optics is also discussed. Particular applications are not, however, considered.

No attempt has been made to provide an exhaustive set of references to research papers or necessarily to note the first contribution in each field. The references that are supplied have been chosen both for the way in which they add to the general understanding of the subject and to complement the text in places where the reader may require additional information. Various review articles exist from which a more comprehensive list can be obtained.

I am indebted to many colleagues at STL and elsewhere who have helped me in the layout and preparation of this book. Especially I would like to thank J. E. A. Whiteaway, A. G. Steventon, J. E. Carroll, K. Unger, S. E. H. Turley, R. G. Plumb, and L. D. Westbrook for critical reading of the manuscript and useful suggestions. I am very grateful to the management at STL both for the facilities they have provided for laser research and for support during the preparation of the book. Particular thanks are due to F. Kerry for editing and correcting the material and to Mrs Cheryl Vaughan for typing the various versions of the text.

List of Principal Symbols

A	= amplitude of forward wave in corrugated waveguide
$[A]$	= $A \exp(-j\beta_b z)$
A_b	= forward wave component associated with backward wave component B in composite backward eigen solution for corrugated waveguide
A_{21}	= Einstein coefficient for rate of spontaneous transitions per unit volume per unit energy interval of $h\nu$
B	= $\{\pm(b^2 + 1)^{1/2} - b\}^{1/2}$ anti-focusing parameter
B	= (also) amplitude of backward wave in corrugated waveguide
$[B]$	= $B \exp(j\beta_b z)$
B_b	= backward wave component associated with forward wave component A in composite forward eigen solution for corrugated waveguide
$B_{21}(E_c, E_v)$	= Einstein coefficient for stimulated radiative transitions of electrons from energy E_c to E_v
C	= proportion of spontaneous emission coupled to lasing modes
D	= normalized width of centre layer of slab dielectric waveguide = $\beta_0 \delta \epsilon^{1/2} d$
D	= (also) diffusion coefficient of minority carriers
D	= (in Chapter 8) real part of eigen wave propagation coefficient β_e
E with subscripts x, y, etc.	= component of optical electric field

E	= energy of electron
E_c	= energy of electron in conduction band
E_v	= energy of hole in valence band
E_g	= energy interval of forbidden band-gap
E_t	= energy characterizing depth of band-tail
F	= photon flux per unit area
F	= (also) $\Delta\epsilon_f/\Delta\epsilon_m + 1$
F_x	= Fourier component of E_x
G	= stimulated emission per photon per mode
G'	= dG/dn = derivative of gain with respect to minority carrier concentration
G	= (in Chapter 8) imaginary component of eigen wave propagation coefficient β_e
H with subscripts x, y, etc.	= component of optical magnetic field
I	= current
I_{th}	= threshold current
J	= current density per unit volume (carriers per second)
J_c	= current density per unit area at contact
J_0	= threshold current density per unit area of wide laser
J_n	= nominal current density per unit area referred to standard thickness of 1 μm (or more generally thickness of d_n)
J_t	= current density per unit volume that gives zero gain
J_{th}	= threshold current density per unit volume
J_{th0}	= threshold current density per unit volume of very long laser
K	= degrees Kelvin
K_0	= wave vector of corrugation in corrugated guide
L	= length of laser
L	= (also) dynamic diffusion length
L_s	= screening length

M	$= \frac{1}{2} \times$ effective number of longitudinal modes in gain spectrum
M	$=$ (also) matrix element of momentum operator for calculating radiative transition probabilities
M_{bb}	$=$ band-to-band matrix element
M_{bi}	$=$ band-to-impurity matrix element
N	$=$ total number of possible optical modes in laser cavity over effective spectral width of gain
N_A	$=$ acceptor concentration
N_D	$=$ donor concentration
P	$=$ normalized transverse optical decay coefficient $(=p/\delta\epsilon^{1/2}\beta_0)$
Q	$=$ normalized transverse optical propagation coefficient $(=q/\delta\epsilon^{1/2}\beta_0)$
R	$=$ normalized transverse optical decay coefficient $(=r/\delta\epsilon^{1/2}\beta_0)$
R	$=$ (also) reflection coefficient for optical intensity
R	$=$ (also) radius of curvature of wavefront
R_{eff} R_{e1}, R_{e2}, etc.	$=$ effective reflection coefficient of composite eigen waves in corrugated waveguides
S	$=$ normalized effective width of optical distribution in slab dielectric waveguide $(=\beta_0\delta\epsilon^{1/2}s)$
S	$=$ (also) normalized effective width of gain distribution in parabolic guide $(=s/(2n+1)|B|s_0)$
S_{eff}	$=$ normalized effective width of optical distribution in parabolic guide $(=s_{eff}/(2n+1)|B|s_0)$
S_1	$= s/(2n+1)s_0$
T	$=$ absolute temperature
T_{12}	$=$ transmission coefficient of composite eigen waves in corrugated waveguides
V	$=$ volume
V	$=$ (also) voltage
X	$=$ normalized position co-ordinate $(=y\delta\epsilon^{1/2}\beta_0)$

Y = normalized admittance

Y_0 = characteristic admittance of free space

Z = characteristic impedance of free space

Z = (also) density of optical modes per unit volume per unit spectral bandwidth

a = coefficient for describing intensity distribution in guide with parabolic distribution of dielectric constant $(= \exp(-a/x^2))$

a = (also) $2\pi/w$

a_1 and a_2 = real and imaginary parts of a

b = ratio of real to imaginary part of dielectric constant due to injected carriers

c = velocity of light

d = thickness of active layer of heterostructure

e = electronic charge

f = shape factor of optical distribution (Chapter 7)

f_c = fractional occupation of states in conduction band

f_v = fractional occupation of states in valence band

f_r = ringing frequency in transient oscillation

g = electrical conductivity

g = (also) gain coefficient per unit length of optical intensity, except in Chapter 8 where g is the amplitude rather than intensity gain coefficient

g_z = mode gain at threshold

g_m = peak gain at centre of stripe

g_+ = positive contribution to mode gain g_z

g_- = negative contribution to mode gain g_z

h = Planck's constant, $\hbar = h/2\pi$

h = (also) $\Delta\epsilon_m/\Delta\epsilon_z - 1$

$\mathbf{k}$ = wave-vector, particularly for electron wave-function

$\mathbf{k}_c$ = wave-vector of electron in conduction band

$\mathbf{k}_v$	= wave-vector of hole in valence band
k	= coupling coefficient for region of gain in slab-dielectric waveguide
k	= (also) coupling coefficient per unit length in corrugated guide
l	= diffusion length of injected carriers
l_s	= spreading length in stripe laser
l_{eff}	= effective diffusion length (due to diffusion + spreading)
l'	= l_{eff}/s_1
m	= longitudinal mode number
m_{eff}	= effective number of longitudinal modes $\times \frac{1}{2}$
m_{eff}	= (also) effective mass of carrier
m_c	= effective mass of electron
m_v	= effective mass of hole
n	= electron concentration
n	= (also) number of transverse mode perpendicular to junction
n_{th}	= electron concentration at threshold
n_0, n_1	= (in dynamic analysis) steady state and oscillatory components of n
n_m	= maximum effective concentration of one type of carrier with which a carrier of the opposite type can recombine
p	= hole concentration
p	= (also) transverse decay constant for electric field in outer layer of dielectric slab waveguide
q	= transverse propagation constant for electric field in centre layer of dielectric slab waveguide
q	= (also) transverse mode number in junction plane
r	= radial position co-ordinate
r	= (also) transverse decay constant for electric field in outer layer of lower dielectric constant in asymmetric dielectric-slab waveguide
r_{stim}	= net rate of stimulated emission per unit volume per unit bandwidth

r_{spon}	= rate of spontaneous emission per unit volume per unit bandwidth
s	= effective width of optical distribution in dielectric-slab waveguide
s	= (also) width of gain distribution in gain guide
s	= (in Chapter 8) ratio of backward to forward wave amplitude in eigen solutions for corrugated waveguide
s_{eff}	= width to $1/e^2$ points of optical intensity in Gaussian distribution and $1/\cosh^u$ distributions of optical intensity
s_0	= characteristic gain-guide dimension ($= 1/\beta_0 \Delta \epsilon_z^{1/2}$)
s_1	= characteristic gain-guide dimension modified for antiguiding and slope of gain/current characteristic ($= \beta^{1/2} B s_0$)
s_2	= characteristic gain-guide dimension further modified to take diffusion into account ($= (4 l_{eff} s_1 / 3)^{1/2}$)
t	= time
t	= (also) thickness of layer of heterostructure in which current spreading occurs in stripe lasers
t_d	= delay time for laser switch on
u	= coefficient for describing field distribution in guide with $\cosh^{-2}$ distribution of dielectric constant
u_1 and u_2	= real and imaginary parts of u
$u(r)$	= Bloch function of crystal lattice
w	= width of stripe
w_0	= width of Gaussian beam at waist
w_0	= (also) fictional width of stripe for evaluating peak injected carrier concentration in terms of current
w_{eff}	= fictional width of stripe for evaluating threshold current in terms of threshold current density of broad laser
w'	= w/s_1
w_{stim}	= rate of stimulated emission per photon per mode ($= r_{stim}/\phi$)
w_{spon}	= rate of spontaneous emission per mode
$\left.\begin{array}{c} x \\ y \\ z \end{array}\right\}$	= (mainly) position co-ordinates

z_f	= position of virtual waist of Gaussian emitted beam behind front face of stripe laser
Γ	= spreading or 'dilution' factor for gain in centre layer of slab-dielectric waveguide
$\Delta\epsilon_f$	= imaginary part of dielectric constant of unpumped semi-conductor far from centre of stripe. However, for parabolic transverse distribution of dielectric constant a nominal value of $\Delta\epsilon_f$ is defined at arbitrary points $s/2$ from centre of distribution
$\Delta\epsilon_m$	= maximum or minimum value of imaginary part of dielectric constant at centre of transverse distribution
$\Delta\epsilon_z$	= imaginary part of effective dielectric constant of guided mode (corresponds to mode gain with $\Delta\epsilon_z = g_z/2\beta_z$)
Λ	= corrugation length in corrugated waveguide
Λ_b	= wave length for Bragg reflection in corrugated waveguide (multivalued)
Φ	= normalized emission angle of output wave ($= \sin\theta/\delta\epsilon^{1/2}$)
$\Phi_{1/2}$	= normalized half angle of emission ($= \sin\theta_{1/2}\delta\epsilon^{1/2}$)
α	= optical absorption coefficient per unit length (intensity)
β	= $(1 - J_t/J_{th})$ for describing steepness of gain/current characteristic
β	= (also) wave propagation coefficient
β	= (also) coefficient for obtaining recombination rate from product of electron and hole concentration
β_o	= propagation coefficient in free space
β_b	= Bragg wave vector for corrugated waveguide
β_e	= propagation coefficient for composite eigen wave solution for corrugated waveguide
β_z	= propagation coefficient along z axis (axis of waveguide)
γ	= $w_{spon}(\max)/w_{stim}(\max)$
γ	= (also) ratio of dielectric constant of built-in waveguide to imaginary dielectric constant due to gain (Chapter 6)
δ	= phase error per unit length between propagation coefficient of guided wave and Bragg wave-vector in corrugated waveguide

δ_m = spontaneous emission rate in photons per unit volume in mode m

ϵ = dielectric constant

ϵ_0 = permittivity of free space

ϵ_1 = real part of ϵ (or dielectric constant in region 1)

ϵ_2 = imaginary part of ϵ (or dielectric constant in region 2)

ϵ_{eff} = effective dielectric constant of slab waveguide $(=\beta_z^2/\beta_0^2)$

ϵ_z = effective dielectric constant of guide in junction plane

ζ = $D_1 l_2/D_2 l_1$ to determine transverse distribution of injected carriers

η = $(\epsilon_1 - \epsilon_3)^{1/2}/(\epsilon_1 - \epsilon_2)^{1/2}$ to describe symmetry of slab waveguide

η = (also) external incremental quantum efficiency

η_0 = internal incremental quantum efficiency

η_{sp} = internal spontaneous quantum efficiency

θ = angle or phase

$\theta_{1/2}$ = half angle of emitted beam to half intensity points

θ_0 = angle to the normal of far-field peak for waveguide with $\cosh^{-2}$ distribution of dielectric constant

λ = wavelength

λ_b = Bragg wavelength

λ_0 = wavelength in free space

μ = refractive index

$\bar{\mu}$ = $\mu + E d\mu/dE = \mu - \lambda d\mu/d\lambda$ = refractive index modified for dispersion (i.e. group refractive index)

μ_0 = permeability of free space

ν = frequency

ξ = $(J/J_{\text{th}} - 1)/\beta$

ρ = (Chapter 7) shape factor of current distribution

ρ = density of electronic states per unit energy interval

ρ_c = density of electronic states for conduction band

ρ_v = density of electronic states for valence band

ρ_{red} = $\frac{1}{2}(1/\rho_c + 1/\rho_v)^{-1}$ (applying to states with one spin direction only)

σ = photon lifetime in resonant cavity

τ = lifetime of minority carrier

τ_1 = damping time constant for oscillatory modulation

τ_{tr} = damping time constant for envelope of transient oscillation

ϕ = phase angle

ϕ = (also) photon density per mode in laser resonator

ϕ_0 = steady state component of ϕ (in dynamic analysis)

ϕ_1 = oscillatory component of ϕ (in dynamic analysis)

ψ_1 = wave-function of electronic state in valence band

ψ_2 = wave-function of electronic state in conduction band

ω = angular frequency

ω_0 = resonant angular frequency of laser modulation.

CHAPTER 1

Introduction and Background

1.1 INTRODUCTORY REMARKS

The semiconductor laser is now approaching maturity after a relatively long period of development. The original concept dates from 1961, when Basov *et al.*[1] suggested that stimulated emission of photons could be produced in semiconductors by the recombination of carriers injected across a p–n junction. The first working devices came into existence in 1962 when successful operation at low temperature was announced almost simultaneously by three groups of workers in the US,[2–5] only three years after Maiman[6] demonstrated the first operating laser of any type—the ruby laser—and two years after the first gas laser was demonstrated.[7] However, despite being only a little younger than the other types of laser the semiconductor laser has lagged considerably behind them in its development and has taken a longer time to come of age.

The slower maturing of the semiconductor laser has been partly due to the specific problems commonly associated with developing a new semiconductor technology. It is also bound up with the particular nature of the device. Stimulated emission in semiconductors is more intense, for a given degree of inversion, than in virtually any other laser material. Special efforts have therefore had to be made to accommodate the high rates of energy generation and heat dissipation that occur. In the course of this development the semiconductor laser has had to undergo a very considerable metamorphosis, and it now bears little resemblance to the device first operated in 1962. The simple p–n junction has been discarded and has been replaced by a heterostructure containing several semiconductor layers of different compositions. Heterostructures were first introduced in 1969[8–10] when they had an immediate impact on device performance. They were further developed and improved in the ensuing years.[11,12] The result of this radical redesign was to change the semiconductor laser from a specialist device operating only at cryogenic temperatures into a practical and efficient component capable of running continuously at room temperature.

One further factor has probably been necessary to bring the semiconductor laser to maturity. This has been the advent of an important new application that sets considerable demands on device performance. The application concerned is the use of the laser as a signal source in optical fibre communication systems. To provide a device which performs satisfactorily for such a purpose it has been necessary to investigate a wide variety of performance characteristics and to modify and improve them in the appropriate ways. Particular emphasis has been placed on the reliability of the laser, its reproducibility, and the length of its operating life. As a result the general usefulness of the device has been vastly improved and it should soon find employment in a variety of other applications.

1.2   REVIEW OF LASER DESIGN AND DEVELOPMENT

The first injection lasers consisted of chips of GaAs of rectangular shape into which a planar p–n junction was diffused. The external appearance of such a laser is illustrated in Figure 1.1(a). The figure shows the GaAs chip bonded to a metal base with a wire contact applied to the top. The chip has smooth cleaved end-faces, out of which the light is emitted, and rough sawn sides. The position of the p–n junction and the direction of light emission is shown in Figure 1.1(b). The passage of current through the contact causes minority carriers, particularly electrons, to be injected across the p–n junction into a region approximately a diffusion length thick where they recombine with the majority carriers. Stimulated emission starts to occur in this region when the current density is raised to a sufficient level. Because of the high refractive index of the GaAs the end-faces of the chip possess a considerable reflectivity and form a Fabry–Perot resonator. This resonator is excited into laser oscillation, approximately over the thickness of the region where the injected carriers recombine, when the current is raised above a certain value known as the 'threshold'. Because of the high rate of stimulated emission possible in semiconductors the length of the Fabry–Perot resonator may be made much smaller than in most other lasers, a length of between 0.2 and 1 mm being suitable.

The threshold current density in the simple p–n junction semiconductor laser described above is very high, particularly if it is not cooled below room temperature, lying in the range 35–100 kA/cm^2. This high value is mainly a fundamental property of the semiconductor and results from the high density of electron states in the conduction and valence bands (see Chapter 2). However, in the simple structure that we have described the current density is increased even further (a) because there is no very satisfactory means of keeping the light confined to the region where the inversion is created, and (b) because the inversion region is not precisely defined but tails away in the direction in which the carriers diffuse.

Figure 1.1(a) Broad-contact semiconductor laser mounted on heat sink, with lead wire. Scanning electron micrographs showing complete laser chip and detail of cleaved end-face and sawn sidewalls. Pictures taken with current passing so that position of p-n junction is delineated by spontaneous electroluminescent output

At a relatively early stage in the development of the semiconductor laser Kroemer[13] and Alferov and Kazarinov[14] suggested that both the above shortcomings of the laser could be remedied by incorporating into the device, on each side of the GaAs inversion layer, an additional layer composed of a semiconductor with a higher band-gap. Such a structure provides a means of confining the injected carriers entirely within the active layer and also of confining the light substantially to the same region. The injected carriers are confined by the potential barriers that exist at the higher band-gap interface and the light is confined by the waveguide that is created by the higher refractive index of the lower band-gap layer, as described in Chapter 3. The necessary inverse relation between band-gap and refractive index occurs with very few exceptions over almost the whole range of III/V mixed semiconductors, which are predominantly used for injection lasers (see Section 1.3). These multilayer laser structures have been called 'heterostructures' and, for distinguishing purposes, the original simple p–n structure has been renamed a 'homostructure'. The particular advantages of the heterostructure are (a) that a waveguide is created, (b) that the active region can be made much thinner than in the homostructure, and (c) that the concentration of carriers injected into it is much more uniform.

The potential improvement in laser performance which the heterostructure might be expected to provide cannot be achieved without the use of 'heterojunctions' of near-ideal electrical characteristics. The properties of a heterojunction are determined mainly by its crystalline perfection and one necessary criterion that must be satisfied for satisfactory performance is that the crystal lattice dimensions of the two constituent semiconductors should be very similar. The combination of GaAs with the mixed semiconductor $GaAs_{1-x}P_x$ that was used for the first heterostructures[15] was inadequate in this respect and the resulting crystalline defects at the heterojunctions introduced an excessive amount of non-radiative recombination of injected carriers. In 1967 Woodall et al.[16] demonstrated that $Ga_{1-x}Al_xAs$ could be successfully grown by liquid phase epitaxy (LPE) on a GaAs substrate and that the lattice match with GaAs was excellent. This work prompted three separate groups, namely Alferov et al.[8,12] Kressel et al.,[9] and Panish and Hayashi[10] to fabricate heterostructure lasers using the GaAs/(GaAl)As system. These devices performed well. Threshold current density was lowered by stages as the heterostructures were developed and eventually lasers were made which would operate continuously at room temperature.[11,12]

Various types of heterostructure have been developed for optimizing different aspects of laser performance. By varying the number and dimensions of the different layers it has been possible to obtain, for instance, either particularly low threshold current density or much reduced

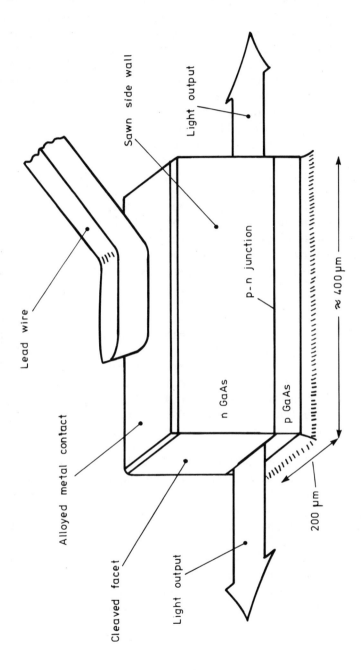

Figure 1.1(b) Broad-contact semiconductor laser mounted on heat sink, with lead wire. Schematic diagram of laser to same scale as micrograph in Figure 1.1(a) to indicate various particular features

divergence of the emergent beam or an emission area at the facet that is considerably extended in the direction perpendicular to the junction. The latter characteristics is relevant in maximizing the peak output power when facet damage is the limiting factor. The different heterostructures and the performance that can be obtained from them are described in detail in Chapter 5. Of the various structures the most widely used are the single heterostructure and the double heterostructure. The former has one layer of higher band-gap material adjoining the active layer and is used particularly for high peak-power applications. The latter has the active layer sandwiched between two layers of higher band-gap material and is used for low current continuous working.

In most semiconductor lasers it is also important to limit the spread of injected carriers and the spread of the lasing emission in the plane parallel to the junction, and for this purpose the operating current has to be confined to a narrow stripe aligned along the axis of the laser. The necessary insulation to block the flow of current outside the stripe can be incorporated in a variety of ways leading to a range of different possible devices. A simple design using SiO_2 insulation is illustrated in Figure 1.2. These devices are classified under the general name of stripe-geometry structures. The performance of the different structures is found to differ in various subtle yet significant respects, and a considerable amount of detailed investigation has had to be carried out to understand the behaviour. The precise form of the transverse distribution of stimulated emission in the junction plane plays an important part in determining the width of the lasing filament and the threshold condition, The factors involved are treated in Chapter 4, Section 4.2. Other effects that depend on small changes in refractive index are also important and can affect the stability of the optical distribution. The different types of stripe-geometry laser are described in Chapter 6, where their performance is also discussed in detail. The development of the stripe laser has been of particular significance in the successful application of semiconductor lasers in optical communication systems.

The semiconductor laser can be efficiently modulated by direct variation of the current up to high frequencies, the practical limit lying around 2 GHz. In this respect it is much superior to other types of laser which will not respond nearly so rapidly to modulation of their pump supply. The direct modulation capability of semiconductor lasers is very useful for application in communications systems, and it has therefore become important to understand the mechanism and its limitations. Basically the process involves an interaction in the laser resonator between the injected carriers and the photon population. This interaction is described in detail in Chapter 7 for the two cases of sinusoidal and step-function drive. In certain conditions the spectrum of the laser is affected by the modulation. This particularly applies when the laser is either operated only slightly

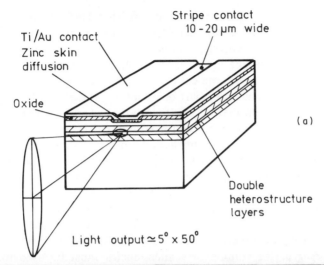

Stripe contact
10 - 20 μm wide

Ti /Au contact

Zinc skin
diffusion

Oxide

(a)

Double
heterostructure
layers

Light output ≃ 5° x 50°

(b)

Figure 1.2 Oxide-insulated GaAs/(GaAl)As double heterostructure stripe laser. (a) Schematic diagram of laser showing heterostructure, oxide insulation, metallic contact, and Zn skin diffusion for improved contact characteristics. (b) Scanning electron micrograph of mounted stripe laser. Both end facets and side-walls of chip are created by cleaving

above threshold or is pulsed from below threshold. Many longitudinal modes are then excited. This behaviour is also treated in Chapter 7. A related subject to the current modulation of lasers is the noise or the fluctuation that is present in the laser output. The source of the noise is the shot modulation of the optical drive to the laser due to the individual photon interactions. The latter part of Chapter 7 is devoted to this subject.

Much work has been carried out to produce a more sophisticated laser resonator than the simple Fabry–Perot structure. The motivation has either been to obtain better mode control or to make a structure that is more easily incorporated in an integrated optical assembly. To obtain superior mode control the laser chip can be made part of an external cavity using one or two mirrors in a suitable optical system, often in conjunction with anti-reflection coatings on the laser end-face. To some extent the need for such external cavities has now diminished since mode control in conventional stripe geometry Fabry–Perot cavities has improved. However, where a larger active volume of semiconductor must be used than in the normal stripe laser, as in high peak power systems, external cavities still have an application. It is also possible that external cavities will prove useful for narrowing the linewidth of individual modes and generally stabilizing the wavelength of the semiconductor laser so that it may be used in holographic applications where a long coherence length is required.

An alternative form of laser resonator can be made which uses an optical grating incorporated into the multilayer structure to perform the function of the normal end reflectors. Such gratings can be used in slightly different configurations, in so-called distributed feedback lasers and distributed Bragg reflection lasers, respectively. These lasers are described in detail in Chapter 8 and their mode of operation is discussed. In such laser designs the multilayer structure may be further adapted to enable passive output guides to be fabricated which may be used to direct the light to various other integrated optical components. At the present time only very simple devices of this type have been made. We briefly describe some of them later in this chapter.

1.3 SEMICONDUCTOR MATERIALS FOR LASERS

A large number of semiconductor materials, in addition to GaAs, have been used for making injection lasers. The main aim in investigating the use of different materials has been to extend the range of wavelengths that may be produced. The various materials that have so far been made to lase, both in the form of simple p–n junction lasers (homostructure) and as heterostructures, are listed in Table 1.1, together with their emission wavelength. The wavelengths that have been obtained cover a very considerable range from 0.59 μm for (GaIn)P[17] at the short end to around

Table 1.1 Examples of lasers using various III/V and IV/VI mixed semiconductors in the active layer

| Material | | Substrate | | | | | |
Active layer	Passive layer	Material	Lattice match	Laser type	λ (μm)	J_{th} (A cm^{-2})	Ref.
Ga$_{1-x}$Al$_x$As	Ga$_{1-y}$Al$_y$As	GaAs	Yes	DH	0.9–0.7	10^3–10^4	34
(GaIn)P	—	GaAs	No	Hom	0.59	>10^4 (77 K)	17
Ga(AsP)	(GaIn)P	GaAs	No	DH	0.70	3.4 × 10^{13}	33
(GaIn)(AsP)	InP	InP	Yes	DH	1.15–1.65	1–2 × 10^3	21, 22
Ga(AsSb)	(GaAl)(AsSb)	GaAs	No	DH	1.0	2 × 10^3	26
(GaAl)Sb	(GaAl)(AsSb)	GaSb	Yes	DH	1.35	≃2 × 10^3	23
(GaIn)(AsSb)	(GaAl)(AsSb)	GaSb	Yes	DH	1.80	5 × 10^3	96
(PbSn)Te	—	PbTe	No	Hom	Up to 28	≃150 (12 K)	18
					Up to 15	≃ 5 × 10^3 (77 K)	18
(PbSn)Se	—	PbSe	No	Hom	Up to 34	≃150 (12 K)	18
(PbSn)Te	PbTe	PbTe	No	DH	8–15	6–20 × 10^3 (70–110 K)	40
Pb(SSe)	PbSe	Pb(SSe)	No	SH	5	10^3–10^4 (20–90 K)	36
(PbSn)Se	PbSe	(PbSn)Se	No	SH	11	≃10^4 (90 K)	36

30 μm for (PbSn)Te at the long end.[18] However, the range where c.w. operation at room temperature is at present possible is much more restricted, lying between 0.7 and 1.67 μm.

The semiconductor material used in the active layer of an injection laser must have a direct gap. As explained in Chapter 2, only materials with a direct gap exhibit sufficiently strong radiative recombination to produce satisfactory stimulated emission. None of the normal elemental semiconductors is direct-gap but there are a considerable number of binary compounds that are. In addition it is possible to produce direct-gap semiconductors which cover a continuous variation of band-gap by employing solid solutions between the different binaries.

The most important set of binary compounds are the so-called III/Vs. These comprise compounds between one of the group III elements—Al, Ga, or In—and one of the group V elements—P, As, or Sb. Of these all except GaP and the three compounds of Al (AlP, AlAs, and AlSb) are direct-gap and have been made to lase, at least as homostructure lasers, in the pure binary form. Various ternaries and quaternaries have also been made to lase, including those containing a proportion of GaP or of the Al compounds, such as Ga(AsP) and (GaAl)As, which are also direct-gap materials up to a certain limiting composition.

Heterostructure lasers of these materials have been investigated with a variety of compositions for the active layer. The design has in general followed that developed for the GaAs/(GaAl)As system, with mixed solid solutions of different III/V compounds being used to obtain the appropriate characteristics for the different heterostructure layers. However, in contrast to (GaAl)As there are no other three-component (ternary) solid solutions whose lattice constants do not vary appreciably with composition. Instead, four-component (quaternary) solid solutions are necessary. The quaternaries provide an extra degree of freedom for attaining lattice match. It is no longer necessary that the substituent atoms should be the same size as those that they replace, only that one of the substituent atoms should be smaller and the other should be larger. Then the proportions of the two substituents can be adjusted so that the lattice constant stays the same as the composition is changed. Careful experiment is necessary to find the correct proportions, but once they are found the reproducibility that can be obtained in the preparation of these materials is as good as for the (GaAl)As/GaAs system.

Figure 1.3 shows the relationship between the lattice constant and the band-gap in a number of ternary solid solutions of III/V compounds. This is a useful diagram for showing the range of band-gaps that can be obtained without altering the lattice constant by changing the composition of the solid solution. The behaviour of the quaternaries can be interpolated from the behaviour of the ternaries and corresponds to the region contained

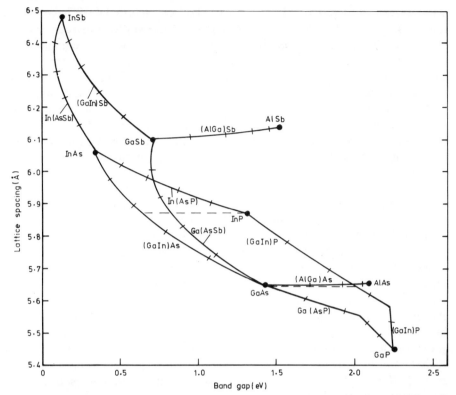

Figure 1.3 Relationship between band gap and lattice spacing in a number of mixed III/V semiconductors containing ternary combinations of Al, Ga, In and P, As, and Sb

within the four-sided figure the corners of which represent the four possible pure binary compounds.

As an example let us consider the important (GaIn)(AsP) system. The four corners of the figure concerned represent, respectively, InAs, InP, GaAs, and GaP and the four sides represent the solid solutions (GaIn)As, In(AsP), (GaIn)P, and Ga(AsP). In all epitaxial growth of layers of a semiconductor it is necessary to start with a substrate wafer and in general it is preferable that the material in the layers is chosen to match the lattice constant of the substrate. In the present quaternary system only the two pure binaries with intermediate lattice constants, i.e. GaAs and InP, provide substrates on which a range of lattice matched compositions may be grown. Reference to Figure 1.3 shows that on a GaAs substrate higher band-gap material may be grown, terminating with the maximum band-gap of $Ga_{0.50}In_{0.50}P$ (lying on a horizontal straight line), and that on an InP substrate lower band-gap quaternary material may be grown, terminating with lowest band-gap of $Ga_{0.47}In_{0.53}As$. Heterostructure lasers have been made using both the above systems. Those on the GaAs substrate largely repeat the behaviour of (GaAl)As lasers but involve a more complicated growth process.[19,20] Of more practical interest is the second system which uses the quaternary compound for the active layer of the laser and can produce emission wavelengths in the range from around $1.1\,\mu m$ (sufficiently greater than the InP wavelength of $0.92\,\mu m$ for InP passive layers to give a satisfactory heterostructure) up to $1.67\,\mu m$ which corresponds to the $Ga_{0.47}In_{0.53}As$ ternary. At the time of writing satisfactory operation at room temperature has been obtained between wavelenths of 1.15 and 1.67 μm.[21,22]

GaSb can also be used as a lattice matched substrate for quaternary layers of (GaAl) (AsSb) and (GaIn) (AsSb). These systems can potentially cover the wavelength ranges $1.3\text{–}1.7\,\mu m$ and $1.7\text{–}4.4\,\mu m$, using (GaAl) (AsSb) in both cases for the passive layers. They have been successfully operated between 1.3 and 1.4 μm[23] and at 1.8 μm[96].

Work has also been carried out on the system Ga(AsSb)/(GaAl)(AsSb), which is not lattice matched to any pure III/V material.[24–26] In this work GaAs was used as the substrate and composition grading was employed in the initial growth to suppress the incidence of mismatch dislocations. The heterostructure lasers that were produced had good performance but it is probable that the grading was not sufficiently effective to make the devices reliable and long lived. At present lattice matching appears to be necessary in the III/V compounds to produce lasers with a generally satisfactory performance in practical use.

The shortest wavelengths at which any of the III/V semiconductor lasers can be made to operate lie at the long wavelength end of the visible spectrum. The very shortest wavelengths have been obtained with homojunction lasers at low temperature in pulsed operation. The lower limit for these lasers is determined by the approach of the direct/indirect transition. When the composition brings the operation too close to this point excessive non-radiative transitions occur and lasing becomes impossible. With heterostructure lasers the minimum wavelengths achieved at room temperature are somewhat longer both because at higher temperature the band-gap of the materials decreases and also because heterostructure lasers suffer additional limitations. Specifically, the need in these lasers to provide lattice matched passive layers of higher band-gap does not allow such a wide choice of active layer composition.

Let us consider the values of the band-gap, and the associated wavelength, at which the direct/indirect transition (cross-over) occurs in several of the III/V semiconductors (see, for example, Figure 3.9 in Chapter 3). The materials with the highest value for cross-over are, in order: (AlIn)P, 2.33 eV (5320 Å);[27] (GaIn)P, 2.25 eV (5510 Å);[28] (AlIn)As,

2.04 eV (6080 Å);[29] and (GaAl)As[30] and (GaAs)P,[31] 1.97 eV (6290 Å). At cross-over by far the greater proportion of the conduction electrons are contained in the indirect band because the density of states of these electrons is so much greater than that of the electrons in the direct band. The figure is around 98 per cent. The electrons in the indirect band do not take part in radiative transitions and hence cannot contribute to lasing. They mainly introduce additional non-radiative recombination and therefore add greatly to the lasing threshold, although a proportion may return to the direct band before recombining. Lasing is possible in these materials up to a composition where the direct band still lies about 0.15 eV below the indirect band. In such compositions not only are electrons largely excluded from the indirect band but also from the deep donor levels that usually accompany the indirect band. Hence, the lasing threshold is only somewhat raised above the normal level.

The shortest wavelength that has been obtained in any III/V injection laser is 5900 Å in a homojunction (GaIn)P laser at 77 K.[17] A further reduction in wavelength should in principle be possible with this ternary material but in practice there are problems in obtaining a sufficiently high p-doping.

(GaIn)P cannot be conveniently employed in the active layer of a double heterostructure laser. As shown in Figure 1.3 there is no suitable III/V compound which can be used in conjunction with it to form the confinement layers. (GaIn)P can itself be used for the confinement layers in conjunction with (GaAs)P in the active layer.[32,22] However, a combination which is much more convenient than (GaAs)P/(GaIn)P and is little inferior to it uses two compositions of (GaAl)As, one just below the cross-over composition for the active layer and the other considerably above it for the passive layer. The typical threshold current density that can be obtained from such a composition in a broad contact laser at room temperature is plotted in Figure 1.4 as a function of the AlAs content x of the active layer. Threshold starts to rise for x greater than 0.16 (<7700 Å) and increases by a factor of about 10 for $x = 0.28$ (6900 Å). The shortest wavelength that has been obtained c.w. from a stripe laser of this material is 7140 Å.[35]

In addition to the III/V compounds the II/VI and IV/VI compounds produce semiconductors with direct band-gaps. Of the II/VI compounds only CdTe has been successfully used for a laser (homostructure device). The other II/VI compounds of Cd and the II/VI compounds of Zn cannot be doped to form a p–n junction and are therefore not suitable for injection lasers.

The IV/VI semiconductors of interest for injection lasers comprise the Pb salts of S, Se, and Te, their mixed solid solutions amongst themselves, and also the mixed solid solutions with the corresponding in Sn salts of Se

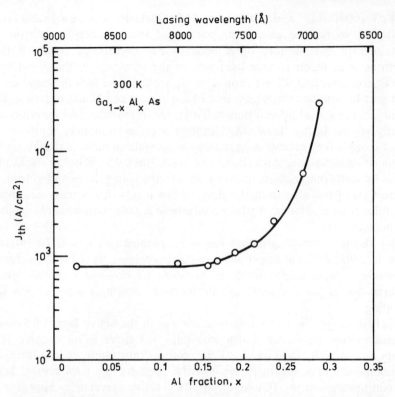

Figure 1.4 Room temperature threshold current density of broad contact double-heterojunction $Ga_{1-x}Al_xAs$ lasers as a function of composition x. Lasing wavelength also shown. $Ga_{0.4}Al_{0.6}As$ passive layers doped with 10^{19} cm^{-3} Zn and $1-2 \times 10^{18}$ cm^{-3} Te. From Kressel and Hawrylo[34]

and Te. These Pb salts are direct-band-gap semiconductors, although they differ from the other direct-gap materials in that the minima in the conduction band and the maxima in the valence band both occur at the L points (non-zero k) rather than the Γ point (zero k) as in the III/V materials (see Chapter 2). The Sn salts have negative band-gaps, i.e. there is an overlap between the conduction and the valence bands. Since there is a continuous variation of properties in the (PbSn)Se and (PbSn)Te solid solutions it is possible by appropriate choice of Sn content to obtain band-gaps ranging from that of the pure materials (0.17 eV for PbSe and 0.22 eV for PbTe at 77 K) down to zero (the point of band inversion). For (PbSn)Te a zero band-gap at 77 K occurs for an Sn content of approximately 40 per cent. Using material close to the zero band-gap, homojunction lasers have been made to operate out to 34 μm with (PbSn)Se and to 28 μm with (PbSn)Te. These results were obtained at temperatures of 12 K.[18]

Heterostructure lasers have been made in the Pb(SSe), the (PbSn)Se,[36] and the (PbSn)Te systems[37-39] using composition variations of the ternary to give the appropriate layers. These systems are not lattice matched. The effect of the mismatch is not fully known although it is possible that it is not so deleterious as in the wider band-gap materials because the defect states may not lie to the same extent within the band-gap. None of the lasers from Pb salts has so far operated above the cryogenic range of temperature and the maximum operating temperatures reported in the case of the heterostructure lasers have been 100 K using (PbSn)Se at 8.6 μm[36] and 114 K using (PbSn)Te.[40]

The reason why the long wavelength Pb salt lasers require so much cooling is not fully understood. At least two factors are involved. First, there is the optical absorption due to free carriers. This increases approximately as the square of the wavelength. Secondly, there is the non-radiative recombination of carriers via the Auger interaction.[95] In this process the recombination energy of the injected carriers is dissipated in raising the thermal energy of the remaining free carriers. The probability of such a process occurring increases as the band-gap of the semiconductor is reduced. Both of these effects become more important at higher temperature because of the higher concentration of free carriers. They tend to raise the carrier concentration at threshold to even higher levels. The feedback that occurs can create a temperature ceiling above which lasing is not possible. However, no quantitative analysis has been carried out to determine how well this explanation applies to the behaviour actually observed.

1.4   PROBLEMS OF DEVICE FABRICATION

Before treating the physics of the semiconductor laser in its various forms, which is the main subject of this book, it is perhaps helpful to enlarge the perspective by briefly describing the fabrication of the laser including the materials growth and also commenting on the present status of the laser as a reliable and practicable component. Considerable problems are naturally encountered in both the preparation of the very perfect single crystal material needed for the laser, in the fabrication of the laser chip with its small dimensions and close tolerances, and in the execution of all these operations with sufficient care and precision to produce long-lived and reliable devices with satisfactory performance. To overcome the problems it has been necessary for technology and physics to advance hand in hand, and the new concepts that have been introduced have had to be continuously modified to satisfy the exigencies of fabrication. The various present designs of laser are therefore determined to a considerable extent by the way in which the different fabrication processes can be combined to the best advantage. This must be taken into account when comparing the different possible devices and when considering the direction in which lasers may further develop.

In the following sections we sketch in some of the background by describing not only the methods for growing the single crystal material in the multilayered form needed for heterostructure lasers, but also the processes involved in fabricating the laser chips. We also consider the factors that determine the operating life and the reliability of the present devices. The processing background is important because it can be said to have influenced the design of the lasers the physics of which we shall be studying. The improvement in operating life that is now being achieved is, of course, very significant to the user and is the reason why so much serious consideration is now being given to the employment of semiconductor lasers in a variety of systems. It is also largely responsible for the more widespread need for a better understanding of the operation of the devices.

1.5   CRYSTAL GROWTH

1.5.1   Liquid Phase Epitaxy

The most successful and the most widely used growth technique has been liquid phase epitaxy (LPE). It owes its success more to the quality of the crystalline material that it produces, which exhibits high efficiency of light emission, rather than to the accuracy of composition and thickness with which the necessary multilayer structures can be grown. Other growth methods, such as chemical vapour deposition (CVD) and molecular beam epitaxy (MBE), are in general superior in the latter respect, but only recently have they been developed to a state where the radiative emission efficiency of the material produced, both in the bulk and close to the heterojunction boundaries, approaches that of LPE material.

Liquid phase epitaxy may be defined as the growth from solution of thin layers of single crystal material on an oriented single crystal substrate. It is carried out by first creating a saturated solution of the necessary components in some suitable solvent at an appropriate temperature, and then moving the solution into contact with the substrate wafer by some appropriate method. Growth is instigated either by lowering the overall temperature or by cooling the substrate only. Liquid phase epitaxy can be used for growing almost all the semiconductor materials that have been used for making injection lasers.

For the growth of the III/V compounds, the group III elements Ga and In, which have melting points around room temperature, are very suitable materials to use as solvents. They do not, of course, introduce unnecessary additional elements into the system. To grow the pure binaries (excluding the pure Al compounds which anyway are never used in heterostructure lasers) it is therefore only necessary to provide one of the above group III elements in sufficient excess to dissolve the group V element. The growth temperature is chosen so that enough of the group V element is dissolved to give reasonable growth rates. This depends on the particular compound being grown. In general a suitable temperature lies in the range 600–900°C, tending towards the lower end for those constituents with the higher atomic weight.

Mixed semiconductors containing three or four elements may be grown in a similar way to the binaries from solutions containing the appropriate additional constituents. In these cases it is necessary to know how the composition of the grown solid is related to that of the liquid in order to grow any particular material. In general the elements of lower atomic weight tend to concentrate in the solid. In the cases where two group III elements are present [e.g. in (GaAl)As, and (GaIn)(AsP)] the solvent consists predominantly of the group III element with the higher atomic weight. Thus, for (GaIn)As of any appreciable In content the solvent is mainly In and similarly for (GaAl)As the solvent is almost entirely Ga. This characteristic is helpful for growing (GaAl)As because it cuts down the amount of highly reactive Al that needs to be used. It would, however, make the growth of materials containing three different group III elements difficult, since only a very small proportion of the component with the lowest atomic weight would be required to be present.

A relatively wide range of dopants can be used in liquid phase epitaxy. They are added directly to the solution in the appropriate concentration. The various dopants differ in some of their characteristics and the best one to choose depends on the circumstances. One consideration is the relative proportion of the dissolved dopant that is actually incorporated in the solid, as determined by the segregation coefficient. For most dopants and impurities the value of this coefficient is such as to largely exclude them from the solid. The result of this behaviour is, of course, to enhance the average purity of LPE material. Also, it makes doping more convenient since the impurities may be added in greater concentration. Sn exhibits this behaviour particularly strongly. Sn in an n-dopant in large number of III/V semiconductors and is so strongly excluded from the solid phase that growth, for instance of GaAs from a pure Sn solution, gives an Sn content of little more than 10^{18} cm^{-3}. Such behaviour is also exhibited, but to a lesser extent, by Ge, Zn, Cd, and Mg. Zn, Cd, and Mg are p-dopants in a large range of III/V semiconductors, whereas Ge is amphoteric but is a useful p-dopant in GaAs and (GaAl)As. S, Se, and Te are exceptions to the above rule and, particularly in the case of Se, are actually incorporated preferentially into the solid. These three dopants are n-type for all the

III/V compounds. Because of their segregation coefficient they are used mainly only for high n-doping levels.

The three dopants, Cd, Zn, and Mg, are capable of considerable diffusion in the solid in the III/V compounds at the growth temperature and as a result may penetrate material adjacent to the deliberately doped layers up to a depth of several microns. This is usually inconvenient, and so these p-type dopants are not normally used if an alternative is available. In GaAs, Ge can be used for p-doping and does not diffuse. However, in InP and its mixed derivatives Ge is n-type and so Cd, Zn, or Mg have to be used as p-dopants and appropriate measurers must be taken to prevent them converting regions to p-type that should be n-type. In certain applications, however, of which fabrication of the single heterostructure is an important example, the diffusion of the p-type impurities is put to useful effect in converting a certain thickness of the n-type GaAs substrate to p-type.

Cd and Zn suffer from one further disadvantage. They are highly volatile at the growth temperature and precautions have to be taken to prevent them, first from being lost from the solutions and, secondly, from contaminating other solutions or the substrate itself. Mg and particularly Be are much less volatile in the solution, although they are more subject to oxidation.

For the growth of multilayer structures by liquid phase epitaxy a suitable boat must be designed to move the appropriate solutions successively over the substrate. Most workers use a basically similar type of boat, as originally constructed by Nelson et al.[41] The minor differences that have arisen are concerned particularly with controlling the degree of saturation of the melts. A typical example is illustrated in Figure 1.5. It is composed of two parts, both fabricated in graphite: an upper part into which a series of holes are machined for containing the melts, and a lower part on which the upper part rests. This lower part forms a base for the melt holes and also contains a recess for the substrate wafer. The boat is placed in a silica chamber within the furnace and purified hydrogen is passed over it. Prior to growth the melts are brought to a saturated condition by holding them at a fixed temperature for an appropriate equilibriation time.

Various methods have been used to control the precise saturation of the melt. One way is accurately to weigh out a particular melt composition so that it has the appropriate degree of saturation at the growth temperature. Alternatively a saturated seed may be provided, either floating on top of the melt or located in an additional recess in the lower section of the boat, which is brought into contact with the melt shortly before the substrate wafer. To initiate growth a certain amount of supersaturation must be induced in each of the melts as they are moved successively over the substrate. Supersaturation may be achieved either by dropping the

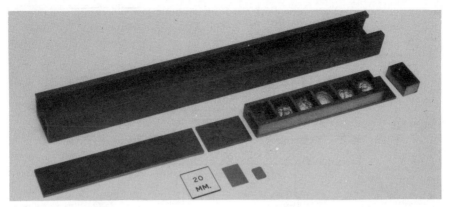

Figure 1.5 Graphite boat for the liquid phase epitaxial growth of III/V compounds. Exploded view showing melt holes in movable slider and recess for holding substrate wafer in baseplate

temperature slightly before the melts are moved or by steadily cooling the boat at a slow rate during the growth of all the layers. The former method gives, in principle, a thickness of growth which depends on the square root of the time the melt is in contact with the slice and the latter method can, under certain circumstances, give a much more linear growth rate provided no supersaturation is generated before the melt moves over the slice. In general it is difficult to prevent some supersaturation being produced during steady cooling because, even in the presence of a saturation seed, the relatively slow rate of diffusion of the solute in the direction of the seed allows some supersaturation to build up in the melt at points remote from the seed. These pockets of supersaturation may then be circulated through the melt as a result of the disturbance induced by moving the slider.

Some designs of heterostructure lasers require the growth of an active layer that is less than 0.1 μm thick and to do this satisfactorily considerable effort must be directed to preventing the occurrence of pockets of supersaturation. A method which seems to help is to use a thin Ga melt (e.g. 2 mm thick) with a saturation wafer pressed against its upper surface by a suitable weight to overcome the balling effect of surface tension, as illustrated in Figure 1.6. Such a method was first described by Lockwood *et al.*[42] and with care it can be used to grow layers reasonably reproducible down to a thickness of around 0.05 μm.

Even after a considerable amount of experimental development of liquid epitaxial methods it is still not easy to grow layers with good uniformity of compositions and thickness and with smooth interfaces of good crystalline quality. For laser applications some non-uniformity of doping level and

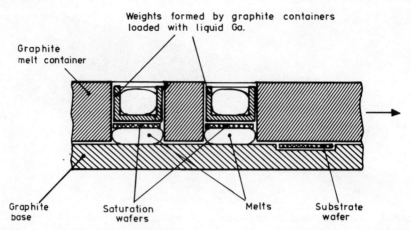

Figure 1.6 Graphite boat designed for LPE from shallow melts. Cross section showing saturation wafers and weights to compress melts

some grading of the heterojunction have little effect. Other inperfections, such as thickness variations across the wafer, poor dimensional control, and lack of surface smoothness are more important and lead to a variation in the performance characteristics of the lasers and to poor yield. Crystalline defects which grow through from the substrate and which are introduced during growth are particularly deleterious and affect the life of the lasers. Experience has shown how such defects can be minimized during growth by eliminating impurities (particularly O_2), by optimizing crucible clearances, by adjusting temperature, etc. As a result laser life is coming under better control. Considering the small dimensions of the laser the relative success of liquid phase epitaxy has been remarkable. However, perfection has not yet been obtained and considerable efforts are now being applied to develop alternative growth methods that inherently permit greater precision and better dimensional control. The aim is to produce material with the same standard of radiative recombination efficiency as is obtained from liquid phase epitaxy but with better reproducibility of the other characteristics.

1.5.2 Chemical Vapour Deposition

In the method of crystalline growth of III/V materials by chemical vapour deposition (CVD) or vapour phase epitaxy (VPE), the constituent elements for the growth are introduced into the growth chamber in the form of gaseous compounds. They first enter a mixing zone, held at such a temperature that little reaction takes place between them, and then pass into a lower temperature deposition zone (typically 700–800°C) where the single crystal substrate wafer is located. As a result of the reduction in temperature the chemical equilibrium between the gaseous components is shifted in such a direction as to cause deposition of solid material in single crystal form on the substrate wafer. Very uniform and smooth growth may be achieved in this way. The rate of growth is about $10–30\ \mu m\ h^{-1}$ depending on the gas flow rates. Dopants may also be introduced in gaseous form. The system is therefore very flexible, and both doping and composition changes can be controlled by appropriate metering valves. Multilayer heterostructures may be grown by simply adjusting gas flows without removing the wafer from the furnace.

In the growth of III/V compounds the group V elements may conveniently be introduced as hydrides, i.e. PH_3, AsH_3, and SbH_3. The group III elements Ga and In are normally introduced as monochlorides, obtained by passing HCl in an H_2 gas stream over a heated boat containing the pure metal. For growth of ternary compounds containing two group III elements both elements may be introduced simultaneously by providing each with a separately controlled HCl stream. (GaIn)/(AsP), for instance, can be effectively grown by this method.[43] Al is more difficult to deal with since the gases produced from it are highly reactive and tend to attack the walls of the reactor.

An alternative means of introducing the metals is in the form of the metal–organic alkyl (di-ethyl or di-methyl) compounds. These materials are liquids at normal temperatures and may be conveyed into the system as vapour by bubbling hydrogen through the containers in which they are held. In most cases this provides a more controllable supply of the gas than does the use of HCl in conjunction with the pure metal, so that the changes in composition required in the growth of heterostructures can be made more easily. Also, the method is more satisfactory for the growth of Al-containing compounds. (GaAl)As/GaAs lasers have been made in this way and the performances that have been achieved in the best cases have been closely comparable with those of lasers fabricated from LPE material.[44]

In the CVD process the stoichiometry of the material that is grown can be considerably affected by adjustment of the relative flow rates of the group III and group V elements, whereas in most LPE processes only small changes can be made in the stoichiometry by altering the temperature. This additional degree of control in CVD processes might at first sight appear to be an advantage. However, optimum stoichiometry is normally obtained when the group III element is in excess. Such a condition is automatically present in liquid phase epitaxy but is much more difficult to sustain in the CVD process. Since the radiative efficiency of the semiconductor deteriorates as the stoichiometry moves away from balance it has in general been found difficult to produce as good a radiative material using CVD processes as when using liquid phase epitaxy. Development is still continuing to bring the CVD material consistently up to the standards of the LPE material.

1.5.3 Molecular Beam Epitaxy

In the growth method known as molecular beam epitaxy (MBE) the constituent materials are introduced into the growth chamber by direct evaporation in an ultra-high vacuum environment in the form of molecular beams which impinge on the substrate. The substrate is normally heated to around 500–600°C and in this condition good single crystal material can be grown. The relative rate of arrival of the constituents in the different beams is adjusted by means of shutters to give the correct stoichiometry and the correct composition to the grown material. The growth rate is relatively low, 60–600 Å min^{-1}, and good dimensional control of layer thickness can be obtained.

A variety of III/V compounds have been grown using this method.[45] In some cases radiative recombination efficiency equal to the best in LPE material has been obtained, but it has proved particularly difficult to produce good material when Al is present. Despite this some good (GaAl)As/GaAs heterostructure lasers have been made from MBE-grown layers.[46] However, development of this method needs to continue before it can be regarded as a really satisfactory way of growing laser material.

1.6   LASER FABRICATION

There are a considerable number of stages necessary for the fabrication of a stripe laser beyond the growing of the epitaxial layer, as follows.

(1) Selection and preparation of a substrate wafer.

(2) Epitaxial growth of the heterostructure layers for double heterostructure lasers, growth and junction diffusion for single heterostructures, or diffusion only for homostructures.

(3) Reduction of the wafer thickness by chemical polishing to facilitate the subsequent cleaning, mounting, etc.

(4) Delineation of the stripe, if required, by deposition of SiO$_2$ insulation followed by photolithography to open up appropriate windows, or by proton bombardment, etc.

(5) Metallization of the wafer on both sides. This may be preceded by a shallow Zn diffusion to improve the p-contact conductivity.

(6) Cleaving the wafer into bars equal in width to the required length of the laser (e.g. 200–500 μm).

(7) Application of protective facet coatings to the cleaved facet, e.g. by evaporation or sputtering of Al$_2$O$_3$, etc.

(8) Separation of bars into individual laser chips by cleaving (or sawing for simple broad contact lasers).

(9) Mounting of the laser chip onto a header by low melting point, soft solder, e.g. In, and attachment of a lead to the top contact.

We will consider some of these processes in more detail below.

1.6.1 Substrate Preparation

First let us take substrate preparation. This is important because the quality of the epitaxial growth is considerably affected by the crystalline quality of the substrate. Substrates should be substantially free of crystalline defects, dislocations, and inclusions (e.g. $<5 \times 10^3$ cm^{-2} in GaAs) doping non-uniformity and strain. Such imperfections arise both during the growth of the substrate material and during subsequent sawing and polishing of the slices. The substrate material should therefore first be carefully selected, using appropriate methods to reveal dislocations (e.g. AB etch* for GaAs), and then all saw damage, which may extend more than 100 μm down from the surface, should be removed. This may be done by chemical polishing (i.e. etching accompanied by light abrasion) followed by a short period of free chemical etching in a suitable solution to remove any residual effects of the chemical polishing. Bromine methanol solution, for instance, is suitable for etching a variety of III/V compounds. The final removal of material from the surface of the wafer may be carried out in the LPE furnace immediately prior to growth by using an unsaturated solution of Ga or In at the growth temperature to dissolve a further 10 or 20 μm of material.

Item (2) above—epitaxial growth—has already been discussed. The processes involved in stripe delineation are described in Chapter 6, Section 6.1. We will therefore omit these items in the present section and move on to item (5)—wafer metallization.

1.6.2 Wafer Metallization

Three factors are important in the metallization of the wafer. First, the metal should adhere adequately, secondly it should provide a low resistance electrical contact, and thirdly it should not introduce excessive strain into the laser chip. Strain, as described in Section 1.7, has a deleterious effect on laser life.

Let us consider the electrical behaviour of the metallized contact. This is difficult to particularize in detail, but it is generally similar to that in an

---

*2 ml H$_2$O, 8 mg AgNO$_3$, 1 g CrO$_3$, 1 ml HF. M. S. Abrahams and C. J. Buiocchi, *J. Appl. Phys.*, **36**, 1965, 855.

ideal Schottky contact. The resistivity thus depends approximately exponentially on the height of the potential barrier between the metal and the appropriate band of the semiconductor, and also depends on the doping level, decreasing fairly rapidly as the doping level is increased.[47] When the barrier height is low, good contact can be relatively easily obtained by locally increasing the doping level and using a simple evaporated metallic layer. This applies to p-type contacts in GaAs where a p-doping level of greater than 3×10^{18} cm^{-3} may be used in conjunction with a well adhering metal such as Ti or Cr. When the barrier is larger, as in n-type GaAs, some form of alloying is necessary. This gives a high local doping level and also probably introduces a grading of the transition between the metal and the semiconductor which is advantageous. Evaporation of Au/Sn or Au/Ge, followed by alloying at around 500°C, gives a satisfactory contact for GaAs. Because the n-contact is more remote from the laser junction (an n-type substrate is used for the LPE growth) the strains of alloying are much less important than for the p-contact.

Contact behaviour has not been investigated to the same extent in the other III/V compounds as in GaAs. However, as a rough rule the barrier height between the metal and the semiconductor is mainly determined, in n-type materials, by the group III element, and in p-type materials by the group V element. In both cases the barrier height decreases as the atomic weight of the element concerned increases. Thus in InP, for instance, the barrier height for n-type material is considerably reduced compared with that in GaAs, but the barrier height for p-type material is somewhat increased. At present, for this reason, alloyed contacts are used on both the p-side and the n-side in InP, but they cannot be regarded as entirely satisfactory. More investigation is needed of the behaviour of Schottky evaporated contacts with these materials.

1.6.3 Facet Coating

The protective coating mentioned in item (7) of the list of fabrication processes is useful for preserving the end-faces of the laser. Over long periods of operation without protective coatings facet erosion has been observed which may be due either to direct thermal damage or to some form of photochemical reaction.[48] This can be largely eliminated at normal operating output power levels by coating the facets with a layer of Al_2O_3 or SiO. This layer is designed to be half a wavelength thick so that it does not alter the reflectivity of the end-face. As a result it has no effect on the optical electric field intensity at the facet, and therefore probably only exerts a protective function.

1.6.4   Separation of Laser Chips and Mounting

As with all other steps in laser manufacture the important points to be emphasized in connection with chip separation and mounting are to avoid processes that damage the laser and shorten its life. Separation of stripe lasers by cleaving can be carried out without significant harm to the devices. Sawing, by a diamond or wire saw, provides an alternative method which has frequently been used as a convenient means of separating chips without current confinement stripes (so-called broad-contact lasers) since it provides non-specularly-reflecting edges to the device to suppress transverse optical modes. However, in most cases sawing introduces damage the effects of which eventually spread across the whole width of the laser and can have a very drastic effect on its operating life. A more reliable method of separating broad contact lasers is first to use proton bombardment of the wafer to form a grid constituted of lines of inactive material and then to cleave down the centre of these lines. The proton bombarded region is electrically non-conducting and optically absorbing and suppresses optical reflection from the cleaved edges.[49]

Mounting of the laser chip is also a process that needs care to avoid the introduction of stress. Various materials have been used to form the base to which the laser is attached, including metallized diamond, silicon, and copper. Metal-to-metal contact is normally required between the laser chip and the base to provide adequate heat-sinking, and the bond requires heat for its formation. Of the above materials silicon has an expansion coefficient which is most closely matched to that of GaAs, but even with Si only a relatively small amount of heating can be tolerated before excessive strains are placed on the GaAs. The solution to this problem that is at present employed is to use any of the above materials in the laser mount but to employ a soft, low melting point solder such as pure indium to make the bond. In general the indium can be relied upon to yield, at least if in sufficient thickness, before excessive stresses arise. Many workers have obtained long-lived lasers using this method. However, the lasers suffer from the disadvantage of being limited to ambient temperatures of less than about 130°C.

1.7   DEGRADATION OF LASERS

One of the most important advances that has been made in recent years in the performance of the heterostructure laser has been the very significant improvement of its operating life. (GaAl)As/GaAs lasers, in selected samples, are now close to meeting the stringent requirements of communications applications which demand lives in excess of 10^5 h.[50-53]

(GaIn)(AsP)/InP) lasers, although at a much earlier stage of development, are also showing considerable promise of reliable operation.[54,55] The situation is very different from that which existed when double heterostructure lasers were first introduced, when lives could often be measured in minutes only. In the early days, and after the unfortunate experience of the continued failure of GaAs tunnel diodes, there were fears that some similar fundamental property of the material might be limiting the lives of lasers. The relief amongst the laser workers was therefore considerable when it was first established that dislocations in the crystalline structure were the major cause of the rapid laser degradation. These dislocations had either been introduced during crystal growth or had been generated in the material as the result of rough handling during processing, and were certainly not fundamental properties of GaAs.

The discovery of the effect of dislocations came about after it had been noticed that the degradation of the early heterostructure stripe lasers was associated with the formation of elongated regions of zero luminescence within the active layer.[56] These dark areas were generated at random within the stripe and spread sideways during further operation of the device. They have come to be known as dark-line defects (DLDs). Petroff and Hartmann[57] carried out an examination of the DLDs using transmission electron microscopy and showed that they consisted of a tangled network of dislocations. There was evidence that these networks had originated from a single dislocation that had originally threaded directly through the heterostructure layers but had subsequently grown and spread to a very considerable extent in the plane of the structure. A typical network is illustrated in Figure 1.7. This network naturally gives rise to a large amount of non-radiative recombination within the active layer, and its effect on the laser is both to increase threshold current density and also to decrease incremental efficiency. Two additional effects may also be produced, namely a decrease in the uniformity of the optical distribution across the output facet of the laser and a decrease in the stability of the laser that may lead to self-pulsing. When the DLD becomes large enough, or when several DLDs are created, the laser ceases to operate c.w.

DLDs have been found to grow only in the presence of recombing holes and electrons, whether the holes and electrons are introduced by injection as in laser diodes or by optical pumping as in certain deliberate experiments that have been carried out.[58] Lasing light appears to play no part in the process and the behaviour is the same whether the device is below or above threshold. Examination of the DLDs shows that the dislocation network has grown predominantly by climb,[57] but possibly also partly by glide.[59] Climb is a process by which the length of the dislocation is increased as the result either of addition or of removal of material from any crystalline half plane whose edge constitutes a part of the dislocation

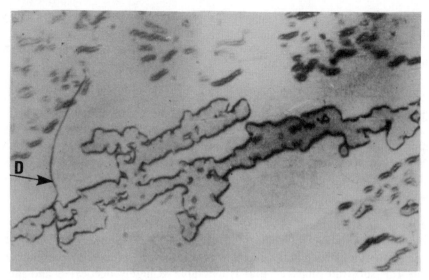

Figure 1.7   Dislocation network found in the active layer of a (GaAl)As DH laser after degradation. It originated from the threading dislocation D. Magnification approx. 2.5×10^4. After Huchinson and Dobson[60]

loop. In the DLDs it is established that addition rather than removal of material is involved, giving rise to so-called interstitial dislocation dipoles.[60]

The fact that point defects in GaAs (both interstitials and vacancies) can be induced to move in the presence of recombining carriers[61] has led to the conjecture that the DLDs might be formed by the 'mopping-up' of interstitial material already present in the lattice. However, in view of the large amount of interstitial material that would be required for this process a more plausible explanation might be that the dislocation grows by incorporating material liberated in the process of generating vacancies in its immediate neighbourhood.[62] The vacancies may then move away, assisted by the 'lubrication' of the recombination energy. The latter explanation concentrates the activity of defect generation and movement in the region close to the dislocation, where marked heating has been observed to occur,[63] in what may be considered a more plausible way. Also, the model does not demand the intital presence of large numbers of crystalline point defects for its operation.

One way of combating the effect of DLDs is to exclude all threading dislocations from the active region of the laser. There are three possible sources, namely:

(a) dislocations which grow up from the substrate during liquid phase epitaxy,

(b) dislocations that are locally produced in the layers during epitaxy, and

(c) dislocations that are generated after growth by harsh treatment during contacting and bonding.

By selecting substrates with low dislocation counts, by optimizing the epitaxy (a small proportion of Al added to the composition of the active layer appears to be helpful in (GaAl)As/GaAs lasers), and by using appropriate methods of contacting and bonding it is possible to produce lasers that are predominantly dislocation-free and not subject to DLDs. These methods have been very successfully applied to (GaAl)As/GaAs lasers.

A second possible method of combating DLDs follows from the observation that lasers in certain materials other than GaAs seem to be less sensitive to the presence of dislocations. For instance, (GaIn)(AsP) lasers are not particularly subject to DLDs even though, at present, the only InP substrate material that is available is highly dislocated and must be the source of many threading dislocations in the active layer. Two suggestions for the reason for this immunity have been made. First, the band-gap of the material is smaller than that of GaAs, and so it is possible that the recombination energy that is liberated by each electron–hole pair is insufficient to cause the growth of DLDs. Secondly, the quaternary active layer consists of a mixed solid solution containing substituent atoms of considerably differing radius, which may cause a certain degree of dislocation pinning and prevent the climb process from proceeding freely.[64] At present these suggestions are only conjecture and further investigation is required before a convincing explanation can be given.

The elimination of DLD formation does not entirely remove all degradation in stripe laser diodes but provides devices with lives at 25–30°C in the region of $2-5 \times 10^4$ h. The remaining residual degradation which does not appear to be particularly dependent on the stripe fabrication methods used is normally observed as a gradual rise in device threshold. In an attempt to gain further information on the mechanism involved, life-tests have also been carried out at elevated temperatures. In general the degradation rate has been found to depend exponentially on reciprocal temperature as $\exp(-E_a/kT)$, where E_a is an activation energy. To obtain a meaningful value of E_a from life-tests care has to be exercised to ensure (a) that the same specific property of the material is being measured at the different temperatures (there has been some controversy as to whether the end of c.w. life of the laser at the life-test temperature fits this criterion since lasers that have been pronounced 'dead' at the higher temperatures will still lase at the lower temperatures) and (b) that the same degradation mechanism is dominant at the different temperatures.

Various workers have obtained activation energies of around 0.7 eV[65,66] (corresponding to a reduction in life by a factor of approximately 30 for a 40°C rise in temperature) although values as small as 0.2 eV have also been reported.[67] Accelerated life-testing at around 70°C has been carried out routinely in various laboratories, and extrapolated room temperature (20°C) lives of as high as 10^6 h have been deduced from the measurements on the basis of a value of 0.7 eV for E_a.[68]

Some contributions to residual degradation in (GaAl)As/GaAs lasers have been identified. One contribution arises from erosion of the laser end-faces which appears to occur as the result of a photochemical reaction in the presence of the lasing light.[48,52] This contribution can be eliminated by applying protective coatings of SiO or Al_2O_3 to the facets with a thickness normally chosen to given minimum change in reflectivity (around a half wavelength). Another contribution to degradation that can be discerned in oxide-insulated stripe lasers depends on the strain introduced by compression in the SiO coating.[68] The stresses involved are of the order of $1-5 \times 10^8$ dyn cm^{-2}, depending on the thickness of the oxide layer. Appreciable stresses exist, even in the absence of oxide, in the heterostructure layers of a (GaAl)As/GaAs laser at room temperature as a result of the slightly greater lattice constant in the (GaAl)As (approximately a 1 in 1500 increase). Values of stress are around 5×10^8 dyn cm^{-2} compression in the passive layers and about 10^8 dyn cm^{-2} tension in the active layer. These stresses can be removed by the addition of about 1.5% P to the (GaAl)As of the passive layer. It has not however been established that laser life is significantly increased as a result.

In view of the amount of progress that has been made in improving laser life, and in view of the way this progress has been made, it no longer appears that there is anything particular about the laser that distinguishes it in reliability terms from other semiconductor devices. Success in achieving reliable operation is related to the amount of effort that is expended. At present, after suitable screening, devices can be confidently expected to exceed 10^4 h of operation, and these figures are likely to continue to improve in the future and, furthermore, to be achieved with continuously increasing yield.

1.8   INTEGRATION OF SEMICONDUCTOR LASERS WITH OTHER OPTICAL COMPONENTS

Many of the techniques that have been developed for the fabrication of semiconductor lasers can be applied to a wider range of optical devices, all constructed in the (GaAl)As/GaAs or similar heterostructure systems. This introduces the possibility of a complete integrated assembly of optical components linked with the semiconductor laser and all based on a common technology. The total technology encompasses multilayer epitaxial growth of the semiconductor heterostructure, photolithographic grating techniques as used in the distributed feedback laser (see Chapter 8), proton bombardment, impurity diffusion, anodization, and selective etching as used for the stripe laser and possibly also two-stage epitaxy and epitaxial growth on grooved substrates as used for the buried-heterostructure and channelled-substrate lasers described in Chapter 6. Integration becomes important as optical systems progress beyond the simplest stage and as the amount of optical processing that must be carried out increases. Coupling of many discrete optical components with cross-sectional dimensions comparable to that of a stripe laser becomes inefficient and unreliable because of the large optical diffraction losses involved and because the possibly high optical density may cause damage at the interfaces. In components where the phase of different optical paths must be balanced integration provides the only practicable solution. Electronic components such as FETs and tunnel diodes can also be integrated in the (GaAl)As/GaAs and other similar systems. This is advantageous in cutting down inductance in the laser drive circuitry and also cutting down capacitance in detector/amplifier combinations and so increasing the range of frequency response of the system.

At present only a limited amount of progress has been made toward realizing a genuine integrated optical concept. More success has been obtained with individual heterostructire components. The various devices that have been fabricated and tested comprise first, of course, lasers, particularly those with distributed feedback as described in Chapter 8, followed by passive waveguides,[69–75] waveguides with bends or corners,[76] directional couplers,[77] a range of optical switches and amplitude phase modulators using both the electro-optic effect[78–82] and the Franz Keldysh effect,[83] and stripe laser pairs with differential phase modulation for output beam sweep.[84]

One problem that arises when lasers are combined with passive components in an integrated heterostructure system is that the material that forms the active part of the laser waveguide becomes optically absorbing when unpumped and does not provide a satisfactory guide when extended to provide the basis for the other components. Possible ways to overcome this problem are to grade the composition of the layer concerned[85] to taper it away[86,87] or to truncate it.[88] The first two alternatives have been achieved by ingenious adaptations of liquid phase epitaxy.[85,86] Tapers have also been fabricated in a controlled fashion by appropriate shadow masking of MBE.[87] Truncation is a relatively simple operation using an appropriate selective etch. A way of avoiding the problem is to fabricate the laser using additional layers of the heterostructure which lie on top of layers to be used for the passive waveguide, but sufficiently closely spaced so that there is coupling between them. This arrangement has been used in the integrated twin-guide laser.[89]

The various integrated arrangements that have been reported so far are relatively simple and represent only the first stages along the route. A laser has been combined with a monitoring detector, connected by a short length of passive waveguide.[90] A frequency modulator has been incorporated into a Fabry–Perot laser cavity[91] and an amplitude modulator has been incorporated into a cavity with Bragg reflectors.[92] A laser has been combined with an FET, both being based on the same semi-insulating substrate.[93] An array of distributed feedback stripe lasers have been built with interconnecting waveguides on a single chip to form a frequency-multiplexing light source.[94]

The more widespread use of integrated optical circuits awaits the development of a more dimensionally reproducible growth system such as MBE or metal-organic CVD. With improved growth more elaborate heterostructures will become feasible and the full advantage of the distributed feedback and Bragg reflection lasers, which are particularly suited to integrated systems, can effectively be expolited.

REFERENCES

1. N. G. Basov, O. N. Kroklin, and Y. M. Popov, 'Production of negative-temperature states in p–n junctions of degenerate semiconductors'. *Pis'ma Zh. Eskp. Theor. Fiz.*, **40**, 1961, 1879. Also, *Sov. Phys. JETP*, **13**, 1961, 1320.
2. R. N. Hall, G. E. Fenner, J. D. Kingsley, T. J. Soltys, and R. O. Carlson, 'Coherent light emission from GaAs p–n junctions', *Phys. Rev. Lett.,* **9**, Nov. 1962, 366.
3. M. I. Nathan, W. P. Dumke, G. Burns, F. H. Dill, and G. J. Lasher, 'Stimulated emission of radiation from GaAs p–n junctions', *Appl. Phys. Lett.,* **1**, Nov. 1962, 62.
4. T. M. Quist, R. H. Rediker, R. J. Keyes, W. E. Krag, B. Lax, A. L. McWhorter, and H. J. Zeiger, 'Semiconductor maser of GaAs', *Appl. Phys. Lett.,* **1**, Dec. 1962, 91.
5. N. Holonyak, Jr, and S. F. Bevacqua, 'Coherent (visible) light emission from $Ga(As_{1-x}P_x)$ junctions', *Appl. Phys, Lett.,* **1**, Dec. 1962, 82.
6. T. H. Maiman, 'Stimulated optical emission in fluorescent solids', *Phys. Rev.,* **123**, 1961, 1145.
7. A. Javan, W. R. Bennett, Jr, and D. R. Herriott, 'Continuous optical maser oscillation in a gas discharge', *Phys. Rev. Lett.,* **6**, 1961, 106.
8. Zh I. Alferov, V. M. Andreev, V. I. Korol'kov, E. L. Portnoi, and D. N. Tret'yakov, 'Injection properties of $n-Al_xGa_{1-x}As$ p-Gas heterojunctions', *Fiz. Tekh. Poluprov.,* **2**, 1968, 1016. Also, *Sov. Phys. Semicond.* **2**, 1969, 843.
9. H. Kressel and H. Nelson, 'Close confinement gallium arsenide PN junction lasers with reduced optical loss at room temperature', *RCA Rev.,* **30**, 1969, 106.
10. I. Hayashi, M. B. Panish, P. W. Foy, 'A low threshold room temperature injection laser', *IEEE J. Quantum Electron.,* **QE-5**, 1969, 211.

11. I. Hayashi, M. B. Panish, P. W. Foy, and S. Sumski, 'Junction lasers which operate continuously at room temperature', *Appl. Phys. Lett.*, **17**, 1970, 109.
12. Zh. I. Alferov, V. M. Andreev, D. Z. Garbuzov, Yu. V. Zhilyaev, E. P. Morozov, E. L. Portnoi, and V. G. Triofim, 'Investigation of the influence of the AlAs–GaAs heterostructure parameters on the laser threshold current and the realization of continuous emission at room temperature', *Fiz. Tekh. Poluprov*, **4**, 1970, 1826. Also, *Sov. Phys. Semicond.*, **4**, 1971, 1573.
13. H. Kroemer, 'A proposed class of heterojunction injection lasers', *Proc. IEEE*, **51**, 1963, 1782.
14. Zh. I. Alferov and R. F. Kazarinov, Author's certificate 1032155/26–25, USSR, 1963.
15. Zh. I. Alferov, 'Injection luminescence of epitaxial heterojunctions in the GaP–GaAs system', *Fiz. Tverd. Tela*, **9**, 1967, 279. Also, *Sov. Phys. Solid State*, **9**, 1967, 208.
16. J. M. Wodall and G. D. Pettit, 'Efficient visible electroluminescence at 300 K from $Ga_{1-x}Al_xAs$ p–n junctions grown by liquid phase epitaxy', *Appl. Phys. Lett.*, **11**, 1967, 81.
17. I. Ladany and H. Kressel, Final Report NASA Contract NAS1-11421, 1974.
18. I. Melngailis, 'Laser action and photodetection in lead–tin chalcogenides', *J.de Phys.*, **29**, Colloque Suppl. C4, 1968, 84. Also, *Proc. Conf. Short Pulses Coherent Interactions*, Chania, Greece, 1969.
19. C. J. Nuese, G. H. Olsen, and M. Ettenberg, 'CW room temperature $GaAs/In_yGa_{1-y}P$ DH lasers prepared by vapour epitaxy', *Appl. Phys. Lett.*, **29**, 1976, 54.
20. C. J. Nuese and G. H. Olsen, 'Room temperature heterojunction laser diodes of $In_xGa_{1-x}As/In_yGa_{1-y}P$ with emission wavelength between 0.9 and 1.15 μm', *Appl. Phys. Lett.*, **26**, 1975, 528.
21. J. J. Hsieh, 'Room temperature operation of GaInAsP/InP double heterostructure diode lasers emitting at 1.1 μm', *Appl. Phys. Lett.*, **28**, 1976, 283.
22. T. Yamamoto, K. Sakai, S. Akiba, and Y. Suematsu, '$In_{1-x}Ga_xAs_yP_{1-y}$/InP DH lasers fabricated on InP (100) substrates', *IEEE J. Quantum Electron.*, **QE-14**, 1978, 95.
23. L. R. Tomasetta, H. D. Law, K. Nakano, and J. S. Harris, 'GaAlAsSb/GaSb lattice matched semiconductor lasers operating at 1.25–1.40 μm', IEEE International Semiconductor Laser Conference, San Francisco, 30 Oct.–1, Nov. 1978.
24. K. Sugiyama and H. Saito, 'GaAsSb–AlGaAsSb double heterojunction lasers', *Japan J. Appl. Phys.*, **11**, 1972, 1057.
25. R. E. Nahory and M. A. Pollack, 'Low threshold room temperature double heterostructure $GaAs_{1-x}Sb_x/Al_yGa_{1-y}As_{1-x}Sb_x$ injection lasers at 1 μm wavelengths', *Appl. Phys. Lett.*, **27**, 1975, 562.
26. R. E. Nahory, M. A. Pollack, M. A. Beebe, J. C. De Winrer, and R. W. Dixon, 'Continuous operation of 1.0 μm wavelength $GaAs_{1-x}Sb_x/Al_yGa_{1-y}As_{1-x}Sb_x$ double heterostructure injection lasers at room temperature', *Appl. Phys. Lett.*, **28**, 1976, 19.
27. A. Onton and R. J. Chicotka, 'Conduction bands in $In_{1-x}Al_xP$', *J. Appl. Phys.*, **41**, 1970, 4205.
28. R. J. Nelson and N. Holonyak, Jr, 'Excitation absorption, photoluminescence and band structure of n-free and n-doped $In_{1-x}Ga_xP$', *J. Phys. Chem. Solids*, **37**, 1976, 629.
29. M. R. Lorenz and A. Onton, *Proc. 10th Int. Conf. Phys. Semiconduct.*,

Cambridge, Massachusetts (S. P. Keller, J. C. Hensal, and F. Stern, eds.), U.S. Atomic Energy Comm., Washington, D.C., 1970, p. 444.

30. H. C. Casey, Jr, and M. B. Panish, 'Composition dependence of the $Ga_{1-x}Al_xAs$ direct and indirect energy gaps', *J. Appl. Phys.*, **40**, 1967, 4910.

31. A. G. Thompson, M. Cardona, K. L. Shaklee, and J. C. Wooley, 'Electro reflectance in the GaAs–GaP alloys', *Phys. Rev.*, **146**, 1966, 601.

32. J. J. Coleman, W. R. Hitchens, N. Holonyak Jr., M. J. Ludowise, W. O. Groves, and D. L. Keune, 'Liquid phase epitaxial $In_{1-x}Ga_xP_{1-z}As_z/GaAs_{1-y}P_y$ quaternary (LPE)–ternary (VPE) heterojunction lasers ($x \sim 0.70$, , $z \sim 0.01$, $y \sim 0.40$; $\lambda < 6300$ Å, 77 K)', *Appl. Phys. Lett.*, **25**, 1974, 725.

33. H. Kressel, G. H. Olsen, and C. J. Nuese, 'Visible $GaAs_{0.7}P_{0.3}$ c.w. heterojunction lasers', *Appl. Phys. Lett.*, **30**, 1977, 249.

34. H. Kressel and F. Z. Hawrylo, 'Red-light-emitting diodes operating c.w. at room temperature', *Appl. Phys. Lett.*, **28**, 1976, 598.

35. T. Kajimura, T. Kuroda, S. Yamashita, M. Nakamura and J. Umeda 'Transverse mode stabilized $Ga_{1-x}Al_xAs$ visible diode lasers', *Applied Optics*, **18**, 1979, 1812.

36. K. J. Linden, K. W. Nill, and J. F. Butler, 'Single heterostructure lasers of $PbS_{1-x}Se_x$ and $Pb_{1-x}Sn_xSe$ with wide tunability', *IEEE J. Quantum Electron.*, **QE-13**, 1977, 720.

37. S. H. Groves, K. W. Nill, and A. J. Strauss, 'Double heterostructure $Pb_{1-x}Sn_xTe$–PbTe lasers with c.w. operation at 77 K', *Appl. Phys. Lett.*, **25**, 1974, 331.

38. J. N. Walpole, A. R. Calawa, R. W. Ralston, T. C. Harman, and J. P. McVittie, 'Single heterojunction $Pb_{1-x}Sn_xTe$ diode lasers', *Appl. Phys. Lett.*, **23**, 1973, 620.

39. L. R. Tomasetta and C. Fonstad, 'Threshold reduction in $Pb_{1-x}Sn_xTe$ laser diodes through the use of double heterostructure geometries', *Appl. Phys. Lett.*, **25**, 1974, 440.

40. J. N. Walpole, A. R. Calawa, T. C. Harman, and S. H. Groves, 'Double heterostructure PbSnTe lasers grown by molecular beam epitaxy with cw operation up to 114 K', *Appl. Phys. Lett.*, **28**, 1976, 552.

41. H. Nelson, U.S. Patent 3,565,702, 1971.

42. H. F. Lockwood and M. Ettenberg, 'Thin solution multiple layer epitaxy', *J. Crystal Growth*, **15**, 1972, 81.

43. G. H. Olsen, C. J. Nuese, and M. Ettenberg, 'Low threshold 1.25 m vapour grown InGaAsP CW lasers', *Appl. Phys. Lett.*, **34**, 1979, 262.

44. R. D. Dupuis and P. D. Dapkus, 'Very low threshold $Ga_{1-x}Al_xAs$–GaAs double heterostructure lasers grown by metal organic chemical vapour deposition', *Appl. Phys. Lett.*, **32**. 1978, 473.

45. A. Y. Cho, M. B. Panish, and I. Hayashi, 'Molecular beam epitaxy of GaAs, $Al_xGa_{1-x}As$ and GaP', *Proc. Symp. GaAs and Related Compounds*, Aachen, Germany, 1970.

46. W. T. Tsang, 'Low-current-threshold and high-lasing-uniformity GaAs-$Al_xGa_{1-x}As$ double-heterostructure lasers grown by molecular beam epitaxy', *Appl. Phys. Lett.*, **34**, 1979. 473.

47. C. Y. Chang, Y. K. Fang, and S. M. Sze, 'Specific contact resistance of metal-semiconductor barriers', *Solid State Electron.*, **14**, 1971, 541.

48. H. Kressel and I. Ladany, 'Reliability aspects and facet damage in high power emission from (AlGa)As cw laser diodes at room temperature', *RCA Rev.*, **36**, 1975, 230.

49. G. D. Henshall, 'The suppression of internally circulating modes in

(GaAl)As/GaAs heterostructure lasers and their effect on catastrophic degradation and efficiency', *Appl. Phys. Lett.*, **31**, 1971, 205.

50. B. W. Joyce, R. W. Dixon, and R. L. Hartman, 'Statistical characterization of the lifetimes of (AlGa)As double heterostructure lasers', *Appl. Phys. Lett.*, **28**, 1976, 684.

51. H. Kan, H. Namizaki, M. Ishii, and A. Ito, 'Continuous operation over 10,000 hours of GaAs/GaAlAs double heterostructure lasers without mismatch compensation', *Appl. Phys. Lett.*, **27**, 1975, 138.

52. I. Ladany, M. Ettenberg, H. F. Lockwood, and H. Kressel, 'Al_2O_3 half-wave films for long life cw lasers', *Appl. Phys. Lett.*, **30**, 1977, 87.

53. A. R. Goodwin, J. R. Peters, M. Pion, and W. O. Bourne, 'GaAs lasers with consistently low degradation rates at room temperature', Appl. Phys. Lett., **30**, 1977, 110.

54. T. Yamamoto, K. Sakai, and S. Akiba, '10,000-h continuous CW operation of $In_{1-x}Ga_xAs_yP_{1-y}$/InP DH lasers at room temperature', *IEEE J. Quantum Electron.*, **QE-15**, 1979, 684.

55. G. H. Olsen, C. J. Nuese, and M. Ettenberg, 'Reliability of vapor-grown InGaAs and InGaAsP heterojunction laser structures, *IEEE J. Quantum Electron.*, **QE-15**, 1979, 688.

56. R. L. Hartman and A. R. Hartman, 'Strain induced degradation of GaAs injection lasers', *Appl. Phys. Lett.*, **23**, 1973, 147.

57. P. Petrov and R. L. Hartman, 'Defect structure induced during operation of heterojunction GaAs lasers', *Appl. Phys. Lett.*, **23**, 1973, 467.

58. P. Petroff, W. D. Johnston, Jr, and R. L. Hartman, 'Nature of optically induced defects in $Ga_{1-x}Al_xAs$–GaAs double heterojunction laser structures', *Appl. Phys. Lett.*, **25**, 1974, 226.

59. J. Matsui, K. Ishida, and Y. Nannichi, 'Rapid degradation in double heterostructure lasers. I: Proposal of a new model for the directional growth of dislocation networks', *Japan J. Appl. Phys.*, **14**, 1975, 1555.

60. P. W. Huchinson and P. S. Dobson, 'Defect structure of degraded GaAlAs–GaAs double heterojunction lasers', *Phil. Mag.*, **32**, 1975, 745.

61. D. V. Lang and L. C. Kimmerling, 'Observation of recombination-enhanced defect reactions in semiconductors', *Phys. Rev. Lett.*, **33**, 1974, 489.

62. S. O'Hara, P. W. Huchinson, and P. S. Dobson, 'The origin of dislocation climb during laser operation', *Appl. Phys. Lett.*, **30**, 1977, 368.

63. T. Kobayashi, T. Kawakami, and Y. Furukawa, 'Thermal diagnosis of dark lines in degraded GaAs–GaAlAs double heterostructure lasers', *Japan J. Appl. Phys.*, **14**, 1975, 508.

64. P. A. Kirkby, 'Dislocation pinning in GaAs by the deliberate introduction of impurites', *IEEE J. Quantum Electron.*, **QE-11**, 1975, 562.

65. R. L. Hartman and R. W. Dixon, 'Reliability of DH GaAs lasers at elevated temperatures', *Appl. Phys. Lett.*, **26**, 1975, 239.

66. T. Kobayshi, H. Wakita, T. Kawakami, G. Iwane, Y. Horikoshi, Y. Seki, and Y. Furukawa, 'Accelerated life test of AlGaAs–GaAs DH lasers', International Conference on Integrated Optics and Optical Fiber Communication (Post-deadline Papers) Tokyo, Japan, 18–20 July, 1977.

67. S. Ritchie, R. F. Godfery, B. Wakefield, and D. H. Newman, 'The degradation of (GaAl)As DH lasers at high temperatures', Third European Conference on Optical Communication, Munich, 14–16 Sept., 1977.

68. A. R. Goodwin, P. A. Kirkby, I. G. A. Davies, and R. S. Baulcomb, 'The effects of processing stresses on residual degradation in long lived $Ga_{1-x}Al_xAs$ lasers', *Appl. Phys. Lett.*, **34**, 1979, 647.

69. A. Y. Cho and F. K. Reinhart, 'Growth of three-dimensional dielectric waveguides for integrated optics by molecular beam epitaxy', *Appl. Phys. Lett.,* **21**, 1972, 355.

70. J. C. Tracy, W. Wiegman, R. A. Logan, and F. K. Reinhart, 'Three dimensional light guides in single-crystal GaAs-Al$_x$Ga$_{1-x}$As', *App. Phys. Lett.*, **22**, 1973, 511.

71. J. L. Merz, R. A. Logan, and A. M. Sergent, 'Loss measurements in GaAs-dielectric waveguides between 1.1 eV and the energy gap', *J. Appl. Phys.,* **47**, 1976, 1436.

72. J. L. Merz and A. Y. Cho, 'Low loss AlGaAs waveguides grown by MBE', *Appl. Phys. Lett.,* **28**, 1976, 456.

73. T. Kawakami and Y. Furukawa, 'GaAs core embedded in Al$_x$Ga$_{1-x}$As matrix', *Japan J. Appl. Phys.,* **14**, 1975, 409.

74. F. K. Reinhart, R. A. Logan, and T. P. Lee, 'Transmission properties of rib waveguides formed by anodization of epitaxial GaAs on AlGaAs layers', *Appl. Phys. Lett.,* **24**, 1974, 270.

75. E. Garmire, M. Stoll, A. Yariv, and R. G. Hunsperger, 'Optical waveguiding in proton-implanted GaAs', *Appl. Phys. Lett.,* **21**, 1972, 87.

76. N. Matsumoto, 'Bent-guide-structure semiconductor lasers', *Rev. Electron. Commun. Lab.* (Japan), **26**, 1978, 1027.

77. S. Somekh, E. Garmire, A. Yariv, H. L. Garvin, and R. G. Hunsperger, 'Channel optical waveguide directional couplers', *Appl. Phys. Lett.*, **22**, 1973, 46.

78. F. K. Reinhart and B. I. Miller, 'Efficient GaAs–Al$_x$Ga$_{1-x}$As heterostructure light modulators', *Appl. Phys. Lett.,* **20**, 1972, 36.

79. J. C. Campbell, F. A. Blum, D. W. Shaw, and K. L. Lawley, 'GaAs electro-optic directional coupler switch', *Appl. Phys. Lett.,* **27**, 1975, 202.

80. F. K. Reinhart, W. R. Sinclair, and R. A. Logan, 'Single heterostructure AlGaAs phase modulator with SnO$_2$ doped In$_2$O$_3$ cladding layer', *Appl. Phys. Lett.,* **29**, 1976, 21.

81. F. J. Leonberger, J. P. Donelly, and C. O. Boyler, 'GaAs p$^+$n$^-$n$^+$ directional coupler switch', *Appl. Phys. Lett.*, **29**, 1976, 652.

82. J. C. Shelton, F. K. Reinhart, and R. A. Logan, 'Single mode GaAs–Al$_x$Ga$_{1-x}$As rib waveguide switches', *Appl. Optics,* **17**, 1978, 890.

83. F. K. Reinhart, 'Electro-absorption in Al$_y$Ga$_{1-y}$As–Al$_x$Ga$_{1-x}$As heterostructures', *Appl. Phys. Lett.,* **22**, 1973, 372.

84. D. R. Scifres, W. Streifer, and R. D. Burnham, 'Beam scanning and wavelength modulation with branching waveguide stripe injection lasers', *Appl. Phys. Lett.,* **33**, 1978, 616.

85. F. K. Reinhart and R. A. Logan, 'Monolithically integrated AlGaAs double heterostructure optical components', *Appl. Phys. Lett.,* **25**, 1974, 622.

86. F. K. Reinhart and R. A. Logan, 'GaAs–AlGaAs DH lasers with taper-coupled passive waveguides', *Appl. Phys. Lett.,* **26**, 1975, 516.

87. F. K. Reinhart and A. Y. Cho, 'Al$_y$Ga$_{1-y}$As–Al$_x$Ga$_{1-x}$As laser structures for integrated optics grown by molecular beam eptiaxy', *Appl. Phys. Lett.,* **31**, 1977, 457.

88. H. Namizaki, M. K. Shams, and Shyh Wang, 'Large-optical-cavity GaAs–(GaAl)As injection laser with low-loss distributed Bragg reflectors', *Appl. Phys. Lett.,* **31**, 1977, 122.

89. H. Kawanashi, Y. Suematsu, and K. Kishino, 'GaAs–GaAlAs integrated twin-guide lasers with distributed Bragg reflectors', *IEE J. Quantum Electron.,* **JQE-13**, 1977, 64.

90. J. L. Merz and R. A. Logan, 'Integrated GaAs–AlGaAs injection lasers and detectors with etched reflectors', *Appl. Phys. Lett., 30*, 1977, 530.
91. F. K. Reinhart and R. A. Logan, 'Integrated electro-optic intra-cavity frequency modulation of double heterostructure injection laser', *Appl. Phys. Lett., 27*, 1975, 532.
92. M. K. Shams, H. Namizaki, and Shyh Wang, 'Monolithic integration of GaAs-(GaAl)As light modulators and distributed Bragg reflector lasers', *Appl. Phys. Lett., 32*, 1978, 314.
93. I. Uri, 'Integration of lasers with high speed devices—FET and tunnel diodes', Post deadline papers, International Semiconductor Laser Conference, San Francisco, 30 Oct.–1 Nov., 1978.
94. K. Aiki, M. Nakamura, and J. Umeda, 'Frequency multiplexing light source with monolithically integrated DFB diode lasers', *Appl. Phys. Lett., 29*, 1976, 506.
95. J. S. Blakemore, 'Semiconductor Statistics' Pergamon Press, 1962, p. 214.
96. N. Kobayashi, Y. Horikoshi and C. Uemura, 'Room temperature operation of the InGaAsSb/AlGaAsSb DH laser at 1.8 μm wavelength,' *Jap. J. Appl. Phys., 19*, 1980, L30.

CHAPTER 2

Light Emission Processes and Laser Action in Semiconductors

2.1 ELECTRONIC RADIATIVE TRANSITIONS

The electronic radiative transitions that take place between the bands in a semiconductor laser play a very similar role to the transitions between individual pairs of electronic states in a simple two-level laser system. In both cases the electrons participate in the same three types of interaction with the photons, namely spontaneous emission, absorption, and stimulated emission. In a direct band-gap semiconductor in thermal equilibrium the conduction band usually contains only a few filled states and the valence band only a few empty states. The small number of electrons in the conduction band have a certain probability of falling into the small number of empty states in the valence band, in the process of which a photon is created by spontaneous emission. When a photon of suitable energy passes through such a semiconductor it has a high probability of being absorbed and passing its energy to one of the many electrons in the valence band. In the process the electron concerned is raised to an empty state in the conduction band. This is not, however, the only interaction possible for the photon. It can also stimulate an electron in the conduction band to move downwards to a state in the valence band and emit a second photon. The emitted photon has very nearly the same frequency and phase as the incident photon. This is an unlikely process when the semiconductor is in thermal equilibrium because of the small number of electrons in the conduction band. However, with sufficient excitation by other means, the number of electrons in the bottom of the conduction band can be made to exceed the number of holes in the top of the valence band, and the probability of the photon causing stimulated emission can be made greater than the probability of its being absorbed. This condition is the familiar one of population inversion and it provides optical gain. The considerable number of electrons in the conduction band still retain their capability of random recombination and so the inverted state of the semiconductor is characterized also by a high rate of spontaneous emission.

Naturally, the change from a limited number of individual pairs of localized electronic states in the two-level laser, where the active ingredient is normally a dopant, to the larger number of relatively unlocalized electronic states in the bands of a semiconductor, results in some change in the lasing properties of the system. First, the higher concentration of electronic states in the bands of the semiconductor provides the capability for higher optical gain. Secondly, there is a very considerably greater interaction between the different excited states in the same band of the semiconductor compared with the excited states of different atoms in the two-level material. The time constants of the collision processes by which the carriers in the bands of the semiconductor interact are short compared with those of the radiation processes, so that quasi-equilibria are maintained amongst the excited states within each band. Once electronic transitions have taken place the empty states that remain are rapidly filled by carriers not originally involved in the transition processes. This almost instantaneous redistribution of carriers confers on the semiconductor a considerable advantage over most other laser materials in the high rate of energy generation that may be achieved.

A third and obvious difference between the two-level laser material and the semiconductor is that in the semiconductor the excited electronic states may be transported through the material by diffusion or conduction. This makes it possible to invert the material in a particularly simple manner by the direct injection of carriers at, say, a p–n junction.

A fourth difference between the semiconductor and the two-level laser material, which is normally observed in practice, may perhaps be attributed to the less than ideal behaviour of most actual semiconductors. This difference concerns the uniqueness of every possible electronic transition. In the two-level laser each excited electron has only one ground state to which it can return, namely that of the particular atom concerned. In an ideal semiconductor at low excitation levels a similar such restriction might still be taken to apply. Selection rules exist which prescribe that for each conduction band state there is only one unique valence band state to which a transition can be made. In practice, owing to a lack of purity and to a certain amount of interaction between injected carriers, the selection rules are relaxed and transitions may occur with little discrimination between considerable numbers of electrons in the conduction band and considerable numbers of holes in the valence band. Before discussing further the results of this behaviour, let us consider how the selection rules in a semiconductor arise and the general consequences that ensue.

The probability of electrons undergoing radiative transitions between given states in the conduction band of a semiconductor and given states in the valence band is strongly dependent upon the relative quantum mechanical wave-vectors associated with the initial and final states of the electrons. The behaviour can conveniently be described in terms of the energy/wave-vector interrelation of the band structure. Semiconductors can be classified into two groups which differ very markedly in their behaviour, namely the 'direct' and the 'indirect' band-gap materials. Only in the 'direct' band-gap semiconductors do carriers of normal energy exhibit high radiative transition probabilities. In these materials, of which GaAs and many other of the III/V and II/VI materials mentioned in Chapter 1 are examples, states at the lowest energy minimum of the conduction band and at the highest energy maximum in the valence band have the same wave vector **k** in the Brillouin zone (or in other words the same momentum). In contrast in materials like Si and Ge, which are indirect, the **k** values of the aforementioned extreme conduction and valence band states differ by an amount up to a value as large as the reciprocal lattice vector. Figure 2.1 shows a schematic diagram of the relation between electron energy and **k** in GaAs. Both the conduction band minimum and the valence band maximum occur at **k** = 0. A similar general picture is true of the majority of the other direct gap semiconductors. In some direct gap materials, however, of which the IV/VI materials are an important example, there are several equal energy conduction band minima and valence band minima that occur in pairs for a series of differently directed but symmetrically related values of **k** of equal and non-zero magnitude. The main effect is simply to increase the density of states.

In photon absorption and emission processes the total momentum or **k** value must be conserved. The photon has negligible momentum and hence

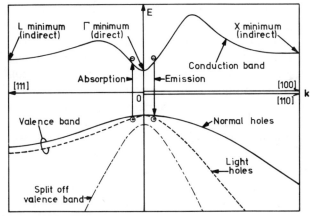

Figure 2.1 Plot of energy versus wave-vector for electrons in conduction and valence bands of direct-gap semiconductor, e.g. GaAs (diagrammatic).

only the momenta or **k** values of the electronic states need be taken into account. As a result the electronic transitions take place predominantly between initial and final states with near-identical **k** values. In a direct band-gap semiconductor simple electronic transitions with no change of **k** are possible between the minimum energy states at the bottom of the conduction band and the maximum energy states at the top of the valence band. In an indirect material, however, no such transitions are available. Certain radiative transitions do, however, take place across the minimum energy gap, but they involve the participation of another particle, e.g. a phonon, to balance the **k** relation. Since a four-particle interaction is much less probable than a three-particle interaction, transitions across the narrow part of the band-gap have a much lower probability in indirect than in direct gap materials.

In practice the transitions in a doped direct band-gap semiconductor or in an undoped direct band-gap semiconductor at high injection rate are not so simply determined by the **k** values of the states as suggested above, and the energy band structure is not such a straightforward function of **k** as indicated in Figure 2.1. In the part of the band structure around the conduction band minimum and the valence band maximum the energy versus **k** relation is smeared because the charge of the impurities and the injected carriers causes a locally varying potential which interferes with the momentum of the carriers. As a result each electronic state can no longer be ascribed the single **k** value that would apply to a carrier with rectilinear motion, but must be described in terms of a **k** spectrum. This reduces the transition probability between those pairs of states in the conduction and valence band which would previously have been highly interactive, but on the other hand introduces the possibility of transitions occurring between many new pairs of states. As a result the overall radiative interaction of, say, an electron with all the new possible empty states in the valence band remains much the same as with the fewer states available previously. However, the conditions required to ensure that these states are empty are different from the previous situation and the emitted or absorbed photons instead of being of one precise wavelength now have a spread of energies. Proper allowance for such effects is one of the major problems in producing a good theoretical analysis of stimulated and spontaneous emission in semiconductor lasers, and areas of controversy remain that have not yet been entirely settled by experiment.

A semiconductor that is pumped into an inverted state imparts optical gain to a propagating wave but it will not cause laser oscillation until it is enclosed within a suitable optical resonator. The resonator provides the necessary feedback by reflecting a proportion of the photons that are generated back into the inverted region. The criterion that must be satisfied for lasing to start is that the stimulated emission from the inverted medium should be sufficient to compensate for the loss of photons at the output and elsewhere in the resonator: A steady oscillation can then be maintained indefinitely. According to this simple concept the threshold for laser oscillation occurs abruptly, as the pump level is increased, at the point where the condition of photon balance is first fulfilled.

The reflection from the ends of the optical resonator provides maximum feedback at a specific set of optical frequencies which give an integral number of half wavelengths (as measured within the semiconductor) in the total length separating the mirrors. The optical field distributions at the different frequencies are called modes.

The lasing output increases approximately linearly as the pump current is raised above threshold. This simple response hides a somewhat more subtle chain of events. The instantaneous effect of increasing the current is to cause the stimulated emission into the optical resonator to exceed the losses from it. The photon population therefore builds up, but obviously only for a very brief period. In a short time (e.g. 100 ps) the drain of the increasing stimulated emission lowers the injected carrier concentration back to the point where the stimulated emission once more exactly balances the losses, and the photon population of the resonator stabilizes at such a value that the additional photon output compensates the increase in the pump level.

If pumping is supplied by direct injection of carriers, as in a semiconductor diode laser, the above model suggests that above threshold the laser is a highly efficient convertor of electrons into photons. If all photons lost from the resonator appear in the output it has 100 per cent incremental efficiency. Optical losses or scattering of light in the resonator reduces this somewhat, but since the processes are linear the output should remain a linear function of the input. In practice there are circumstances in which non-linear effects can intervene, as described in Section 2.7 of this chapter and in Chapter 6, but in most cases the behaviour approximates to a linear relation.

Combining the concept of a threshold—in the case of a diode laser a threshold current—with a linear relation between light and pumping level (or current) gives the simple light/current characteristic of Figure 2.2. This is entirely described in terms of the threshold current I_{th} and the incremental quantum efficiency (although ohmic and other electrical losses must of course be taken into account in evaluating the overall efficiency).

In the following sections of this chapter we develop in greater detail the topics that we have just introduced. We review the fundamental physics of the interaction in semiconductors between electro-magnetic radiation and electrons and derive the expression for optical gain as a function of the pumping current. In Section 2.2 we consider the various relationships that exist between stimulated and spontaneous emission and optical absorption. The Einstein relations provide the starting point for this treatment. These

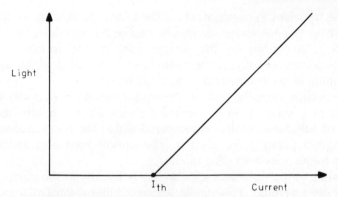

Figure 2.2 Idealized light/current characteristic in semi-conductor laser showing threshold current I_{th} and linear slope

relations were originally applied to a system with two discrete electronic levels and need to be treated somewhat differently for a semiconductor. Fermi rather than Boltzmann statistics must be applied. On this basis it is possible to derive the condition that must be satisfied in a semiconductor to make the net stimulated emission rate positive, as first formulated by Bernard and Duraffourg.[1] It is also possible to show the relationship between the shape of the absorption edge and the spectrum of the spontaneous emission.

In Section 2.3 we discuss the probability of electron radiative transitions between conduction and valence band and impurity states. We introduce the dipole matrix element and show how the **k** selection rules determine the transition probability in different situations. By considering the behaviour of a bound electron we introduce the concepts necessary in treating the localized electron states in the band tails of highly doped semiconductors.

In Section 2.4 we consider the density of states distribution in the conduction and valence band of the semiconductor and again use the bound impurity state as a means of introducing the band-tailing effects in highly doped material.

In Section 2.5 we discuss the radiative recombination rate between electrons and holes. This is important in determining the current density that accompanies any particular degree of inversion. It leads to the relation between optical gain and current density that is presented in Section 2.6.

In Section 2.7 we consider the threshold condition for lasing and discuss the behaviour of the light/current characteristic as the current is increased beyond threshold. This treatment includes the effect on incremental efficiency of both the gain saturation at high output and of the spontaneous contribution to the lasing mode at currents close to threshold. In the latter instance the number of modes excited in the laser resonator must also be taken into account and this is dealt with in Section 2.8.

2.2   RELATION BETWEEN EMISSION AND ABSORPTION PROCESSES

In this section we investigate the various general relations that exist in semiconductor materials between spontaneous emission, stimulated emission, absorption and gain. These relations depend not on the particular characteristics of the semiconductor but on the fundamental properties of photons, as enunciated by Einstein, and on the laws of Fermi–Dirac statistics. The treatment is a development of that used for a simple atomic system with pairs of discrete electron energy levels only, and parallels it in many respects. However, the continuous nature of the allowed electronic energy bands in the semiconductor, which broadens the spectrum and demands the use of Fermi–Dirac statistics to determine the occupation of the states, changes certain aspects of the picture and leads to different forms for expressing the relationships.

A considerable understanding of the radiative interactions can be obtained by considering the behaviour of the electron/photon system in the semiconductor under conditions of thermal equilibrium. This leads to the so-called Einstein relations. The system can then be investigated under non-equilibrium conditions and further relationships between stimulated and spontaneous emission can be obtained. In the process of the analysis it is necessary to utilize the general expression for the spectral density of thermal radiation and to employ Fermi–Dirac statistics in conjunction with the distribution of states in the bands of the semiconductor. For completeness we briefly introduce these topics before proceeding with the rest of the analysis.

2.2.1   Thermal Radiation

The standard procedure[2] for deriving the spectral density of thermal radiation in a material is to consider the effect of isolating an appreciable volume of the material in an optical resonator and to treat the modes of the resonator. To yield a useful result the resonator must be large enough for the spectral modes to approach reasonably close to a continuum. Then it is possible to define a meaningful average value of the spectral density over a bandwidth which is small but still large enough to contain at least several modes. Further insight can be obtained by limiting the range of radiation under consideration in other ways. For instance, it may be restricted to a certain solid angle in space. In the case of a laser it is frequently of interest to consider the radiation density in a single mode. We will consider here the two descriptions which are most generally used, namely the radiation density per mode and the total radiation density per unit bandwidth.

The Bose–Einstein distribution, which applies to particles like photons that are not subject to the Pauli exclusion principle, gives the number of photons of energy $h\nu$ per mode of the optical resonator at temperature T. If the photon density per mode is ϕ and the volume of the resonator is V then the expression for the number of photons per mode ϕV is

$$\phi V = \left\{ \exp\left(\frac{h\nu}{kT}\right) - 1 \right\}^{-1} \tag{2.1}$$

The photon density per unit frequency range at energy $h\nu$, which we will represent by $P(h\nu)$, is obtained by multiplying the photons per mode in (2.1) by the mode density at energy $h\nu$ per unit bandwidth in the resonator, which we will denote by $Z(h\nu)$. $Z(h\nu)$ tends to a fixed value as the size of the resonator is increased, as we show below.

For convenience we take the resonator to be a cube of edge dimension L. Let the modes be made up of plane waves of wave-vector $\mathbf{k}$ within the material whose components along the x, y, and z axes of the cube are given by k_x, k_y, and k_z. Such waves are resonant when

$$k_x = \frac{m\pi}{L}; \qquad k_y = \frac{p\pi}{L}; \qquad k_z = \frac{q\pi}{L} \tag{2.2}$$

where m, p, and q are integers. Each mode can therefore be considered to occupy a volume π^3/L^3 in $\mathbf{k}$ space.

Let us evaluate the density Δm of modes spanning a range δk in the magnitude of the wave-vector. These modes occupy one quadrant of a spherical shell in $\mathbf{k}$ space of radius k, thickness δk, and volume $\frac{1}{2}\pi k^2 \delta k$. The total number of modes per unit volume is obtained by dividing by the volume per mode with $L = 1$ and is given by

$$\Delta m = \left(\frac{k}{\pi}\right)^2 \delta k \tag{2.3}$$

where an additional factor of 2 is introduced to allow for the two possible polarizations of the modes.

We may express the magnitude of $\mathbf{k}$ and its derivative in terms of the photon energy E in eV as follows

$$k = \frac{2\pi\mu E}{hc}$$

$$\delta k = 2\pi \left\{ \frac{\mu + E\,d\mu/dE}{hc} \right\} \delta E \tag{2.4}$$

where μ is the refractive index and h is Planck's constant. $(\mu + E\,d\mu/dE)$ is a group refractive index which takes account of dispersion and which crops up in various contexts. In what follows we will represent it by $\bar{\mu}$.

To evaluate $\Delta m/\delta E$, which is equal to $Z(h\nu)$, the mode density at photon energy $h\nu$ per unit energy interval of bandwidth, we insert the expression for k and δk in (2.4) into (2.3). This gives

$$Z(h\nu) = \frac{8\pi}{(hc)^3}\, \mu^2 \bar{\mu} E^2$$

$$= 13.17\, \mu^2\bar{\mu}\left(\frac{h\nu}{e}\right)^2 \mu m^{-3}\, eV^{-1} \tag{2.5}$$

where e is the electronic charge and $(h\nu/e)$ is measured in electronvolts.

Multiplying the expression for the mode density in (2.5) by the number of photons per mode in (2.1) gives the thermal photon density $P(E)$ at energy E per unit energy interval of bandwidth as follows

$$P(E) = \frac{\{8\pi/(hc)^3\}\mu^2\bar{\mu}E^2}{\exp(E/kT) - 1}$$

$$= \frac{13.17\, \mu^2\bar{\mu}(h\nu/e)^2}{\exp(h\nu/kT) - 1}\, \mu m^{-3}\, eV^{-1} \tag{2.6}$$

where $(h\nu/e)$ is measured in electronvolts.

2.2.2. Density of Electron States and Occupation Probability

The distribution of electrons in the conduction band and of holes in the valence band of a semiconductor can be conveniently expressed in terms of the density $\rho(E)$ of states at any particular energy E, multiplied by the fractional occupation of the states. This is closely analogous to the description used for the spectral distribution of photons in the previous section. The energy states are modes of the electronic wave-function which are very similar to the optical modes. However, the occupation of the states is different from that of the optical modes, being determined by Fermi–Dirac statistics rather than by Bose–Einstein statistics. This is because electrons differ from photons in being subject to the Pauli exclusion principle which prevents more than one electron occupying an indentical state.

The density of states per unit energy for electrons and holes in a pure semiconductor can be derived from the electronic wave functions in a very similar way to the mode density per unit energy for radiation. This is described in very many standard texts on semiconductors.[3] Each state of the electron corresponds to a particular standing wave pattern of the wave-function with a particular value of the wave-vector $\mathbf{k}$. Again we consider the properties of a cube of side L isolated within the semiconductor. The components of $\mathbf{k}$ in each state must satisfy the same conditions

$$k_x = \frac{m\pi}{L} ; \qquad k_y = \frac{p\pi}{L} \quad \text{and} \quad k_z = \frac{q\pi}{L} \tag{2.7}$$

Each state occupies the same volume in **k** space of π^3/V where $V = L^3$ is the volume of the cube. The number of states $\rho(k)\delta k$ per unit volume in an interval δk of $|\mathbf{k}|$ is given as before by the volume of one-eighth of a spherical shell of thickness δk as follows

$$\rho(k)\delta k = \left(\frac{1}{\pi^2}\right) k^2 \, \delta k \tag{2.8}$$

where the concentration has been doubled to take account of the two possible spin directions. Band theory shows that the electrons and holes in the bands generally have values of effective masses that are different from that of a free electron. We will denote them by m_c and m_v, respectively. To obtain the density of states in terms of energy rather than k we use the relation $p = \hbar k$ for the momentum p and the relation energy $= p^2/2m$ to give the following expression for the energy E_c of the electron with respect to the bottom of the conduction band

$$E_c = \frac{\hbar^2 k^2}{2m_c} \tag{2.9}$$

and for the energy E_v of the hole also measured with respect to the same zero

$$-(E_v + E_g) = \frac{\hbar^2 k^2}{2m_v} \tag{2.10}$$

where E_g is the band gap. Substituting E for k in equation (2.8) gives the density of states ρ_c for the conduction band and ρ_v for the valence band in the form

$$\rho_c = \frac{m_c (2m_c E_c)^{1/2}}{\pi^2 \hbar^3}$$

$$\rho_v = \frac{m_v \{2m_v(-E_g - E_v)^{1/2}\}}{\pi^2 \hbar^3} \tag{2.11}$$

In addition to the normal hole band, III/V semiconductors also have a light hole band the maximum energy of which is identical to that of the heavy hole band. Light holes have an effective mass that is not much greater than that of the electron, and their density of states is accordingly only a small fraction of the heavy hole density of states. Because of the small density of states the light holes are very much in the minority, and their presence can normally be neglected in comparison with the heavy holes.

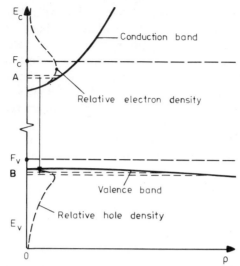

Figure 2.3 Diagrammatic plot of relation between density of electron states and electron energy in conduction and valence bands of typical semiconductor. Distribution of electrons and holes versus energy also shown for specific values of conduction band quasi-Fermi level F_c and valence band quasi-Fermi level F_v

A schematic illustration of a typical distribution of the density of states for both the conduction and valence band according to the above equations is given in Figure 2.3. In all the direct-gap III/V compound semiconductors the effective mass of an electron in the conduction band is almost an order of magnitude smaller than that of a normal hole in the valence band. For instance, in GaAs the ratio of the conduction band electron mass to the mass of a free electron is 0.067 whereas the same ratio for the normal hole is 0.55. Because the density of states is proportional to $m^{3/2}$ the density of states in the valence band is almost 25 times as great for comparable energy as that in the conduction band. This is indicated in the figure.

High-injected carrier concentration and particularly high doping modifies the density of states distribution given in equation (2.11), and this must be taken into account in considering the behaviour of many semiconductor lasers. The charge of the randomly distributed impurities and the charge of the injected free carriers result in potential fluctuations that create tails of states at the bottom of the conduction band and the top of the valence band. This behaviour will be treated separately in Section 2.4.

The second factor that determines the carrier distribution in the bands is the occupation of the available states. We will denote the average proportion of occupied states in the conduction band at some particular energy by f_c and the average proportion in the valence band by f_v. Fermi–Dirac statistics describes the occupation in terms of a Fermi energy. When there is perfect thermal equilibrium between the conduction and valence band a single Fermi level can be defined that uniquely determines the distribution of f_c and f_v over the whole range of energies of both hands. Injection of minority carriers into one or both bands destroys the equilibrium and upsets this simple description. However, provided the injection rate is not too large, the carriers in each of the bands may remain in close thermal equilibrium amongst themselves even though they are not in equilibrium with those in the opposite band. Under these conditions two different Fermi levels, so called quasi-Fermi levels, can be defined for the two separate bands in such a way as to give a very good approximation to the distribution of carriers within the bands. Let F_c be the energy of the quasi-Fermi level in the conduction band and F_v be the energy in the valence band. Then the occupation factors f_c and f_v at energy levels E_c and E_v in the two bands are given by

$$f_c = \left\{ \exp\left(\frac{E_c - F_c}{RT}\right) + 1 \right\}^{-1}$$

$$f_v = \left\{ \exp\left(\frac{E_v - F_v}{kT}\right) + 1 \right\}^{-1}$$

(2.12)

The Fermi levels F_c and F_v represent the points where the states are 50 per cent occupied.

The dashed curves in Figure 2.3 show the distribution of the electron and hole concentrations as a function of energy in the two bands. The curves represent the product of the Fermi function in equation (2.12) with the density of states in equation (2.11). A peak in the distribution of carrier concentration versus energy exists in both bands. At low total carrier concentration it lies very close to the bottom of the bands. As the total carrier concentration is increased the peak remains fairly stationary until the Fermi level moves into the band when it starts to move in the same direction.

The total carrier concentration is obtained by integrating the distribution of occupied states over the whole range of energy. The electron concentration n is thus given by

$$n = \int \left[\frac{\rho_c(E_c)}{\exp(E_c - F_c)/kT + 1} \right] dE_c$$

(2.13)

and the hole concentration p is given by

$$p = \int \left[\frac{\rho_v(E_v)}{\exp(F_v - E_v)/kT + 1} \right] dE_v \qquad (2.14)$$

2.2.3 Einstein Relations Between Transition Probabilities

There are certain relations between the stimulated, spontaneous, and absorptive transition probabilities in a semiconductor which can be derived by considering the conditions in thermal equilibrium. These are the so-called Einstein relations. We will carry out this derivation below, limiting our consideration to transitions between some particularly compact group of levels in the conduction band and some similar group in the valence band, as indicated in Figure 2.3 at A and B. First, however, we must discuss the factors that control the transition rates in each of the three processes.

One factor that affects the transition rates is the occupancy of the electronic levels concerned. Transitions cannot start at empty levels nor end at filled levels. The probability of a particular type of transition occurring is therefore proportional to the fraction of the starting levels that are occupied and of the finishing levels that are vacant.

The second factor, which is only of concern for stimulated and absorptive transitions, is the density of incident photons. We will classify the photons in two ways. In one case we will limit our consideration to the spectrally pure photons associated with a single mode of the resonator. In the second case we will take into account photons moving in a range of directions with energies spread over a spectral band. In the first case the photon emission rate per transition is taken to be proportional to the photon density in the single mode, which we will denote by ϕ. In the second case it is taken to be proportional to the incident photon density per unit bandwidth, which we will denote by $P(h\nu)$.

The third factor is the density of possible optical transitions per unit energy interval of optical bandwidth. This must obviously be taken into account if the photons cover a range of spectral energies. However, it must equally be taken into account when the exciting photons belong to a single mode of the optical resonator and are spectrally pure. The reason is that photons of one specific energy can excite electron transitions spanning a range of energies. Such excitations occur because the interaction time is finite. The quicker the interaction takes place the wider the range of transitions that may be involved. A quantum mechanical treatment[4] shows that the probability of a photon interacting with a single pair of levels is proportional to the square of the time. When a range of pairs of levels is involved the probability becomes directly proportional to the time because, as mentioned above, the number of interacting levels diminishes in inverse proportion to the time. Since we have already taken the probability to be linear with time we therefore need to include the density of states in the total expression for the probability.

We will denote the density of optical transitions per unit bandwidth for electrons of one of the two possible spin directions by $\rho_{red}(h\nu)$, the reduced density of states. $\rho_{red}(h\nu)$ is limited by the **k** selection rules and we need to determine which levels in the conduction band of the semiconductor can interact with which levels in the valence band. Perfect **k** conservation would require that each level in the conduction band be linked to only one level of similar spin in the valence band. Then $\rho_{red}(h\nu)$ could be written in the form $\delta N/2(\delta E_c + \delta E_v)$, where $\delta N/2$ is the incremental number of electronic states of one of the two spin directions (equal in the two bands) and δE_c and δE_v are the respective increments of energy in the conduction and valence band which, encompassing the same number of states, ensure that **k** values are equal. $\rho_{red}(h\nu)$ is therefore given by

$$\rho_{red}(h\nu) = \frac{1}{2}\left(\frac{1}{\rho_c} + \frac{1}{\rho_v}\right)^{-1} \tag{2.15}$$

where ρ_c and ρ_v are the density of states in the conduction and valence band, respectively. In practice there is considerable laxity in the selection rules but this does not affect the present argument and will not be further considered until the next section.

The fourth factor that determines the transition rate is the probability coefficient. We will define three probability coefficients, namely B_{12} for absorptive transitions, B_{21} for stimulated transitions, and A_{21} for spontaneous transitions. Because we have chosen exact selection rules these B and A coefficients describe all the transitions that take place for photon energy $h\nu$. We could alternatively define B and A as distribution functions that require to be integrated over a spread in energy of the initial and final states of the transitions. This is the form in which they will be presented in the next section. However, in either case the treatment that follows gives the same interrelationships between them.

Having defined the quantities upon which the transition rates depend we will now use the condition of detailed balance between the upward and downward transitions to relate the three different probability coefficients. We consider a condition of thermal equilibrium such that the two quasi-Fermi levels that describe the occupation of the states in equation (2.12) coincide. Let us first take the case where the incident photons have a continuous spectral distribution. The rate r_{12} of absorptive transitions per unit volume per unit bandwidth is given by

$$r_{12} = B_{12}f_v(1 - f_c)\rho_{red}(h\nu)P(h\nu) \tag{2.16}$$

The rate r_{21} of stimulated transitions per unit volume per unit bandwidth is given by

$$r_{21} = B_{21}f_c(1 - f_v)\rho_{red}(h\nu)\, P(h\nu) \tag{2.17}$$

B_{21} and B_{12} have dimensions (energy × volume/time). The rate of spontaneous transitions per unit volume per unit bandwidth is given by

$$r_{21}(\text{spon}) = A_{21}f_c(1 - f_v)\rho_{red}(h\nu) \tag{2.18}$$

A_{21} has dimensions of time^{-1}. In equilibrium the rate of upward and downward transitions must be equal. Using this condition and substituting in the above equations for f_c and f_v from equation (2.12) with equal values of the Fermi energy in the conduction and valence band, gives the following expression for the thermal radiation spectrum $P(h\nu)$

$$P(h\nu) = \frac{A_{21}}{B_{12}\exp(E_c - E_v)/kT - B_{21}} \tag{2.19}$$

Comparing this expression with equation (2.6) for $P(h\nu)$ obtained in a previous section shows that the two expressions can be made consistent at all temperatures if we put

$$B_{12} = B_{21} \tag{2.20}$$

and

$$A_{21} = Z(h\nu)B_{21} \tag{2.21}$$

We can perform the same analysis whilst limiting the consideration to transitions associated with a single optical mode. In this case we compare transition rates per unit volume rather than per unit volume per unit bandwidth. By equating the resulting expression for photon density ϕ with equation (2.1) we obtain the same equality between B_{12} and B_{21}. However the A coefficient, which we denote in this case by A'_{21}, is different, being given by:

$$A'_{21} = B_{21}/V \tag{2.22}$$

Its dimensions are also different, namely energy^{-1} time^{-1} rather than time^{-1} as previously.

2.2.4 Total Stimulated Emission Rate

We have so far only considered transitions between certain selected states in the conduction band and the states in the valence band that are appropriately separated from them to produce photons of a particular energy $h\nu$. In general, as mentioned above, there are a range of possible starting and finishing states that are capable of emitting photons of the same energy, and so we must widen the number of states that we consider. The extent of the range concerned is associated with the degree of **k** selection involved in the transition. Strong **k** selection limits the number of states that participate. Without committing ourselves to any particular amount of **k** selection we can formally make allowance for this behaviour by allowing the transition probability B_{21} between pairs of states to depend on the starting and finishing energy of the states involved. We may, for instance, specify the particular transition by quoting the energy of the conduction band state E_c and the photon energy $h\nu$ of the transition. We therefore write the transition probability per unit spread of energy in the conduction band for the value of $h\nu$ and E_c concerned and for volume V as $B_{21}(E_c,h\nu)\rho_c(E_c)V$. $B_{21}(E_c,h\nu)$ has dimensions energy^2 × volume^2/time. It normally contains V^{-1} so that V cancels out in the whole expression. (Note that we could equally well have written the transition probability in terms of the valence band energy E_v and $B_{21}(E_v,h\nu)\rho_v(E_v)$, where $E_v = E_c - h\nu$.) To obtain the total rate of stimulated emission we multiply the transition probability per unit energy by the density $\rho_{red}(h\nu)$ of optical transition per unit bandwidth and by the appropriate occupation factors and the photon density, as for equations (2.16) and (2.17), and integrate over E_c.

Let us first use this procedure to write down an expression for the net stimulated emission rate per unit volume per unit energy interval of bandwidth at photon energy $h\nu$. The net rate per unit volume is obtained by integrating over E_c the difference between the downwards transitions as given by equation (2.17) and the upwards transitions as given by equation (2.16) using $B_{21} = B_{12}$. We represent the rate by $r_{stim}(h\nu)$ and after substituting $\rho_{red}(h\nu)$, using equation (2.15), obtain the following expression

$$r_{stim}(h\nu) = P(h\nu) \int_{-\infty}^{\infty} B_{21}(E_c, h\nu)V\rho_c(E_c)\rho_v(E_c - h\nu)(f_c - f_v)\left(1 + \frac{\rho_v}{\rho_c}\right)^{-1} dE_c$$

$$= P(h\nu)w_{stim}(h\nu) \qquad (2.23)$$

where we have introduced a symbol $w_{stim}(h\nu)$ to represent the value of the integral. (Note, if we had integrated with respect to dE_v we would replace the term $(1 + \rho_v/\rho_c)^{-1}$ in the integral by $(1 + \rho_c/\rho_v)^{-1}$.

The dimensions in which we choose to express r_{stim} and P in equation (2.23) are immaterial provided that they match one another. Thus, the equation might equally well represent a relation between the stimulated emission per unit volume in a single mode of a cavity and the photon density in that mode. Alternatively, we might restrict $r_{stim}(h\nu)$ and $P(h\nu)$ to a particular solid angle of photon density per unit bandwidth. The latter is a useful form for the consideration of gain in plane waves.

2.2.5 Condition for Net Stimulated Emission

A study of equation (2.23) shows that it is possible to write down the condition that the net stimulated emission be positive, provided equilibrium amongst electrons in each band is sufficient to enable equation (2.12) to be used for f_c and f_v. For instance, if f_c is greater than f_v over the whole range of the integration then there must be net positive stimulated emission. Inserting $E_v = E_c - h\nu$ into the expression for f_v in equation (2.23) one finds that the requirement for f_c to be greater than f_v is

$$\exp \frac{(E_c - h\nu - F_v)}{kT} > \exp \frac{(E_c - F_c)}{kT} \qquad (2.24)$$

or, more simply

$$F_c - F_v > h\nu \qquad (2.25)$$

Notice that E_c has been eliminated from the inequality in (2.25). Hence, if (2.25) is satisfied $f_c - f_v$ is positive in equation (2.23) over the whole range of E_c (although not constant). The stimulated emission is therefore positive irrespective of the selection rules that determine B_{21} and the exact form of the density of states distributions in the bands. The condition in (2.25) was first pointed out by Bernard and Duraffourg.[1] It states that net stimulated emission occurs for all transitions where the photon energy $h\nu$ is less than the separation of the two quasi-Fermi levels $(F_c - F_v)$. If the material concerned has a definite forbidden gap E_g then $(F_c - F_v)$ must be greater than E_g before any stimulated emission can occur. The E/k diagram in Figure 2.4 illustrates an example of the Bernard and Duraffourg condition. Typical values of the Fermi energies are indicated and the range of transitions is shown that can produce net stimulated emission when **k** is conserved.

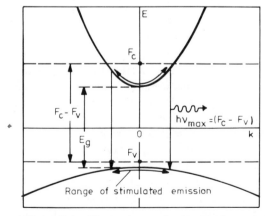

Figure 2.4 Illustration of Bernard and Duraffourg condition. Shows range of k for transitions with net stimulated emission for particular value of quasi-Fermi level separation

2.2.6 Spontaneous Emission Rate and Relation with Stimulated Emission and Absorption

We will use the same procedure to write down the expression for the total spontaneous emission at photon energy $h\nu$ that we used in a previous section to obtain the stimulated emission, and we will then relate the two expressions. Denoting the rate of spontaneous emission per unit volume per unit bandwidth for photons of energy $h\nu$ by $r_{spon}(h\nu)$ and using the relation between the A and B coefficients given in equation (2.21) leads to the following expression

$$r'_{spon}(h\nu) = Z(h\nu) \int_{-\infty}^{\infty} B_{21}(E_c, h\nu) V \rho_c(E_c) \rho_v(E_c - h\nu) f_c (1 - f_v) \left(1 + \frac{\rho_v}{\rho_c}\right)^{-1} dE_c$$

$$= Z(h\nu) w_{spon}(h\nu) \tag{2.26}$$

Once again we have represented the value of the integral by a separate symbol, $w_{spon}(h\nu)$.

The expressions for $w_{stim}(h\nu)$ and $w_{spon}(h\nu)$ in equations (2.23) and (2.26) are very similar, and an exact relation can be obtained between them. To obtain w_{stim} from w_{spon} we must insert the factor $(f_c - f_v)/f_c(1 - f_v)$ into the integral over E_c for w_{spon}. However, if we assume quasi-equilibrium in the band and use equation (2.12) for f_c and f_v we find that the ratio $(f_c - f_v)/f_c(1 - f_v)$ is independent of E_c and may be taken outside the integral. This gives

$$w_{stim}(h\nu) = w_{spon}(h\nu) \left[1 - \exp\left(\frac{h\nu - (F_c - F_v)}{kT}\right)\right] \tag{2.27}$$

Since $w_{spon}(h\nu)$ is always positive, equation (2.27) is an alternative formulation of the Bernard and Duraffourg condition in equation (2.25) showing that there is only net positive stimulated emission if $(F_c - F_v) > h\nu$. Another interesting point arises when $(F_c - F_v) \gg h\nu$. Equation (2.27) then shows that $w_{stim}(h\nu) \simeq w_{spon}(h\nu)$. According to equations (2.23) and (2.26) this means that at high pumping rates the spontaneous emission at any wavelength is equal to the stimulated emission that would occur with one photon per mode—which is the relation familiar in two-level lasers.

We can use equation (2.27) to find the shape of the spontaneous emission spectrum in terms of the shape of the absorption edge of the semiconductor, provided the excitation is well below the lasing level. Thus, at low pumping rates, when $F_c - F_v$ in equation (2.27) is small, $w_{stim}(h\nu)$ turns negative and becomes proportional to the passive absorption coefficient $\alpha(h\nu)$ in the semiconductor. The exact relation, whose derivation is analogous to that for optical gain given in section 2.2.7, is as follows

$$\alpha(h\nu) = -(\mu/c)\, w_{stim}(h\nu) \tag{2.28}$$

where c is the velocity of light. Using the relation between the spontaneous emission rate r_{spon} and w_{spon} in equation (2.26), inserting this into equation (2.27) and ignoring unity compared with the exponential term in the bracket of that equation, gives the following relation between the spontaneous emission spectrum and the absorption spectrum

$$r_{spon}(h\nu) \simeq \exp\left\{\frac{F_c - F_v}{kT}\right\} \frac{cZ(h\nu)\alpha(h\nu)}{\mu \exp(h\nu/kT)} \tag{2.29}$$

This relation continues to apply with an increasing injection level until the population of the bands approach inversion. Figure 2.5 shows the application of the relationship.[5] The measured spectral distribution of the absorption coefficient of GaAs at 300 K is illustrated in Figure 2.5a and the spontaneous emission spectrum calculated from it is illustrated in Figure 2.5b.

2.2.7   Optical Gain

An optical wave passing through an inverted region of the semiconductor experiences gain as a result of the stimulated emission. The gain of the wave can be expressed in the form

$$F(z) = F_o \exp(gz) \tag{2.30}$$

where z is the direction of propagation, $F(z)$ is the photon flux per unit area, F_o is a constant, and g is the gain per unit length. We wish to express the gain in terms of the stimulated emission rate. Differentiating equation (2.30) with respect to z and converting it to an expression for g shows that the gain is given by the ratio of the additional flux of photons created per unit volume divided by the total photon flux of the optical wave.

The additional flux of photons created per unit volume is equal to the stimulated emission rate r_{stim} in that volume. In the situation which frequently occurs in practice, where the optical wave extends sideways into a loss-free region outside the pumped region and occupies a larger effective cross section, the average rate of stimulated emission per unit volume over the whole cross section is reduced in the ratio of the effective cross sections, which we represent by a confinement factor Γ, giving an average rate of Γr_{stim}.

The photon flux F of the wave should be expressed in terms of the photon density $P(h\nu)$, since this is the quantity used in equation (2.23) for r_{stim}. F corresponds to the flux of photons resulting from photons of density $P(h\nu)$

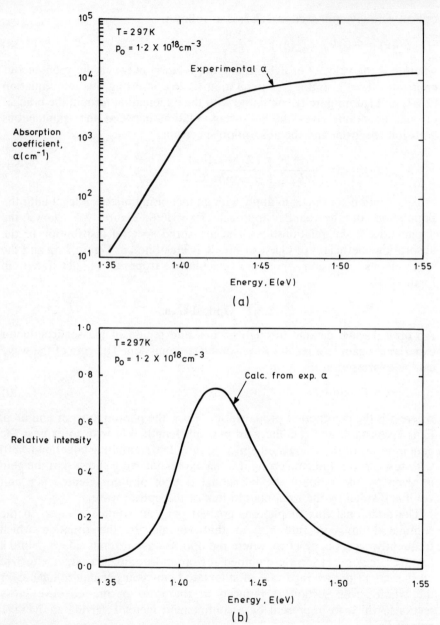

Figure 2.5   (a) Measured absorption coefficient of GaAs for $p = 1.2 \times 10^{18}$ cm^{-3}.
(b) Spontaneous emission spectrum calculated from measured absorption coefficient.
After Casey and Stern[5]

travelling at the velocity c/μ of light in the material. Hence, from equation (2.23) we obtain the following relation for the gain g

$$g(h\nu) = \left(\frac{\Gamma\mu}{c}\right)\int_{-\infty}^{\infty} B(E_c)\rho_c(E_c)\rho_v(E_c - h\nu)(f_c - f_v)\left(1 + \frac{\rho_v}{\rho_c}\right)^{-1} dE_c$$

$$g(h\nu) = \left(\frac{\Gamma\mu}{c}\right) w_{\text{stim}}(h\nu) \tag{2.31}$$

which in view of the definition of the quantities in equation (2.23) is equally valid for plane waves and for guided modes.

2.3   TRANSITION PROBABILITIES

The transition probability $B_{21}(h\nu)$ is the basic quantity that determines the transition rate of electrons between upper and lower levels in the presence of radiation, as given in equation (2.23), and also determines the rate of spontaneous emission between the same levels, as given in equation (2.26). To evaluate B_{21} we must consider the mechanisms by which the electrons in the semiconductor interact with radiation. This involves the quantum mechanics of the system. It is necessary to investigate how the wave-functions of the electron, as they are determined by the spatially varying potentials associated with the lattice, are affected by the potential associated with the incident electro-magnetic field. The appropriate treatment is to use time dependent perturbation of the Schroedinger equation, as described in standard texts on quantum mechanics.[4] By this means the effect of the incident radiation can be expressed in terms of the wave-functions that describe the system in the absence of radiation. We will take this as our starting point and quote the value of the transition probability that is obtained in terms of atomic constants and in terms of a momentum matrix element which associates the wave-functions of the initial and final states of the system. The expression is

$$B_{21}(h\nu) = \frac{e^2 h}{2m^2\epsilon_0\mu^2(h\nu)}|M|^2 \tag{2.32}$$

where ϵ_o is the permittivity of free space, e and m are the charge and mass of the electron and M is the matrix element of the momentum operator connecting the wave-function of the upper state, say $\psi_2(\mathbf{r})$, to the wave-function of the lower state, say $\psi_1(\mathbf{r})$. B_{21} has the dimensions (energy × length^3 + time) such that when multiplied by a density of either electron states or optical modes per unit energy per unit volume it gives a rate in s^{-1}. M is given by

$$M = \left(\frac{h}{2\pi j}\right)\int \psi_2^*(\mathbf{r})\nabla_A\psi_1(\mathbf{r})d^3\mathbf{r} \tag{2.33}$$

where ∇_A is the component of the grad operator along the direction of the electrical vector of the electromagnetic field. M is also referred to as the dipole matrix element and the quantity $2|M|^2/m(h\nu)$, which is a dimensionless number, is called the oscillator strength.

From equations (2.33) and (2.32) it can be seen that the evaluation of the matrix element M and the transition probability B_{21} involves first finding the wave-functions that describe the conduction and valence band states of the semiconductor and then performing the integration. The basic wave-functions for a pure semiconductor are of course those that must be derived in the course of determining the band structure of the material. We will consider them only in general terms to illustrate the behaviour in the presence of impurities. In an impure material the wave-functions, which are perturbed, can be expressed in terms of an infinite series of the unperturbed wave-functions of the ideal semiconductor, and the emission and absorption properties can similarly be expressed in terms of a 'smeared' version of the properties of the pure semiconductor.

2.3.1 Band-to-band Transition (k selection)

First we discuss the transition probability for a pure semiconductor and indicate how the **k** selection rules arise. For this purpose it is not necessary to evaluate the wave-functions but simply to consider certain general properties that they exhibit stemming from the periodicity of the lattice. General solutions[6] of the wave equation show that in a periodic potential all wave-functions can be expressed as the product of a function that has the periodicity of the lattice, commonly called a Bloch function, which we will denote by $u(\mathbf{r})$, and a phase function determined by some wave-vector **k**. Let us consider a single electron and a single hole confined within a volume V. According to the preceding argument we may therefore write normalized wave-functions $\psi_2(\mathbf{r})$ for the electron and $\psi_1(\mathbf{r})$ for the hole in the form

$$\psi_2(\mathbf{r}) = V^{-1/2}u_2(\mathbf{r})\exp(j\mathbf{k}_c \cdot \mathbf{r}) \tag{2.34}$$

$$\psi_1(\mathbf{r}) = v^{-1/2}u_1(\mathbf{r})\exp(j\mathbf{k}_v \cdot \mathbf{r}) \tag{2.35}$$

where $\mathbf{k}_c$ and $\mathbf{k}_v$ are the plane wave vectors appropriate to the conduction and valence band states respectively, and the functions $u(\mathbf{r})$ are normalized to unit volume. Inserting these two relationships into equation (2.33) for the matrix element M and taking the direction of polarization of the light to be parallel to $\mathbf{k}_v$ gives the following expression for the band-to-band matrix element M_{bb}

$$M_{bb} = \frac{h}{2\pi j} V^{-1} \int \exp\{j(\mathbf{k}_v - \mathbf{k}_c) \cdot \mathbf{r}\}u_2^*(\mathbf{r})(j\mathbf{k}_v + \nabla_A)u_1(\mathbf{r})d^3\mathbf{r} \tag{2.36}$$

Of the functions of $\mathbf{r}$ within the integral in the above expression $u_1(\mathbf{r})$ and $u_2(\mathbf{r})$ both have a periodicity equal to that of the lattice, whereas $\exp\{j(\mathbf{k}_v - \mathbf{k}_c) \cdot \mathbf{r}\}$ has in general a different periodicity, in which case the interaction of $\exp\{j(\mathbf{k}_v - \mathbf{k}_c) \cdot \mathbf{r}\}$ with the first two functions reduces the value of the integral to zero. Only if $(\mathbf{k}_v - \mathbf{k}_c)$ is zero does the integral have a non-zero value. Thus, the only states in the conduction and valence band between which transitions can be made are those with identical $\mathbf{k}$ values.

To obtain the value of M_{bb} from (2.36) when $\mathbf{k}_v = \mathbf{k}_c$ it is necessary to know the form of the Bloch functions. We will not investigate these functions more specifically but use the value of $|M_{bb}|^2$ that has been reported for III/V compounds in the literature. The appropriate value averaged over all directions in space, is given approximately by[7]

$$|M_{bb}|^2 \simeq \frac{m^2 E_g}{3m_c} \frac{1 + \Delta/E_g}{1 + \frac{2}{3}\Delta/E_g} \left\{1 - \frac{m_c}{m}\right\} \tag{2.37}$$

where m is the free electron mass, m_c is the effective mass of the electron in the conduction band, E_g is the band-gap, and Δ is the spin–orbit splitting. For GaAs with $m_c = 0.067$ m, $E_g = 1.42$ eV, and $\Delta = 0.33$ eV we have

$$|M_{bb}|^2 = 4.96 \, m E_g \tag{2.38}$$

Inserting (2.37) into equation (2.32) for the transition probability and taking $h\nu \simeq E_g$ we find

$$B_{21} = \frac{e^2 h}{6m_c \epsilon_0 \mu^2} \frac{1 + \Delta/E_g}{1 + \frac{2}{3}\Delta/E_g} \left\{1 - \frac{m_c}{m}\right\} \tag{2.39}$$

This expression for B_{21} contains relatively few variables. It is largely independent of the band-gap E_g and the only quantity that varies much between different semiconductors is m_c, the effective mass of the electron.

2.3.2   Transition between Impurity Level and Opposite Band

As a second example we will consider the interaction between a carrier from one band that is bound to a charged impurity and a free carrier in the opposite band, and derive the transition probability. This illustrates a situation where the $\mathbf{k}$ selection rules are relaxed. The wave-function $\psi_b(\mathbf{r})$ for the bound carrier can be written as the product of a Bloch function $u_2(\mathbf{r})$ associated with the lattice and a wave-function $\psi_{env}(\mathbf{r})$ that has the properties of the 1s state of hydrogen atom.[6] Thus

$$\psi_b(\mathbf{r}) = \psi_{env}(\mathbf{r}) \, u_2(\mathbf{r}) \tag{2.40}$$

$\psi_{env}(r)$ has the form

$$\psi_{env}(\mathbf{r}) = \pi^{-1/2}\left(\frac{1}{a^*}\right)^{3/2} \exp\left(\frac{-\mathbf{r}}{a^*}\right) \tag{2.41}$$

where $a^* = \epsilon_o \epsilon h^2 / \pi m_{eff} e^2$ is the effective Bohr radius of the bound carrier (typically 10^{-6} cm for electrons and 10^{-7} cm for holes in GaAs).

The free carrier of opposite type is taken as occupying a volume V and its wave function is the same as given previously in equation (2.35).

The expression for the band to impurity matrix element M_{bi} is obtained by inserting these two wave-functions into equation (2.33). Manipulation of the expression in equation (2.33) shows that M_{bi} can be represented by the product of the band-to-band matrix element M_{bb} and a second term associated with the envelope function $\psi_{env}(\mathbf{r})$ which we will call M_{env}. Thus

$$M_{bi} = M_{bb}M_{env} \tag{2.42}$$

Performing the appropriate integration of equation (2.33) gives

$$|M_{env}|^2 = \frac{64\pi a^{*3}}{(1 + a^{*2}k_v^2)^4 V} \tag{2.43}$$

This relation, which was first derived by Eagles[8] and Dumke,[9] is illustrated in Figure 2.6, in which $|M_{env}|^2(V/a^{*3})$ is plotted against a^*k_v. The curve shows that the transitions available to the bound electron are mainly to hole states with a value of k_v less than $1/a^*$. As the hole concentration is increased, the transition probability of the bound electron at first rises approximately in proportion but then tends to a limiting value as the lower holes states are filled and as $|M_{env}|^2$ for the higher energy hole states tends towards zero. Let us calculate this limiting value. The number of hole states δp per unit volume of the same spin as the electron and lying between k_v and

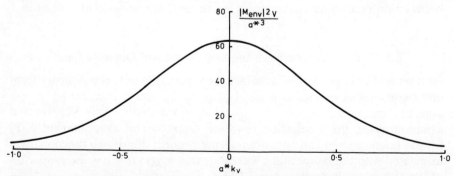

Figure 2.6 Probability of radiative recombination between carrier bound to impurity and free carrier in opposite band as a function of product of wave vector $\mathbf{k_v}$ of free carrier and Bohr radius a^* of bound state. Probability given in terms of envelope matrix element

$k_v + \delta k_v$ is half the number given in equation (2.8), namely

$$\delta p = \frac{k_v^2 \delta k_v}{2\pi^2} \tag{2.44}$$

Taking the product of δp with the expression for $|M_{\text{env}}|^2$ and integrating to infinity gives

$$\int \left(\frac{|M_{\text{env}}|^2}{\pi^3} \right) d^3 \mathbf{k}_v = 1 \tag{2.45}$$

Hence

$$\int |M_{\text{bi}}|^2 \, d^3 \mathbf{k}_v = |M_{\text{bb}}|^2.$$

This result illustrates the general rule that any state of the electron or hole which is modified on a macroscopic scale (large compared with the lattice spacing) but remains describable in terms of the normal wave-functions of the lattice has a combined matrix element coupling it to all states in the other band, whether similarly modified or not, which is always equal to the quantity M_{bb}. In other words, the total oscillator strength remains the same as before the modification.

It is informative to estimate the total concentration of hole states with which a bound electron can interact strongly or conversely the total concentration of electron states with which a bound hole can interact strongly. This is approximately obtained by dividing the transition probability per unit volume to a low energy state, into the total transition probability and multiplying the result by two to take into account both spin directions (since it is not possible to isolate only those carriers that have the same spin as the bound carrier). The concentration is $1/(32\pi a^{*3})$. Thus, setting $a^* = 10^{-6}$ cm for a bound electron and 10^{-7} cm for a bound hole we obtain values of the maximum concentrations that interact strongly of 10^{16} cm^{-3} hole states for a bound electron and 10^{19} cm^{-3} electron states for a bound hole. The transition probability to these states constitutes 0.43 of the total transition probability of the bound carrier. Of course to provide this concentration of fully occupied states an actual concentration of carriers must be injected which becomes progressively greater as the temperature rises.

2.2.3 Band-to-band Transition–Highly Doped Semiconductor

As a third example we consider the transition probabilities in a highly doped semiconductor between carriers in the opposite bands. As the doping level of the semiconductor is increased so the spacing between the impurity atoms decreases and eventually the orbitals of the neighbouring bound carriers start to overlap. The potential wells of individual impurities merge together and the carriers can no longer be described by simple hydrogenic wave-functions. A group of bound carriers becomes associated with an aggregate of impurity atoms and hence the individual carriers spread over a larger volume. This occurs in a random way since the impurities are not ordered with respect to the crystal lattice. Ionized free carriers are also present and additionally interfere with the binding by screening the bound carriers from the charge of the impurities. At a certain impurity concentration the distinction between bound and free carriers becomes vague. There is a continuous variation in the energy of the bound carriers and the degree of localization decreases on the average as the energy of the carrier increases.

Stern[10,4] has made a theoretical analysis of the transition probabilities in a highly doped semiconductor. To represent the semi-localized electronic states he has devised *ad hoc* wave-functions which have the combined properties of regular periodicity, as for a free electron, with exponentially decaying amplitudes away from the centre of localization, as for a bound electron. The *ad hoc* wave function is expressed in the form of a product between an envelope function and a Bloch function in the same way as for the bound electron, but the envelope function $\psi_{env}(\mathbf{r})$ is modified as follows

$$\psi_{env} = \left(\frac{\beta^3}{\pi}\right)^{1/2} \exp(j\mathbf{k} \cdot \mathbf{r}) \exp\{-\beta(\mathbf{r} - \mathbf{r}_i)\} \tag{2.46}$$

β is a coefficient which determines the rate at which the wavefunction decays away from the central point at $\mathbf{r} = \mathbf{r}_i$ and $\mathbf{k}$ is a wave-vector that describes the plane wave character of the wave-function. The allocation of values of $\mathbf{k}$ and β is carried out on the basis of the modified distribution of the density of states versus energy that applies in these conditions in which a tail is drawn out at the bottom of the band (see Section 2.4). The value of $\mathbf{k}$ for a particular state of the highly doped semiconductor, say the nth from the bottom on the energy scale, is taken to be equal to that of a free carrier in an undoped semiconductor in the nth state above the bottom of the parabolic band. The value of β is related to the amount in energy by which the nth state for the highly doped semiconductor is lower than the nth state in the parabolic band. These assumptions are largely arbitrary but have the merit of being accurate at the high and low energy limit.

The matrix element is obtained by substituting the *ad hoc* wave-functions into equation (2.33), integrating, and averaging over all the directions of the wave-vector and over all the positions where the localized wave-functions are centred. The result can be expressed in the same way as for the single bound carrier as the product of an envelope matrix element M_{env} with the band-to-band matrix element M_{bb}. All the information on the perturbation that exists in the highly doped semiconductor is contained in M_{env}.

The way that $|M_{env}|^2$ depends on the carrier energy in a highly p-doped

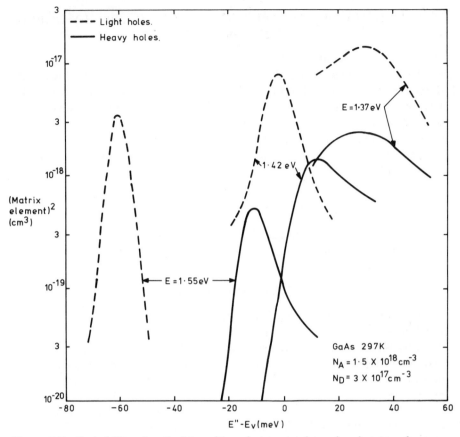

Figure 2.7   Probability of optical transitions between valence band states of energy given on abscissa and appropriate conduction band states to give photons of the three indicated energies. Applies to GaAs with 1.2×10^{18} cm^{-3} net p-doping. Note there are two sets of results for heavy hole and light hole band, respectively. After Casey and Stern[5]

sample is illustrated in Figure 2.7 $|M_{env}|^2 (1 + \rho_c/\rho_v)^{-1}$ is plotted as a function of the energy of the hole state measured from the nominal edge of the unperturbed valence band for three different photon energies. The valence band proper extends to the left of the diagram. The range of holes contributing to a given transition reduces as the energy of the holes increases, indicating that **k** selection increases as the states concerned move into the bands. Stern has used these matrix elements to calculate the spectral distribution of absorption and gain in doped GaAs and obtained good agreement with the measured results.

2.4 DENSITY OF ELECTRON STATES IN THE HIGHLY DOPED SEMICONDUCTOR

In this section we discuss the way the density of electronic states in the conduction and valence bands of the semiconductor are modified when the doping levels are high. The factor that causes the change is the electric field associated with the charge on each impurity. Regular spacing of concentrated impurities on a super-lattice would simply have the effect of broadening the isolated impurity levels into a continuous band. However, because in practice the spacing between the impurities is random, a considerably greater perturbation may occasionally occur as the result of a chance close spacing of several impurities. To take such effects into account a statistical analysis must be made. We first discuss a single impurity state and then give a brief account of the statistical analysis of many impurity states and present an example of a perturbed distribution of the density of states for high doping.

2.4.1 Impurity States

Let us consider a single impurity in an unionized condition with its carrier still bound to it. The carrier is confined in an orbital around the charged impurity which is very similar (see Section 2.3.2) to the 1s ground state in a hydrogen atom.[6] The radius of the orbital is, however, much greater than that in a hydrogen atom because (a) the electrical binding force is reduced by the high dielectric constant of the semiconductor (in GaAs, for example, the value of the dielectric constant is 13), and (b) the effective mass of the carrier, particularly in the case of an electron, is much less than that of a free electron. The Bohr radius a^* of the localized state is given by

$$a^* = \frac{\epsilon \epsilon_0 h^2}{\pi m_{\text{eff}} e^2} \tag{2.47}$$

where ϵ is the delectric constant, ϵ_0 is the permittivity of free space, m_{eff} is the effective mass of the carrier and e is the electronic charge. For GaAs a^* has a value of 100 Å for an electron and 10 Å for a hole. The binding energies of the states are respectively, 0.006 and 0.031 eV. One might have reservations about using an effective mass in equation (2.47) if a^* had dimensions not much greater than the lattice spacing but they are obviously dispelled when the above large values of a^* are obtained.

At high impurity concentration this simple picture of an impurity is no longer appropriate. The ionized carriers which are also present partially screen the charge of the impurity so that the orbital of the bound carrier enlarges and its binding energy decreases. The screening effect may be calculated as follows. In the potential well around each impurity there is a slight accumulation of free carriers. The additional concentration of these carriers can be derived from the effect of the local depression in the potential, say δV, on the filling of the states in the band. Thus, in equation (2.13) for the carrier concentration n the Fermi energy F_c is altered by an amount $e\delta V$. The additional free carriers contribute charge which modifies the potential. To find the change in the potential distribution a charge density that depends in an appropriate way on δV is inserted into Poisson's equation. The radial distribution of δV around the impurity can then be found. Instead of varying as $1/r$, as in the unscreened state, δV is found to depend approximately on r as follows[11]

$$\delta V = \frac{-e}{\epsilon\epsilon_0}\frac{1}{r}\exp\left(\frac{-r}{L_s}\right) \tag{2.48}$$

where L_s is a quantity with the dimensions of length which is reasonably constant for small changes in δV and is called the screening length. L_s is given by

$$L_s = \left\{\left(\frac{e^2}{\epsilon\epsilon_0}\right)\frac{dn}{dF}\right\}^{-1/2} \tag{2.49}$$

where dn/dF is the rate of change of carrier concentration with the Fermi energy F. When F lies in the band-gap (2.49) becomes

$$L_s \simeq \left(\frac{kT\epsilon\epsilon_0}{e^2 n}\right)^{1/2} \tag{2.50}$$

and when F lies well within the band (2.49) becomes

$$L_s \simeq \left(\frac{\epsilon\epsilon_0 h^2}{4\pi m_{\mathrm{eff}} e^2}\right)^{1/2}\left(\frac{\pi}{3n}\right)^{1/6} \tag{2.51}$$

The value of n taken in these relations should in principle be an appropriate average of the free carrier concentration in the vicinity of the impurity, but if the binding energy of the ground state of the impurity is small the value of the bulk free carrier concentration is adequate. Typically L_s lies around 1000 Å for $n = 10^{15}$ cm^{-3} and 100 Å for $n = 10^{17}$ cm^{-3}.

Figure 2.8 shows how the screened potential distribution of equation (2.48) compares with the normal unscreened distribution round a charged impurity. The depth and radius of the potential well is very considerably reduced in the screened case. The difference between the two distributions becomes proportionally greater with increasing radius and becomes important at a radius which is about one-third of the screening length.

Measurements in GaAs show that the ionization energy of donors starts to decrease at an electron concentration of 10^{15} cm^{-3} and goes to zero at about 2×10^{16} cm^{-3}.[12] Similarly, the ionization energy of acceptors starts to decrease at a hole concentration of 10^{17} cm^{-3} and goes to zero at about

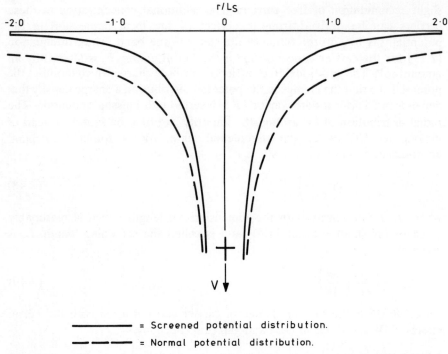

——————— = Screened potential distribution.

— — — — = Normal potential distribution.

Figure 2.8   Effect of screening by free carriers on the shape of the potential well in the vicinity of a charged impurity. Radial position co-ordinate r normalized to screening length L_s

$4 \times 10^{18} \, \text{cm}^{-3}$.[13] At the carrier concentration where the ionization energy goes to zero the screening length falls to around three times the Bohr radius in both cases. Such a reduction in the screening length is sufficient to indicate that the effect of screening is largely responsible for the fall in the ionization energy.

2.4.2   Band Tails

There is a second effect on the binding of the unionized carriers that occurs as the concentration of impurities increases: the orbitals of adjacent impurities start to overlap. This is of course enhanced by the effect of screening which causes the size of the orbitals to increase as their spacing decreases. The wave-functions of the electrons in adjacent orbitals interact and their energy levels are spread in such a way that an impurity band is formed. The breadth of the impurity band increases with increasing impurity concentration, and of course its centre also moves towards the conduction band as the ionization energy that we have already considered diminishes.

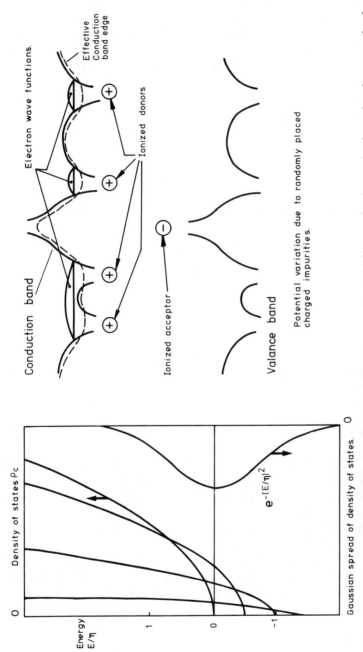

Figure 2.9 Diagramatic representation at right of fluctuations of potential in conduction and valence band as a result of charge of randomly spaced impurities. If fluctuations have a Gaussian distribution then average density of states in bands is summed from distributions of the type illustrated at left

When the two bands merge, bound and free carriers become virtually indistinguishable and the effective ionization energy is zero. However, the impurities are not regularly spaced and there will be certain regions where an aggregate of impurities produces a stronger local electrical binding field. The carriers associated with these impurities have an intermediate character between bound and free states and introduce a modification to the density of states at the edge of the band. This model provides a way of picturing how the charge of the impurities continue to have an influence on the band properties of the semiconductor even when the individual ionization energies of the carriers have decreased in zero.

The above model may be put into a quantitative statistical form. Figure 2.9 shows a schematic diagram of the way a high concentration of charged impurities affects the band structure. There are random up and down excursions of potential associated with local deficiencies and excesses of impurity charge. This irregularity on the average causes a smearing of the edges of the bands. The effect of such variations on the effective density of states was first treated by Kane.[14] He ascribed a Gaussian probability distribution to the size of the upward and downward excursions of potential and expressed the distribution of the effective density of states $\rho_{\text{eff}}(E_c)$ in terms of a root mean square voltage fluctuation V_{rms} as follows

$$\rho_{\text{eff}}(E_c) = \left\{ \frac{m_c(2m_c)^{1/2}}{\pi^2 \hbar^3} \right\} \eta^{1/2} \mathbf{y}\left(\frac{E_c}{\eta} \right) \tag{2.52}$$

where

$$\eta = 2^{1/2} V_{\text{rms}} \tag{2.53}$$

and where the coefficient in the first bracket is the same as for the normal density of states expression [see equation (2.11)] but where $E_c^{1/2}$ in the previous expression is replaced by $\eta^{1/2} \mathbf{y}(E_c/\eta)$, the function $\mathbf{y}$ being given by

$$\mathbf{y}(x) = \pi^{-1/2} \int_{-\infty}^{x} (x - z)^{1/2} \exp(-z^2) \, dz \tag{2.54}$$

Figure 2.10 shows how the function $\mathbf{y}(E_c/\eta)$ depends on E_c/η. When $E_c > \eta$, $\mathbf{y}(E_c/\eta) \simeq (E_c/\eta)^{1/2}$ and the expression in equation (2.52) for ρ_{eff} is very similar to the normal parabolic form. When $E_c < 0$, $\mathbf{y}(E_c/\eta)$ approaches the Gaussian form $\exp(-E_c^2/\eta^2)$ and causes a tail to be formed on the density of states distribution. The parameter η gives a convenient measure of the depth of the tail.

The magnitude of the root mean square voltage fluctuation V_{rms} that determines η depends on the square root of the total impurity concentration, of both donors and acceptors, and the square root of the screening length according to the relation

$$V_{\text{rms}} = \left(\frac{e^2}{4\pi\epsilon\epsilon_0} \right) \{ 2\pi(N_D + N_A)L_s \}^{1/2} \tag{2.55}$$

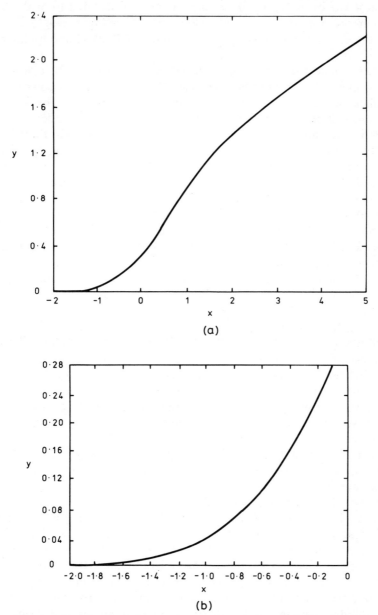

(a)

(b)

Figure 2.10   Density of states versus energy for the Kane bandtail model. Function y, described in text, plotted as a function of E_c/η where η depends on the r.m.s. voltage fluctuation of the bands. After Kane[14]

Typical values of the band tail parameter η, calculated from the above equation using a self-consistent value of the screening length L_s,[14] are $0.017\,\text{eV}$ for a p-doping of $10^{18}\,\text{cm}^{-3}$ and $0.027\,\text{eV}$ for a p-doping of $3 \times 10^{18}\,\text{cm}^{-3}$.

Kane's simple treatment, as expressed in equation (2.52), considerably over-estimates the depth of the band tail. This is because it assumes that all the tail states can be accounted for in the same way, i.e. by a random downwards displacement of the band edge to the necessary depth with no change in the band structure. However, any large downwards displacement is likely to occur very locally over a small volume close to an aggregate of charged impurities. Such a small volume no longer has the large number of closely spaced energy states for the carriers that are necessary to define a continuous density of states function. Indeed, the confinement may be so tight that the state of lowest energy lies appreciably above the bottom of the potential well. Because of this effect the regions of deeper downwards displacement in the band do not make a contribution to tail states that is proportionally equivalent to the shallower regions. The total depth of the tail is therefore reduced. This effect shows up more strongly in the conduction band than the valence band because of the lower effective mass of the electron and the consequent greater spacing of the states. Figure 2.9 gives a schematic indication of the behaviour in the conduction band and the dashed line indicates the position of the effective conduction band edge.

Halperin and Lax[15] have made an improved analysis of the density of tail states that takes into account the effect of the localization of the carriers in the deeper potential wells. The results that they have presented are expressed in terms of a normalized carrier energy related to the energy of the lowest state of the carrier in a potential well of width equal to π times the screening length. Generalized curves are given in terms of this normalized variable from which the density of states distribution can be computed. The reader who requires greater detail should consult the original publication.

Hwang[16] has compared the density of tail states as calculated for particular doping levels of the semiconductor by the Kane method and by the Halperin and Lax method, respectively. The curves are illustrated in Figure 2.11. They apply to a highly p-doped sample, half compensated by donors, and represent an extreme case of band-tailing. It is evident that the Halperin and Lax treatment gives a tail depth that is considerably reduced compared with that obtained from the Kane model, particularly for the case of the conduction band. The Halperin and Lax treatment is only applicable for the deeper tail states and it is necessary to use an interpolated curve, as shown in the figure, to join the tail states to the distribution in the main part of the band.

In many experimental measurements the band tails appear to have an

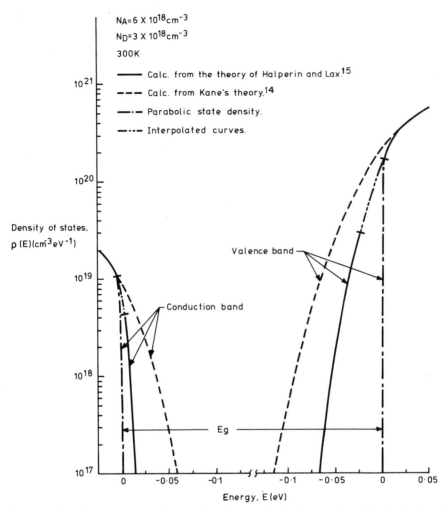

Figure 2.11 Comparison of the density of states in the band tails of GaAs obtained from the Kane model and the Halperin and Lax model. Curves apply for $N_A = 6 \times 10^{18}$ cm^{-3}, $N_D = 3 \times 10^{18}$ cm^{-3} at a temperature of 300 K and with the injection level required to give a gain of 100 cm^{-1}. After Hwang[16]

exponential shape. It is therefore often convenient to define the effective depth of the tails in terms of an empirical energy E_t such that

$$\rho_c \propto \exp \left(\frac{E_c}{E_t} \right)$$

$$\rho_v \propto \exp \left\{ \frac{-E_g - E_v}{E_t} \right\}$$

(2.56)

The presence of the tails increases the number of available states up to any particular value of the electron energy. Unger[17] has shown that the total concentration of injected carriers, for a given quasi-Fermi level F, is increased by the same amount as if the temperature were increased from T to $\{T^2 + (E_t/k)^2\}^{1/2}$.

Figure 2.12 shows a schematic band diagram for a p-type semiconductor of intermediate doping. Here the parabolic density of states distribution in the main part of both bands is combined with band tails and also with a hole impurity band. The hole impurity band is a significant feature for doping levels less than about 10^{18} cm^{-3} lying fairly deep in the valence band tail. In n-type material electron impurity bands would be a much less conspicuous feature because of the shallowness of the donor states and would merge with the conduction band at doping levels greater than about 3×10^{16} cm^{-3}.

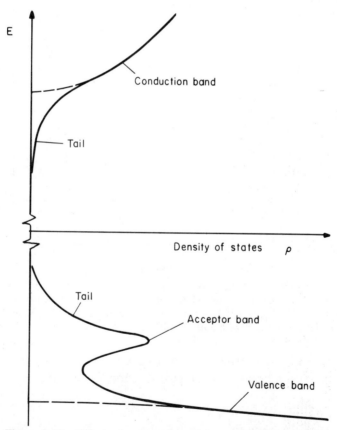

Figure 2.12   Effect of p-type impurities on density of states distribution for conduction and valence band, showing tails on both bands and impurity band (diagrammatic)

2.5   CARRIER RECOMBINATION AND SPONTANEOUS EMISSION

So far we have only considered the rate of spontaneous emission at a certain photon energy $h\nu$. It is necessary, however, to derive the total spontaneous emission over the whole spectrum in order to obtain an estimate of the injection current density and hence provide a reference level against which the other properties of the material may be evaluated. In a good semiconductor the spontaneous recombination represents the major part of the total recombination in the absence of lasing. The remainder involves non-radiative processes and occurs at deep centres and imperfections in the material or by the transference of the recombination energy into kinetic energy of free carriers (Auger effect, significant for narrow band-gap materials).

In this section we consider the total spontaneous emission not only in terms of the quasi-Fermi levels but also as a function of the concentration of carriers in the two bands. This will enable us to analyse the carrier recombination processes and to obtain the recombination times. First, we treat the condition where **k** selection is rigorous. The carrier radiative recombination times that apply in this condition are the minimum that can be observed in any circumstances. We then consider the effect of relaxing the selection rules and discuss the somewhat different recombination laws that then apply.

2.5.1   Recombination with Rigorous k Selection

The total spontaneous recombination per unit volume can be obtained by integrating over the whole range of $h\nu$ the expression in equation (2.18) for rigorous **k** selection or the expression in equation (2.26) for general selection rules. Let us take equation (2.18) first. Substituting for A_{21} from equation (2.21) we obtain

$$r_{\text{spon}}(\text{total}) = \int_a^\infty Z(h\nu)B_{21}(h\nu)f_c(1 - f_v)\rho_{\text{red}}(h\nu)\mathrm{d}(h\nu) \qquad (2.57)$$

where a is a suitable lower limit for the integration somewhat less than the band-gap energy. We express the integral in terms of the concentration of the minority carriers which, for example, we take to be electrons. We may put $f_c\rho_{\text{red}}(h\nu)\mathrm{d}(h\nu)$ in the integral of (2.57) equal to $\mathrm{d}n/2$, where n is the electron concentration (the $\frac{1}{2}$ arises because ρ_{red} applies to electrons of one spin only) and obtain

$$r_{\text{spon}}(\text{total}) = \frac{1}{2} \int_0^n Z(h\nu)B_{21}(h\nu)(1 - f_v)\,\mathrm{d}n \qquad (2.58)$$

The time constant τ associated with the recombination of each increment dn of the electron concentration within the integral is therefore given by

$$\tau = 2\{ZB_{21}(1 - f_v)\}^{-1} \tag{2.59}$$

where we have ignored the small variation of Z and B_{21} with $h\nu$. The minimum value of τ occurs when f_v tends to zero so that the valence band states to which a given electron can make a transition are completely empty. τ then tends to a value of $1/ZB_{21}$. Z and B_{21}. are given in equations (2.5) and (2.39), respectively. However, the expression for B_{21} applies to the recombination of electrons with normal holes only. When light holes are also taken into account, as they must be if the Fermi level in the valence band is low enough for the light hole states also to be vacant of electrons, the value of B_{21} is doubled.[7] The minimum limiting value of τ for electrons in all direct band-gap III/V semiconductors is then given by

$$\tau_{\text{limit}} = \frac{3m_c c\epsilon_0\lambda_0^2}{4\pi e^2\bar{\mu}} \frac{1 + \frac{2}{3}\Delta/E_g}{1 + \Delta/E_g} \left(1 - \frac{m_c}{m}\right)^{-1} \tag{2.60}$$

Inserting, for example, the following value appropriate to GaAs of $m_c = 0.067$ m, $\lambda_o = 0.87$ μm, $\bar{\mu} = 4.5$, $\Delta = 0.33$ eV, and $E_g = 1.42$ eV gives

$$\tau_{\text{limit}} = 0.25 \text{ ns} \tag{2.61}$$

The minimum recombination time for holes when the Fermi level lies sufficiently high in the conduction band is twice the above value.

As we explained in Section 2.3 on transition probability the above value of the recombination time is also applicable in the case where the selection rules are upset by any macroscopic perturbation of the carrier wave-functions provided that the hole concentration is sufficiently large that all holes are present with which the given electron can recombine. The results are of course reciprocal and apply equally well to n-doped material in which the recombination time of holes is considered.

2.5.2 Recombination with Relaxed k Selection

Let us now consider specifically the total spontaneous emission under more general conditions of **k** selection. For this case we take equation (2.26) and integrate it over the frequency band, obtaining

$$r_{\text{spon}}(\text{total}) = \int Z(h\nu)w_{\text{spon}}(h\nu) \, \text{d}(h\nu) \tag{2.62}$$

which can be represented as an integral over $h\nu$ and E_c as follows

$$r_{\text{spon}}(\text{total}) = \int_a^\infty Z(h\nu) \int_{-b}^\infty B(E_c, h\nu)V\rho_c(E_c)\rho_v(E_c - h\nu)f_c(1 - f_v)$$
$$\left(1 + \frac{\rho_v}{\rho_c}\right)^{-1} \text{d}E_c \, \text{d}(h\nu) \tag{2.63}$$

or as an integral over E_c and E_v as follows

$$r_{spon}(total) = \int_{-\infty}^{-b-a} \int_{-b}^{\infty} Z(E_c - E_v)B(E_c, E_v)V\rho_c(E_c)\rho_v(E_v)f_c(1 - f_v)$$

$$dE_c \, dE_v \qquad (2.64)$$

where the limits a and b are chosen so that the integrations terminate within the forbidden band. The second form of the integral as in equation (2.64) is useful because it contains the two composite terms $\rho_c(E_c)f_c dE_c$ and $\rho_v(E_v)(1 - f_v)dE_v$ which represent increments dn in electron concentration and dp in hole concentration, respectively.

We may therefore write

$$r_{spon}(total) = Z \int_0^n \int_0^p B(p_\rho, n_\rho)V \, dp \, dn \qquad (2.65)$$

where the variables n_ρ and p_ρ in terms of which B is expressed are alternatives to E_c and E_v and represent the total concentration of electron and hole states (whether occupied or not) up to energies E_c and down to energy E_v. Z is taken outside the integral as being approximately constant over the small range of $h\nu$ involved in the integration. Equation (2.65) is a useful form when the term $B(n_\rho p_\rho)$ can be satisfactorily handled. This is true for two cases; first the non-inverted Boltzmann condition where both the quasi-Fermi levels lie in the band-gap, and secondly the situation where B is constant over the important part of the integral, that is if the matrix element can be taken as invariant with the energy of the initial and final states.

In the Boltzmann condition the distribution of the electrons and holes over the available states in the band remains unchanged, except for a constant factor, as the total concentration is varied. This factor, which is proportional to the product of the two concentrations, may be taken outside the integral of (2.65) giving

$$r_{spon}(total) = \beta np \qquad (2.66)$$

where β is obtained by integrating the remaining terms, and is a constant at given temperature. This result is no longer true in general when the Fermi levels move up into the bands. However, if B is independent of n_ρ and p_ρ, as in the case of no selection rules, it may itself be taken outside the integral and equation (2.66) becomes true over whatever range of carrier concentration the selection rules may be disregarded.

To see what happens if there are partial selection rules it is more convenient to consider B as being a function of the electron and hole wave vectors $\mathbf{k}_c$ and $\mathbf{k}_v$. The way B might vary with, say, the x components of $\mathbf{k}_c$ and $\mathbf{k}_v$, for equal y and z components, is illustrated schematically in Figure 2.13. Here, as an example, the selection rules are chosen so that B only has a non-zero value when the difference in $\mathbf{k}$ between the conduction

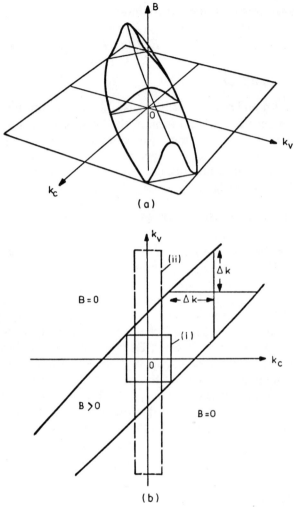

Figure 2.13   Illustration of selection rules. A schematic plot of transition probability B as a function of **k** vectors in both conduction and valence band. Only one component of **k** vectors plotted, other components taken as equal. (a) Plot of B against particular components of k_c and k_v. (b) Plan view of above illustrating maximum allowable difference Δk between k_c and k_v. Examples also given of relevant regions in k-space for recombination at two different injection levels

and valence band states is less than Δk. In three dimensions this would mean that any electron could recombine with holes with values of **k** contained within a sphere of radius Δk centred on the **k** values of the electron, and vice versa for the recombination of holes.

Any effect that increases the volume of the **k** sphere in the valence band reduces the probability that the electron will make a transition to any given one of the states within it in inverse proportion. This is an example of the general principle, mentioned in Section 2.3, that the total oscillator strength of an electron is independent of the number of possible transitions that it can make. The concentration of states contained within the effective **k** sphere, which varies according to the selection rules, will be represented by n_m. The total recombination probability [i.e. $1/\tau_{\text{limit}}$ in equation (2.59)] will be represented by the product $\beta_m n_m$, where β_m is an appropriate constant.

To obtain a general picture of the behaviour we need to change the variables on which B depends back to E_c and E_v of equation (2.65). However, for a qualitative understanding it is adequate to consider the two extreme cases in which either (a) the average **k** value of the injected carriers is less than $\Delta k/2$, or (b) the average **k** value of at least one of the carrier types is much greater. The former corresponds to low injected carrier concentration at not too high a temperature and the latter corresponds to high injected carrier concentration. In case (a) all transitions are allowed [all the electrons are contained within the small square (i) in Figure 2.13(b)]. Hence β in equation (2.66) becomes β_m giving

$$r_{\text{spon}}(\text{total}) = \beta_m np \tag{2.67}$$

This applies when neither n nor p are greater than n_m.

In case (b) we find

$$
\begin{aligned}
r_{\text{spon}}(\text{total}) &= \beta_m n_m p, \quad \text{for minority holes} \\
&= \beta_m n_m n, \quad \text{for minority electrons}
\end{aligned}
\tag{2.68}
$$

Here the carriers are contained within the large rectangle (ii) in Figure 2.13(b) but only pairs which lie within the allowed strip can recombine with one another.

The overall conclusion is that a product recombination law of the form of equations (2.66) and (2.67) can be used for values of the injected carrier concentration either up to the point where the Fermi level for at least one carrier type moves into the band, or where the concentration reaches a value of n_m, whichever is greater. A linear recombination law of the type in equation (2.68) can be used at a carrier concentration beyond the point where the Fermi level for both carriers has moved into the band and where the carrier concentration of one carrier type exceeds n_m. Only in the latter case does the recombination time for the minority carriers reach its minimum theoretical value.

In practice a product recombination law seems to occur in the range of interest and the experimentally measured value of β_m is of the order of $1.5 - 2 \times 10^{-10} \text{ cm}^3 \text{ s}^{-1}$ at room temperature.[5,51]

2.6   GAIN/CURRENT RELATION

The relation between optical gain and current density in a semiconductor can be derived in principle by solving the integrals of equation (2.31) for gain and equation (2.26) for the spontaneous emission rate per unit volume for a series of appropriately related values of the quasi-Fermi energies F_c and F_v. The current density J_n for some particular thickness d_n in a semiconductor with no non-radiative recombination is of course related to the total spontaneous emission rate per unit volume by

$$J_n = e d_n r_{spon}(\text{total})$$ (2.69)

and it has become customary to describe J_n as the nominal current density when d_n is set equal to 1 μm.

In practice the derivation of the gain/current relation is not straightforward because of the difficulty of obtaining satisfactory relationships for the density of states functions ρ_c and ρ_v and the Einstein coefficient B which appear in the integrals. These topics have been treated in Sections 2.4 and 2.3. The results of a rigorous treatment of the gain/current characteristic are given in Section 2.6.5. However, before proceeding to describe the complete treatment it is useful to consider the behaviour in terms of some more familiar parameters of the semiconductor and perhaps, thereby, obtain a better physical insight into the gain process. Despite the lack of full information it is still possible by these means to make reasonably adequate semi-empirical estimates of the order of magnitude of the quantities involved. We present such a treatment in the following section.

2.6.1   Phenomenological Treatment

We can obtain two very useful pieces of information about the gain/current relation in semiconductors by applying some of the general relationships on light emission presented in Section 2.2. The first of these is the current density necessary to just produce positive optical gain. Knowledge of this quantity is particularly useful because gain increases so rapidly with current that the current density need be increased little further beyond the zero gain point to bring most lasers to threshold. The Bernard and Duraffourg condition for zero stimulated emission in equation (2.25) provides the basis for the analysis. This treatment was described in early papers on the derivation of threshold current[18,19] and will be discussed in more detail in Section 2.6.1.1 below.

The second feature of the gain/current relation that we can estimate in a simple way is the ratio of optical gain to current at high current density, close to the point of gain saturation. The starting point for the derivation is the relation between the rates of stimulated and spontaneous emission. This is a universal relation, irrespective of the material concerned, and is given in equation (2.27). The only characteristics of the semiconductor on which the resulting gain/current relation explicitly depends are the linewidth and the wavelength of the spontaneous emission and the refractive index. The result also depends on temperature because this affects the maximum degree of inversion that can be attained without excessively broadening the linewidth. A treatment of this type was first described by Mayburg.[20] We will discuss it in greater detail in Section 2.6.1.2 below.

2.6.1.1 Current Density for Zero Gain

According to the condition of Bernard and Duraffourg [equations (2.25) and (2.27)] the optical gain in the semiconductor becomes positive when the difference in the quasi-Fermi energies $(F_c - F_v)$ becomes greater than the bandgap E_g. Using this condition in conjunction with the condition for charge neutrality, whereby the concentrations of holes and electrons injected over and above the initial doping level must be equal, makes it possible to calculate the electron and hole concentrations at zero gain for any initial doping level. For undoped GaAs one finds that the injected concentration of both carriers is about 1.3×10^{18} cm^{-3} at room temperature and that it varies as $T^{3/2}$. Using the experimental value of the recombination constant β_m quoted in the previous section in conjunction with equation (2.67) gives a corresponding current density of about 4000 A cm^{-2} μm^{-1} at room temperature which would be expected to vary according to a power of T lying between 3/2 and 3 depending on how β_m varies with temperature. This is in reasonable agreement with experiment.[21]

If the calculation is applied to doped material it suggests that n-doping should considerably reduce the current density required to attain the Bernard and Duraffourg condition whereas p-doping should have little effect. For instance, with an electron concentration of 5×10^{18} cm^{-3} an injected hole concentration of only 3×10^{16} cm^{-3} should be required and the current density would be cut by an order of magnitude compared with the undoped case. The effect occurs because the density of states in the conduction band is considerably less than that in the valence band, so that the relative increase of the electron concentration with upward displacement of the two Fermi levels is much less than the relative increase of hole concentration with downward displacement of the levels.

As has been shown, perturbations introduced by the doping interfere with the perfection of the band edges, and this calculation cannot be regarded as accurate. It is, however, qualitatively correct and more exact calculations[22,23] and experimental results[24] indicate that n-doping is particularly beneficial in reducing current density for given optical gain if the optical gain is low.

2.6.1.2   *Current Density for High Gain*

To estimate the current density at high optical gain we start by considering and intensity and spectral width of the total spontaneous emission. The spectrum is represented, according to equation (2.26), by $w_{spon}(h\nu)$. We will denote the peak spectral value of this quantity by $w_{spon}(max)$ and its effective bandwidth by ΔE (see Figure 2.14), such that the total spontaneous emission rate per unit volume is $Z\,w_{spon}(max)\Delta E$. The nominal current density J_n as defined in equation (2.69) is therefore

$$J_n = d_n e\, Z\, w_{spon}(max)\Delta E \tag{2.70}$$

Let us next consider the maximum spectral gain, say g_{max}. From equation (2.31) this is given by

$$g_{max} = (\mu\Gamma/c)w_{stim}(max) \tag{2.71}$$

where $w_{stim}(max)$ is similarly defined as the maximum value of $w_{stim}(h\nu)$ over

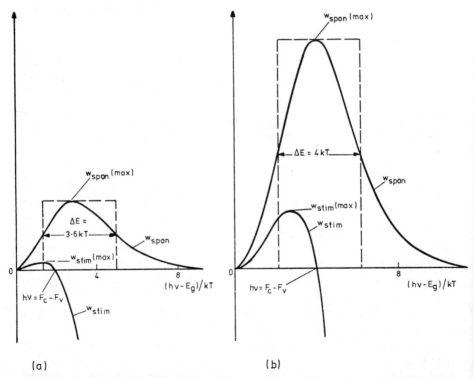

(a)   (b)

Figure 2.14   Spectra of stimulated emission rate w_{stim} and spontaneous emission rate w_{spon} for two different pumping levels to show relative increase in stimulated emission as pumping current is raised (approximate)

the whole spectral width. The fundamental relation of equation (2.27) shows that $w_{stim}(max)$ can never be greater than $w_{spon}(max)$. Let us therefore write

$$w_{stim}(max) = w_{spon}(max)/\gamma \qquad (2.72)$$

where γ is a factor greater than unity (introduced by Lasher and Stern[25]) which depends on the shape of the spontaneous spectrum and on the quasi-Fermi level separation $(F_c - F_v)$. Figure 2.14 illustrates how γ is decreased by increasing $(F_c - F_v)$. Combining equations (2.70), (2.71), and (2.72) gives the following relation between current density per unit volume and gain

$$J_n = d_n(ceZ_{av}\Delta E \gamma/\mu\Gamma)g_{max} \qquad (2.73)$$

It is convenient for a numerical example to express the linewidth in terms of kT as follows:

$$\Delta E = qkT$$

where we expect q to be a number somewhat greater than unity. Then inserting the band-gap, wavelength, and refractive index of GaAs at room temperature into equation (2..73) we obtain

$$\frac{J_n}{g_{max}} = d_n\left(\frac{T}{300}\right)5.38\frac{q\gamma}{\Gamma} \text{ (A cm}^{-2}\ \mu\text{m}^{-1}) \text{ cm} \qquad (2.74)$$

This relation becomes useful under conditions where γ is not too large and can therefore be estimated with reasonable accuracy. This applies when the quasi-Fermi level separation $F_c - F_v$ becomes at least $2kT$ greater than the bandgap E_g, i.e. the current is about a factor of four greater than that estimated in Section 2.6.1.1 above to be necessary to reach zero gain. Once this condition is reached then equations (2.73) and (2.74) imply that the subsequent increase in gain with current becomes remarkably independent of the properties of the semiconductor or its doping level. The major factors which control the gain are the linewidth and the wavelength of emission (which enters into Z). As the laser is driven harder the linewidth broadens with the increase in the quasi-Fermi separation [see Figure 2.14(b)], but over a considerable range this is compensated by a reduction in γ. Over one to two orders of magnitude in gain the product γq can be taken as around 4.5 (compare more exact results in Figure 2.15 which are given in the next section) giving

$$\frac{J_n}{g_{max}} \simeq d_n\frac{24(T/300)}{\Gamma} \text{ A cm}^{-1} \qquad (2.75)$$

for GaAs at temperature T, provided that T is greater than about 80 K. The linewidth over this range is varying from about 3 to $6kT$ (450–900 Å at room temperature).

2.6.2   Gain/Current Relation for 'Ideal' Semiconductor

We now present the theoretical derivation of the gain/current characteristics for a pure semiconductor, using a model with parabolic density of states in the bands and rigorous **k** selection. This model is probably not exactly representative of any true situation, for even if the semiconductor were sufficiently pure the injected carriers themselves would upset the perfection of the bands and the precise nature of the **k** selection to some extent. However, the gain/current characteristic is not particularly sensitive to the conditions, and the 'ideal' characteristic provides a useful and reasonably easily derived standard with which to compare the more correct curves.

For the spontaneous emission rate with **k** selection we use equation (2.18) which we integrate over $h\nu$ to obtain r_{spon}(total), and hence find the nominal current density according to equation (2.69). For the stimulated emission rate we take the difference between r_{21} and r_{12} in equations (2.17) and (2.16), and hence find the nominal gain per unit length by multiplying by μ/c [cf. equation (2.31)]. The gain depends on $h\nu$. Normally we will be concerned with the peak value of the gain over the spectral width as a function of current density, but in circumstances where the current density is

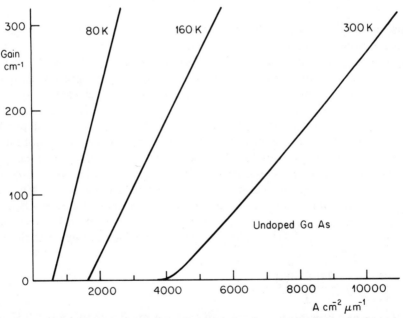

Figure 2.15   Theoretical relation between peak optical gain and injected current density at various temperatures in pure GaAs assuming rigorous **k** selection—after Stern[23]

not uniform we will also need to know how the gain at a fixed value of $h\nu$ varies with current density.

To evaluate the expressions for spontaneous and stimulated emission we must substitute for the density of optical transition $\rho_{red}(h\nu)$ using equations (2.15) and (2.11) and for the occupation factors f_c and f_v using the Fermi relations in equation (2.12). The requisite integration for the current and the maximization for the gain must then, in general, be carried out numerically.

Results for the peak gain versus current density characteristics for GaAs that have been obtained for rigorous **k** selection by Stern[23] are illustrated in Figure 2.15. Curves are given for a range of temperatures. The current densities that are listed apply to an active layer $1\,\mu\text{m}$ thick. Over a considerable range of gain (from 20 to $500\,\text{cm}^{-1}$) the curves can be represented by a linear relation of the form

$$g = A(J - J_t) \tag{2.76}$$

where the gradient A and the intercept J_t depend on temperature. J_t is the current density per unit volume at which the gain becomes positive, and is of the order of $4000\,\text{A cm}^{-2}$ at room temperature. It varies approximately with temperature as $T^{3/2}$. The gradient A is of the order of $0.045\,\text{cm}^{-1}/\text{Acm}^{-2}$ μm^{-1} at room temperature and varies with temperature approximately as $1/T$. This behaviour is illustrated in Figure 2.16 (a) and (b) where $1/A$ and J_t are respectively plotted against T.

2.6.3 Gain/Current Relations with relaxed k selection

In this section we consider various ways in which the theoretical model for light emission can be modified to take into account less rigorous **k** selection in the transition processes. The aim is to make the model capable of dealing with a more highly doped semiconductor and also capable of explaining specific aspects of the recombination properties of the injected carriers and of the spectral distribution of the gain and spontaneous emission as well as producing a satisfactory relation between gain and current density.

The simplest way of allowing for the relaxation of the **k** selection rules is to assume equal probability for all significant transitions between the bands. Although some authors have attempted to estimate a reasonable value for this probability and equated it, for instance, with the probability appropriate to transitions between a state bound to an impurity and a free state in the band[25] [see equations (2.42) and (2.43)], it is equally useful to ascribe it an empirical value and to use the model to give the various functional relationships. We first take the latter approach and investigate some approximate functional relationships. We return later in Section 2.6.5 to the problem of obtaining the best representation of the selection rules where we present

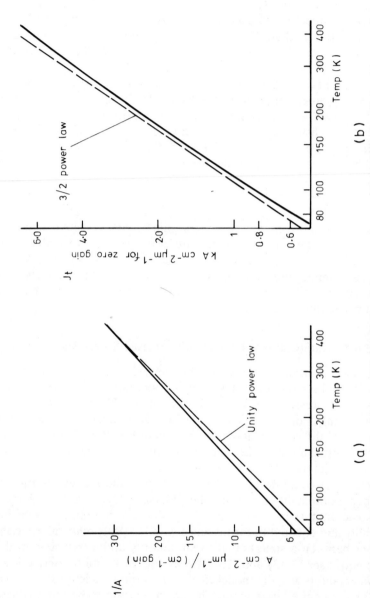

Figure 2.16 Temperature sensitivity of theoretical gain/current characteristics in pure GaAs (rigorous **k** selection): (a) slope of characteristic versus temperature, (b) current density for zero gain versus temperature

various numerical results that have been obtained by Stern using a more sophisticated treatment with a variable transition probability.

The constant transition probability approximation has been applied both to bands with parabolic densities of states[25,26] and to bands with tails with, in the latter instance, the quasi-Fermi levels being located in the tails.[16,17,27,28] The parabolic treatment is applicable at pumping levels which are high enough to drive the quasi-Fermi levels well into the bands. The treatment using band tails may either be limited such that all the carriers reside within the band tails,[28] in which case the model is only applicable at low temperature, or alternatively the bulk of the carriers may lie within the parabolic part of the band whilst the quasi-Fermi levels remain in the tail,[29] in which case the model has wider applicability. A reasonably simple form of the gain/current characteristic is obtained in the latter circumstances. It applies at room temperature for a current somewhat below the normal operating level but sufficiently close to be useful in analysing the behaviour of real lasers. A description is given below.

2.6.3.1 Constant matrix element for all transitions

We consider a model of the semiconductor where the main transitions take place between an impurity band and the tail of the opposite band with a uniform probability for all transitions. As a suitable example we consider a heavily doped p-type material in which the acceptors form a half-filled band (occupation factor $f_v = \frac{1}{2}$). Take the conduction band tail to have the exponential form given in equation (2.56). Take the Fermi level for the electrons to lie in the conduction band tail at an energy-F_c below the bottom of the parabolic part of the band. Consider states in the tail close to the Fermi level so that the occupation factor f_c in equation (2.12) can be approximated by

$$f_c \simeq \frac{1}{2} + (F_c - E_c)/4kT \qquad (2.77)$$

Inserting the value of $(f_c - f_v)$ and the density of tail states into equation (2.31) for the gain then gives

$$g \propto \left\{ \frac{F_c - E_c}{kT} \right\} \exp\left(\frac{E_c}{E_t} \right) \qquad (2.78)$$

for E_c negative and for a photon energy $(E_g + E_c)$ which is less than the nominal band-gap. The gain has a maximum value g_{max} over the spectrum with respect to electron energy E_c of

$$g_{max} \propto \left(\frac{E_t}{kT} \right) \exp\left(\frac{F_c}{E_t} - 1 \right) \qquad (2.79)$$

Substituting the value of E_c appropriate for g_{max} gives a corresponding value of the photon energy of $(E_g + F_c - E_t)$.

We can express equations (2.78) and (2.79) in terms of the injected carrier concentration N, and eliminate F_c by using Unger's relation[17]

$$n = N_c \exp\left(\frac{F_c}{\{(kT)^2 + E_t^2\}^{1/2}}\right) \qquad (2.80)$$

where N_c is an effective density of states which is itself proportional to $\{(kT)^2 + E_t^2\}^{3/2}$. Equation (2.79) for maximum spectral gain becomes

$$g_{max} \propto \left(\frac{n}{N_c}\right)^{\{(kT/E_t)^2 + 1\}^{1/2}} \qquad (2.81)$$

Since the injected electron concentration is directly proportional to current in the high p-doped material that has been considered, this relation corresponds to a superlinear dependence of gain on current with an index of $\{(kT/E_t)^2 + 1\}^{1/2}$. The value of this index increases with temperature from a minimum value of unity. For a typical value of E_t at room temperature of 0.01 eV the index has a value of about 3. Experimental measurements approximately confirm this result for values of n up to about 10^{18} cm^{-3}.[30]

Consider also how the gain at fixed wavelength varies with the injected carrier concentration. This relation has certain practical applications as described below. We take E_c in equation (2.78) as constant so that the equation applies to a fixed photon energy and F_c is the variable. Then the substitution of F_c for n, using equation (2.80) gives

$$g \propto \ln(n/n_0) \qquad (2.82)$$

where n_0 is chosen to represent the injected carrier concentration which arises when the Fermi level coincides with the tail states under consideration, i.e. when $F_c = E_c$. In contrast to equation (2.81) this shows a sublinear dependence of g on n. g for the wavelength concerned lies at the peak of the gain spectrum for a particular injected carrier concentration n given by

$$\ln\left(\frac{n}{n_0}\right) = \left\{\left(\frac{kT}{E_t}\right)^2 + 1\right\}^{-1/2} \qquad (2.83)$$

Figure 2.17 shows an example of peak spectral gain according to equation (2.81) (curve a), and gain at fixed wavelength according to equation (2.82) (curve b) plotted against injected carrier concentration. These curves apply to a tail depth E_t which is one-third of kT—reasonably typical at room temperature. The plots show the concave and convex nature of the respective curves which touch at the point determined by equation (2.83). Since the two curves are so obviously different it is appropriate to point out their different applications.

Curve a and equation (2.81) apply under conditions where the lasing spectrum can centralize on the gain spectrum. For instance, if the length or

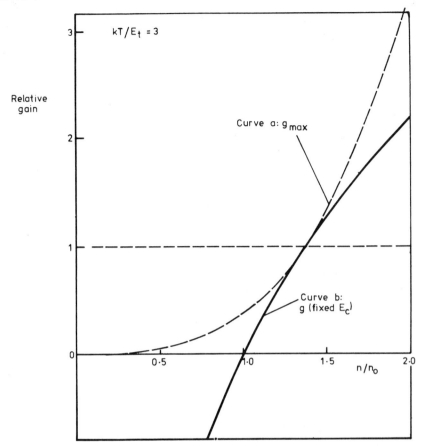

Figure 2.17 Relative gain versus injected carrier concentration as obtained by approximate analysis of transitions from conduction band tail to acceptor level. Tail depth $E_t < kT$. Curves shown both for maximum spectral gain and gain at fixed wavelength

the reflection coefficient of a laser is changed the gain requirement alters and equation (2.81) is appropriate for calculating the new threshold current density. The lasing wavelength changes slightly in the new situation.

Curve *b* and equation (2.82) applies under conditions where the wavelength of the laser is unaltered. This is true under transient conditions where any given mode approximately retains its wavelength. Equation (2.82) must also be used under non-uniform conditions when different parts of the laser, for whatever reason, have different concentrations of injected carriers, but interact with the same cavity modes.

Both equations are, of course, only approximate because of the initial assumptions involved. It can be shown, however, that they have a wider range of validity than the particular case of high p-doped material considered here.[29]

2.6.3.2 Matrix element varying over band tail

The most sophisticated theoretical model that has been investigated for obtaining the gain/current relation in highly doped semiconductors is that due to Stern.[22,23] He has made elaborate approximations to allow for the effect of the band tails both on the density of states distribution and on the transition probability. The density of states distribution is represented by a Kane Gaussian function, modified to fit the Halperin and Lax results for deep states as described in Section 2.4. The transition probability and the degree of **k** selection for the tail states varies according to the depth of the states as described in Section 2.3.3. Gain/current characteristics for a range of temperatures, obtained using this model for a highly compensated GaAs simple with net n-doping of 10^{18} cm^{-3}, are illustrated in Figure 2.18. For comparison the curve for pure GaAs at 300 K is also illustrated, although because of the greater number of approximations made for the present curves too precise comparisons should not be made.

At 300 K the general effect of the higher doping is to cause curvature in the characteristic where the gain is low in such a way as to give increased gain for given current density up to gains of the order of 100 cm^{-1}. Above this level the two sets of gain characteristics are reasonably similar. At low temperatures higher doping in general reduces the optical gain, although there remains a small region of low current where the gain is increased.

These results can be interpreted qualitatively in terms of the phenomenological treatment given at the beginning of this section. It was shown that a condition is reached at high pumping levels where the gain/current relation depends only on the bandwidth of the emission and no longer on the properties of the semiconductor, and that this condition is reached when the bandwidth becomes appreciably greater than kT. High doping increases the bandwidth of the emission by distorting the band structure, but the effect becomes proportionally less significant at high temperature or high current. At room temperature and at currents sufficient to give 300 cm^{-1} gain, the effect is negligible and high doping causes no appreciable diminution of gain attributable to electronic effects. However, at 80 K where the current required for 300 cm^{-1} gain is much lower, the effect of doping on the bandwidth is significant and the gain is considerably reduced.

At low currents higher doping increases the optical gain. This can be expressed in the alternative form that higher doping reduces the current at which the optical gain first becomes positive. The reason is simply that the deeper the band tail the lower the Fermi energy required to produce

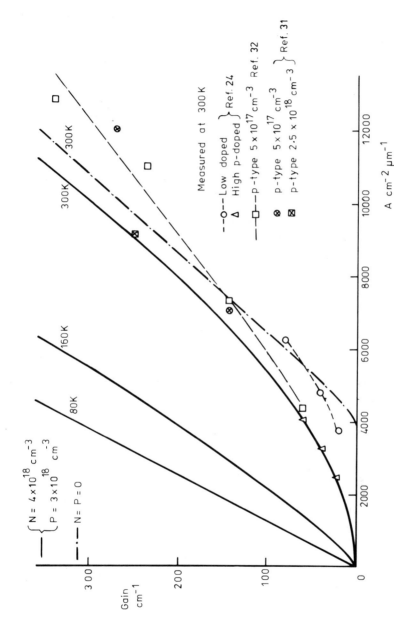

Figure 2.18 Theoretical relation between peak gain and injected current density at various temperatures in doped GaAs after Stern.[23] Comparison curve for pure GaAs also shown together with some experimental measurements at 300 K

inversion of the lowest states. The number of states occupied by injected carriers in this condition is much less than if Fermi level lay in the parabolic band. The current is low both because of the small number of injected carriers and because of the long recombination time which Stern deduces for deep tail states. At low temperatures the gain advantage at low currents is rapidly lost with increasing current owing to the relatively greater bandwidth associated with the band tails whereas at room temperature this advantage may be maintained over the whole operating range of current (compare Figures 2.18 and 2.15).

Various workers have measured the relation between gain and current density in GaAs at room temperature. Direct measurement is not easy on account of gain saturation effects in the higher range of injected carrier concentration. However, Bakker and Ackett[31] have obtained good results using optical pumping and by varying the length of the semiconductor heterostructure wafer over which it is applied. Some of their results are indicated in Figure 2.18. The gain relation may also be obtained by measurement of the threshold current density of a range of lasers of different but known threshold gain.[32] Results obtained by this method by two sets of workers are also indicated in Figure 2.18. An alternative method of gain measurement has been developed by Hakki and Paoli.[33] In this method the spectral resonances of the Fabry–Perot laser cavity are observed below threshold as a function of current and the net gain is deduced from the ratio of the maxima to the minima that occurs half way between the resonances (see Section 2.8.2). This allows both the peak gain (up to the threshold gain) and a part of the gain spectrum versus wavelength to be found.

As can be seen from Figure 2.18 the agreement between the measured results and the theoretical curves is in general within 20 per cent. This is approximately of the same order as the accuracy of the measurement. The measured trend of the effects produced by doping is also generally in line with the theoretical predictions although the results are too scattered to establish it with real precision. The discrepancy is perhaps greatest with the lowest doped material; the observed difference between low and high doped material being less than is suggested by the theory. The precise shape of the gain spectra, where measured, also tends to show a smaller distinction between low and high doping than might be expected from the very different selection rules that theory suggests apply to the two cases. It is possible that the high concentration of injected carriers, which is not taken into account in the theoretical treatment, may modify the selection rules to some extent. It is also possible that the high concentration of injected carriers may affect the peak gain at the high gain end of the characteristic and account for the fact that the measured gains in this region tend to be significantly below the theoretical curves.

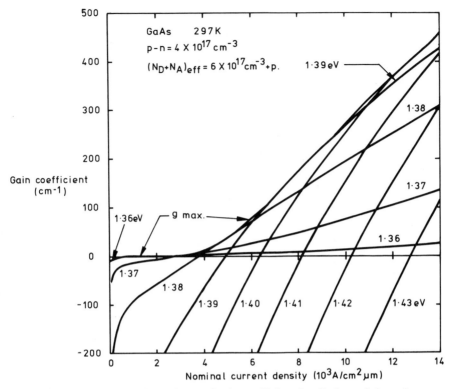

Figure 2.19 Calculated dependence of gain coefficient for GaAs on injected current density, showing variation of gain at fixed photon energy and also variation of peak gain. Applies at 297 K with net acceptor concentration of 4×10^{17} cm^{-3}. After Stern[34]

Stern[34] has also made calculations of the variation of the complete gain spectrum with current density. These are illustrated in Figures 2.19 and 2.20. The curves apply to lightly p-doped GaAs at 300 K ($p = 4 \times 10^{17}$ cm^{-3}). In Figure 2.19 the gain for a variety of fixed values of $h\nu$, both below and above the nominal band-gap, is plotted against current density. The envelope curve for maximum gain is also shown. All the curves follow the general shape suggested by the approximate functional treatment of Section 2.6.3.1, although there are detailed differences particularly for the lower photon energies. The envelope curve of maximum gain lies very close to the theoretical result obtained for pure GaAs with rigorous **k** selection given in Figure 2.15. The only real discrepancy is in the region of current density below 4000 A cm^{-2} μm^{-1}, where the maximum gain in the present instance is not zero, although small.

Figure 2.20 repeats the same information as Figure 2.19 but with gain

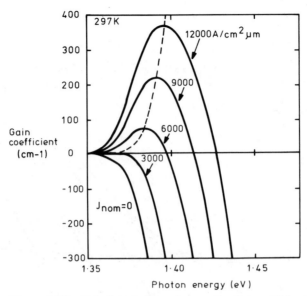

Figure 2.20   Calculated dependence of gain coefficient for GaAs at 297 K on photon energy for several values of the injected current density. The same parameters are used as in Figure 2.19. After Stern[34]

plotted as a function of optical energy $h\nu$ for several different values of current density. This form of plot clearly shows the shift of the photon energy of peak gain with increasing current, rapidly at first in the band tail region, but more slowly as the current density rises beyond $6000 \text{ A cm}^{-2} \mu\text{m}^{-1}$.

2.7   LIGHT/CURRENT CHARACTERISTICS

We now investigate more closely the relation between current input and light output in semiconductor lasers using the concepts of optical gain derived in the previous section. In this section we shall be particularly concerned with the threshold condition and the incremental efficiency. We will extend consideration of the threshold condition to deriving in some detail the light/current characteristic that occurs in the proximity of the nominal threshold current, and we will extend the consideration of efficiency to the higher range of current where saturation effects start to occur. However, we will leave the main discussion of the way multimode operation can affect the behaviour to section 2.8.

In order to oscillate, a laser requires feedback and the behaviour around threshold is particularly associated with the way the feedback approaches the critical threshold condition. Threshold is normally defined as the condition where the loop gain first becomes unity, such that no input signal is required to sustain the oscillation. In fact some driving signal is available from the spontaneous emission, and in semiconductor lasers close to threshold this signal can be significant. The laser can then be regarded as an amplifier of spontaneous emission. It is instructive to consider to what extent this behaviour modifies the simple concept of threshold as presented in Section 2.1.

Semiconductor lasers differ from most other varieties of laser in that they are normally operated with a relatively small proportion of feedback. This is because (a) a flat end-face, which provides a convenient output, has a power reflection coefficient of only about 30 per cent, and (b) because the gain/current characteristics of the material are such that there is little sacrifice in threshold current in providing the necessarily rather high optical gain (50 cm^{-1}). The small feedback means that the optical intensity must vary considerably along the length of the laser. Simple resonant cavity treatments which equate stimulated emission rates to photon loss rates and assume uniform conditions over the length of the resonator are not necessarily adequate. Spatial effects are important and the analysis should be tailored to take them into account. For this reason it is preferable to treat the problem in terms of the optical gain of travelling waves and to take account of the exponential-like distributions of intensity which exist along the length of the laser.

2.7.1 Threshold Conditions

Figure 2.21 shows a typical distribution along the length of a laser of the intensity of the forward and reflected waves. Under conditions where the

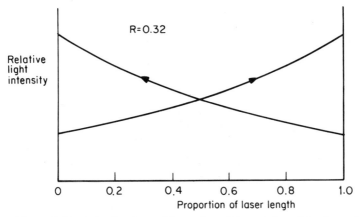

Figure 2.21 Distribution of intensity of forward and backward waves along length of laser resonator at low output power levels. Reflection coefficient appropriate for cleaved facets of GaAs

optical gain is approximately constant over the whole length of the laser the light has an exponential distribution with position z along the laser axis of the form

$$F_\pm = F_{0\pm} \exp \pm (g - \alpha)z \qquad (2.84)$$

where F is the optical flux density; the positive and negative signs and subscripts refer to the forward and reverse components of the wave; g is the optical gain per cm provided by the stimulated emission $[= \mu\Gamma w_{stim}/c$ from equation (2.31)]; α is the optical loss per cm from processes not directly associated with the gain mechanism, such as diffraction, scattering, and free-carrier absorption; and F_{0+} and F_{0-} are appropriate constants to be determined. This relation becomes less exact as the current is increased towards twice threshold and beyond as a result of gain saturation processes. These are treated in a later section.

To make the optical distribution of equation (2.84) satisfy the boundary reflections at the end-faces of the laser the following condition must apply

$$\exp 2(g - \alpha)L = \frac{1}{R_1 R_2} \qquad (2.85)$$

where R_1 and R_2 are the power reflection coefficients at the two ends of the resonator and L is the length. From this expression we may obtain the relation for the nominal threshold gain g_{th}, which is constant over the whole length of the laser, in terms of R_1, R_2, and L, as follows

$$g_{th} = \alpha + \ln(1/R_1 R_2)/2L \qquad (2.86)$$

This equation shows that the gain per unit length must be sufficient to cancel out the optical losses due to absorption, etc. and also the appropriate proportion of the end losses due to light emission. The proportion of end losses concerned depends inversely on the length of the laser. The general concept of the gain cancelling out the losses applies not only at the threshold current but at all currents above threshold. However, as the current is increased saturation effects start to reduce the gain per unit length in some parts of the laser compared with others so that there is no longer the exact balance between gain and loss at all points along the laser as represented by equation (2.86), but the loop gain must still be unity.

Threshold occurs quite abruptly as a function of current. As threshold is approached a proportion of the spectral width of the spontaneous emission is split up into peaks corresponding to modes of the Fabry–Perot cavity, and amplified. This situation is illustrated in Figure 2.22. Raising the current causes the magnitude of a few of the central peaks to increase, but the amplification must become very considerable before a significant amount of the total power is contained within them. The loop gain for these modes is then very close to unity and any further current causes them to grow

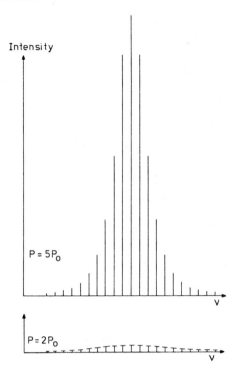

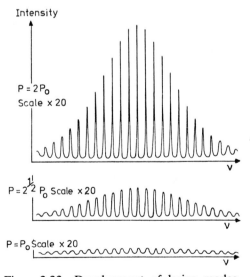

Figure 2.22   Development of lasing modes from spontaneous emission as current is increased (diagrammatic)

enormously. This constitutes threshold. In most cases threshold according to this definition occurs very close to the condition represented by equation (2.86).

Equation (2.86) for the gain continues to remain true up to 10–50 per cent above threshold at which stage longitudinal saturation effects start to interfere. The gain per unit length is therefore effectively clamped to its threshold value along the whole length of the laser over a significant current range beyond threshold. In view of the relation between gain and injected carrier concentration one might expect that the injected carrier concentration and the spontaneous emission would also be clamped. This is true in certain circumstances. Experiments which have carried out show that if .conditions are uniform within the laser, so that equation (2.86) applies throughout, very effective clamping does take place.[35] However, there are many exceptions, particularly in situations where there is a variation of light intensity and injected carrier concentration in the direction transverse to the laser axis, as occurs in stripe lasers. Here the gain g is averaged over the width. To maintain constant g in this condition there is no necessity that the total injected carrier concentration should stay constant, only that over the cross section a certain integrated product of the carrier concentration with the light intensity should do so.

When precise clamping occurs all the current that exceeds the threshold level produces stimulated emission. This applies even if some of the threshold current is causing non-radiative recombination. The non-radiative component also remains constant beyond threshold. Hence, the lasing emission increases linearly with additional current. The incremental efficiency will be less than 100 per cent only if there is optical loss in the resonator additional to the band-edge absorption and re-emission processes within the active medium. Such loss is described by the term α.

If the relation between gain and current density is known then equation (2.86) may be used to find the threshold current density. In general there is no simple relation for gain, as has been discussed in Section 2.6. However, in low-doped material an offset-linear characteristic approximately applies (offset in that finite current is required for zero gain) as given in equation (2.76). This expression is satisfactory even for appreciable doping provided that the current density is high enough. Combining this relation with equation (2.86) gives a useful expression for threshold current density per unit volume in cases where the current density is not too low. The expression is

$$J_{th} = J_t + \left(\frac{1}{\Gamma A}\right) \alpha + \frac{\ln(1/R_1 R_2)}{2L} \tag{2.87}$$

The confinement factor Γ has been included to allow for spreading of the light outside the active region [see equation (2.31)]. At room temperature J_t, which is the current density for zero gain, lies around 4000 A cm^{-2} μm^{-1}. In practice A is of the order of 0.035 cm^{-1}/Acm^{-2} μm^{-1}, somewhat lower than predicted theoretically (see Figure 2.8).

2.7.2 Efficiency (Low Power)

For lasers in which the light/current characteristic beyond threshold is linear an incremental quantum efficiency η may be defined to relate the optical output power P in photons per second to current I in electrons per second in the form

$$P = \eta(I - I_{th}) \tag{2.88}$$

where I_{th} is the threshold current.

If conditions are such, as described above, that all the current beyond threshold is directed to stimulated emission then only optical losses contribute to lowering the incremental efficiency. The incremental efficiency can conveniently be obtained by comparing the total net rate of stimulated emission P_{stim} and the total dissipated optial power P_{lost}. These quantities can be expressed respectively in terms of the gain g and the loss α per cm of the optical wave. The loss concerned is a combination of absorption, scattering, and diffraction loss but excludes any process which regenerates minority carriers at a point where they can be used again for stimulated emission (i.e. band-to-band reabsorption). The expressions for P_{stim} and P_{lost} are

$$\begin{aligned} P_{stim} &= \int g(F_+ + F_-)\, dz \\ P_{lost} &= \alpha \int F_+ + F_-)\, dz \end{aligned} \tag{2.89}$$

where F_+ and F_- are the forward and backward components of optical flux, and where α is assumed to be constant over z. At currents reasonably close to threshold g does not vary over the length of the laser. This is true when the stimulated emission, which does vary along the length of the laser, is too small to cause appreciable variations in the injected carrier concentration, and is more easily satisfied when the end-face reflection coefficient is large. If g does not vary appreciably it may be taken outside the integral. The incremental quantum efficiency η is then given by:

$$\eta + \eta_0\left(1 - \frac{P_{lost}}{P_{stim}}\right) = \eta_0\left(1 - \frac{\alpha}{g}\right) \tag{2.90}$$

where the adjustable quantity η_0 (normally referred to as the internal efficiency) is introduced to take into account any incomplete clamping of the injected carrier concentration and any other factors that may empirically affect the behaviour. Using the value of g given in equation (2.86) we obtain

$$\eta = \frac{\eta_0}{1 + 2\alpha L/\ln(1/R_1 R_2)} \tag{2.91}$$

This relationship was first obtained by Biard *et al.*[36] At high output powers it becomes less accurate and an alternate relation should be used, as described in Section 2.7.4.

When the end-faces of the laser are not symmetrical and $R_1 \neq R_2$ the output P_1 from end 1 is no longer equal to the output P_2 from end 2. The ratio is given by

$$\frac{P_1}{P_2} = \frac{R_1^{-1/2} - R_1^{1/2}}{R_2^{-1/2} - R_2^{1/2}} \tag{2.92}$$

This can be deduced using the fact that $F_+ F_-$ is everywhere constant and the output is proportional to $\pm(F_+ - F_-)$ at each mirror (assuming no mirror absorption).

The overall efficiency depends on the incremental quantum efficiency but it is also affected by the relative value of the threshold current and by any resistive losses which raise the voltage across the laser above the band-gap voltage. Let us consider the means of optimizing the overall efficiency.

The incremental quantum efficiency can be increased, according to equation (2.91), by reducing the laser length or by decreasing the end-face reflection coefficient, both of which increase the output coupling, by increasing the internal efficiency η_0 and also, of course, by decreasing the optical dissipation loss. Decreasing the dissipation loss and increasing the internal efficiency is a benefit in all circumstances but compromise is involved in altering the other two parameters. First let us consider the dissipation loss.

2.7.2.1   *Optical dissipation loss*

There are usually three contributions to the dissipation loss, namely free carrier absorption, band-edge absorption, and scattering loss. They can all be important in different circumstances.

Free carrier absorption results from a direct interaction between the optical waves and the electrons and holes. The absorption is directly proportional to the carrier concentration and approximately proportional to the square of the wavelength. For instance, in GaAs with an electron concentration of 10^{18} cm^{-3} the absorption coefficient at the GaAs emission wavelength is approximately 3 cm^{-1}. Free carrier absorption in the passive layers of a heterostructure can be reduced by decreasing the doping level and for the GaAs emission wavelength it becomes insignificant for doping below 3×10^{17} cm^{-3}. Decreasing the doping level in the active layer may be of some benefit but the situation here is more complicated since it is the concentration of injected carriers at the lasing threshold that must be considered. Paradoxically a condition where the injected carrier concentration in the active layer at threshold is high is an advantage because it is the ratio of gain to loss which determines the efficiency [see equation (2.90)] and the gain increases proportionally more than does the loss with injected carrier concentration as a result of (a) its offset linear dependence on current [equation (2.76)] and (b) by the square root dependence of injected carrier concentration on current [equation (2.67)]. To realize this advantage with normal values of end-face reflection (which impose relatively low mode gain) the laser must be designed with a low confinement factor Γ [see equation (2.31)] so that the local gain within the active layer is high. In general free carrier absorption is not an important factor in GaAs lasers but it becomes significant for lasers with longer wavelengths, e.g. (GaIn)As.

The second dissipation loss to be considered is band-edge absorption. Although this takes place most strongly in the central part of the active layer it is of no significance in this region since it simply causes regeneration of the injected carriers. Some band-edge absorption can also occur in other parts of the laser. In heterostructure lasers the light spreads from the active layer into the adjacent passive layers but they are normally designed to be of sufficiently greater band-gap to be transparent, and provided the light does not penetrate through the passive layers into further layers of lower band-gap (e.g. substrate or contacting layers) there is no band-edge absorption. However, this is not true of the single heterostructure laser (see Chapter 3) where the immediately adjacent n-type GaAs layer may cause appreciable band-edge absorption and may be an important cause of low efficiency. In stripe lasers the light spreads sideways into regions where the active layer is unpumped and where band-edge absorption can take place. This reduces the efficiency. However, care has to be taken in applying equation (2.91) because the band-edge absorption generates carriers and alters the injected carrier profile. This can change the gain requirement of the laser and affect factors which are not taken into account by equation (2.91). The behaviour is treated in more detail in Chapter 6.

The third cause of dissipation loss and decreased efficiency is optical scattering. Scattering occurs in heterostructure lasers particularly as a result of lack of planarity of the heterostructure interfaces. Under ideal conditions the heterostructure forms a perfect waveguide, but irregularities in the boundary allow a certain amount of light to escape. If the irregularities are random the scattering is proportional to the square of the amplitude of the roughness.[37] Alternatively there may be missing sections of guide, in which case the loss is approximately proportional to the missing length.[38] This sort of optical loss is obviously very dependent upon the perfection of growth of the laser heterostructure. In practice it is frequently

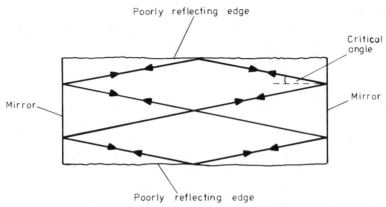

Figure 2.23   Totally reflected internally circulating mode in sawn cavity laser

the major cause of optical dissipation, giving loss coefficients of 5–10 cm^{-1}, or even greater in bad cases.

A final cause of optical absorption should be mentioned here which in certain circumstances may have a very considerable effect on efficiency. This is the loss associated with totally internally reflected circulating modes. This condition can occur in broad lasers if there is a small amount of coherent reflection from the sides sufficient to provide feedback for light travelling at more than 16° to the laser axis and therefore beyond the critical angle for emerging from the end-faces, see Figure 2.23. Energy in these modes is entirely dissipated within the laser, and the external incremental efficiency of the wanted Fabry–Perot modes depends on the strength with which the circulating modes are excited. Under such circumstances suppression of reflection from the sides can give a considerable increase in efficiency.[39,40] This subject is treated further in Chapter 5, Section 5.4.1.

2.7.2.2   *Optimization of reflectivity and length*

Let us now consider how the overall efficiency of the laser may be maximized for a given dissipation loss by adjusting the mirror reflectivity and the length of the device. Normally light is taken out of one end of the laser only, and this is the output we should consider in making the optimization. If the reflectivity R_1 and R_2 of the two end-faces is entirely at our disposal then it is always possible, by imposing 100 per cent reflectivity at one end (say $R_2 = 1$), to take all the light out of the other end without limiting our control of threshold current density and incremental efficiency. Both the latter quantities depend on the product $R_1 R_2$ and may be equally well adjusted by varying R_1 only. The situation is more complicated under conditions where there is, say, an upper limit to the value of R_2, less than unity, because in this case variation of R_1, with R_2 held at its maximum, not only alters the threshold and incremental efficiency but also varies the power division between the two ends of the laser. However, we will not consider this case since in most possible practical situations R_2 can be made sufficiently large for this effect not to be important. Throughout the following treatment we will assume that R_2 is unity. First let us consider the effect on overall efficiency of varying R_1 and then consider the effect of varying laser length.

A change in the reflection coefficient R_1 in the direction that increases incremental efficiency also increases threshold current. The two effects influence the overall efficiency in opposite ways. This suggests that there must be some intermediate value of reflection coefficient where neither effect is too strong and where maximum efficiency will be achieved. Analysis confirms this. The optimum reflectivity concerned is conveniently expressed in terms of the associated threshold current density $J_{th}(opt)$, as may be appreciated by appropriate manipulation of equation (2.87) and (2.91). For convenience we will denote $J_t + \alpha/\Gamma A$, the threshold current density for a laser of infinite length, by J_{tho} [see equation (2.87)]. Then the optimum threshold current density $J_{th}(opt)$ may be expressed in the form

$$(J_{th}(opt) - J_t) = \{(J_{tho} - J_t)(J - J_t)\}^{1/2} \tag{2.93}$$

and the corresponding overall output L, per unit volume, measured in the same units as J (e.g. particles s^{-1}), is given by

$$L = (J_{tho} - J_t)(1 + x - 2x^{1/2}) \tag{2.94}$$

where x is a function of J given by

$$x = \frac{J - J_t}{J_{tho} - J_t} \tag{2.95}$$

Equation (2.93) for the optimum threshold current may be interpreted as follows. When all the current densities are measured in terms of their excess over J_t then optimum operation is obtained if the threshold current density is adjusted, by varying the reflection coefficient, so that its excess over J_t is equal to the geometric mean of the excesses of the applied current density and the threshold current density for an infinitely long laser.

The optimum light output according to equation (2.94) is plotted against x in Figure 2.24. The dashed lines represent the light/current relation for fixed values of the reflectivity and the full line shows the output when the reflectivity is optimized for each value of current.

Let us now consider the effect of laser length. Decreasing the laser length increases the incremental efficiency and also reduces the total threshold current. Thus, the shorter length increases the overall efficiency in two ways.

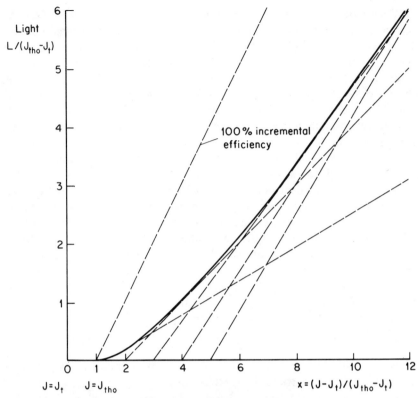

Figure 2.24   Curve showing maximum light obtainable from a laser as a function of current by optimizing reflectivity for each current. Curves for light output at constant reflectivity also shown. Applies to a laser of fixed length with fixed optical absorption coefficient

However, if series resistance is present the improvement in quantum efficiency with decreasing laser length is eventually counteracted by the effect of the rising current density which increases the overall voltage. Hence, there is a certain length for the laser which gives optimum overall efficiency. The optimization concerned has been treated both by Sommers[41] for $J_t = 0$, and by Whiteaway et al.[42] for other values of J_t. It was found that the overall optimized behaviour is determined by only one dimensionless parameter in addition to J_t/J_{tho}. This parameter, which we call δ, is related to the series resistivity of the laser, and is defined as the ratio of the band-gap voltage to the voltage developed across the series resistance at current density J_{tho}. The remaining parameters, including the absorption coefficient, the laser length, the reflectivity of the facets, and the required output power do not affect the optimized efficiency, although they must be suitably traded off against one another to obtain the desired result.

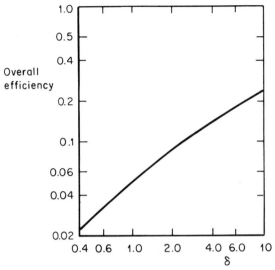

Figure 2.25 Plot of optimum overall efficiency of light output from laser including resistive heating against series resistivity parameter δ. Applies for $J_t = 0$. After Sommers[41]

The optimized overall efficiency for $J_t = 0$ is plotted against δ in Figure 2.25. The value of δ encountered in practice for room temperature laser operation lies in the range 3–10. Hence, the optimum efficiency, not taking into account an internal efficiency which may be appreciably less than unity, lies between 0.1 and 0.2. However, this result is subject to certain limitations. Equation (2.91) for incremental efficiency is only approximately accurate for current more than twice threshold if $\ln(1/R_1 R_2) < 4$. The optimized result for $3 < δ < 10$ requires the current to be between two and three times threshold. Satisfying the condition for R means restricting the output power for the laser to around 10 mW per square micron of emitting area. The necessary analysis for higher output power is given in Section 2.7.4.

2.7.2.3 Laser analysis by efficiency measurement

In addition to being of interest in itself measurement of the incremental efficiency provides a useful experimental means of investigating the gain and loss characteristic of a laser. It is instructive to examine the way the efficiency η varies either in similar lasers of different length, or as a result of varying the reflection coefficient in a given laser. The latter can be carried out non-destructively by immersing the laser in liquids of different refractive index. It is then convenient to plot $1/η$ against $2L/\ln(1/R_1 R_2)$. According to

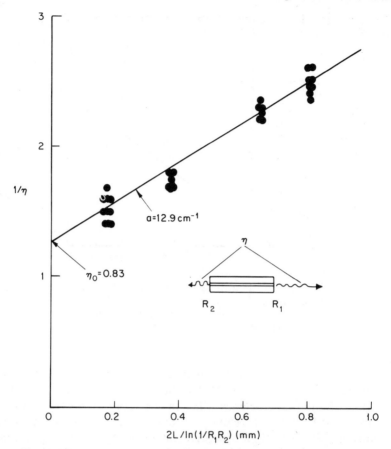

Figure 2.26   Example of effect of varying length on incremental efficiency of broad contact laser. Reciprocal of efficiency plotted against normalized length. After Henshall[40]

equation (2.91) a straight line should be obtained with an intercept on the vertical axis of $1/\eta_0$ and an intercept on the horizontal axis of $1/\alpha$. An example is shown in Figure 2.26 for a set of broad contact lasers in which efforts were made to suppress internally circulating modes.[40] The value obtained for η_0, which approaches unity, shows that this has been successful. The absorption coefficient that is found of $13\,\text{cm}^{-1}$ is typical of a heterostructure laser.

In some circumstances the loss α may vary with the emission wavelength, which itself is dependent on current. However, with a series of measurements of efficiency on lasers with different values of $2L/\ln(1/R_1R_2)$ it is possible to obtain an estimate of the variation of the gain with current and hence deduce the variation of α. Thus, equations (2.86) and (2.91) can be manipulated to give

$$g = \left(\frac{\eta_0}{\eta}\right) \frac{\ln(1/R_1 R_2)}{2L} \tag{2.96}$$

Provided that η_0 remains constant the relative values of gain can be found as the length or reflection coefficient are varied. Such a method was successfully used to find the relation between gain and current (threshold current) in single heterostructure lasers with appreciable wavelength shift and deduce the variation of α.[43]

2.7.3 Light Output Around Threshold

At low light levels the longitudinal distribution of optical intensity in the laser given in equation (2.84) is modified by the contribution of spontaneous emission. Let us calculate the effect that is produced on the light/current characteristic. The portion of spontaneous emission which should be considered is that which lies within the bandwidth and the solid angle appropriate to the mode or modes concerned (i.e. within the frequency interval which separates longitudinal modes and the angular interval which separates transverse modes, both of which can be expressed in similar terms, if desired, as vector increments in wave number). If a single mode is being considered, and if all the light is contained within the active medium, the total contribution of spontaneous emission is (r_{spon}/Z) photons s^{-1} per mode where Z is the mode density per unit bandwidth According to equation (2.26) this is equal to w_{spon}. If the light spreads beyond the active layer so that the confinement factor Γ becomes less than unity, the contribution of spontaneous emission is reduced to Γw_{spon}.

The differential equation which describes the intensity variation in a single mode along the z axis of a laser with resonator volume V and with spontaneous emission included becomes

$$\frac{dF}{dz} = (g - \alpha)F + \frac{\Gamma w_{\text{spon}}}{2V} \tag{2.97}$$

where F is the average light intensity in photons per unit area per second per mode travelling in one direction. Integration gives

$$F_{\pm} = F_{0+/-} \exp\{\pm(g - \alpha)z\} - \frac{\Gamma w_{\text{spon}}}{2V(g - \alpha)} \tag{2.98}$$

where F_+ and F_- apply to the forward and backward waves respectively and where F_{0+} and F_{0-} are appropriate respective constants. The relation between these two constants, and the total output power of the laser, may be determined by fitting the forward and backward waves to the reflecting boundaries. We will take the length of the laser to be L and the respective reflection coefficients at the two ends of the laser to be R_1 and R_2. The total output power P_1 in photons per second from face i (where $i = 1$ or 2) is given in terms of g by

$$P_i = \frac{(1 - R_i)[\exp\{(g - \alpha)L\} - 1][1 + R_j \exp\{(g - \alpha)L\}]}{(g - \alpha)[1 - R_i R_j \exp\{2(g - \alpha)L\}]} \left\{\frac{\Gamma w_{\text{spon}}}{2}\right\} \quad (2.99)$$

where j has the opposite value to i. For a symmetrical laser, where $R_1 = R_2 = R$, this reduces to

$$P = K\,\Gamma w_{\text{spon}} \qquad\qquad (2.100a)$$

where the magnification factor K is given by

$$K = \frac{[\exp\{(g - \alpha)L\} - 1](1 - R)}{(g - \alpha)L[1 - R\exp\{(g - \alpha)L\}]} \qquad (2.100b)$$

$$= \frac{\sinh\{(g - \alpha)L/2\}(1 - R)}{(g - \alpha)LR^{1/2}\sinh[\{\ln(1/R) - (g - \alpha)L\}/2]} \qquad (2.100c)$$

and where P is the combined output power from the two ends of the laser. The second form (2.100c) of the expression for K is written so that terms of the same type as appear in equation (2.86) for the threshold gain appear in the exponent of sinh in the denominator. This shows that when the gain g actually reaches the nominal threshold value g_{th} that satisfies equation (2.86) the denominator in equation (2.100c) becomes zero and the output power becomes infinite. In the vicinity of this value of g the power output is a very sensitive function of g. For all finite values of P the gain g must, in fact, be slightly less than the nominal threshold gain.

In the interesting range where the laser output is much greater than the spontaneous level w_{spon} we can put $(g - \alpha)L \simeq \ln(1/R)$ in all terms except the difference terms in equation (2.100c), and in this term we can substitute the exponent of sinh for sinh. This gives

$$K \simeq \left[\frac{(1 - R)^2}{R\{\ln(1/R)\}^2}\right]\left[\frac{(\eta/\eta_0)}{1 - gL/\{\ln(1/R) + \alpha L\}}\right] \qquad (2.101)$$

with the incremental efficiency η as defined in equation (2.91). The term in the first brackets in this expression is unity when R is close to 1 and, for example, only increases to 1.11 when R is reduced to the value of 0.32 appropriate to a cleaved end mirror in a GaAs laser. In most cases therefore it is adequate to take it to be approximately unity.

Many authors derive a simpler equivalent to equation (2.101) ignoring the exponential variation of light intensity between the two ends of the resonator. An average photon density is used to describe the photon population in the resonator, say ϕ_{mpq} for mode mpq, and an average photon lifetime σ is stipulated which depends on the length of the resonator, its end reflectivity, and the loss coefficient. The derivation is simply carried out by equating the spontaneous emission rate per mode per unit volume, i.e. $\Gamma w_{spon}/V$, plus the stimulated rate $\Gamma w_{stim} \phi_{mpq}$ to the output rate per unit volume, i.e. ϕ_{mpq}/σ. This gives the following expression for the magnification factor K

$$K = \frac{1}{1 - \Gamma w_{stim} \sigma}$$

$$= \frac{1}{1 - cg\sigma/\mu} \tag{2.102}$$

where the second form is obtained by using the relation between w_{stim} and g in equation (2.31). Equations (2.101) and (2.102) can be made reasonably similar by choosing the value of the photon lifetime σ according to

$$\sigma = \frac{\mu}{c\{\ln(1/R)/L + \alpha\}} \tag{2.103}$$

Equation (2.101) or (2.102) with (2.100) enables the output power P of the laser to be expressed in terms of the gain g, whereas its relation to the driving current density J would be of much more interest. We cannot use equation (2.76) directly for the relation between current and gain since the stimulated emission in the present instance takes additional current. This component of current is diverted from its previous function of maintaining the level of the injected carrier concentration and so supplying its complement of gain. We therefore divide the total current density J into the portion J_{st} which provides the stimulated emission and the remaining portion J_{sp} which provides the gain g and can be treated as in equation (2.76).

This enables us to write the quantity $cg\sigma/\mu$ in the denominator of equation (2.102) in terms of the above J_{sp}, the threshold current density J_{th}, and the transparency current density J_t [see equation (2.76)] as follows

$$\frac{cg\sigma}{\mu} = \frac{J_{sp} - J_t}{J_{th} - J_t} \tag{2.104}$$

Substituting this into equation (2.102) gives an expression for K. This expression is illustrated in Figure 2.27 curve a, plotted against the convenient current parameter $x = (J_{sp} - J_t)/\beta J_{th}$, where $\beta = (1 - J_t/J_{th})$. K initially increases gradually with x from unity at $x = 0$ until x approaches unity $(J_{sp} \to J_{th})$ when K tends to infinity.

A more meaningful plot of the current magnification K would be produced if the variable on the horizontal axis of Figure 2.27 were related to the total current J rather than J_{sp}. The missing contribution J_{st} of current density is equal to the density of spontaneous emission output in all the laser

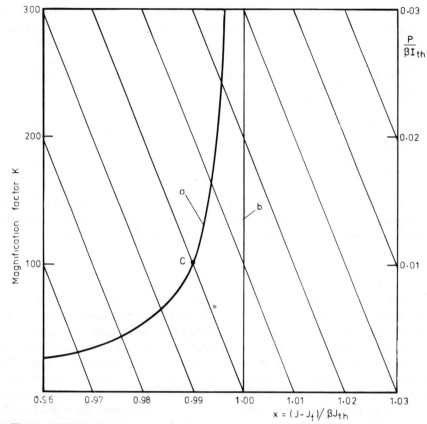

Figure 2.27   Magnification factor for spontaneous emission into lasing mode as a function of spontaneous component of total current, and example of inclined grid for obtaining total current

modes multiplied by K, i.e. $Km_{\text{eff}}\Gamma w_{\text{spon}}/V$ where m_{eff} is the effective number of laser modes and V is the volume of the laser resonator. The abscissa x in Figure 2.27 can be shifted by an amount $J_{\text{st}}/(J_{\text{th}} - J_t)$ corresponding to the missing contribution by tipping the vertical lines in the cartesian grid so that they have a slope dK/dx given by

$$\frac{dK}{dx} = \frac{-V(J_{\text{th}} - J_t)}{m_{\text{eff}}w_{\text{spon}}} \tag{2.105}$$

Then using the distorted grid the total current J corresponding to any point on the curve for K can be read off the x axis in the form $(J - J_t)/(J_{\text{th}} - J_t)$. The total output is obtained by multiplying K on the vertical axis by the total spontaneous output $m_{\text{eff}}\Gamma w_{\text{spon}}$ into the laser modes. This requires knowledge of the value of w_{spon} at threshold.

The total spontaneous emission at threshold is approximately equal to the threshold current, so the spontaneous emission into a single mode Γw_{spon} is given by

$$\Gamma w_{spon}(\text{threshold}) = \frac{\eta_{sp} J_{th} V}{N} \tag{2.106}$$

where η_{sp} is the internal spontaneous efficiency, V is the laser volume, and N is the total number of spontaneous modes in the bandwidth of the spontaneous emission and can be obtained from equation (2.5).

Let us make an estimate of Γw_{spon} for a typical laser. If most of the light is contained within the active layer the threshold current density is normally approximately 4000 A cm^{-2} μm^{-1}, irrespective of the precise design of the laser. (As shown in Figure 2.18 this current density is the value at which the optical gain starts increasing rapidly with current.) Using such a value of current (converted into carriers cm^{-3} s^{-1}) in conjunction with the mode density for a linewidth of $3kT$ gives an emission rate of spontaneous photons at threshold into a single laser mode which corresponds to a current of 0.32 μA or a power, for $h\nu = 1.42$ eV, of 0.5 μW. For a limited reduction of Γ below unity this becomes 0.5 $\Gamma\mu$W.

The range of values which might be found for Γw_{spon} can be estimated in another way. According to equations (2.27) and (2.72) Γw_{spon} is expected to be somewhat greater than Γw_{stim} by a factor γ. γ is a measure of the degree of inversion and increases from unity as the inversion is reduced. Γw_{stim} is related to laser gain [see equation (2.31)]. For a typical laser of length, say, 300 μm the total gain lies around 40 cm^{-1} and Γw_{stim} has a value of 3.4×10^{11} photons s^{-1}. The spontaneous emission power injected into each mode at threshold for a photon energy of 1.42 eV, obtained by multiplying Γw_{spon} by photon energy, is therefore $0.077 \gamma\mu$W. If, for instance the inversion were complete, the spontaneous emission power into each mode in the laser considered would be about an order of magnitude lower than that calculated previously in terms of a current density of 4000 A cm^{-2} μm. Complete inversion cannot, of course, be produced. However, lasers with a thin active layer having threshold current density per unit area of around 600 A cm^{-2} could have a value of Γw_{spon} as low as 0.2 μW.

Substituting equation (2.104) into (2.103) we find that the slope of the inclined grid in Figure 2.27 is given by

$$\frac{dK}{dx} = \frac{-\beta N}{m_{eff}}$$

$$\simeq \frac{-118 \beta V}{m_{eff}} \tag{2.107}$$

for $\mu^2(\mu - \lambda d\mu/d\lambda) = 56$, $\lambda = 0.85$ μm, $\eta_{sp} = 1$, V measured in μm^3,

$\Delta(h\nu) = 0.075$ eV, where $\beta = (1 - J_t/J_{th})$ and where we have used equation (2.5) to find N in terms of V. In Figure 2.27 we have drawn the slope of the grid with $118\,\beta V/m_{eff} \simeq 10^4$, corresponding to a stripe laser of average volume with $\beta = 0.3$ and, say ten modes. In addition to the vertical scale for K there is an alternative scale for P/I_{th}, the total output in photons per second relative to the total input at nominal threshold in injected carriers per second. As described above the output power for given total current is obtained by tracing upwards the relevant line of the inclined grid to the point where it intersects curve a. The output power which the simple linear light/current characteristic would predict is shown by the point where the sloping line intersects the vertical line b. Point C on curve a, which lies on the sloping line that passes through $x = 1$, gives the output power P_0 obtained at the nominal threshold current. P_0 is given by

$$\frac{P_0}{I_{th}} = \left(\frac{\beta m_{eff}}{N}\right)^{1/2}$$

$$\simeq 0.092\left(\frac{\beta m_{eff}}{V}\right)^{1/2} \tag{2.108}$$

where the various constants in the second version have been given the same values as for equation (2.107). The corresponding magnification K is given by

$$K = \left(\frac{\beta N}{m_{eff}}\right)^{1/2}$$

$$\simeq 11\left(\frac{\beta V}{m_{eff}}\right)^{1/2} \tag{2.109}$$

Substituting the same laser parameters as we used for Figure 2.27 into equation (2.108), we find that the relative output power at threshold, P_0/I_{th}, has a value less than 1 per cent. Hence, in the average laser spontaneous emission does not contribute a great deal to the intensity of the lasing modes at nominal threshold. However, the behaviour changes considerably as the volume V is reduced by reducing the cross section of the laser resonator. Lasers with a cross section of less than 1 μm^2 characteristic is 'softer' as a result. Reducing the volume by reducing the length does not have the same effect because this also reduces the number of modes m_{eff}.

To obtain a more exact treatment of the light/current characteristic around threshold we need to consider in more detail the number of modes m_{eff} that may be present under any particular circumstances. m_{eff} depends not only on the length of the laser but also on the current. In section 2.8.3 we consider how m_{eff} is affected by these variables and examine the consequences.

2.7.4 Efficiency (high power)

At high pumping levels the analysis of incremental efficiency described in Section 2.7.2 and giving equations (2.88)–(2.90) is no longer strictly accurate. The injected carrier concentration, which was assumed uniform, cannot in fact be maintained constant over the length of the laser under conditions where the stimulated emission itself varies appreciably with position. Since the optical intensity is greatest at the ends of the laser the stimulated emission is also greatest at these points, and the higher recombination rate reduces the injected carrier concentration and the optical gain. Saturation sets in and eventually, when the power level is high enough, the saturation becomes complete and the gain adjusts itself so that the stimulated emission rate is everywhere equal to the carrier injection rate. Light is generated uniformly throughout the bulk of the laser rather than more strongly close to the end-faces as is the case just above threshold. This results in a lowering of the incremental efficiency since the light, on average, has to suffer optical absorption over a greater length before it exits from the end-faces. The effect becomes appreciable for lasers with a low end-face reflection coefficient and of a length comparable to an absorption length.

To analyse the behaviour at high power it is first necessary to find the optical distribution along the length of the laser. This no longer obeys the exponential distribution of equation (2.84). When the current is increased greatly above threshold the distribution is described by a differential equation, first derived by Gooch,[44] of the form

$$\frac{\mathrm{d}F_+}{\mathrm{d}z} = \frac{JF_+}{F_+ + F_-} - \alpha F_+$$

$$\frac{\mathrm{d}F_-}{\mathrm{d}z} = \frac{-JF_-}{F_+ + F_-} + \alpha F_-$$

(2.110)

where F is the optical flux density in photons/cm^2, the positive and negative subscripts refer to the forward and reverse components of the wave, J is the volume current density (electrons cm^{-3}), and α is the optical absorption coefficient. These equations are based on the assumption that the current, at the high level concerned, is almost entirely directed to stimulated emission and that this stimulated emission is divided between the two oppositely directed waves in proportion to their intensity. Useful solutions can be obtained from the equations under normal circumstances where the current density J can be taken as constant over the whole area of the laser. Examination of the equations shows that the product $F_+ F_-$ is constant ($= F_0^2$ say) over the whole length of the laser. (Hasuo and Ohmi[45] have shown that the constancy of the product is a universal property of lasers irrespective of current.) The two above equations may be combined. To show the generality of the resulting expression it is convenient to express F_+ and F_- in terms of F_0 as $F_+/F_0 = \rho = F_0/F_-$ and to express z in terms of the absorption length α^{-1} as $\alpha z = Z$. The general differential equation becomes

$$\frac{d\rho}{dZ} = -\rho + \frac{A}{1 + \rho^{-2}} \tag{2.111}$$

where $A = J/\alpha F_0$ is a measure of the pumping strength. Hasuo and Ohmi have shown that this equation can be integrated to give Z in terms of ρ and A in the following terms

$$Z = \ln \rho + \left(1 - \frac{4}{A^2}\right)^{-1/2} \ln\left\{\frac{(\rho - b)(c - 1)}{(1 - b)(c - \rho)}\right\} \tag{2.112}$$

where b and c are the roots of the quadratic $b^2 - Ab + 1 = 0$. This equation is unfortunately not in the form which allows ρ to be obtained in terms of Z with pumping strength A as a parameter. To solve the optical flux distribution for any given laser of length L (giving a value of Z at the mirrors of $\pm \alpha L/2$) and reflection coefficient R ($\rho = R^{-1/2}$ at $Z = \pm \alpha L/2$) numerical methods must be used to find the value of A which allows the above boundary conditions on ρ and Z to be satisfied.

The curves in Figures 2.28 and 2.29 give examples of the calculated optical distributions well beyond threshold for lasers respectively with small

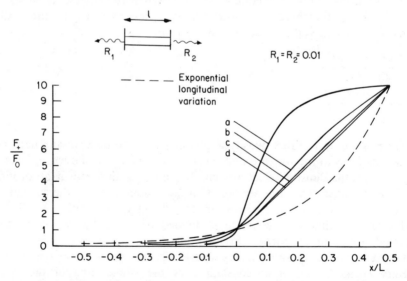

Figure 2.28 Longitudinal intensity profiles in lasers with low end-face reflectivity—comparison of low and high power behaviour. Curves for high power: (a) $\alpha L = 10$, (b) $\alpha L = 2.0$, (c) $\alpha L = 0.5$, (d) $\alpha L = 0.2$, $R_1 = R_2 = 0.01$. Low power behaviour which is independent of αL is indicated by dashed curve. After Whiteaway et al[42]

and large end-face reflection coefficients for a range of values of αL.[42] The precise value of αL is not significant up to about 0.5. As a comparison the exponential optical distributions according to equation (2.84) for currents just above threshold are also given for both cases. When the end-face reflection coefficient is large there is little difference between the low and high level results. When it is small the difference is considerable. At high current levels in this case the region of high optical intensity extends much further into the laser from the end-face, decreasing linearly rather than exponentially with distance.

The laser incremental efficiency η at high current levels can be derived from this treatment. It is given by the ratio of the output optical flux density $2F_0(\rho - 1/\rho)$ to the current input per unit cross section JL. Assuming an internal incremental efficiency of η_0 the expression for η in terms of R, αL, and A becomes

$$\eta = \frac{2\eta_0(R^{-1/2} - R^{1/2})}{A\alpha L} \tag{2.113}$$

In this expression, as in equation (2.91) for the efficiency of lasers just above threshold, the efficiency is a function of R and αL, in this case both explicitly and via the parameter A. As indicated above, numerical methods are necessary to find A.

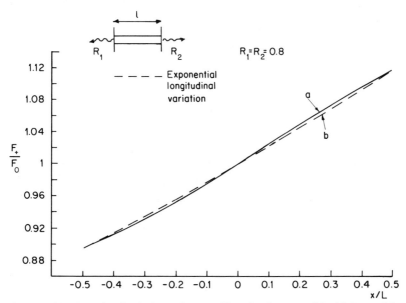

Figure 2.29 Longitudinal intensity profiles in lasers with high end-face reflectivity—comparison of low and high power behaviour. Curves for high power: (a) $\alpha L = 10$, (b) $\alpha L = 2.0, 0.5, 0.2$. Low power behaviour which is independent of αL is indicated by dashed curve. After Whiteaway et al[42]

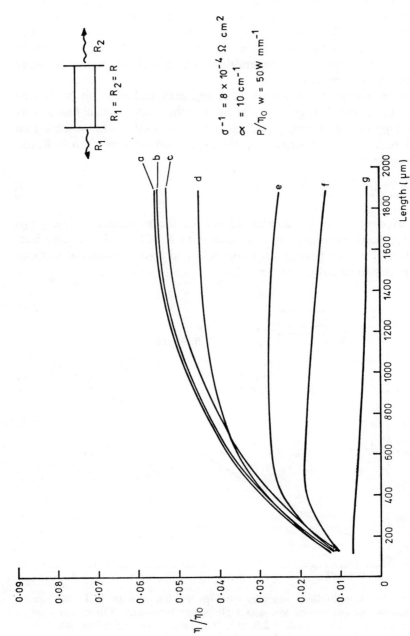

Figure 2.30 Theoretical plot of relative incremental efficiency η/η_0 against laser length L and reflectivity R for lasers operating far beyond threshold: (a) $R = 0.0001$, (b) $R = 0.001$, (c) $R = 0.01$, (d) $R = 0.1$, (e) $R = 0.32$, (f) $R = 0.5$, (g) $R = 0.8$. After Whiteaway et al[42]

   The effect in a typical case of using the accurate high power relation for incremental quantum efficiency according to the above equation rather than the approximate relation of equation (2.91) is illustrated in Figures 2.30 and 2.31. These figures give curves showing how the overall efficiency of a typical laser can be optimized by adjusting the laser length and the mirror reflectivity. The overall efficiency includes the voltage drop across the laser contacts and the effect of the threshold current. The absorption length is taken in this instance as 10 cm^{-1}, the contact resistivity as 8×10^{-4} Ωcm^2, and the required output power as 50 W mm^{-1} width. The curves of Figure 2.30 are based on equation (2.113) for the efficiency at currents well beyond threshold, and the curves of Figure 2.31 are based on equation (2.91) which applies for current close to threshold. The point that emerges clearly is that at high currents it is not possible to obtain good efficiency by using low values of the reflection coefficient in conjunction with a long laser resonator. Thus, Figure 2.30 shows little advantage in reducing the facet reflectivity below 0.01 for the case considered and increasing the laser length beyond 1.5 mm, whereas the approximate curves of Figure 2.31 suggest that much lower reflectivity and much longer lasers would give optimum performance. Whiteaway et al[42] have analysed the general case and shown that optimum performance is obtained in a variety of situations for laser length close to the absorption length and for facet reflectivity between 0.1 and 0.01.

2.8   OPTICAL MODES

The optical mode pattern of the lasing emission in a semiconductor laser is determined to a large extent by the properties of the laser resonator. The laser resonator in general has a rectangular shape, flattened in the direction perpendicular to the p–n junction (y axis) and elongated along the laser axis (z axis). The end mirrors terminate the resonator in the z direction. In a heterostructure laser the two hetero-junctions enclose the resonator in the y direction. A variety of boundaries, depending on the particular design of the laser, are used for enclosing the resonator in the second transverse direction (x direction). The relevant constructional details of the various devices are described in Chapters 3, 5, and 6. In a rectangular resonator the resonant optical modes can be indexed in terms of the number of complete half wave periods existing in the three spatial directions. In a dielectric waveguide resonator the number of half wave periods is non-integral and the index is conventionally taken as the nearest integer below the actual value. The treatment of slab waveguides in Chapter 4 describes how this behaviour occurs. For the present we simply exploit it to provide a three-index identification for each mode of the form mpq where m applies to the z direction (laser axis), p applies to the y direction (perpendicular to junction

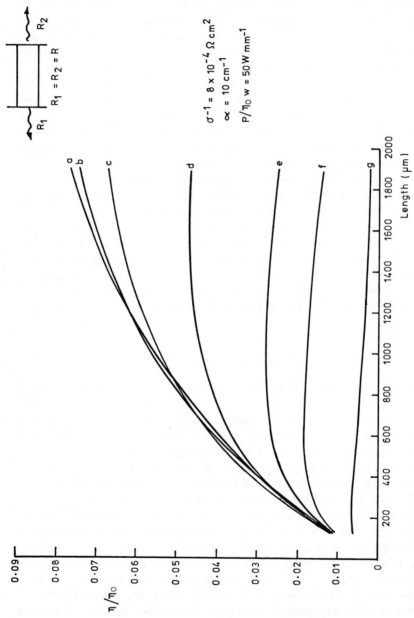

Figure 2.31 Theoretical plot of relative incremental efficiency η/η_0 against laser length L and reflectivity R for lasers operating close to threshold: (a) $R = 0.0001$, (b) $R = 0.001$, (c) $R = 0.01$, (d) $R = 0.1$, (e) $R = 0.32$, (f) $R = 0.5$, (g) $R = 0.8$. After Whiteaway et al[42]

plane), and q applies to the x direction (transverse direction in junction plane). m is a large number but p and q may have values from zero upwards.

A three-dimensional rectangular optical resonator can in general support a large number of resonant modes, and the plane waves into which the resonances may be resolved can be directed over a wide range of angles in space. The resulting close spacing of the resonances in the optical frequency spectrum and the resulting wide range of angles of the emergent beams would be a drawback to the operation of a laser. The resonator must therefore be designed to limit the number of possible modes. In the direction perpendicular to the laser junction this is normally done by restricting the thickness of the resonator to a size where only one half period of the wave can be accommodated. The thickness lies in the range 0.5–2 μm, depending on the properties of the heterostructure waveguide, as described in Chapter 4. In the transverse direction in the junction plane the reflection of oblique waves which excite the higher order modes is normally cut down by leaving the sides of the resonator open. However, there is usually some weak form of optical confinement at the sides, and in practice lasers which are wider than 20 or 30 μm exhibit low order transverse modes ($q > 0$) with thresholds that are not much higher than that of the axial mode ($q = 0$). The transverse modes may be identified in lasers of not too great width by the regular pattern of antinodes that they produce across the output face. In lasers that are wider than about 50 μm, variations in the uniformity of the junction tend to destroy the regular pattern.

Even when the transverse modes are suppressed there is still a considerable spectral density of the remaining pure longitudinal modes. As shown below they have a spectral separation in the range 2–5 Å. Many lasers are sufficiently uniform such that the discrimination exerted by the gain spectrum (width about 400 Å) is sufficient substantially to select a single longitudinal mode. However, as shown below, such discrimination can only occur when the lasing output is raised sufficiently above the spontaneous level. At lower levels the mode spectrum broadens until, at around the nominal threshold current, there may be ten or more longitudinal modes with more than half the intensity of the central mode (see Figure 2.22). This considerable number of modes adds to the light output in these circumstances. It also affects other aspects of the behaviour, particularly the modulation response, which is treated in Chapter 7, Section 7.3.3.

2.8.1 Separation of Longitudinal Modes

The frequency interval separating longitudinal modes in a semiconductor laser depends on the length L of the resonator and on the refractive index and dispersion of the semiconductor material. Let δN be the difference in the wave number (reciprocal wavelength) between adjacent longitudinal modes as measured within the laser. Then because successive modes contain an extra half wavelength we find the following relation

$$\delta N = \frac{1}{2L} \tag{2.114}$$

We require to relate δN to the change $\delta\lambda$ in the free space wavelength. We use $N = \mu_{eff}/\lambda$ where μ_{eff} is the effective refractive index for the guided wave within the laser resonator (see Section 4.1.2). Because the semiconductor is dispersive μ_{eff} depends on λ. Differentiation of N with respect to λ gives

$$\frac{dN}{d\lambda} = \left(\frac{1}{\lambda}\right) \frac{d\mu_{eff}}{d\lambda} - \frac{\mu_{eff}}{\lambda^2}$$

Using this expression in conjunction with equation (2.114) gives

$$\delta\lambda = \frac{\lambda^2}{(\mu_{eff} - \lambda d\mu_{eff}/d\lambda)2L} \tag{2.115}$$

In practice the group index $(\mu_{eff} - \lambda \, d\mu_{eff}/d\lambda)$ is found to have a value in GaAs of about 4.5 which gives a typical mode spacing for, say, $L = 400 \ \mu$m and $\lambda = 0.87 \ \mu$m of 2 Å.

2.8.2   Spectrum of Individual Modes

We now consider the spectral distribution of the lasing output within each mode. Spontaneous emission causes some broadening of the linewidth. Even well above threshold the laser can be considered in some respects to be an amplifier of spontaneous emission rather than an oscillator. The contribution of spontaneous emission means that the stimulated emission does not have to compensate completely the optical losses from the resonator. The active Q of the resonator is therefore not infinite and the bandwidth is not zero. Saturation effects caused by the limited amount of pump current (which are treated in section 7.7.2) restrict the amplitude fluctuations associated with the finite bandwidth but have no effect on the frequency fluctuations.

To derive the bandwidth of the resonator under active conditions it is necessary to consider the amplitude and phase of the forward and backward waves within it rather than just their intensity. Consider the interrelation of the two sets of waves at one end of the resonator, as illustrated in Figure 2.32. Wave A incident on the mirror is derived from a combination of the wave reflected from the opposite mirror together with the spontaneous

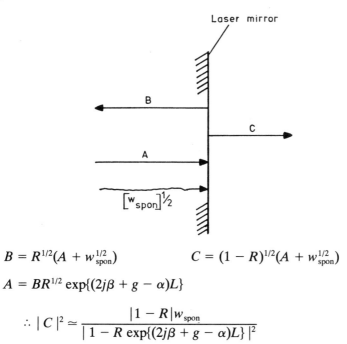

Laser mirror

$$B = R^{1/2}(A + w_{\text{spon}}^{1/2}) \qquad\qquad C = (1 - R)^{1/2}(A + w_{\text{spon}}^{1/2})$$

$$A = BR^{1/2} \exp\{(2j\beta + g - \alpha)L\}$$

$$\therefore |C|^2 \simeq \frac{|1 - R| w_{\text{spon}}}{|1 - R \exp\{(2j\beta + g - \alpha)L\}|^2}$$

Figure 2.32 Relation between amplitudes of forward and reflected and transmitted wave at laser mirror and contribution from spontaneous emission

emission produced over the whole length of the resonator within the solid
angle and band width appropriate to the mode concerned. The contribution
from the opposite mirror is itself derived from the wave B reflected from the
first mirror after it has traversed the double length of the resonator,
undergoing in the process amplification and reflection from the far end.
Taking into account the fact that the amplitude reflection coefficient is $R^{1/2}$
and the double pass gain for the amplitude is half that for the intensity we
may write a self-consistent equation equating the round trip loss in
amplitude to the amplitude contribution of the spontaneous emission. By
this means we find we can replace the term $(1 - R)/(1 - R \exp\{(g - \alpha)L\})$
in equation (2.100b) for K, to substitute in equation (2.100a) for the total
output, by a term $f(\nu)d\nu$ over the frequency range $d\nu$ where $f(\nu)$ is given by

$$f(\nu)d\nu = \frac{|1 - R|}{|1 - R \exp\{j2\pi\nu/\Delta\nu + |(g - \alpha)L\}|^2} \frac{d\nu}{\Delta\nu} \qquad (2.116)$$

and where $\Delta\nu$ is the frequency interval between modes. The integral of this expression over $\Delta\nu$ naturally gives the original term gain. The equation represents a Lorentzian spectral distribution with a linewidth $\delta\nu$ to the half power points given by

$$\delta\nu \approx \frac{[1 - R \exp\{(g - \alpha)L\}]\Delta\nu}{\pi} \qquad (2.117a)$$

The term on the right-hand side of equation (2.117a) is the same as the term which appears in the denominator of expression (2.100b) for the amplification factor K and determines the level of the output. Hence we may re-express (2.117a) in terms of the total output power of the mode, say P_m. Using the same approximations on (2.100b) as were used on (2.100c) in obtaining (2.101) and putting $(1 - R)^2/R\{\ln(1/R)\}^2$ equal to unity and substituting into (2.117a) gives

$$\delta\nu \simeq \ln\left(\frac{1}{R}\right)\frac{\Gamma w_{\text{spon}}\Delta\nu}{\pi P_m} \qquad (2.117b)$$

The linewidth is therefore inversely proportional to the power output in the mode and to the length of the resonator (via $\Delta\nu$) and decreases with increase of the reflectivity R according to $\ln(1/R)$. With a longitudinal mode separation of, say, 3 Å a power output of 5 mW in one mode and a spontaneous emission input of 0.5 μW (as estimated in Section 2.7.3) we would expect a linewidth of 10^{-4} Å, or approximately 3 MHz. Linewidths as narrow as this have not yet been confirmed. However the best results reported on temperature-stabilized lasers at room temperature showed stability within 40 MHz, the measurement being limited by the resolution of the etalon employed.[46] The above results also apply to the linewidth of individual modes in a multimode laser.

2.8.2.1 Derivation of gain from mode spectrum

In this section we analyse a method of deriving the gain spectrum in a laser below threshold by observing the magnitude of the Fabry–Perot resonances in the longitudinal modes. These resonances can still be observed even well below threshold. The number of peaks increases as the current is lowered and they spread over a greater width of the spectrum. The maxima occur at frequency intervals corresponding to $\nu/\Delta\nu$ in equation (2.116) changing by an integer and the intervening minima lie half way in between. According to equation (2.116) the intensity ratio ρ between any maximum and the nearby minimum is given by

$$\rho = \left\{\frac{(1 + R \exp\{(g - \alpha)L\}}{1 - R \exp\{(g - \alpha)L\}}\right\}^2 \qquad (2.118)$$

Hence, the net gain $(g - \alpha)$ is given in terms of ρ by

$$(g - \alpha) = \left(\frac{1}{L}\right) \ln \left\{ \frac{(\rho^{1/2} - 1)}{R(\rho^{1/2} + 1)} \right\} \tag{2.119}$$

This is a useful relation which provides the means for experimentally deriving $(g - \alpha)$ in a laser as a function of current up to the threshold current and as a function of wavelength over some fraction of the spontaneous emission linewidth. This is the method referred to in section 2.6.3.2 and pioneered by Hakki and Paoli.[34]

2.8.3 Evolution of Mode Spectrum and Intensity with Current

In order to obtain a precise understanding of how the light output of the laser depends on current in the vicinity of threshold and how the overall spectrum evolves with current it is necessary to consider how the total light is divided amongst all the laser modes. In a uniform laser the optical intensity in the modes of different wavelength is determined by the way the optical gain varies across the spectrum. Equations (2.100a) and (2.101) in section 2.7.3 can be used to find the output in each longitudinal mode when the appropriate gain is inserted into the expression. We will carry out this analysis for the case where only the zero-order transverse mode is present and all the longitudinal modes therefore belong to this zero-order set.

2.8.3.1 Analysis

As a starting point for the analysis we require an expression for the shape of the gain spectrum. A suitable approximation is to take the spectrum to be in the form of an inverted parabola. The width of the parabola is more conveniently related to the longitudinal mode number m than to wavelength. The modes will be arbitrarily numbered from zero at the centre of the spectrum through positive and negative numbers to $+M$ and $-M$ at the short and long wavelength edges, respectively. The edges of the spectrum are defined to be where the gain is zero. Then we may use the following approximate expression for the gain g_m of mode m in terms of the gain g_0 of the central mode

$$g_m = g_0 \left(1 - \left(\frac{m}{M}\right)^2 \right) \tag{2.120}$$

as illustrated in Figure 2.33(a). Consider the case where the net gain of the zero-order mode is slightly less than the overall losses by a factor $(1 - \epsilon)$ where ϵ is small. Then we have

$$g_0 = \left\{ \frac{\ln(1/R)}{L} + \alpha \right\} (1 - \epsilon) \tag{2.121}$$

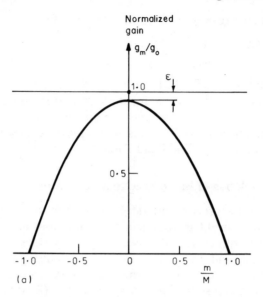

(a)

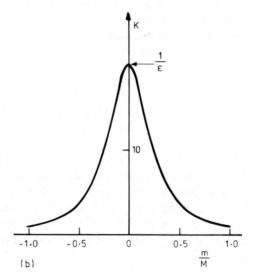

(b)

Figure 2.33 (a) Example of spectral distribution of relative gain and loss plotted as a function of relative longitudinal mode number m/M, and (b) corresponding spectral distribution of magnification factor K for spontaneous emission into lasing mode and

$$g_m \simeq \left\{ \frac{\ln(1/R)}{L} + \alpha \right\} \left\{ 1 - \epsilon - \left(\frac{m}{M} \right)^2 \right\} \tag{2.122}$$

for m/M small. The output power P_m for m can then be obtained from equations (2.100a) and (2.101) in terms of the spontaneous emission as follows

$$P_m \simeq \frac{\eta \Gamma w_{\text{spon}}}{\epsilon + (m/M)^2} \tag{2.123}$$

where $\eta_0 = 1$ [see equation (2.101)]. The relative distribution of P_m is illustrated in Figure 2.33(b). The total output ΣP_m from all the longitudinal modes can be obtained by summing the expression in equation (2.123) with respect to m between $-M$ and $+M$. This is approximately the same as summing between $m = \pm \infty$, which gives[47]

$$\Sigma P_m \simeq \eta \left(\frac{\pi M}{|\epsilon^{1/2}} \right) \Gamma w_{\text{spon}} \coth(\pi M \epsilon^{1/2}) \tag{2.124}$$

The total number of modes whose intensity is greater than half that of the central mode, say $m_{1/2}$, can be obtained from equation (2.123) and is given by

$$m_{1/2} = 2M\epsilon^{1/2} \tag{2.125}$$

Multiplying the two expressions together and noting that coth $(\pi M\epsilon^{1/2})$ may be taken as unity for $M\epsilon^{1/2} > 1$ shows that the output power times number-of-modes product is approximately constant for given M provided there is more than one mode with appreciable intensity. We call this product P_B and it is given by

$$P_B \simeq 2\eta \pi M^2 \Gamma w_{\text{spon}} \tag{2.126}$$

We now derive the relationship between total current and the combined output power ΣP_m in all modes. As in section 2.7.3 we divide the total current density per unit volume J into two components: a stimulated component J_{st} related to the total light output by

$$J_{\text{st}} = \frac{\Sigma P_m}{\eta V} \tag{2.127}$$

and a spontaneous component J_{sp} to which the gain g_0 of the central mode is related by

$$g_0 = \left\{ \frac{\ln(1/R)}{L} + \alpha \right\} \left\{ 1 + \frac{\Delta J_{\text{sp}}}{\beta J_{\text{th}}} \right\} \tag{2.128}$$

where ΔJ_{sp} is the amount by which J_{sp} exceeds the nominal threshold J_{th}, where $\beta = (1 - J_t/J_{\text{th}})$, and where J_t is the current density for zero gain.

Hence ϵ in equation (2.121) is given by

$$\epsilon = \frac{-\Delta J_{sp}}{\beta J_{th}} \tag{2.129}$$

We now have the information required to express the stimulated output in equation (2.124) in terms of the spontaneous component of current density and hence, by adding the stimulated component of current, in terms of the total current density. To simplify the equations it is helpful to re-express the total optical output ΣP_m as a flux per unit volume of the laser resonator, measured relative to the threshold current density per unit volume J_{th}. We define this quantity as ρ so that

$$\rho = \frac{\Sigma P_m}{J_{th}} \tag{2.130}$$

where P_m and J_{th} are measured in comparable units, e.g. photons s^{-1} and carriers s^{-1}, respectively.

Similarly the spontaneous emission per unit volume can be expressed as a proportion of the spontaneous current density by dividing by the total number N of spontaneous modes in the laser cavity within the bandwidth of the spontaneous emission [by analogy with equation (2.104)]. Expressing the spontaneous component of the current density as $J_{th} + \Delta J_{sp}$ this gives

$$\frac{\Gamma w_{spon}}{V J_{th}} = \frac{\eta_{sp}(1 + \Delta J_{sp}/J_{th})}{N} \tag{2.131}$$

where N can be obtained from equation (2.5) in terms of the volume of the laser resonator. Substituting (2.129), (2.124) with $\coth(\pi M \epsilon^{1/2}) \approx 1$, and (2.131) into (2.130) we obtain the following relation between the relative light output ρ and the amount ΔJ_{sp} by which the spontaneous current input differs from threshold

$$\rho = -\eta \eta_{sp} \pi M \beta^{1/2} \left(\frac{J_{th}}{\Delta J_{sp}} \right)^{1/2} \frac{1 + \Delta J_{sp}/J_{th}}{N} \tag{2.132}$$

The total current density J is the sum of the spontaneous component of current density, and the stimulated light output per unit volume, less the contribution to the stimulated light output of spontaneous emission. This gives the following relation for J when expressed relative to the threshold current density J_{th}

$$\frac{J}{J_{th}} = \left(1 + \frac{\Delta J_{sp}}{J_{th}} \right) \left(1 - \frac{2M}{N} \right) + \frac{\rho}{\eta} \tag{2.133}$$

We can ignore $\Delta J_{sp}/J_{th}$ in equation (2.132) compared with unity in most circumstances and then use this equation to give a relatively simple expression for $\Delta J_{sp}/J_{th}$ in terms of the relative light output ρ. This can be substituted into equation (2.133) giving the following concise relation between the relative excess current above threshold and a normalized version of the light output y,

$$\frac{\Delta J}{J_{th}} = \rho_0 \left(y - \frac{1}{y^2} \right) \tag{2.134}$$

where M/N has been ignored compared with unity and where

$$\rho_0 = \beta^{1/3} \left(\frac{\eta_{sp} \pi M}{N} \right)^{2/3} \tag{2.135}$$

$$y = \frac{\rho}{\eta \rho_0} \tag{2.136}$$

$$\Delta J = J - J_{th} \tag{2.137}$$

The total number of modes $m_{1/2}$ with intensity more than half of that of the central mode is given by

$$\begin{aligned} m_{1/2} &\simeq 1 + 2M\epsilon^{1/2} \\ &\simeq 1 + \frac{2\eta\eta_{sp}\pi M^2}{N\rho} \\ &\simeq 1 + \frac{2M\rho_0^{1/2}}{y\beta^{1/2}} \end{aligned} \tag{2.138}$$

2.8.3.2 Results

Let us now consider the actual magnitude of the effects introduced by spontaneous emission in a practical laser both in the multimode behaviour and the total-intensity-versus-current relations.

The (power × mode number) product P_B gives the minimum power output at which the laser will operate in substantially a single longitudinal mode, with the intensity in the central mode more than twice as great as that in the adjacent modes. The important parameters on which P_B depends, according to equation (2.126), are the number of longitudinal modes $2M$ within the gain spectrum and the spontaneous emission rate Γw_{spon} into a single laser mode.

M is given in terms of the length L of the laser and the bandwidth $\Delta\lambda$ of the gain spectrum, by

$$M = \frac{L\Delta\lambda(\mu - \lambda \, d\mu/d\lambda)}{\lambda^2} \tag{2.139}$$

as derived from the mode spacing given in equation (2.115). $\Delta\lambda$ varies with injection level, doping and temperature. On average it lies around 250 Å.[49] This gives a value of M for, say, a 400-μm long laser of about 60. Γw_{spon} is

also not known accurately. We will use our estimate in section 2.7.3 of
$0.5\,\Gamma\,\mu$W and take a reasonable value of Γ of around 0.5. Inserting these
values into equation (2.126) gives a value of the total output P_B for near
single mode operation of 5 mW, or taking the external efficiency to be, say,
40 per cent, a power out of one end of the laser of 1 mW. This power
depends on the square of the laser length and would drop to 0.25 mW for a
laser of length 200 μm.

It may seem that a power within the laser of 5 mW is a surprisingly large
value to be required for single mode operation. However, it must be
compared with the total internal power associated with the whole
longitudinal spectrum of spontaneous modes at threshold, which amounts to
0.05 mW. We see therefore that the laser power concerned is only two
orders of magnitude greater than the total spontaneous power, which makes
the result more reasonable. The large value of laser power required is simply
a consequence of the relatively wide bandwidth of the spontaneous light
emission from the semiconductor.

Let us now consider the variation of light output in the vicinity of
threshold in multimode operation. This is given by equation (2.134) and is
plotted in Figure 2.34 curve A. The characteristic obtained is fairly slowly

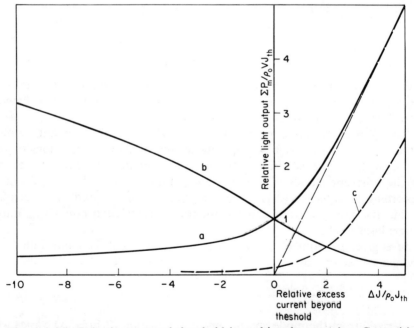

Figure 2.34   Behaviour around threshold in multimode operation. Curve (a)
output in all modes as a function of excess current above threshold. Curve (b)
relative number of modes. Curve (c) output in central mode as a function of
excess current

varying below threshold. Above threshold it steepens up and approximates to the ideal linear characteristic when the relative excess current $\Delta J/J_{th}$ is greater than about $2\rho_0$. At nominal threshold, where $y = 1$, the emitted light relative to the threshold current is ρ_0. The number of modes at this current is $1 + 2M\rho_0^{1/2}/\beta^{1/2}$ [see equation (2.138)]. Hence, ρ_0 is the major factor that determines behaviour and it is interesting to estimate its value.

The main parameter on which ρ_0 depends according to equation (2.135) is M/N. M is given in equation (2.139) and is proportional to the laser length L. N can be obtained from equation (2.5) and is proportional to laser volume. Hence M/N is proportional to the cross-sectional area of the laser. It is given by

$$\frac{M}{N} = \frac{B\lambda^2}{8\pi\mu^2 ws} \tag{2.140}$$

where B is the ratio of the width of the gain spectrum to the spontaneous spectrum, w is the width, and s is the thickness of the laser resonator. For typical values of $\lambda = 0.85 \ \mu\text{m}$, $B = 0.75$, and $\mu^2 = 12.5$ and for w and s measured in micrometres we have

$$\frac{M}{N} = \frac{0.001725}{ws} \tag{2.141}$$

and

$$\rho_0 = \frac{0.02}{(ws)^{2/3}} \tag{2.142}$$

for a typical value of β of 0.3.

According to equation (2.142) the cross-sectional area ws of the laser is the most important factor in determining the value of ρ_0 and hence in determining the behaviour of the laser around threshold. Let us compare the typical behaviour of lasers of, say, $5 \ \mu\text{m}^2$ and $1 \ \mu\text{m}^2$ cross section, the former representative of a normal stripe laser and the latter representative of a buried heterostructure laser.

For $ws = 5 \ \mu\text{m}^2$ we find $\rho_0 \simeq 0.007$. Hence the output of amplified spontaneous emission at nominal threshold is equivalent to 0.7 per cent of the threshold current. The number of longitudinal modes with intensity more than half the central mode at nominal threshold is, according to equation (2.138), proportional to laser length, and for a laser of length $400 \ \mu\text{m}$ is about 15. The minimum relative current required to give substantially single mode operation is given according to equations (2.134) and (2.138) by

$$\frac{\Delta J}{J_{th}}(m = 1) = \frac{2M\rho_0^{3/2}}{\beta^{1/2}} \tag{2.143}$$

and for a 400-μm long laser is approximately 13 per cent above threshold.

For $ws = 1\ \mu\mathrm{m}^2$, $\rho_0 = 0.02$. The power output at nominal threshold now corresponds to 2 per cent of the threshold current. The number of modes in a 400-μm long laser at nominal threshold is about 25. The minimum current required to give substantially single mode operation is 65 per cent above threshold. The latter characteristic in particular represents a significant change in behaviour compared with the laser of large cross section.

The multimode behaviour also affects the intensity/current relation of the central longitudinal mode, introducing superlinearity in the region where the number of modes is diminishing. The intensity of the central mode is obtained by dividing the total intensity of all the modes by the effective mode number $\pi M \epsilon^{1/2}$ (slightly different from the number of modes with more than half the intensity of the main mode). This shows that the intensity of the central mode is proportional to the square of the intensity of the sum of all the modes up to the point where the central mode starts to dominate. Such a characteristic is plotted in Figure 2.34 curve C for the case of a laser where the effective mode number at nominal threshold is 10.

The modal behaviour of actual lasers is frequently complicated by non-uniformity of injected carrier concentration and refractive index in the active layer. Carrier concentration variations become more obvious as the laser is driven harder. Longitudinal variations with the periodicity of the standing wave pattern may arise as a result of stimulated depletion of carriers which is only partially compensated by carrier diffusion.[48] This situation can encourage multimode operation to re-appear at higher currents. Refractive index variations are more obvious in wider lasers where they interfere with the regular pattern of the transverse modes.

In good stripe lasers, the widths of which are not too great, the modal behaviour in the vicinity of threshold conforms reasonably closely to that predicted theoretically. The number of modes diminishes rapidly as the current is increased through threshold and the output moves smoothly from amplified spontaneous emission into true lasing.[49]

Measurements that have been made on the light/current characteristics of stripe lasers of various widths show that the lasers with the smaller cross-sectional area show a 'softer characteristic' with a more gradual transition between the spontaneous and lasing regimes, in agreement with the theoretical analysis.[50]

REFERENCES

1. M. G. A. Bernard and G. Duraffourg, 'Laser conditions in semiconductors', *Phys. Status Solidi*, **1**, 1961, 699.
2. R. M. Eisberg, 'Fundamentals of modern physics' John Wiley and Sons, Inc. 1961, pp. 47 et seq.
3. R. A. Smith, *Semiconductors*, Cambridge University Press, London, 1959, p. 22.
4. L. Schiff, *Quantum Mechanics*, 3rd edn., McGraw Hill Kogakusha, Ltd, Tokyo, pp. 280, 398.

5. H. C. Casey, Jr and F. Stern, 'Concentration dependent absorption and spontaneous emission in heavily doped GaAs', *J. Appl. Phys.* **47**, 1976, p. 631.

6. J. Callaway, *Energy Band Theory* Academic Press, New York, 1964, Section 1.1 and p. 240.

7. E. O. Kane, 'Band structure-indium antimonide', *J. Phys. Chem. Solids*, **1**, 1957, 249.

8. D. M. Eagles, 'Optical absorption and recombination radiation in semiconductors due to transitions between hydrogen-like acceptor impurity levels', *J. Phys. Chem. Solids*, **16**, 1960, 76.

9. W. P. Dumke, 'Interband transitions and maser action', *Phys. Rev.*, **127**, 1962, 1559.

10. F. Stern, 'Band tail model for optical absorption and for the mobility edge in amorphous silicon', *Phys. Rev.*, **B3**, 1971, 2636.

11. F. Stern, *Solid State Physics* (F. Seitz and D. Turnbull, eds.), vol. 15, Academic Press, New York, 1963, p. 398.

12. O. V. Emel'yanenko, T. S. Lagunova, D. N. Nasledov, and G. N. Talalakin, 'Formation and properties of an impurity band in n-type GaAs', *Sov. Phys. Solid State*, **7**, 1965, 1063.

13. F. Ermanis and K. Wolfstirn, 'Hall effect and resistivity of Zn-doped GaAs', *J. Appl. Phys.*, **37**, 1966, 1963.

14. E. O. Kane, 'Thomas–Fermi approach to impure semiconductor band structure', *Phys. Rev.*, **131**, 1963, 79.

15. B. I. Halperin and M. Lax, 'Impurity-band tails in the high density limit. I Minimum counting methods', *Phys. Rev.*, **148**, 1966, 722.

16. C. J. Hwang, 'Properties of spontaneous and stimulated emission in GaAs junction lasers', *Phys. Rev. B.*, **2**, 1970, 4117.

17. K. Unger, 'Spontaneous and stimulated emission in junction lasers. I Bands with parabolic state densities, II Bands with density of states tails', *Zeitscrift fur Physik*, **207**, 1967, 322–341.

18. G. J. Lasher, 'Threshold relations and diffraction loss for injection laser', *IBM J. Res. Develop.*, **7**, 1963, 58.

19. J. L. Moll and J. F. Gibbons, 'Threshold current for p–n junction lasers', *IBM J. Res. Develop.*, **7**, 1963, 157.

20. S. Mayburg, 'Threshold current for line narrowing in GaAs junction diodes', *J. Appl. Phys.*, **34**, 1963, 1791.

21. M. J. Adams, 'A simple approximation for high temperature properties of the injection laser', *Brit. J. Appl. Phys. (J. Phys. D)*, **2**, 1969, 1549.

22. F. Stern, *Semiconductor Lasers: Theory*, Laser Handbook, North-Holland, Amsterdam, 1972.

23. F. Stern, 'Gain current relation for GaAs lasers with n-type and undoped active layers', *J. Quant. Electron.*, **QE-9**, 1973, 290.

24. E. Pinkas, B. I. Miller, I. Hayashi, and P. W. Foy, 'GaAs–Al$_x$Ga$_{1-x}$As double heterostructure lasers—effect of doping on lasing characteristics of GaAs', *J. Appl. Phys.*, **43**, 1972, 2827.

25. G. Lasher and F. Stern, 'Spontaneous and stimulated recombination radiation in semiconductors', *Phys. Rev.*, **133**, 1964, A553.

26. M. J. Adams and P. T. Landsberg, 'The theory of the injection laser', *Gallium Arsenide Lasers* (C. H. Gooch, ed.) Wiley–Interscience, 1969, pp. 5–79.

27. F. Stern, 'Effect of band tails on stimulated emission of light in semiconductors', *Phys. Rev.*, **148**, 1966, 186.

28. M. J. Adams, 'Theoretical effects of exponential band tails on the properties of the injection laser', *Solid State Electronics*, **12**, 1969, 661.

29. G. H. B. Thompson, 'Theory of filamentation in semiconductor lasers including the dependence of dielectric constant on injected carrier density', *Opto-Electronics*, **4**, 1972, 257.

30. A. R. Goodwin and G. H. B. Thompson, 'Superlinear dependence of gain on current density in GaAs injection lasers', *J. Quantum Electron.*, **QE-6**, 1970, 311.

31. J. Bakker and G. A. Acket, 'Single-pass gain measurements on optically pumped $Al_xGa_{(1-x)}As–Al_yGa_{1-y}As$ double heterostructure laser structures at room temperature', *J. Quantum Electron.*, **QE-13**, 1977, 567.

32. G. H. B. Thompson, G. D. Henshall, J. E. A. Whiteaway, and P. A. Kirkby, 'Narrow-beam five-layer (GaAl)As/GaAs heterostructure lasers with low threshold and high peak power', *J. Appl. Phys.*, **47**, 1976, 1501.

33. B. W. Hakki and T. L. Paoli, 'CW degradation of GaAs lasers II Electronic gain', *J. Appl. Phys.*, **44**, 1973, 4113.

34. F. Stern, 'Calculated spectral dependence of gain in excited GaAs', *J. Appl. Phys.*, **47**, 1976, 5382.

35. T. L. Paoli, 'Saturation behaviour of the spontaneous emission from double-heterostructure junction lasers operating high above threshold', *J. Quantum. Electron.*, **QE-9**, 1973, 267.

36. J. R. Biard, W. N. Carr, and B. S. Reed, 'Analysis of a GaAs laser', *Trans. AIME*, **230**, 1964, 286.

37. G. H. B. Thompson, P. A. Kirkby, and J. E. A. Whiteaway, 'The analysis of optical scattering in double-heterostructure and five-layer heterostructure (GaAl)As/GaAs injection lasers', *J. Quantum Electron.*, **QE-11**, 1975, 481.

38. F. R. Nash, W. R. Wagner, and R. L. Brown, 'Threshold current variations and optical scattering losses in (AlGa)As double heterostructure lasers', *J. Appl. Phys.*, **47**, 1976, 3992.

39. M. Ettenberg, H. F. Lockwood, and H. S. Sommers, 'Radiation trapping in laser diodes', *J. Appl. Phys.*, **43**, 1972, 5047.

40. G. D. Henshall, 'The suppression of internally circulating modes in (GaAl)As/GaAs heterostructure lasers and their effect on catastrophic degradation and efficiency', *Appl. Phys. Lett.*, **31**, 1977, 205.

41. H. S. Sommers, 'Theoretical maximum of the power efficiency of a pulsed injection laser with a Fabry-Perot cavity', *Solid State Electron.*, **11**, 1968, 909.

42. J. E. A. Whiteaway and G. H. B. Thompson, 'Optimisation of power efficiency of (GaAl)As injection lasers operating at high power levels', *Solid State and Electron Devices*, **1**, 1977, 81.

43. A. R. Goodwin and P. R. Selway, 'Gain and loss processes in GaAlAs–GaAs heterostructure lasers', *J. Quantum Electron.*, **QE-6**, 1970, 285.

44. C. H. Gooch, *Proceedings of the 1966 Symposium on GaAs*, Reading (Institute of Physics), p. 62.

45. S. Hasuo and T. Ohmi, 'Spatial distribution of the light intensity in the injection laser', *Japan J. Appl. Phys.*, **13**, 1974, 1429.

46. K. Aiki, M. Nakamura, T. Kuroda, J. Umeda, R. Ito, N. Chinone, and M. Maeda, 'Transverse mode stabilized $Al_xGa_{1-x}As$ injection lasers with channelled-substrate-planar structures', *IEEE J. Quantum Electron.*, **JQE-14**, 1978, 89.

47. L. W. Casperson, 'Threshold characteristics of multimode laser oscillators', *J. Appl. Phys.*, **46**, 1975, 5194.

48. W. Streifer, R. D. Burnham, and D. R. Scifres, 'Dependence of longitudinal mode structure on injected carrier diffusion in diode lasers', *J. Quantum Electron.*, **QE-13**, 1977, 403.

49. Y. Suematsu, S. Akiba, and T. Hong, 'Measurement of spontaneous emission factor of AlGaAs double heterostructure semiconductor lasers', *J. Quantum Electron*, **QE-13**, 1977, 596.
50. T. Kobayashi, H. Kawaguchi, and Y. Furukawa, 'Lasing characteristics of very narrow planar stripe lasers', *Japan J. Appl. Phys.*, **16**, 1977, 601.
51. R. J. Nelson and R. G. Sobers, 'Minority carrier lifetime and internal quantum efficiency of surface-free GaAs', *J. Appl. Phys.*, **49**, 1978, 6103.

CHAPTER 3

Laser Heterostructures and Properties of Heterojunctions

GaAs injection laser design has now evolved to a large extent from the original simple p–n junction devices. This development can be attributed predominantly to the great improvement in performance which has been obtained by the incorporation of GaAs/(GaAs)Al heterojunctions into the structure. In this chapter we describe the various 'heterostructure' lasers, and give a general account of the properties of the (GaAl)As heterojunctions which are exploited in these designs.

3.1 HOMOSTRUCTURE LASERS

The simple type of p–n junction GaAs laser in which lasing action was first demonstrated is illustrated in Figure 3.1. The p–n junction is created in n-type material by diffusing in a p-type dopant, and a rectangular Fabry–Perot optical cavity is made by cleaving the end-faces of the laser and using an appropriate method to produce non-specularly reflecting side-faces, (e.g. sawing). In contrast to the later designs of heterostructure lasers these lasers are made from a semiconductor of uniform composition and have been since called homostructure lasers.

The n- and p-type regions in homostructure lasers are highly doped except for a thin region close to the diffusion front of the p-type impurity, mainly on the p-side of the junction where the dopant concentration grades down to zero. Under forward bias the current is predominantly carried by the electrons injected into the p-region. This selective injection takes place both because of the higher mobility of the electrons and because the band gap of the GaAs is slightly reduced on the p-side of the junction by the high acceptor concentration.

The potential variations around the p–n junction and the flow of carriers under forward bias are illustrated in the band diagram of Figure 3.2(a). If the p- and n-type regions are sufficiently highly doped, such that the

132

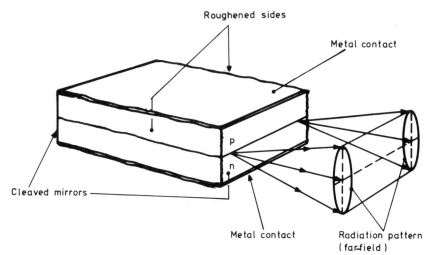

Figure 3.1 Diagram of homostructure laser showing light emission from cleaved end mirrors along junction plane, and roughened sidewalls to suppress transverse and internally circulating modes

respective Fermi levels lie well within the bands, then at a high injection current, as illustrated in the figure, a region of inversion is created, just on the p-side of the junction, where the quasi-Fermi levels are separated by more than the bandgap [see equation (2.5)]. The penetration of this inversion region into the p-type material is determined by the distance that the electrons diffuse in the face of the reverse field which, in general, is created by the doping gradient. When sufficient inversion is created over a sufficient distance into the p-region then the optical gain of a wave propagating along the junction becomes greater than its absorption and diffraction losses and the lasing threshold is reached. At 80 K threshold occurs at a current density J_{th} of the order of 500–1000 A cm^{-2}. However, J_{th} is very temperature sensitive and the minimum threshold that has been measured at room temperature is of the order of 30–50 kA cm^{-2}.

The theoretical dependence on temperature of the current required to maintain a given optical gain, according to the analysis of gain presented in Chapter 2, lies between a $T^{3/2}$ variation for low gain and a linear variation for high gain. Hence the expected factor for the increase in current density between 80 and 300 K due to fundamental gain processes lies between 4 and 8. In practice the current is observed to increase by a factor of 50 over this temperature range. The additional temperature sensitivity can be attributed to other causes. Three interrelated effects may be involved. associated respectively with the thickness of the inversion region, the diffraction losses, and the absorption losses of the optical wave. These effects become critical close to room temperature.

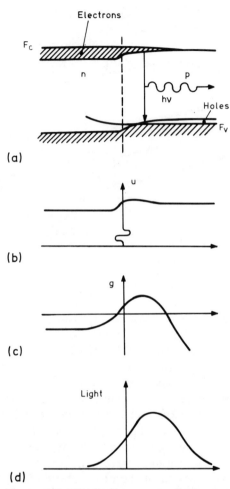

Figure 3.2 Distribution perpendicular to p–n junction in homostructure laser of (a) potential of conduction and valence bands, (b) refractive index, (c) optical gain per unit length, and (d) light intensity

The diffusion length of electrons, and hence the thickness of the inversion region, increases with temperature and also to some extent with current, owing to electric field and hot-carrier effects, up to at least 5 μm at 300 K. Hence the threshold current increases more than proportionately so as to provide both the higher injected carrier concentration and the greater volume of injected carriers needed at higher temperature. A limit is reached when the necessary injected carrier concentration approaches the doping level of the n-region from which the electrons are injected.

The propagation characteristics of the optical wave along the junction of the laser probably deteriorate at higher temperature. It is believed that a refractive index distribution exists, particularly at low temperatures, which tends to guide the wave in the vicinity of the junction. This is illustrated in Figure 3.2(b). The step in the refractive index on the n-side of the junction is readily understandable as the negative contribution of free electrons, although band-to-band processes add a further contribution. The step on the p-side is more conjectural. However, increasing the p-doping in GaAs has been found to lower the refractive index,[1] due to electronic band-to-band effects, and so a p-doping gradient can provide an appropriate refractive index profile.

The absorption edge in p-type GaAs occurs at longer wavelengths than in n-type material and hence the main absorption losses of the guided wave in the laser arise outside the inverted region on the p-side. The distribution of gain and loss which causes this is illustrated in Figure 3.2(c).

As the temperature is raised the concentration of injected electrons required to give threshold gain increases. This causes the refractive index to diminish so that the diffraction losses increase and the optical guiding becomes weaker. Also the lasing wavelength, which at low temperature is somewhat longer than the wavelength of the absorption edge, approaches the absorption edge as the temperature is raised. This provides another contribution to increasing optical losses at high temperature. In c.w. operation the increasing current which is required to compensate all the effects of increased temperature causes greater heating and hence higher threshold. Above a certain limiting heat-sink temperature this feedback process induces thermal runaway which suppresses lasing entirely. The maximum temperature that has been reported for c.w. operation in an optimized device is around 200 K.[2]

Qualitatively we can make the following conclusions about the performance of the homostructure laser at room temperature. The threshold current density is about 8–10 times higher at room temperature than might be expected when judged by its value at 80 K. The additional increase arises from the broadening of the inversion region in the laser and the spreading of the light into the optically lossy p-region. These conclusions suggest that very considerable improvements in performance could be achieved if means were provided for (a) controlling the diffusion of the minority carriers and (b) controlling the spread of the optical wave. By these means the injection and waveguiding characteristics at room temperature could be made comparable to, or even better than, those at 80 K, and threshold current densities could be reduced by at least an order of magnitude.

3.2 HETEROJUNCTIONS

The properties of semiconductor heterojunctions can be exploited very effectively in overcoming the deficiencies of the homostructure laser. Kroemer[3] and Alferov and Kazarinov[4] independently proposed that improved operation could be obtained by sandwiching the active layer of a semiconductor laser between two layers of higher band-gap material. The outer layers would limit the spread of both the injected carriers and the optical wave. Such a laser is not only superior to the homostructure laser but also more versatile. The composition and dimensions of the layer may be adjusted to suit a variety of applications. This design is called a heterostructure, and various identifiable types of heterostructure have been developed, adapted for different purposes. In this section we describe the relevant properties of the heterojunction and in the next section list the various types of heterostructure.

Heterostructure lasers are normally fabricated from mixed semiconductors, i.e. semiconductors with a composition in which one or two of the constituent elements can be replaced in any proportion by certain other elements. Examples are (GaAl)As, (GaIn)(AsP) and (GaAl)(AsSb) where the elements in the brackets can be mutually substituted (see also Chapter 1, section 1.3). These mixed semiconductors have a particularly convenient combination of characteristics for use in heterostructure lasers. Any change in composition that produces a change in the band-gap produces a change in the opposite sense in the refractive index. Hence it is possible to choose the composition of the outer layers of the heterostructure with respect to that of the centre layer so that (a) potential barriers are created on either side of the centre layer which will confine the injected carriers within it, and (b) regions of lower refractive index flank the centre layer on both sides, which are also transparent at the laser wavelength, and therefore form a very efficient optical waveguide.

The confinement of carriers is the more demanding function. The heterojunction must be capable of injecting one carrier type at high current density while substantially blocking the passage of the other. In addition to providing a potential barrier of sufficient height for this purpose, it is also necessary to ensure that the heterojunction is free from excessive recombination centres that would serve as a sink to the flow of the minority carriers. The second condition is the more difficult to satisfy.

Crystalline defects at the heterojunction produce recombination centres, and to prevent their formation the lattice match between the two semiconductors must be very good. The GaAs/(GaAl)As system of solid solutions provides a satisfactory lattice match as a consequence of the similar effective sizes of the Ga and Al atoms in the crystalline structure. Figure 3.3 shows the way the lattice constants of GaAs and AlAs vary with

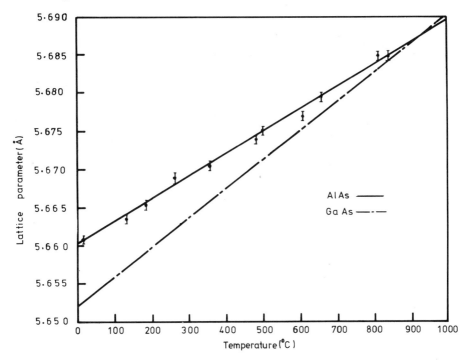

Figure 3.3 Lattice constant of GaAs and AlAs as a function of temperature (after Ettenberg and Paff[5])

temperature.[5] The lattice constants are identical at a temperature of about 920°C and the greater thermal expansion coefficient of GaAs gives it a lattice constant at room temperature which is about 0.2 per cent less than that of AlAs. Heterostructure lasers in the (GaAl)As system are normally fabricated from two compositions of (GaAl)As which differ in AlAs content by about 30 per cent and hence the lattice mismatch at room temperature between the layers is about 0.06 per cent. The lattice match can be improved by the substitution of a small amount of P for the As in the material with the higher AlAs content since P atoms have a smaller effective radius than As atoms in the lattice.[6] However, it has not been definitely proved that such a substitution improves the performance of the lasers.

As described in Chapter 1, Section 1.2, there are no other mixed semiconductors where a pair of substituent atoms are so close in size as Al and Ga in (GaAl)As. Hence in the other systems lattice match can only be obtained by simultaneously introducing two substituents, one larger and one smaller than the atoms which they replace. This gives rise to the quaternary systems such as (GaIn)(AsP)[7] and (GaAl)(AsSb).[8-10] Figure

1.3, Chapter 1, shows how such systems can be adjusted to give constant lattice dimensions and differing band-gap in the layers of the heterostructure. In practice it is found that thin layers of one material (e.g. 0.2 μm thick) can satisfactorily be grown on a second material without mismatch dislocations forming provided the lattice match lies within about 0.5 per cent.[11] Considerable stresses are involved, however, and the lattice of the second layer whilst being constrained to adopt the dimensions of the first lattice in the growth plane expands or contracts in the direction normal to the plane such that the unit cell is distorted from its normal cubic form to a tetragonal symmetry. Although the performance of the laser appears not to be significantly affected by the deformation such strains are liable to induce degradation during operation and are not desirable. With care in controlling the compositions lattice match in quaternary systems can normally be held to within 0.02 per cent.

3.2.1   Carrier Injection and Transport at Heterojunctions

In this section we discuss the electrical properties of heterojunctions in the way that they concern selective carrier injection and carrier confinement in heterostructure lasers. We consider particularly the efficiency with which minority carriers are injected across a heterojunction under the high forward bias conditions that exist during laser action. Initially we assume that the heterojunction interface is free of traps or recombination centres, leaving till Section 3.2.3 a more detailed consideration of the effect that such centres may have on the behaviour. For most purposes it is possible to obtain a good description of the injection and confinement behaviour in a heterostructure laser using a relatively simple model for the heterojunctions. This is particularly true in cases where the composition change at the heterojunction is graded to the extent that normally occurs with liquid phase epitaxy (e.g 100 Å grading distance). When the composition change takes place in less than 20 Å, as can be achieved by molecular beam or vapour phase epitaxy, additional effects may occur which make a more exact theoretical treatment desirable. We will extend our model to indicate how such effects can be taken into account.

The basic model used for describing the behaviour of heterojunctions was developed by Anderson.[11] The two semiconductors that form the heterojunction are assumed, in this model, to retain their bulk properties right up to the point where they join each other. This is a good assumption for abrupt single crystal heterojunctions to a scale only a little larger than the lattice spacing. The properties of the different materials can be defined in terms of two quantities, namely their respective band-gaps E_g and their respective electron affinities χ. The electron affinity is the energy required to raise an electron from the bottom of the conduction band to the 'vacuum level' where the electron is entirely free of the semiconductor. It differs from the work function in taking the initial energy of the electron to be that at the bottom of the conduction band rather than that at the Fermi level. The difference between the electron affinities of the two materials on either side of the heterojunction gives the step in energy ΔE_c in the conduction band at the junction. ΔE_c may, in certain instances, be measured more accurately than the individual electron affinities, and may be regarded as a fundamental quantity in its own right. A complementary step ΔE_v occurs in the valence band given by

$$\Delta E_v = \Delta E_c - \Delta E_g \qquad\qquad (3.1)$$

where ΔE_g is the step in the band-gap. If there is a grading of composition at the boundary, as for instance normally occurs to some extent in mixed semiconductors (e.g. the III/V or II/VI materials), then the change in the conduction and valence band energy is also graded over the same distance.

In addition to the abrupt step in energy that occurs at the heterojunction interfaces, space charge effects cause band-bending in both materials in the vicinity of the heterojunction. In equilibrium the Fermi levels of the majority carriers on the two sides of the heterojunction must have equal energy to prevent current flow. The band-bending provides the means by which this equilibrium is attained in a very similar way to that in p–n and Schottky junctions. Figure 3.4(a) shows the band diagram of an abrupt

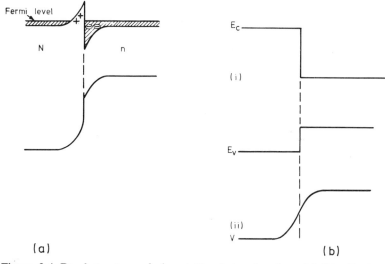

Figure 3.4 Band-structure of abrupt N–n heterojunction. (a) Distribution of total potential of conduction and valence band. (b) Curves (i) energy of conduction and valence band referred to vacuum level. Curve (ii) distribution of potential of vacuum level

junction between two materials of different band-gap but of the same doping type, in this case n-doping. We call this an N–n heterojunction, where N refers to the doping type of the material of the higher bandgap. The band-bending that occurs is the result of a positively charged depletion region being created on the higher band-gap side of the junction and a negatively charged accumulation region being created on the lower band-gap side. Figure 3.4(b) shows how the total potential distribution is made up of the heterojunction step, illustrated by curves (i), and the band-bending due to space charge, illustrated by curve (ii). The result of the combined behaviour is to line up the majority carrier bands (in this case the two conduction bands) of the two materials, albeit with two oppositely directed spikes of potential separating them, and to introduce the main potential step into the minority carrier band.

Figure 3.5(a) shows the band diagram of an n–N heterojunction which differs only from that described in Figure 3.4 in that the band-gap change is graded rather than being abrupt. In this case the band-bending compensates the heterojunction step more exactly than for the abrupt junction and leaves the potential in the majority carrier band almost flat. Figure 3.5(b) shows how the total potential distribution is divided between the band-gap variation illustrated by curves (i), and the band-bending due to space charge, illustrated by curve (ii). In a situation where the grading of the band-gap extends over a distance at least comparable to the sum of the depletion and accumulation widths for the abrupt heterojunctions, we

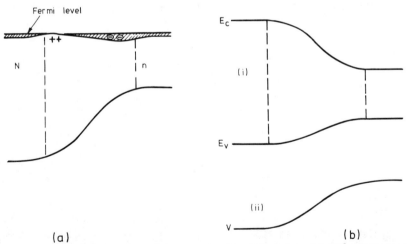

Figure 3.5 Band-structure of graded N–n heterojunction. (a) Distribution of total potential of conduction and valence band. (b) Curves (i) energy of conduction and valence band referred to vacuum level. Curve (ii) distribution of potential of vacuum level

find that curve (ii) for space charge comes close to being the exact inverse of curve (i) for the conduction band energy. The two cannot exactly match because it is only the irregularities in the sum curve of the total potential that generates the space charge on which curve (ii) depends. However, the necessary irregularities are only of the order of kT in amplitude, which is small compared with the total variation in the electron affinity of the conduction band between the two materials.

The potential distributions of the bands, as shown in Figure 3.4 and 3.5, are deduced in principle from Poisson's equation after inserting the charge density of the free carriers and the impurities. This can be done simply in the regions of carrier depletion and where the carrier accumulation is not too great. The following differential equation is obtained for the distribution of the voltage V, which is measured with respect to the free electron level, over the width of the heterojunction (see Figure 3.4(b))

$$\frac{d^2V}{dx^2} = \left(\frac{e}{\epsilon\epsilon_0}\right)[N_D - N_A - n + p] \tag{3.2}$$

where N_D is the donor concentration, N_A is the acceptor concentration, n is the electron concentration, and p is the hole concentration. The carrier concentration are functions of the energy separation ΔF between the Fermi level and the edges of the bands concerned. For the electrons, for instance, ΔF, can be expressed in terms of the voltage V in the form

$$\Delta F = F - eV(x) - \Delta E_c(x) \tag{3.3}$$

where F is the absolute energy of the Fermi level measured with respect to the energy of the free electron level as for V, and $\Delta E_c(x)$, which varies with x, is the change in the electron affinity, measured for convenience with respect to that of the semiconductor material at one selected boundary of the heterojunction. n is related to ΔF using the density of states in the bands and the Fermi functions as given in Chapter 2, Section 2.2.2. However, in the cases of large carrier accumulation this relation is modified because of the small dimensions involved, as mentioned later in this section.

For an abrupt heterojunction the step ΔE_c can be regarded as a boundary condition to the space charge distribution and the solution of equation (3.2) is otherwise the same as in any uniform semiconductor. Two standard types of approximate solution may then be employed, one which is appropriate when a depletion layer exists and the other when the carrier concentration nowhere differs by more than a small amount from the net impurity doping level. In the first case, and when the impurity level can be taken as constant, the potential varies with position in the following way

$$V = V_\infty + \frac{e}{2\epsilon\epsilon_0}(N_D - N_A)(x - x_0)^2 \tag{3.4}$$

where V_∞ is the voltage at the edge of the depletion region and x_0 is an arbitrary constant of position. In the second case the potential varies as

$$V = V_\infty + V_0 \exp\left(\frac{-x}{L_D}\right) \tag{3.5}$$

where V_∞ is the potential when x is large, V_0 is an arbitrary constant (positive or negative), and L_D is the Debye length, given by

$$L_D = \left[\frac{\epsilon\epsilon_{0_i}}{e(\mathrm{d}n/\mathrm{d}V)}\right]^{1/2} \simeq \left[\frac{|\epsilon\epsilon_0 kT|}{ne^2}\right]^{1/2} \tag{3.6}$$

The latter solution can be used in regions of carrier accumulation on the lower band-gap side of the junction, but only when the increase in carrier concentration is small, as occurs for small discontinuities in the band or when the higher band-gap material is much lower doped. Otherwise it is necessary to solve equations (3.2) and (3.3) exactly.

The complete solution is obtained by combining the individual solutions on the two sides of the junction. In the absence of charged interface states there must be continuity of electric field across the junction and an appropriate step ΔE_c in the conduction band energy. This may be satisfied by appropriate choice of the constants of integration.

The above type of analysis of the accumulation region, even using an exact solution of equations (3.2) and (3.3), breaks down in yet another way when the concentration of additional carriers is large. Under such circumstances the potential gradient becomes very large and the downward spike of potential that lies alongside the heterojunction becomes narrow enough for its width to be comparable to the wavelength of the carrier wave-functions. The normal expression for the density of states is then inappropriate and to obtain the true carrier distribution it is necessary to solve Poisson's equation simultaneously with Schroedinger's equation. The situation is very analogous to that in the inversion and accumulation layers which occur in MOS devices at the semiconductor surface, and which have been theoretically investigated by Stern.[12] Figure 3.6, taken from Stern's results for MOS behaviour in Si, shows how the carrier distribution that is obtained close to the semiconductor boundary differs from that derived using the normal form of the density of states. In general the exact treatment indicates that the carrier concentration falls off close to the surface, instead of steadily rising up to a sharp peak at this point as classical theory would suggest. The accumulation region is therefore about twice as wide as deduced classically. A very similar behaviour must occur close to an abrupt heterojunction but computations, which must be performed numerically, have not yet been carried out specifically for such a case.

For graded heterojunctions the variation of the electron affinity ΔE_c with

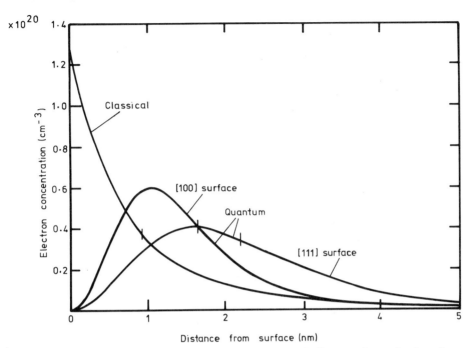

Figure 3.6 Electron concentrations as a function of distance from the interface calculated for strongly inverted silicon surfaces and compared with the classical result for the same carrier concentration. The vertical bars on the curve indicate the effective depth of the accumulation layer. $N_A - N_D = 10^{15}$ cm^{-3}, $T = 4.3$ K (after Stern[13])

position must be taken into account. In general in such devices space charge effects are weaker and the complications associated with large carrier accumulation effects can be ignored. An exact result, however, requires the numerical solution of equations (3.2) and (3.3).

3.2.2 Carrier Confinement at Heterojunctions

Let us consider the mechanism of carrier confinement in the active layer of heterostructure lasers using the GaAs/(GaAl)As system as an example. Alferov[14] and Dingle,[15] have shown that in this system the band discontinuity at the composition boundary is predominantly taken up by the conduction band (85 per cent of the total discontinuity according to the latter author). The effect of the band discontinuity on the potential distribution is illustrated in Figure 3.7 for the pair of heterojunctions formed by enclosing p-type GaAs between, respectively, n- and p-type (GaAl)As. The situation shown applies under conditions of forward bias

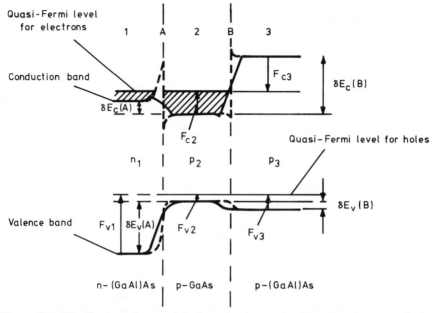

Figure 3.7 Distribution of potential of conduction and valence bands perpendicular to junctions in double heterostructure laser. Dashed line for abrupt heterojunctions and continuous line as example of graded heterojunction. Quasi-Fermi levels in conduction and valence band also shown

with high current. The dashed lines show the way the potentials of the band vary with position if the composition change at the heterojunction boundaries is abrupt. In spite of the imbalance between the discontinuities in the conduction and valence bands the barrier created for the confinement of holes (junction A, valence band), is equally as effective as that created for the confinement of electrons (junction B, conduction band). The former is almost entirely a space charge barrier whereas the latter is mainly a heterojunction barrier comprising an abrupt change in electron affinity over dimensions of the order of a few lattice spacings. Only where the space charge effects and the change in electron affinity are opposed is the particular form of the band discontinuity of real significance. Such a situation arises in the conduction band at the n-(GaAl)As/p-GaAs interface (junction A). The space charge on the average cancels out the discontinuous potential step of the heterojunction, but the depletion and accumulation regions on the two sides of the junction have finite width (a few hundred ångströms) as described in the previous section, and an upward and downward spike of potential results. This could interfere to some extent with the free passage of electrons. It also occurs at N–n heterojunctions. The double spike is greatly reduced if the heterojunction is graded, as described in the previous section; grading over a distance as small as 200 Å being sufficient to reduce the barrier height to less than kT.[16] The solid lines in Figure 3.7 show the band picture under these circumstances. In practice many heterojunctions can be considered as graded. However, as will be described later, laser devices have been made with individual GaAs layers less than 500 Å thick and still well defined. The growth methods used in these instances (particularly molecular beam epitaxy and metal-organic vapour deposition) may give sufficiently abrupt heterojunctions for band discontinuities to become significant.

Figure 3.7 also illustrates the interesting point that the carrier density injected into the centre GaAs layer can exceed that in the injecting layers without losing the efficiency of injection. Thus, in a typical laser with a central layer which is less than a diffusion length thick it is quite feasible to leave the layer undoped and to inject into it approximately equal concentrations of electrons and holes (as required for near electrical neutrality) up to densities, if necessary, in the 10^{18}–10^{19} cm^{-3} range.

Carriers flow by diffusion from the injecting layers across to the opposite barrier layer where they are almost entirely reflected. The reflection may be regarded as generating a reverse diffusion current of such a magnitude as virtually to cancel out the forward flow, and hence the gradient of carrier concentration at the boundary.

The analysis of the carrier distribution in a real situation at high current density is complicated by the presence of the large injected concentration of both carrier types. This results in both a concentration dependent recombination time, which is further affected when lasing takes place, and a concentration dependent diffusion constant and also in ambipolar effects in the diffusion itself (i.e. interaction of the two carrier types). However, in practice two simple situations may be distinguished. The first occurs when the thickness of the central layer is much less than a diffusion length. In this case the concentration of injected carriers may be regarded as constant over the whole thickness. This is true in most normal heterostructure lasers with active layer thickness less than 0.5 μm. The second situation occurs when the thickness of the layer is sufficiently large and the doping level sufficiently high such that the injected carriers are in the minority. The concentration distribution is then the combination of forward and reversed exponentials of the form

$$n \simeq n_b \cosh\left(\frac{x}{l}\right) \tag{3.7}$$

where the position x is measured from the confining barrier, l is the diffusion length, and n_b is the concentration of injected carriers adjacent to the barrier. At currents appreciably above the lasing threshold the situation becomes more complicated because the diffusion length l decreases as a result of the stimulated emission. Behaviour of the type described by equation (3.7) is important in single heterostructure lasers with active layers thicker than 3 μm.

3.2.3   Carrier Recombination at Heterojunctions

Even in a good heterojunction with no misfit dislocations it is still found that there are a certain number of centres present at the interface which induce recombination of injected carriers. Such a recombination normally contributes only a relatively small proportion of the total recombination in heterostructure lasers although its effect becomes more significant when the active layer is particularly thin. The characteristics of the interface have been investigated experimentally in (GaAl)As/GaAs heterostructures[17,18] by comparing the recombination rate in heterostructures with different centre layer thicknesses, and quantitative estimates of the interface recombination have been made.

The total recombination rate in the centre layer of a heterostructure is the combination of the bulk rate and the rate at both interfaces. The bulk recombination can be described in the normal way in terms of a recombination time τ. The interface recombination can be described in terms of a minority carrier recombination velocity s. The recombination rate at the interface is then equal to ns where n is the injected carrier concentration. As for the case of the bulk recombination time there is no absolute requirement that the recombination velocity should be independent of carrier concentration although for simplicity it is normally assumed so. Provided the centre layer has a thickness d that is appreciably less than a diffusion length, as is normally the case, then the total recombination rate per unit volume in the centre layer, expressed as a current density J_{tot} in carriers per unit volume per second, is given by

$$J_{tot} = n\left(\frac{1}{\tau} + \frac{2s}{d}\right)$$
(3.8)

and one can define an effective time constant τ_{eff} to take into account both types of recombination which is given by

$$\frac{1}{\tau_{eff}} = \frac{1}{\tau} + \frac{2s}{d}$$
(3.9)

As expected these relations show that the effect of interface recombination is most pronounced when the active layer is thinnest and when the bulk recombination time is largest.

In line with the above remarks Nelson and Sobers[17] in their measurements of interface recombination in (GaAl)As/GaAs heterostructures used low-doped centre GaAs layers (down to 5×10^{15} cm^{-3} p-type) to give a large bulk recombination time of up to around 400 ns and varied the thickness of the layer between 0.1 and 10 μm. They measured the total lifetime of the injected carriers by monitoring the decay of photoluminescence after the optical excitation was switched off. From these results they deduced that the recombination velocity at the (GaAl)As/GaAs heterojunctions in their samples was 450 cm s^{-1}. In heterostructure lasers where the bulk recombination time at threshold is of the order of 5 ns such interface recombination rates become significant for active layer thicknesses of 0.1 μm and less. The exact nature of the recombination centres remains unknown at the present time.

3.2.4 Effectiveness of heterojunction barrier

The confinement of injected carriers at heterojunctions is not perfect because of a) recombination of carriers at the interface and b) leakage of carriers over the barrier. In this section we consider loss of carriers by leakage over the barrier.

Rode[19] and Goodwin et al.[20] have investigated the effectiveness of the heterojunction barriers in preventing leakage of carriers. The amount of leakage depends on the concentration of carriers injected into the centre layer and the height of the confinement barrier. In measuring the height of the barrier any potential spikes due to space charge are neglected, on the basis that if they exist they are narrow enough for the carriers to tunnel easily through them. The carriers which surmount the barrier diffuse away with a velocity D/l, where D is the diffusion coefficient and l is the diffusion length, or the thickness of the wider band-gap layer, whichever is the less.

To calculate the concentration of leaking carriers it is convenient to express all injected carrier concentrations in terms of quasi-Fermi levels (see Figure 3.7) F_{c2} and F_{c3} in layers 2 and 3 for electrons, and F_{v1} and F_{v2} in layers 1 and 2 for holes. We need first to find how the effective band-gap step ΔE_g is divided, at both heterojunctions, between the total step in the conduction band δE_c and the total step in the valence band δE_v. Each step is a combination of the discontinuity ΔE_c or ΔE_v in the associated band and a potential barrier due to space charge. The derivation of the total step height is similar for the electron- and hole-confining junctions. Let us analyse, for example, the electron-confining junction (junction B) and consider the step $\delta E_v(B)$ in the valence band. This step is determined by the hole concentrations in layers 2 and 3 on the two sides of the junction. The hole concentration in layer 2 is the sum of the original doping level p_2 plus the concentration of holes necessary to neutralize the injected electron concentration n, i.e. $(p_2 + n)$. The hole concentration in layer 3 is approximately p_3 (if the electron leakage were very large it would be greater). If both these concentrations are non-degenerate (as is normally the case) then

$$\delta E_v(B) = kT \log \left[\frac{p_2 + n}{p_3} \right] \tag{3.10}$$

The quasi-Fermi F_{c3} level of the leaking electrons in layer 3 is given by

$$\begin{aligned} F_{c3} &= F_{c2} - \delta E_c(B) \\ &= F_{c2} - \Delta E_g(B) + \delta E_v(B) \end{aligned} \tag{3.11}$$

and their concentration n_3 by

$$n_3 = N_c \exp\left(\frac{F_{c3}}{kT}\right) \tag{3.12}$$

where N_c is the effective density of states. Hence, using equation (3.11) and multiplying n_3 in (3.12) by De/l to obtain leakage current density J_3 into layer 3 we obtain

$$J_3 = \frac{DeN_c}{l} \left\{ \frac{p_2 + n}{p_3} \right\} \exp\left[\frac{F_{c2} - \Delta E_g(B)}{kT} \right] \tag{3.13}$$

where D is the diffusion constant of electrons and l is either the diffusion length of electrons in layer 3 or the thickness of the layer whichever is smaller. e is the electronic charge.

A reasonably similar expression is obtained for the hole leakage[18] although the hole current is in general less important because of the reduced diffusion coefficient of the holes.

Because $\Delta E_g(B)$ occurs as a negative term in an exponential in the above expression, it is possible, by appropriate choice of $\Delta E_g(B)$, to reduce the leakage to negligible proportions. However, the coefficient of the exponential is large and must also be considered. The least favourable case occurs if l is small and if $(p_2 + n)/p_3$ is large (i.e. a narrow and low doped p-(GaAl)As layer). Taking a reasonable minimum value for the former of 1 μm (the smallest probable thickness of the higher band-gap layer) and a maximum likely value for the latter of 8 ($p_3 = 2 \times 10^{17}$ cm^{-3}) and putting $D = 90$ cm^2 s^{-1} gives a value for DeN_c/l at room temperature of 5.5×10^5 A cm^{-2}. For an acceptable leakage current density of, say, less than 100 A cm^{-2} and a typical value of F_{c2} of 2.5 kT (injected electron concentration at room temperature (300 K) of about 1.5×10^{18} cm^{-3}) then $\Delta E_g(B)/kT > 11$ and $\Delta E_g(B)$ should be greater than about 0.29 eV. Under less demanding in conditions with, for instance, the thickness of the wide gap layer increased to greater than 5 μm and a p-doping level in this layer of 10^{18} cm^{-3} the band-gap step could be reduced to about 0.21 eV. However, in practice operation at temperatures of up to about 65°C must be

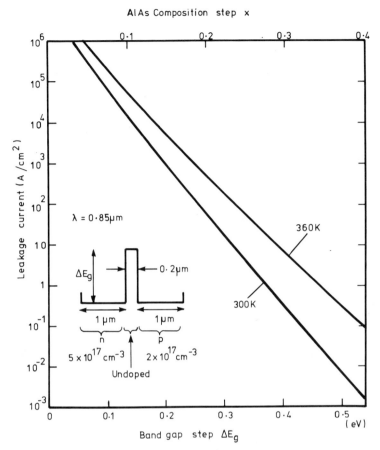

Figure 3.8 Dependence of electron leakage current density at threshold across p-type heterojunction barrier on band-gap step in eV at different temperatures. Thickness of p-passive layer $= 1\ \mu$m. Doping level $= 2 \times 10^{17}$ cm^{-3}. Injected carrier concentration in active layer $= 1.5 \times 10^{18}$ cm^{-3} at 300 K

anticipated (owing to heat sink and junction heating). Under these circumstances the necessary band-gap step is increased in the two situations quoted above to 0.32 and 0.24 eV, respectively.

Figure 3.8 presents the above information in a more complete form, and shows the dependence of the leakage current density on the band-gap step $\Delta E_g(B)$ at different temperatures, assuming a thickness and a doping level of the p-passive layer of 0.1 μm and 2×10^{17} cm^{-3}, respectively. The quasi-Fermi level F_{c2} required in the active layer at threshold is taken to rise with temperature approximately in proportion to kT. The other data used in the calculation is given with the figure.

3.2.5 Band-gap Versus Composition of Semiconductor

Figure 3.9 shows the compositional dependence of the band-gap in the (GaAl)As system at room temperature.[21] The band-gap for the direct Γ minimum increases fairly linearly with AlAs content from 1.43 eV for pure GaAs to 3 eV for pure AlAs. However, the situation is complicated by the

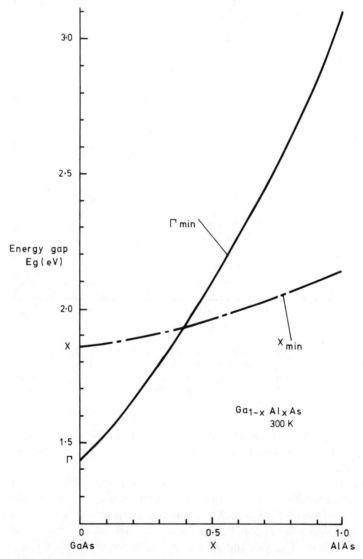

Figure 3.9 The direct and indirect energy gaps of $Ga_{1-x}Al_x$ (after Casey and Panish[21])

presence of the indirect X minimum. This has a higher energy gap than the Γ minimum in pure GaAs, but increases more slowly with AlAs content and crosses the band-gap of the Γ minimum at an AlAs content of around 38 at.% and at a band-gap of around 1.96 eV.

If we take 0.3 eV as the minimum band-gap step which gives useful carrier confinement then Figure 3.9 shows that this can be obtained with the composition for the centre layer lying in the range 0–18 at.% AlAs and with not less than 20–25 at.% greater concentration of AlAs in the outer layers. If the AlAs concentration of the centre layer is allowed to increase beyond 18 at.%, which corresponds to a lasing wavelength of less than 7500 Å, then leakage of heavy electrons into the X minimum of the wide gap starts occurring. This is treated in more detail by Rode[19] and Goodwin et al.[20]

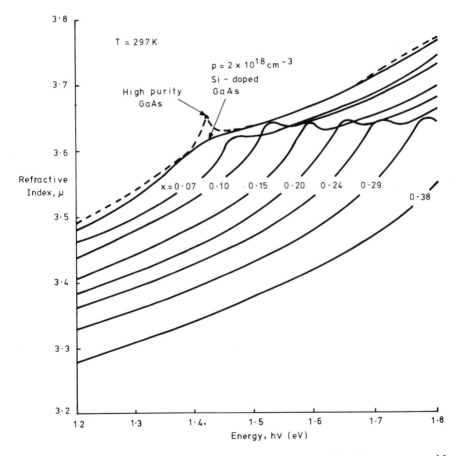

Figure 3.10 Refractive index of $Ga_{1-x}Al_x$ as a function of photon energy with composition as a parameter (after Casey et al.[22])

3.2.6   Refractive Index Versus Composition of Semiconductor

To produce a satisfactory optical dielectric waveguide in a three-layer structure it is necessary for the centre layer to have the higher refractive index. The characteristics of the guiding (spread of light, mode behaviour, etc.), are determined to a large extent by the refractive index differences between the layers. In this section we describe how the composition of the (GaAl)As in the layers, together with the particular wavelength concerned, determine the values of the refractive index. The exact way in which these values affect the waveguiding properties will be treated in detail in Chapter 4.

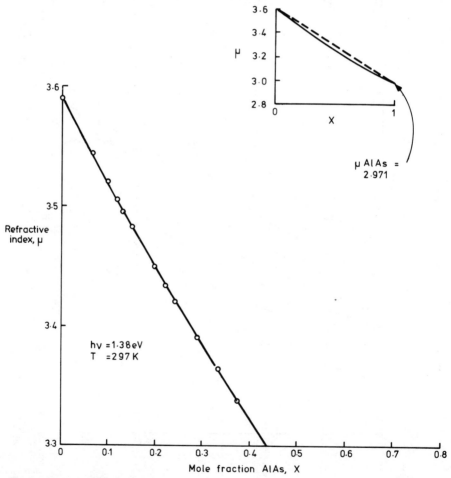

Figure 3.11   Refractive index of n-type $Ga_{1-x}Al_xAs$ at $h\nu = 1.38$ eV as a function of composition x (after Casey *et al.*[22])

Figure 3.10 gives a series of results, obtained by Casey *et al.*[22] showing how the refractive index of $Ga_{1-x}Al_xAs$ depends on composition in the range $0<x<0.38$ for photon energy between 1.2 and 1.8 eV. The results were obtained on low n-doped material but are equally applicable for low p-doped material. The curves of refractive index against photon energy for the different compositions all exhibit similar shapes, steepening towards a maximum at the absorption edge. The main effect of increasing the AlAs content is to move the curves to higher photon energies in accordance with the increase in band-gap. At a fixed photon energy the refractive index increases as the band-gap is narrowed, in the way desired for heterostructure lasers. The variation of refractive index with composition x for a photon energy of 1.28 eV is illustrated in Figure 3.11.

The doping level also has an effect, although much smaller, on the refractive index. Figures 3.12 and 3.13 show the photon-energy-dependence of the refractive index of n- and p-type GaAs as a function of the doping level, as measured by Sell *et al.*[4] Stern[23] and Zoroofchi and Butler[24] have also derived similar results from absorption data, using the Kramers–Kroenig relations. The curves show a shift in the photon energy with doping somewhat similar to that shown by the previous

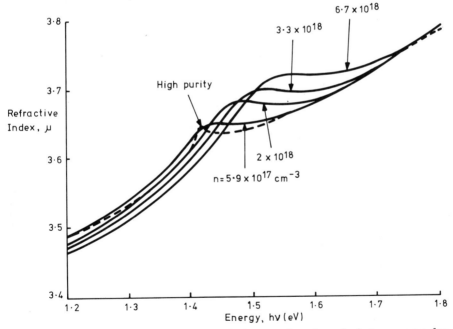

Figure 3.12 Refractive index of n-type GaAs as a function of photon energy for various values of n-doping (after Sell *et al.*[1])

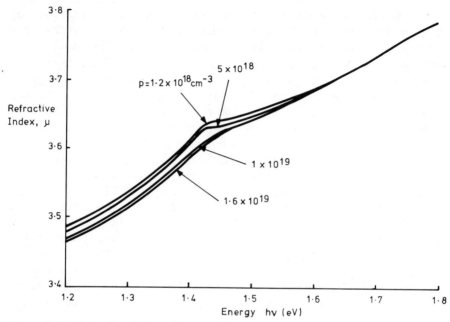

Figure 3.13 Refractive index of p-type GaAs as a function of photon energy for various values of p-doping (after Sell *et al.*[1])

curves with composition. This is related to the Burstein shift in the absorption edge and is stronger in n-type material

3.3   TYPES OF LASER HETEROSTRUCTURES

3.3.1   Single Heterostructure Laser

The first heterostructure reported was the so-called single heterostructure laser which was developed independently by Kressel and Nelson[25] and Panish *et al.*[26] The single heterostructure laser illustrated in Figure 3.14 is a physically simpler device than the symmetrical double heterostructure whose band structure was illustrated in Figure 3.7. The active GaAs layer of the laser has only one wider band-gap layer lying adjacent to it. A p–n junction is formed in GaAs, as in the homostructure laser, and the heterojunction is placed at a certain distance away on the p-side, where it can remedy the major defects of the homojunction laser by preventing the unrestricted diffusion of electrons injected into the p-layer and by providing an abrupt optical waveguiding boundary where otherwise very little optical confinement would exist. The p–n junction itself provides the second injecting contact and the other boundary of the waveguide. To do

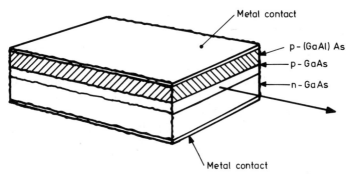

Figure 3.14 Diagram of single heterostructure laser showing layer structure

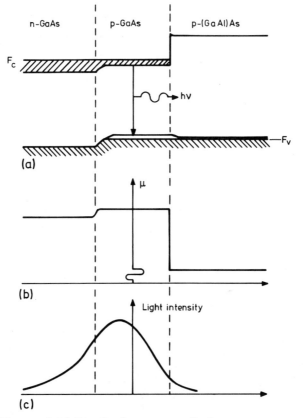

Figure 3.15 Distribution perpendicular to p–n junction in single heterostructure laser of: (a) potential of conduction and valence bands, (b) refractive index, and (c) light intensity

this satisfactorily the n-side of the junction must be highly doped, e.g. $3\text{–}4 \times 10^{18}$ cm^{-3}. The band diagram under forward bias and the distributions of refractive index and light intensity are illustrated in Figure 3.15.

The use of a p–n junction, rather than a second heterojunction, gives lower injection efficiency of electrons and produces an asymmetric optical waveguide. However, the structure is relatively simple. It may be fabricated in one stage by growing a Zn-doped p-type (GaAl)As layer by liquid phase epitaxy on an n-type GaAs substrate and allowing the appropriate time at high temperature for the Zn to diffuse the correct distance back into the substrate, thereby converting it to p-type. The threshold current density at room temperature in this structure is about 5–10 times lower than that in a homostructure laser, being of the order of 6000–8000 A cm^{-2}. The lower limit is set by the minimum thickness to which the p-type GaAs layer may be reduced before the optical guiding and/or the injection efficiency at the p–n junction become unsatisfactory. This minimum thickness is of the order of 1 μm. A lower threshold current density can be obtained in more elaborate heterostuctures, as described below. The single heterostructure laser, however, has other useful properties which make it particularly suitable for high peak power application. These will be described in Chapter 5.

3.3.2 Double Heterostructure Laser

In the double heterostructure laser illustrated in Figure 3.16, the active layer of Ga$_{1-x}$Al$_x$As is sandwiched between n- and p-type layers of Ga$_{1-y}$Al$_y$As, usually of similar AlAs content to each other but with greater AlAs content than the active layer. Alferov[27] reported the first successful

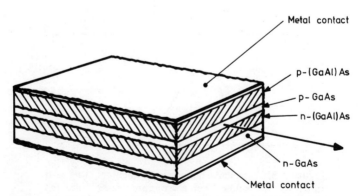

Figure 3.16 Diagram of double heterostructure showing layer structure.

operation of double heterostructure devices and obtained a threshold current density at room temperature of 4300 A cm⁻². The threshold was successively lowered by Hayashi *et al.*[28] and others[29,30] so that c.w. operation at room temperature was achieved. The reduction in threshold was achieved by a steady reduction in the thickness of the central layer from over 2 μm in the first devices down to 0.1 μm in some of the most recent devices. Ettenberg[31] has reported a lowest figure for room temperature threshold of 470 A cm⁻² in a device using an 0.12 μm thick GaAs active layer and outer layers containing 65 at.% AlAs, the high AlAs content being used to give good optical confinement.

Figure 3.17 shows the band energy diagram, under forward bias, and the distribution of refractive index and light intensity in the double heterostructure laser. As described in the previous section, excellent carrier

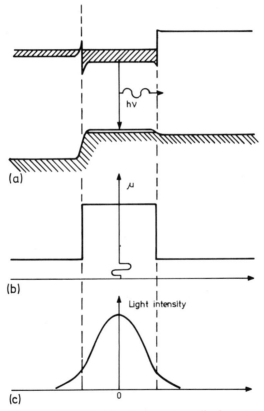

Figure 3.17 Distribution perpendicular to junction in double heterostructure laser of: (a) potential of conduction and valence bands, (b) refractive index, and (c) light intensity

confinement can be obtained in the central layer if the AlAs step is 25 at.% or greater. Optical confinement deteriorates when the thickness of the central layer is reduced below a certain critical value. The critical value can be made smaller by increasing the refractive index difference between the central and outer layers, the lowest critical value being about 0.15 μm. It is this optical guiding effect which sets the lower limit to the possible threshold current density. The optical guiding and its effect on threshold will be treated in greater detail in Chapters 4 and 5.

3.3.3 Heterostructures to Provide Localized Gain

It can be an advantage to build heterostructures in which the injected carriers are confined to a narrow part of the total region in which the light is confined. Two rather different applications are involved. In the first the main requirement is to spread the light into a particularly wide region. This is an advantage in high pulsed-current operation where the optical flux density in the laser is a limiting factor. The power threshold at which damage occurs (normally at the output face) is increased by spreading the light. In the second application the light is as closely confined as the waveguiding structure allows but further reduction in threshold current density is obtained by confining the injected carriers to an even narrower layer. The threshold current density of any particular guiding structure can be approximately halved by this procedure. There also exists, of course, an intermediate range of devices where reasonably wide optical spread and reasonably low threshold current density are both required.

Separate confinement heterostructure lasers for the above purpose are four- or five-layer devices in which the inner junctions or heterojunctions are used for carrier confinement and the outer heterojunctions are used for optical confinement. In the four-layer devices one heterojunction is used in common for the two forms of confinement. In both types of device the inner junctions must be prevented from producing appreciable optical confinement. For this purpose the limiting optical guiding characteristic of both single and double heterostructures with thin central layers may be exploited. Either type may be built into the wider optical cavity by adding an extra layer or layers, and if appropriately dimensioned to be a poor guide itself will allow the light to spread into the wider cavity. The main difference between the two basic structures is that the single-heterostructure-like active layer can be up to about 1 μm thick before it starts to exert some guiding effect whereas the double-heterostructure-like active layer should be less than about 0.1 μm thick. Devices with an intermediate basic structure, or with a basic structure which would not function on its own as a satisfactory laser, are also possible but they tend to give poorer carrier confinement.

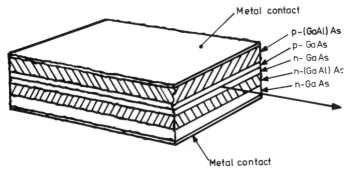

Figure 3.18 Diagram of four-layer separate confinement heterostructure showing layers (LOC laser)

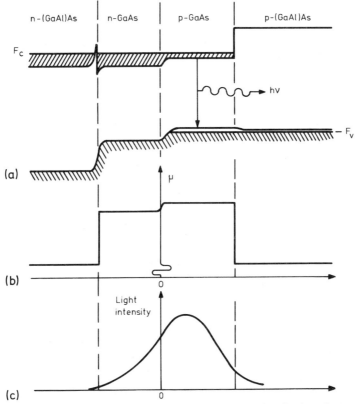

Figure 3.19 Distribution perpendicular to junction in four layer separate confinement heterostructure of: (a) potential of conduction and valence bands, (b) refractive index, and (c) light intensity

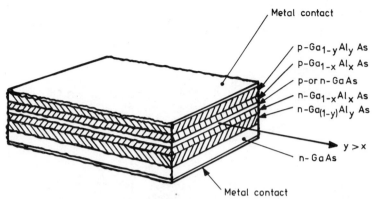

Figure 3.20 Diagram of five-layer separate confinement hetero-structure showing layers (LGR device)

Figure 3.18 shows a four-layer structure based on the carrier confinement of a single heterostructure, and Figure 3.19 shows the associated band structure and the distributions of refractive index and light intensity. One layer of (GaAl)As has been added to the single heterostructure configuration on the n-side. Variations of this device have been developed by Lockwood et al.[33,33] (large optical cavity laser), and by Paoli et al.,[34] for high power applications.

Figure 3.20 shows a five-layer structure based on the carrier confinement layout of the double heterostructure laser, and Figure 3.21 shows the associated band structure and the distributions of refractive index and light intensity. Two additional layers of (GaAl)As with higher AlAs content are added outside the normal passive (GaAl)As layers of a double heterostructure. This structure was developed by Thompson and Kirkby[35,36] and co-workers[37] and by Panish and Hayashi[38] and Casey et al[39,40] for high peak power and low threshold current operation. A threshold current density of 500 A cm^{-2} and below has been reported for structure with optical distributions which are somewhat wider than in the double heterostructure laser.[37] Much wider optical distributions can be obtained without raising the threshold current density beyond around 1000 A cm^{-2}.

The optical guiding characteristics of these structures and the way the guiding affects threshold current density, optical distribution and beam width will be treated in Chapters 4 and 5.

3.4   STRIPE LASERS (TWO-DIMENSIONAL HETEROSTRUCTURE)

All the heterostructures discussed so far have been directed to confining light and injected carriers in the direction perpendicular to the plane of

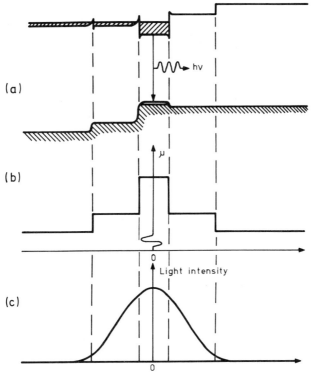

Figure 3.21 Distribution perpendicular to junction in five-layer separate confinement heterostructure of: (a) potential of conduction and valence bands, (b) refractive index, and (c) light intensity

the structure. However, confinement in the plane of the junction is helpful for sufficiently narrow lasers. Optical confinement is required when the aperture width w of the laser is small enough to allow the beam to spread appreciably sideways by diffraction as it propagates along the length L of the laser. Sideways diffraction is significant when the width w is less than $(L\lambda)^{1/2}$, i.e. about 20 μm. Carrier confinement is required when the width of the laser is comparable to or less than a diffusion length, i.e. less than about 10 μm. Devices of the above widths, or narrower, are called stripe lasers.

Figure 3.22 shows the ultimate heterostructure stripe laser as developed by Tsukada.[41] This employs the same heterojunction configuration in the plane of the junction for optical and carrier confinement as is used in the double heterostructure in the perpendicular direction. It consists of a filament of lower band-gap (GaAl)As, entirely embedded in higher band-gap (GaAl)As with the p–n junction passing through it, and has been

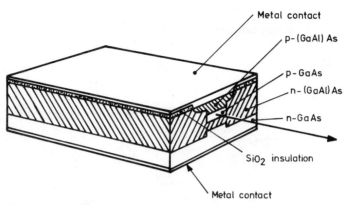

Figure 3.22 Buried heterostructure laser with confinement of
light and injected carriers in both transverse directions

called a buried heterostructure laser. Lasers with a cross section as small as
$0.7 \times 1\ \mu m$ have been made, with threshold current at room temperature
of less than 10 mA. These devices and other stripe devices will be
described in greater detail in Chapter 6.

REFERENCES

1. D. D. Sell, H. C. Casey, Jr, and K. Wecht, 'Concentration dependence of the
   refractive index for n- and p-type GaAs between 1.2 and 1.8 eV', *J. Appl.
   Phys.*, **45**, 1974, 2650.
2. J. C. Dyment and L. A. D'Asaro, 'Continuous operation of GaAs junction
   lasers on diamond heat sinks at 200 K', *Appl. Phys. Lett.*, **11**, 1967, 292.
3. H. Kroemer, 'A proposed class of heterojunction injection lasers', *Proc.
   IEEE*, **51**, 1963, 1782.
4. Zh. I. Alferov and R. F. Kazarinov, Author's certificate no. 1032155/26-25
   USSR, 1963.
5. M. Ettenberg and R. J. Paff, 'Thermal expansion of AlAs', *J. Appl. Phys.*, **41**,
   1970, 3926.
6. J. C. Dyment, F. R. Nash, C. J. Hwang, G. A. Rozgony, R. L. Hartman, H. M.
   Marcus, and S. E. Hassko, 'Threshold reduction by the addition of P to the
   ternary layers of double heterostructure GaAs lasers', *Appl. Phys. Lett.*, **24**,
   1974, 481.
7. J. J. Hsieh, J. A. Rossi, and J. P. Donnelly, 'Room temperature cw operation
   of GaInAsP/InP double heterostructure diode lasers emitting at 1.1 μm', *Appl.
   Phys. Lett.*, **28**, 1976, 709.
8. K. Sugiyama and H. Saito, 'GaAsSb–AlGaAsSb double heterojunction lasers',
   Japan J. Appl. Phys., **11**, 1972, 1057.
9. R. E. Nahory, M. A. Pollack, M. A. Beebe, J. C. De Winter, and R. W.
   Dixon, 'Continuous operation of 1.0 μm wavelength $GaAs_{1-x}Sb_x/Al_yGa_{1-y}
   As_{1-x}Sb_x$ double heterostructure injection lasers at room temperature', *Appl.
   Phys. Lett.*, **28**, 1976, 19.
10. L. R. Tomasetta, H. D. Law, K. Nakano, and J. S. Harris, 'GaAlAsSb/GaSb
    lattice matched semiconductor lasers operating at 1.25–1.40 μm', IEEE

International Semiconductor Laser Conference, San Francisco, 30 Oct.–1 Nov., 1978.

11. K. Oe, Y. Shinoda, and K. Sugiyama, 'Lattice deformations and misfit dislocations in GaInAsP/InP double heterostructure layers', *Appl. Phys. Lett.*, **33**, 1978, 962.

12. R. L. Anderson, 'Experiments on Ge–GaAs heterojunctions', *Solid State Electron.*, **5**, 1962, 341.

13. F. Stern, 'Quantum properties of surface space-charge layers', *CRC Crit. Rev. Solid State Science*, **5**, 1974, 499.

14. Zh. I. Alferov, 'Photo-electric properties of AlGaAs–GaAs heterojunctions', *Sov. Phys. Semicond.*, **3**, 1970, 1373.

15. R. Dingle, 'Confined carrier quantum states in ultra-thin semiconductor heterostructures', *Festkorper Probleme*, vol. XV, Pergamon Vieweg, 1975, 21.

16. J. Womac, and R. H. Rediker, 'The graded-gap $Al_xGa_{1-x}As$–GaAs heterojunction', *J. Appl. Phys.*, **43**, 1972, 4129.

17. R. J. Nelson and R. G. Sobers, 'Interfacial recombination velocity in GaAlAs–GaAs heterostructures', *Appl. Phys. Lett.*, **32**, 1978, 761.

18. R. J. Nelson, 'Interfacial recombination in GaAlAs–GaAs heterostructures', *J. Vac. Sci. Tech.*, **15**, 1978, 1475.

19. D. L. Rode, 'How much Al in the AlGaAs–GaAs laser', *J. Appl. Phys.*, **45**, 1974, 3887.

20. A. R. Goodwin, J. R. Peters, M. Pion, G. H. B. Thompson, and J. E. A. Whiteaway, 'Threshold-temperature characteristics of double heterostructure $Ga_{1-x}Al_xAs$ lasers', *J. Appl. Phys.*, **46**, 1975, 3126.

21. H. C. Casey, Jr and M. B. Panish, 'Composition dependence of the $Ga_{1-x}Al_xAs$ direct and indirect energy gaps', *J. Appl. Phys.*, **40**, 1969, 4910.

22. H. C. Casey, Jr., D. D. Sell, and M. B. Panish, 'Refractive index of $Al_xGa_{1-x}As$ between 1.2 and 1.8 eV', *Appl. Phys. Lett.*, **24**, 1974, 63.

23. F. Stern, 'Dispersion of the index of refraction near the absorption edge of semiconductors', *Phys. Rev.*, **133**, 1964, A1653.

24. J. Zoroofschi and J. K. Butler, 'Refractive index of n-type GaAs', *J. Appl. Phys.*, **8**, 1973, 3697.

25. H. Kressel and H. Nelson, 'Close confinement gallium arsenide p–n junction lasers with reduced optical loss at room temperature', *RCA Rev.*, **30**, 1969, 106.

26. M. B. Panish, I. Hayashi, and S. Sumski, 'A technique for the preparation of low-threshold room temperature GaAs laser diode structures', *J. Quantum Electron.*, **QE-5**, 1969, 210.

27. Zh. I. Alferov, V. M. Andreev, E. L. Portnoi, and M. K. Trukan, 'AlGaAs heterojunction lasers with low room temperature threshold', *Fiz. Tech. Poluprov.*, **3**, 1969, 1328 (*Sov. Phys. Semicond.*, **3**, 1970, 1107).

28. I. Hayashi, M. B. Panish, P. W. Foy, and S. Sumski, 'Junction lasers which operate continuously at room temperature', *Appl. Phys. Lett.*, **17**, 1970, 109.

29. P. R. Selway, A. R. Goodwin, and C. M. Phillips, 4th European Solid State Devices Conference, Exeter, 1970; and P. R. Selway and A. R. Goodwin, 'The properties of double heterostructure lasers with very narrow active regions', *J. Phys. D.*, **5**, 1972, 904.

30. I. Sakuma, M. Yonezu, K. Nishida, K. Kobayashi, M. Saito, and Y. Nannichi, 'Continuous operation of junction lasers at room temperature', *Japan J. Appl. Phys.*, **10**, 1971, 282.

31. M. Ettenberg, 'Very low threshold double heterojunction $Al_xGa_{1-x}As$ injection lasers', *Appl. Phys. Lett.*, **27**, 1975, 652.

32. H. F. Lockwood, H. Kressel, H. S. Sommers, and F. Z. Hawrylo, 'An efficient large optical cavity injection laser', *Appl. Phys. Lett.,* 17, 1970, 499.
33. H. Kressel, H. F. Lockwood, and F. Z. Hawrylo, 'Low threshold LOC GaAs injection lasers', *Appl. Phys. Lett.,* 18, 1971, 43.
34. T. L. Paoli, B. W. Hakki, and B. I. Miller, 'Zero order transverse mode operation of GaAs double heterostructure lasers with thick waveguides', *J. Appl. Phys.,* 44, 1973, 1776.
35. G. H. B. Thompson and P. A. Kirkby, '(GaAl)As lasers with a heterostructure for optical confinement and additional heterojunction for extreme carrier confinement', *J. Quantum Electron.,* QE-9, 1973, 311.
36. G. H. B. Thompson and P. A. Kirkby, 'Low threshold current density in 5-layer-heterostructure (GaAl)As/GaAs localized gain region injection lasers', *Electron. Lett.,* 9, 1973, 295.
37. G. H. B. Thompson, G. D Henshall, J. E. A. Whiteaway, and P. A. Kirkby, 'Narrow-beam five-layer (GaAl)As/GaAs heterostructure lasers with low threshold and high peak power', *J. Appl. Phys.,* 47, 1976, 1501.
38. M. B. Panish and I. Hayashi, 'Heterostructure junction lasers', *Applied Solid State Science* (R. Wolfe, ed.). Vol. 4, 1974.
39. M. B. Panish, H. C. Casey, Jr, S. Sumski, and P. W. Foy, 'Reduction of threshold current density in $GaAs-Al_xGa_{1-x}As$ heterostructure lasers by separate optical and carrier confinement', *Appl. Phys. Lett.,* 22, 1973, 590.
40. H. C. Casey Jr., M. B. Panish, W. O. Schlosser, and T. L. Paoli, '$GaAs-Al_xGa_{1-x}As$ heterostructure lasers with separate optical and carrier confinement', *J. Appl. Phys.,* 45, 1974, 322.
41. T. Tsukada, '$GaAs-Ga_{1-x}Al_xAs$ buried-heterostructure injection lasers', *J. Appl. Phys.,* 45, 1974, 4899.

CHAPTER 4

Optical Waveguides

Two forms of optical waveguide must be considered in the treatment of heterostructure lasers. The first is the dielectric slab waveguide. This is the type of waveguide that is formed by the layers of the heterostructure with their different refractive indices. In the dielectric slab guide total internal reflection is used to confine the light entirely within the central layer. The result is a very effective waveguide. The second optical waveguide is the structure formed by surrounding a region of optical gain with a region of optical loss. This produces a so-called 'gain-guiding' condition which is an important means of confining light in the junction plane of stripe lasers. The optical behaviour in such a guide can be analysed by an extension of the treatment used for a dielectric waveguide, in which complex rather than real values of the refractive index are used.

In Section 4.1 we review the fundamentals of the classic dielectric slab waveguide necessary to understand the heterostructure behaviour, using only the minimum amount of electro-magnetic theory, and derive the properties relevant to laser action. For a more comprehensive treatment of the theoretical background the reader is referred to standard texts on the electro-magnetic theory of guided waves, such as Collin[1] and Marcuse.[2] In Section 4.2 we provide an analysis of gain-guiding as it occurs in a stripe laser context, more comprehensive than for the slab waveguide since the information is not available in standard texts. In Section 4.3 we give a detailed account of the properties of the higher order transverse modes that may propagate in both these types of waveguide.

4.1 DIELECTRIC SLAB WAVEGUIDES

4.1.1 Ray Treatment

A beam of light propagating in a transparent dielectric medium of refractive index μ_1 is reflected completely at the interface with a medium of lower refractive index μ_2 if the angle θ between the beam and the interface is less than the critical angle θ_c, where θ_c is given by

$$\theta_c = \cos^{-1}\left(\frac{\mu_2}{\mu_1}\right) \tag{4.1}$$

At a $Ga_{1-x}Al_xAs/Ga_{1-y}Al_yAs$ heterojunction with a typical AlAs composition step of 25 at % the critical angle is about 15°. Figure 4.1 shows a double heterostructure with the centre layer of highest refractive index μ_1 enclosed between layers of refractive index μ_2 and μ_3 ($\mu_2 > \mu_3$). A beam propagating at an angle θ to the axis which is smaller than the smaller of the two critical angles θ_{c2} (associated with the medium of refractive index μ_2) will zig-zag between the two interfaces and be completely guided.

In such a dielectric waveguide there is, however, a restriction on the allowed angle θ of the beam. Only for certain angles does the wavetrain propagate unchanged down the guide. The condition to be satisfied is that the new wave, which is continually generated from the original wave by two successive reflections from opposite sides of the guide, should remain precisely in step with the original wave at its flank, with no kinks in the wavefront. Figure 4.1 illustrates the condition. A wavefront AC moves to the position BD by the direct path CD and also by the doubly reflected path AB. For constructive interference these two paths must differ by an integral number of wavelengths in the medium μ_1 plus an allowance for phase change at the reflections. The phase change resulting from total internal reflection advances the phase of the wave. The phase advance can be obtained from the Fresnel equations for the reflection of a plane wave or, as shown in the next section, by exact treatment of the guided wave. For the present we will set the phase advance equal to ϕ_2 and ϕ_3 radians at the respective μ_2 and μ_3 interfaces. The condition for proper wave propagation becomes

$$AB - CD = 2DF = \frac{(n + (\phi_2 + \phi_3)/2\pi)\lambda_0}{\mu_1} \tag{4.2}$$

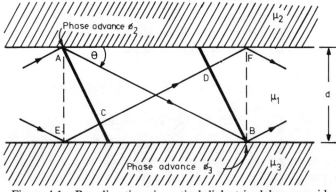

Figure 4.1   Ray directions in optical dielectric slab waveguide

where n is an integer (including zero because $(\phi_2 + \phi_3)$ is positive) and λ_0 is the free space wavelength. The angle of propagation is given by

$$\sin \theta = \frac{(n + (\phi_2 + \phi_3)/2\pi)\lambda_0}{2\mu_1 d} \tag{4.3}$$

where d is the thickness of the centre layer. Only those modes with values of n small enough for θ to be less than the critical angle θ_{c2} are guided modes. The phase change θ_2 at reflection tends to zero as θ approaches θ_{c2}. Hence the criterion for mode n to be guided, using equations (4.1) and (4.3), is

$$n < \frac{2d\,\delta\epsilon^{1/2}}{\lambda_0} - \frac{\phi_3}{2\pi} \tag{4.4}$$

where $\delta\epsilon = \mu_1^2 - \mu_2^2$ is the smaller step in dielectric constant between the centre layer and the other two layers. As d is narrowed the higher order modes $(n > 1)$ successively cease to propagate or, as it is described, are 'cut-off'. The zero-order mode also ceases to propagate for d smaller than a certain value, except in the case where the guide is symmetrical $(\mu_2 = \mu_3)$. In this case ϕ_3 would tend to zero at cut-off so allowing the propagation equation (4.4) to remain satisfied with $n = 0$ even for infinitesimally small d.

4.1.2   Wave Treatment

Figure 4.2 demonstrates the way in which the wavefronts of the plane waves combine to create the guided wave. Individual crests of the two sets of plane waves are shown with propagation directions inclined respectively equally on either side of the guide axis. The overall pattern moves without change along the direction z of the guide. Any longitudinal section of the wave is sinusoidal and has a guided wavelength λ_z which is greater than the plane wavelength λ_0/μ_1 in the centre layer but is less than the plane wavelengths λ_0/μ_2 and λ_0/μ_3 in the adjacent layers. The latter criterion is essential for waveguiding and is associated with the existence of total internal reflection. The transverse section of the guided wave in the y direction perpendicular to the layers is a standing wave of wavelength λ_y. λ_y is greater than $\lambda_0/\delta\epsilon^{1/2}$ but approaches it as the propagation angle tends towards the critical. As can be seen from the triangle ACD the wavelengths within the central layer are related by

$$\frac{1}{\lambda_y^2} + \frac{1}{\lambda_z^2} = \frac{\epsilon_1}{\lambda_0^2} \tag{4.5}$$

or

$$\beta_y^2 + \beta_z^2 = \epsilon_1 \beta_0^2$$

where, for convenience, the square of the refractive index has been

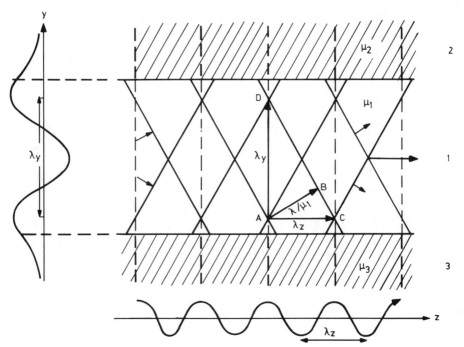

Figure 4.2   Instantaneous disposition of wave crests of component plane waves in a dielectric slab waveguide

replaced by the dielectric constant ϵ with the appropriate subscript for the region concerned. The second version of the equation gives the relation between the propagation constants: $\beta_y = 2\pi/\lambda_y$, $\beta_z = 2\pi/\lambda_z$, and $\beta_0 = 2\pi/\lambda_0$. The propagation constants are convenient for expressing the spatial variations of the optical field. The spatial variations have the form $\cos(\beta_y y)$ for the y direction and $\exp(j\beta_z z)$ for the z direction. We will henceforward deal mainly with propagation constants rather than wavelength.

Although no transmitted wave leaks out of the central layer of the waveguide some local electro-magnetic disturbance is generated in the surrounding layers, and this falls off exponentially with distance from the interface. We will define decay coefficients p and r for layers 2 and 3 so that the respective rates of decay become $\exp(-py)$ and $\exp(ry)$. Comparison of these exponential distributions with the periodic distribution of optical field in the central layer, which can be expressed as $\exp(j\beta_y y) + \exp(-j\beta_y y)$, shows that the mathematical form is very similar in the two cases and that the distribution in the outer regions is obtained by ascribing imaginary values to β_y of jp and $-jr$. For a uniform nomenclature we will ascribe a real value to β_y in the centre region of q. The evaluation of the complete distribution of optical field involves finding self-consistent values of p, q, and r which allow the three parts of the distribution to be combined appropriately together. This gives a complete solution to the waveguiding problem. It is effectively a way of finding the values of ϕ_2 and ϕ_3 in equation (4.2) without directly treating the plane wave behaviour and using the Fresnel equation of reflection.

Equation (4.5) for λ_y (or β_y) is a particular instance, with no x variation, of Maxwell's wave equation

$$\nabla^2 \mathbf{A} = \epsilon \epsilon_0 \mu_0 \mathbf{A} \tag{4.6}$$

where $\mathbf{A}$ represents either the optical electrical or magnetic field and where ϵ_0 and μ_0 are the permittivity and the permeability of free space. From Maxwell's equation one can see that an equally applicable equation to (4.5) occurs when λ_y (and β_y) is imaginary. We may therefore write similar equations, except for change of sign, for p^2 and r^2 in regions 2 and 3 as we write for q^2 in region 1. This gives

$$q^2 = \epsilon_1 \beta_0^2 - \beta_z^2$$
$$p^2 = -\epsilon_2 \beta_0^2 + \beta_z^2 \tag{4.7}$$
$$r^2 = -\epsilon_3 \beta_0^2 + \beta_z^2$$

β_z must be common to all three equations to give a coherently propagating wave. More general equations can be written to take account of any variation of A in the x direction and they will include a β_x term. We shall be concerned predominantly with situations where the field is only slowly varying in the x direction, with very small values of β_x. Except when directly considering the effects of such a variation it is justifiable to ignore β_x, which we shall proceed to do in the present context.

The three equations in (4.7) can be represented in a single plot of β^2 against y as shown in Figure 4.3. The stepped line $\beta^2 = \epsilon \beta_0^2$ shows the variation of the dielectric constant across the layers. The line $\beta^2 = \beta_z^2$ indicates the longitudinal propagation coefficient. The quantities q^2, p^2, and r^2 appear as the vertical separation between the two lines. For a guided wave the line $\beta^2 = \beta_z^2$ must pass through both vertical discontinuities in $\epsilon \beta_0^2$ so that it lies below $\epsilon \beta_0^2$ within the waveguide and above outside the guide. The solution of any particular problem lies in finding the appropriate positioning of the line $\beta^2 = \beta_z^2$ which allows the transverse field distributions to match one another at the layer interfaces. The method may be extended to more than three layers or to problems where there is a continuous rather than an abrupt variation of ϵ with y.

Matching of the transverse optical distributions at a dielectric interface requires that the tangential components of the electric field $\mathbf{E}$ and the

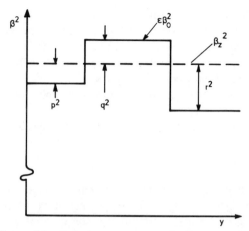

Figure 4.3 Relation between TEM propagation constant $\epsilon\beta_0^2$ and guide propagation constant β_z^2

magnetic field **H** be continuous across the interface. The precise behaviour depends on the polarization of the modes. We limit our consideration to modes with no variation in the x direction, which means that there are only two sets of modes possible, namely the TE modes with the electric field E_x polarized parallel to the junction and the TM modes with a similarly directed magnetic field H_x. In both cases the complementary field, **H** or **E** respectively, has both y and z components. The tangential components to be matched at the dielectric interface are therefore E_x and H_z for the TE modes and H_x and E_z for the TM modes. Maxwell's equations can be used to relate these components of electric and magnetic field. Thus, for the TE modes the standard relation

$$\text{curl } \mathbf{E} = -\mu_0 \dot{\mathbf{H}} \tag{4.8}$$

becomes

$$\frac{\partial E_x}{\partial y} = \beta_0 Z H_z$$

and for the TM modes

$$\text{curl } \mathbf{H} = \epsilon\epsilon_0 \dot{\mathbf{E}}$$

becomes

$$\frac{\partial H_x}{\partial y} = -\left(\frac{\epsilon\beta_0}{Z} E_z\right) \tag{4.9}$$

where $Z = (\mu_0/\epsilon_0)^{1/2}$ is the characteristic impedance of free space.

The significant point about these relations is that for the TE mode $\partial E_x/\partial y$

is continuous across a dielectric boundary as well as E_x and H_z. For the TM modes, on the other hand, $\partial H_x / \partial y$ changes across a dielectric boundary in proportion to ϵ. However, as the step $\delta \epsilon$ across the boundary becomes small compared with ϵ the difference between the characteristic of the two modes becomes small. Since lasers normally operate in the TE mode and since the behaviour in the TE mode is simpler than, but not very different from, the behaviour in the TM mode, we henceforward deal with the TE modes only.

For the TE modes we must find a solution for E_x over the cross section which is sinusoidal with y where β_y is real, which is exponential or hyperbolically sinusoidal where β_y is imaginary, which tends to zero at infinity, and which matches both the field E_x and its gradient $\partial E_x / \partial y$ at the boundaries between the regions. The distribution of E_x for a zero-order mode in a three-layer structure which illustrates these characteristics is shown in Figure 4.4. The general principles are the same for higher order modes, which include in the distribution a number of zeros equal to the mode number, and for structures with more than three layers, except that cosh and sinh distributions as well as cos distributions may occur in the additional central layers.

The boundary condition at the interfaces is mathematically more simply expressed in terms of the continuity of the ratio $(\partial E_x / \partial y)/E_x$ since this eliminates an arbitrary constant. The ratio is a normalized admittance and we will denote it by Y. We can find the way Y transforms from one side of each layer to the other, independent of the number of layers there may happen to be in the structure, and hence write an equation for the condition that Y is a continuous function over the whole width of the waveguide. Consider first those layers where β_y is real $(= q)$ and the electric field E_x varies as $\cos(qy - \phi_1)$, ϕ_1 being an arbitrary phase constant. (If there is more than one such layer q will in general have different values in each layer.) We will

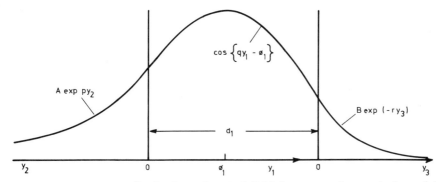

Figure 4.4 Transverse distribution of optical field for zero-order mode in a slab waveguide

take the layer as being the nth layer with thickness d_n. Y can be represented by $-q \tan(qy - \phi_1)$. Suppose $Y = Y_n$ at the left-hand side of the layer, say at $y = 0$. Then the value of ϕ_1 is defined as $\tan^{-1}(Y_n/q)$. Let $Y = y_{n+1}$ at the right-hand side of the layer at $y = d_n$. Then

$$Y_{n+1} = -q \tan\left\{qd_n - \tan^{-1}\left(\frac{Y_n}{q}\right)\right\}, \quad \text{for } E \propto \cos\left\{qy - \tan^{-1}\left(\frac{Y_n}{q}\right)\right\}$$

$$(4.10)$$

which applies for β_y real. For β_y imaginary, say $= jp$, one similarly finds the three possible alternative relations

$$Y_{n+1} = Y_n = p, \qquad\qquad\qquad \text{for } E \propto \exp(py)$$

$$Y_{n+1} = p \coth\left\{pd_n + \coth^{-1}\left(\frac{Y_n}{p}\right)\right\}, \quad \text{for } E \propto \sinh\left\{py + \coth^{-1}\left(\frac{Y_n}{p}\right)\right\}$$

$$Y_{n+1} = p \tanh\left\{pd_n + \tanh^{-1}\left(\frac{Y_n}{p}\right)\right\}, \quad \text{for } E \propto \cosh\left\{py + \tanh^{-1}\left(\frac{Y_n}{p}\right)\right\}$$

$$(4.11)$$

where y is measured from the left-hand side of each region except in the case of the exponential function where the position of the origin is immaterial. Using the above relations a characteristic transcendental equation may be written in terms of the p and the q values for a dielectric structure of any number of layers, with the p and the q values related by equations of the type of (4.7). For the three-layer structure with centre layer thickness d we have

$$Y_1 = p; \quad Y_2 = -q \tan\left\{qd - \tan^{-1}\left(\frac{p}{q}\right)\right\} \quad Y_2 = Y_3 = -r$$

where r is the value of p in layer 3, giving

$$qd = \tan^{-1}\left(\frac{p}{q}\right) + \tan^{-1}\left(\frac{r}{q}\right) + n\pi \tag{4.12}$$

where n is the mode number, and only the principle values of the $\tan^{-1}$ functions are taken. This is the exact form of equation (4.3) that was derived by the ray treatment. ϕ_2 and ϕ_3 are now given by $2 \tan^{-1}(p/q)$ and $2 \tan^{-1}(r/q)$, respectively. The relations between p, q, and r may be simplified by appropriate normalization. Equations (4.7) show that

$$p^2 + q^2 = \delta\epsilon\beta_0^2 \tag{4.13}$$

$$r^2 + q^2 = \eta\delta\epsilon\beta_0^2$$

where

$$\delta\epsilon = \epsilon_1 - \epsilon_2$$

and where an asymmetry factor η is introduced given by

$$\eta\delta\epsilon = \epsilon_1 - \epsilon_3.$$

To normalize these relations we put

$$\frac{p^2}{\delta\epsilon\beta_0^2} = P^2; \qquad \frac{q^2}{\delta\epsilon\beta_0^2} = Q^2; \qquad \frac{r^2}{\delta\epsilon\beta_0^2} = R^2 \quad \text{and} \quad d\delta\epsilon^{1/2}\beta_0 = D \qquad (4.14)$$

so that equation (4.13) becomes

$$P^2 + Q^2 = 1; \qquad R^2 + Q^2 = \eta \qquad\qquad\qquad (4.15)$$

Equation (4.12) can then be written in a simpler form as follows

$$QD = \cos^{-1}Q + \cos^{-1}\left(\frac{Q}{\eta^{1/2}}\right) + n\pi \qquad\qquad (4.16)$$

An interesting point about these equations is that the transverse distribution of field which they describe does not depend on the actual values of the dielectric constant in the various layers but only on the differences $\delta\epsilon$ and $\eta\delta\epsilon$ between the layers. It is only these differences which are involved in the determination of p, q, and r. This feature is also, of course, evident in equation (4.4) for the cut-off condition. The actual values of dielectric constant only enter in determining the longitudinal propagation coefficient β_z and the effective angle θ of propagation of the constituent plane waves.

The longitudinal propagation coefficient β_z can be obtained from equation (4.7). It is given by

$$\beta_z^2 = \epsilon_1\beta_0^2 - q^2 = (\epsilon_1 - \delta\epsilon Q^2)\beta_0^2 = (\epsilon_2 + \delta\epsilon P^2)\beta_0^2 \qquad (4.17)$$

The above relation shows that we can define an effective dielectric constant ϵ_{eff} for the waveguide (square of an effective refractive index) as follows

$$\epsilon_{\text{eff}} = \epsilon_1 - \delta\epsilon Q^2 = \epsilon_2 + \delta\epsilon P^2 \qquad\qquad (4.18)$$

which lies intermediate between the dielectric constant ϵ_1 of the centre layer and the dielectric constant ϵ_2 of the adjacent layer that differs least from it. This is evident from the positioning of the β_z^2 line in Figure 4.3.

4.1.3   Transverse Optical Field Distribution

The analysis of the optical distribution in a three-layer waveguide structure starts with the solution of equation (4.16) for Q in terms of D. P and R may then be obtained from equation (4.15). The total transverse distribution of the electric field E_x, shown in Figure 4.4, may then be found. It is conveniently expressed in terms of a normalized position X defined as $X = y\delta\epsilon^{1/2}\beta_0$ and is given by

$$E_x = E_{max}\cos(QX_1 - \cos^{-1}Q) \tag{4.19}$$

in the centre region, with X_1 measured with respect to the left-hand boundary of the region, see Figure 4.4, and

$$E_x = E_{max}Q\exp(PX_2) \tag{4.20}$$

in region 2 with X_2 measured with respect to the interface with region 1 and

$$E_x = E_{max}\left(\frac{Q}{\eta^{1/2}}\right)\exp(-RX_3) \tag{4.21}$$

in region 3 with X_3 measured with respect to the interface with region 1.

The distribution of optical intensity is in general of more direct interest than the distribution of optical field, and is obtained by squaring the latter. Three characteristics of the intensity distribution are of particular interest in deriving the optical properties and the threshold of the laser. The first is the total integral of the distribution. This can be conveniently defined in terms of an effective optical width s and a peak optical field E_{max}. s is given by

$$s = \int_{-\infty}^{\infty} E_x^2 \, dy / E_{max}^2 \tag{4.22}$$

s provides useful information for various applications. First, it gives a measure of the maximum optical flux which may be generated per unit junction width without exceeding a damaging level of optical field. Secondly, it provides an indication of the divergence of the output beam in the plane perpendicular to the junction. Thirdly s, in conjunction with optical losses in the cavity, is the ultimate quantity which determines the minimum threshold current density of the laser when other parameters are optimized.

The second characteristic of interest is the ratio of the integral of the part of the optical distribution that is located in the central layer of the waveguide to the total integral of the distribution. This is equal to the confinement factor Γ, given in equation (2.10), Chapter 2, which determines the reduction in the optical gain available from the centre layer. Γ can also be regarded as a 'dilution factor' that modifies the gain value that would prevail if all the light were contained within the central pumped layer. Γ is given by

$$\Gamma = \frac{\int_d E_x^2 \, dy}{\int_{-\infty}^{\infty} E_x^2 \, dy} \tag{4.23}$$

where subscript d indicates that the integral concerned is only taken over the width of the centre layer.

It is useful to distinguish between the two integrals that contribute to the confinement factor Γ in the above expression. The one in the denominator is proportional to s. In many circumstances s is a design parameter of the laser and not subject to optimization. However, the one in the numerator can often be maximized. Its maximum value is $E_{max}^2 \, d$, which occurs when the central layer is very narrow and is localized at the peak of the optical distribution. Hence, as a third interesting characteristic of the optical distribution we define a coupling coefficient k to indicate how closely this maximum is achieved

$$k = \int_d E_x^2 \, dy / E_{max}^2 \, d \tag{4.24}$$

where subscript d indicates that the integral is only taken over the width of the active layer. In double heterostructures k normally lies between 0.6 and 0.9. In four- and five-layer structures k may be made to closely approach 1 for the desired mode and to take a much smaller value for undesired modes.

For three-layer structures the above parameters may be expressed quite simply in terms of P, R, D, and η. We first define a normalized effective width S given in terms of s by

$$S = s\delta\epsilon^{1/2}\beta_0 \tag{4.25}$$

Then evaluation of the various integrals shows that

$$S = \frac{(1/P + 1/R + D)}{2} \tag{4.26}$$

$$k = \frac{(P + R/\eta + D)}{2D} \tag{4.27}$$

$$\Gamma = \frac{kD}{S} \tag{4.28}$$

The independent variables are η and D. P and R may be obtained for any three-layer waveguide structure using equations (4.15) and (4.16).

4.1.4 Dielectric Waveguide Characteristics of Heterostructures

The relations derived in the previous section for the effective optical width S, the coupling coefficient k, and the confinement factor Γ are applicable to both double and single heterostructures. In the former case the structure is approximately symmetrical and η lies around unity. In the latter case η is of the order of 20. Let us discuss how S, k, and Γ vary with the normalized thickness D of the centre layer for both types of heterostructure.

In Figure 4.5 we show curves of S against D for the double heterostructure. Curve A for $\eta = 1$ and $n = 0$ applies to the zero-order

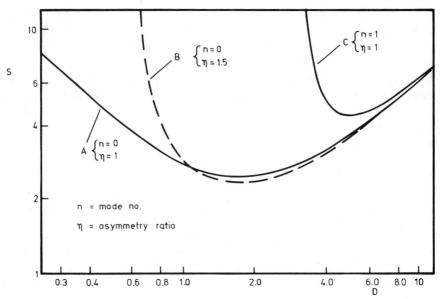

Figure 4.5   Effective optical width in double heterostructure optical waveguide as a function of thickness of central layer. Zero- and first-order modes for symmetrical structure (curves A and C) and zero-order mode for unsymmetrical structure (curve B)

mode in a symmetrical double heterostructure. As in all instances there is a value of D which gives a minimum in the optical spread. For the symmetrical double heterostructure in the zero-order mode minimum spread S occurs for a value of D approximately equal to 1.7, at which point the optical distribution is about 40 per cent wider than the thickness of the centre layer. The thickness of the centre layer which corresponds to this value of D depends on the step in the dielectric constant at the boundary. For a (GaAl)As/GaAs device and for, say, a 30 per cent step in the AlAs content the thickness is about $0.2\,\mu$m. In the symmetrical double heterostructure optical guiding is maintained down to zero D, although it becomes progressively weaker as D approaches zero. For small D, S is approximately equal to $2/D$.

The shape of the optical distribution as well as its width varies as D is altered. Figure 4.6 shows examples of the shape in the range of D from 10 to 0.3. The variation in shape over this range is gradual, but there is an appreciable difference between the first and last patterns, both of which give approximately the same value of S.

Assymetry in the double heterostructure causes waveguiding to cease at a certain minimum value D_{min} of D. As D approaches this value from above, S increases proportionally very rapidly and tends to infinity. This is illustrated

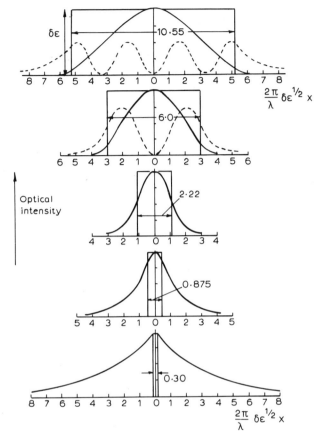

Figure 4.6   Distribution of optical intensity across width of symmetrical slab waveguide for various values of the normalized width D $(=(2\pi/\lambda)\delta\epsilon^{1/2}d)$ of the centre layer between 0.3 and 10.55. Zero-order transverse modes shown by continuous curves and highest order transverse mode shown by dashed curves for cases where higher order modes can propagate

in curve B, Figure 4.5, for the case of $\eta = 1.5$. The guiding stops for D less than about 0.6, which in an average heterostructure corresponds to a central layer thickness of about 0.08 μm. This degree of asymmetry has little effect when D is greater than unity.

The way the effective width of the first-order mode varies with D in the symmetrical double heterostructure is also shown in Figure 4.5, curve C. The minimum value of D for the propagation of this mode is π. The value of D which gives maximum optical confinement is 5. These figures correspond in a typical double heterostructure to centre layer thicknesses of 0.4 and

0.6 μm, respectively. For values of D beyond 5 the effective width of the first-order mode is negligibly greater than that of the zero-order mode.

The coupling coefficient k in the zero-order mode of the symmetrical double heterostructure increases towards unity as D is reduced towards zero. This is illustrated in Figure 4.7. For large D, k has a value of 0.5, and this rises to about 0.75 at the point where D has been reduced sufficiently to prevent the first-order mode from propagating. For the higher order modes k tends to 0.5 both for large D and as D approaches cut-off, and rises only somewhat above this value for intermediate D. This is also illustrated in Figure 4.7.

The dependence of the confinement factor Γ on D for the symmetrical double heterostructure is also illustrated in Figure 4.7. Γ is approximately unity for large D. Γ for the zero-order mode starts decreasing rapidly as D is reduced

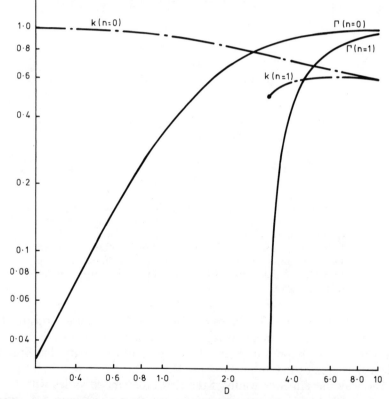

Figure 4.7 Coupling coefficient k and confinement factor Γ for optical distribution in double heterostructure optical waveguide as a function of normalized thickness D of central layer. First- and zero-order modes for symmetrical structure

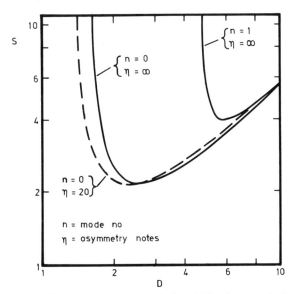

Figure 4.8 Effective optical width for optical distribution in single heterostructure waveguide as a function of normalized thickness D of central layer. Curves shown for two different degrees of asymmetry for zero-order mode, and for one degree of asymmetry for first-order mode

below the value which gives maximum confinement ($D \simeq 1.7$) and tends to $D^2/2$ for small values of D. Γ for the first-order mode is always less than that for the zero-order mode and tends steeply towards zero as D is reduced towards the value that gives mode cut-off.

Figure 4.8 shows the variations of S with D for the zero- and first-order modes of a single heterostructure for values of η of 20 and ∞. $\eta = 20$ is a typical value for a single heterostructure. The general behaviour is similar to that of the first-order mode of a double heterostructure (identical in the case of $\eta = \infty$ if all distances are halved). A minimum value of $S = 2.2$ occurs for D in the region of 2.5 (corresponding to $d \simeq 1.5\ \mu$m in a typical device). S increases rapidly as D is reduced below this value, and tends to infinity as D tends to 1.3–1.5, the exact value depending on the degree of asymmetry. Below this value of D, which we call $D_{\min}$, there is no waveguiding.

For the first-order mode in a single heterostructure the minimum value of the effective width occurs for $D \simeq 6$ (corresponding to $d \simeq 3.5\ \mu$m in a typical device) and the mode cut-off occurs for D in the range 4–4.5, depending on the precise degree of asymmetry. The curve of S against D for $\eta = \infty$ is given in Figure 4.8. There is a three to one range of D in which only the zero-order mode can propagate.

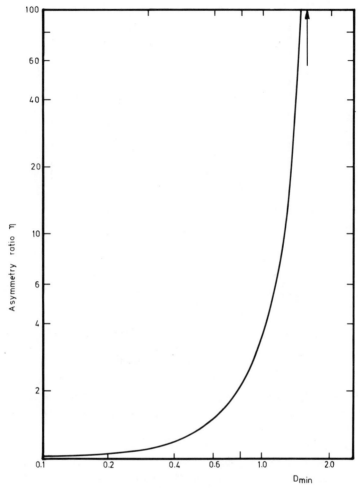

Figure 4.9 Relation between asymmetry ratio and normalized thickness of centre layer for waveguide cut-off condition in asymmetrical heterostructure waveguide

Figure 4.9 shows how the value D_{min} for cut-off for the zero-order mode varies with the asymmetry factor η. The relation is

$$D_{min} = \cos^{-1}(\eta^{-1/2}) + n\pi \qquad (4.29)$$

which can be obtained from (4.16) by putting $Q = 1$. The initial variation of D_{min} with η, as η increases from unity, is relatively rapid but it slows down as the asymmetry factor η approaches the value of around 10 or 20 that is appropriate for a single heterostructure.

Figure 4.10 shows the variation of k and Γ with D for both the zero- and

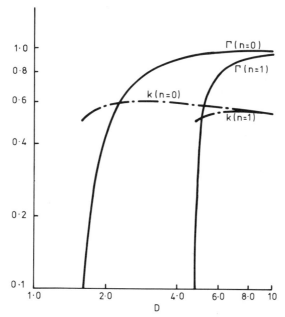

Figure 4.10   Coupling coefficient k and confinement factor Γ for optical distribution in single heterostructure optical waveguide as a function of normalized thickness of central layer. Curves shown for zero- and first order modes ($n = 0$ and 1)

the first-order mode in a single heterostructure with $\eta = \infty$. k tends to 0.5 both for large D and as D approaches the value for the mode cut-off concerned. At an intermediate value of D it reaches a maximum of around 0.6 for the zero-order mode, and successively less for each higher order mode.

Γ is approximately unity for all modes at sufficiently large D. As D is decreased Γ for each mode falls in value. It starts to decrease rapidly when D becomes less than the value which gives maximum confinement for the mode concerned, and tends steeply to zero as D approaches mode cut-off. For any value of D the value of Γ decreases as the mode number increases.

4.1.5   Divergence of Emitted Beam

The beam emitted at the output face of a heterostructure laser diverges considerably in the plane perpendicular to the heterojunctions. In most cases this is caused by the narrow source dimensions provided by the heterostructure waveguide. The thickness of the central layer of a typical double heterostructure waveguide is of the order of one-quarter of a free space wavelength, and the light which it guides is confined to a width which is normally not more than twice the thickness of this layer. When light which has been confined to such dimensions radiates into free space natural diffraction causes the beam to spread into a total angle of about 45°. Increasing the thickness of the central layer does not necessarily reduce the beam divergence because it can easily result in the generation of higher order transverse modes. However much the width of the source is extended the highest order mode still produces a widely divergent far-field pattern which is predominantly twin lobed. A more fundamental cause for the potential widely divergent beam stems from the properties of the dielectric waveguide and the size of the step in dielectric constant at its boundaries. The ray that is emitted at the most oblique angle θ_{max} from the end-face of the laser is that which strikes the waveguide boundary within the laser at the critical angle. It is easy to show that θ_{max} is given in terms of the dielectric step $\delta\epsilon$ by

$$\sin \theta_{max} = \delta\epsilon^{1/2} \tag{4.30}$$

For the limited central layer widths used in practice the spread of the emission remains within an angle of about half θ_{max} as a result of narrowing produced by the appreciable spread of the light into the outer layers of the waveguide. However, the qualitative behaviour is still determined by an expression of the type of equation (4.30) and the spread of the beam tends mainly to be determined by the square root of the dielectric step. Double heterostructure lasers, where $\delta\epsilon \simeq 1$, normally give beam angles of around 45° (total angle to the half intensity points), and single heterostructures, where $\delta\epsilon \simeq 0.01$ at the p–n junction waveguide boundary, give beam angles of 10–15°. Fairly sophisticated methods of mode control can however be used to improve on these figures, as will be evident after carrying out the more precise analysis that is described below.

Let us therefore consider in more detail the specific angular distribution of the beam emitted by some particular guided wave. The beam angle is largely determined by the transverse distribution of optical field in the heterostructure waveguide. Fourier transform methods are normally used for deriving the relation between the source field distribution and the beam angle. They are applicable in the present instance but with the complication that the beam angle is not necessarily sufficiently small to make the usual simplifying linear approximations. This problem has been treated by Hockham,[3] and in greater detail by Lewin.[4] Here we give a descriptive treatment which is less rigorous than that of the latter two authors but which gives the same results for both small and large beam angles.

We take the z direction as the axis of the guide and the y direction to lie perpendicular to the heterostructure interfaces [see Figure 4.11(a)]. As an example we consider the TE mode which has its electric vector polarized parallel to the heterostructure with a component E_x only. The magnetic field

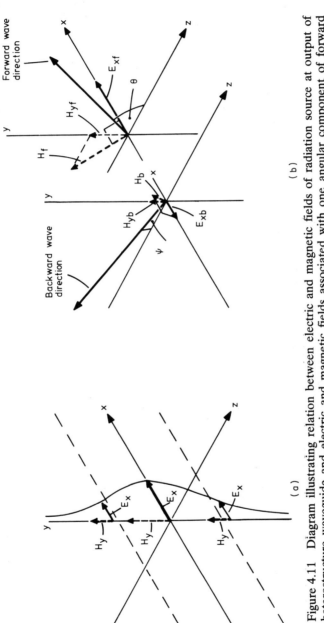

Figure 4.11 Diagram illustrating relation between electric and magnetic fields of radiation source at output of heterostructure waveguide and electric and magnetic fields associated with one angular component of forward radiation pattern and associated component of backward scattered radiation. (a) Field distribution at source. (b) Fields associated with forward- and backward-emitted radiation

has a transverse component H_y and a longitudinal component H_z. The important feature that we must consider is the distribution of E_x and H_y in the y direction. Maxwell's equations show that, because the fields are created by a propagating wave, the ratio H_y/E_x is everywhere constant with a value which, taking account of the reflection at the output face, is approximately equal to Y_0, the free space admittance.

A source field with a sinusoidal transverse distribution of infinite extent gives a simple far-field pattern with two symmetrical lobes directed at an angle to the axis determined by the periodicity of the sinusoid. Hence the first stage in deriving the far-field pattern of the actual transverse distribution of the source is to decompose the source field into its sinusoidal Fourier components.

Consider the Fourier component F_x of the electric field E_x with transverse periodicity defined by a phase constant β_y, in the form

$$F_x(\beta_y) \exp(j\beta_y y) \tag{4.31}$$

where $F_x(\beta_y)$ can be obtained in terms of the y-distribution of E_x using

$$F_x(\beta_y) = \int_{-\infty}^{\infty} E_x \exp(j\beta_y y) \, \mathrm{d}y$$

The corresponding Fourier component of the magnetic field H_y is obtained by multiplying by Y_0. The direction θ of the beam emitted into free space by the above Fourier components of field [see Figure 4.11(b)] is given in terms of β_y by

$$\sin \theta = \frac{\beta_y}{\beta_0}, \qquad \beta_0 = \frac{2\pi}{\lambda} \tag{4.32}$$

However, these Fourier components of E_x and H_y can also radiate a beam back into the dielectric material. The waves which constitute the backward beam are not entirely plane as a result of the refraction caused by the differing dielectric constants of the heterostructure. However, as a first approximation we may ignore the effect of the centre layer. If the heterostructure is symmetrical then the angle ψ of the backward radiated beam [see Figure 4.11(b)] is mainly determined by the common dielectric constant of the two outer layers, say ϵ_2, and is given approximately in terms of β_y by

$$\sin \psi = \frac{\beta_y}{\epsilon_2^{1/2} \beta_0} \tag{4.33}$$

The relative amplitudes of the forward and backward radiated waves, and the relation between the amplitude of the forward wave and the amplitude of the Fourier component of the original source field, can be obtained by equating the transverse components of E and H due to the source to the similar components of E and H of the radiated field at the output face of the waveguide. Let the x components of the electric field of the forward and backward radiated field be E_{xf} and E_{xb}, respectively, and the y components of the magnetic field be H_{yf} and H_{yb}, respectively, as shown in Figure 4.11(b). Equating the combined electric fields due to radiation with the Fourier component of the source gives

$$E_{xf} - E_{xb} = F_x \qquad (4.34)$$

The ratio of the sum of the forward and backward magnetic fields to the sum of the forward and backward electric fields must be equal to the admittance of the source field, i.e.

$$\frac{H_{yf} + H_{yb}}{E_{xf} - E_{xb}} \simeq Y_0 \qquad (4.35)$$

But the transverse components of E and H in the radiated waves are related by the oblique wave admittances as follows

$$\frac{H_{yf}}{E_{xf}} = Y_0 \cos \theta$$

$$\frac{H_{yb}}{E_{xb}} = \epsilon_2^{1/2} Y_0 \cos \psi = Y_0(\epsilon_2 - \sin^2 \theta)^{1/2} \qquad (4.36)$$

Inserting these values into (4.35), finding E_{xb}/E_{xf}, and substituting into (4.34) gives the following expression for the amplitude of the forward radiated wave in terms of the Fourier component of the source field

$$E_{xf} = \frac{F_x\{1 + (\epsilon_2 - \sin^2\theta)^{1/2}\}}{\cos \theta + (\epsilon_2 - \sin^2\theta)^{1/2}} \qquad (4.37)$$

The optical power flux, say $P_\beta \delta \beta_y$, associated with the amplitude E_{xf} of the forward radiated electric field and the amplitude H_{yf} of the corresponding magnetic field over an interval $\delta\beta_y$ of the phase constant β_y is

$$P_\beta \delta \beta_y = E_{xf} H_{yf}^* \, \delta\beta_y$$
$$= Y_0 |E_{xf}|^2 \cos \theta \, \delta\beta_y \qquad (4.38)$$

where * indicates the complex conjugate.

Using the relationship between β_y and θ in equation (4.32) the power flux, say $P\delta\theta$, over the angular interval $\delta\theta$ becomes

$$P\delta\theta \propto |E_{xf}|^2 \cos^2\theta\delta\theta \qquad (4.39)$$

Substituting for E_{xf} in terms of F_x from equation (4.37) gives

$$P\delta\theta \propto \left[\frac{\cos^2\theta\{1 + (\epsilon_2 - \sin^2\theta)^{1/2}\}^2}{\{\cos \theta + (\epsilon_2 - \sin^2\theta)^{1/2}\}^2} \right] |F_x|^2 \delta\theta \qquad (4.40)$$

where F_x is given in terms of θ by

$$F_x = \int_{-\infty}^{\infty} E_x \exp(j\beta_0 y \sin \theta) \, dy \qquad (4.41)$$

A similar derivation for the mode with the electric field polarized perpendicular to the heterojunctions gives

$$P\delta\theta \propto \left[\frac{\cos^2\theta \{\epsilon_2 + (\epsilon_2 - \sin^2\theta)^{1/2}\}^2}{\{\epsilon_2 \cos\theta + (\epsilon_2 - \sin^2\theta)^{1/2}\}^2} \right] |F_x|^2 \delta\theta \qquad (4.42)$$

The expression on the right-hand sides of equations (4.40) and (4.42) for the angular profiles of the emitted beam are the product of Fourier terms that depend on the transverse distribution of the optical field in the waveguide and of additional terms, in square brackets, that depend only on the angle θ. The latter terms are called obliquity factors. They are plotted as a function of θ in Figure 4.12. Curve A applies to the mode with the electric field polarized parallel to the heterojunction which in most cases is

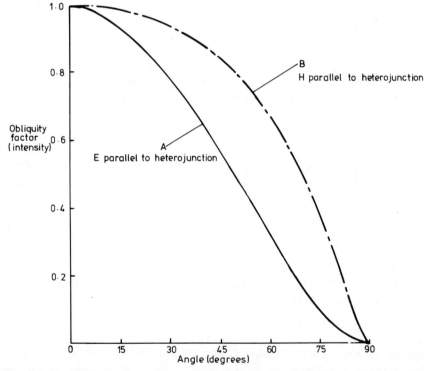

Figure 4.12   Obliquity factor as a function of emission angle for optical intensity of radiated wave from source with (a) electric vector parallel to heterojunctions and (b) magnetic vector parallel to heterojunctions

dominant. Curve B applies to the perpendicular polarized mode. The first curve, in particular, shows that the obliquity factor provides a considerable amount of sharpening up to the beam when the contribution from the Fourier terms gives a wide distribution.

Let us now consider the contribution of the Fourier terms. In order to continue using the normalized quantities introduced in the previous section for the field distribution it is convenient to define a new angular variable $\Phi = \sin\theta/\delta\epsilon^{1/2}$. Then using $X = \beta_0 \delta\epsilon_y^{1/2}$ as a normalized position coordinate we modify equation (4.41) to give a new normalized function $F(\Phi)$ as follows

$$F(\Phi) \propto \int_{-\infty}^{\infty} \frac{E_x}{E_{max}} \exp(j\Phi X) \, dX \qquad (4.43)$$

For the case where θ is small and the obliquity factor is approximately unity this function alone gives a good indication of the far-field pattern.

$F(\Phi)$ can be expressed in terms of the quantities Q, P, R, η, and D which describe the distribution of the waveguide source field. Henshall and Whiteaway[5] give the following expression for $F(\Phi)$ for the nth-order transverse mode in a general unsymmetrical three-layer waveguide

$$F(\Phi) = \frac{Q}{Q^2 - \Phi^2} \left[\frac{P\cos(\Phi X_1) - \Phi\sin(\Phi X_1)}{P^2 + \Phi^2} + \frac{\eta^{1/2}(R\cos(\Phi X_2) - \Phi\sin(\Phi X_2)}{R^2 + \Phi^2} \right.$$
$$\left. -j\left\{ \frac{\Phi\cos(\Phi X_1) + P\sin(\Phi X_1)}{P^2 + \Phi^2} - \frac{\eta^{1/2}[\Phi\cos(\Phi X_2) + R\sin(\Phi X_2)]}{R^2 + \Phi^2} \right\} \right]$$

$$(4.44)$$

where $X_1 = (\cos^{-1}Q + n\pi)/Q$ and $X_2 = D - X_1$. For the symmetrical three-layer structure this expression simplifies very considerably to[6,7]

$$F(\Phi) = \frac{2Q\{P\cos(\Phi D/2) - \Phi\sin(\Phi D/2)\}}{(Q^2 - \Phi^2)(P^2 + \Phi^2)} \qquad (4.45)$$

The square of the modulus of $F(\Phi)$ gives the optical intensity per unit beam angle which is the quantity of the more direct interest. The intensity distribution is symmetrical on either side of $\Phi = 0$ irrespective of the symmetry of the near field.

The effect of varying D in a three-layer structure with fixed asymmetry is to vary both the width and the shape of the far-field intensity distribution. Figure 4.13 shows the extremes of shape that can be encountered for various zero-order distributions of near field. To provide a good comparison all the curves have been scaled up so that the curvatures at $\Phi = 0$ are equal. The inset curves in the figure show the near-field distributions that apply to each of the far-field curves. Curves A and B refer respectively to asymmetric and symmetric guide structures very near

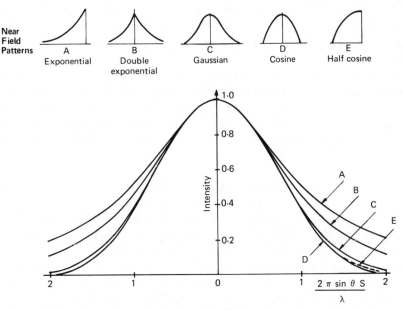

Figure 4.13 Comparison of shape of far-field patterns that originate from dielectric guides with the various near-field distributions shown

cut-off. In the near fields to which these curves apply the majority of the light spreads outside the central layer in the form of an exponential tail either on one side or on both sides. Curve D refers to a strongly guiding structure with large D where the near-field distribution is a pure cosine function. Curve C refers to an intermediate near-field distribution. It can be seen that as the guiding becomes weaker or more asymmetrical the skirts of the far-field pattern become more pronounced.

Figure 4.14 shows examples of multilobed far-field patterns which are produced by higher order transverse mode distributions in the near field (the obliquity factor is not included). The curves shown apply to wide guides, where the penetration of the optical field into the outer layers can be ignored. However, they illustrate the main points of the typical behaviour. For the nth order mode ($n > 1$) the far field has two dominant lobes close to the edge of the distribution, separated by ($n - 1$) subsidiary and narrower maxima that lie between them. If the very small maxima which lie outside the main lobes are ignored the far field can be considered to have an equal number of maxima to the near field.

The subsidiary maxima which lie between the main lobes become more prominent for narrower, and hence more weakly guiding, structures. This arises because of the additional contribution from the near field of the light which penetrates in exponential tails into the outer layers of the guide. The

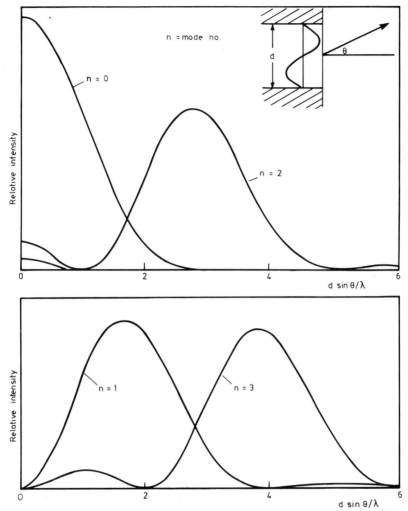

Figure 4.14 Multi-lobed far-field patterns produced by higher order transverse guided modes. Limiting case of strong guiding. Symmetrical for negative angles

pair of exponential tails constitute. a double source which produces interference fringes and intensifies the subsidiary maxima.

The width of the far-field pattern may be defined in various ways. Two useful definitions are in terms (a) of the angle from the axis at which the intensity drops by a given amount and (b) of the angle which contains a certain fraction of the total power. The first definition is normally used and an angle $2\Phi_{1/2}$ is defined as the total normalized angle to the points of half intensity [alternatively the (normalized) full angle at half power]. It is

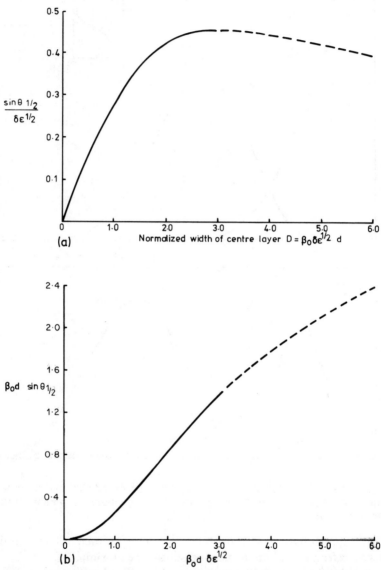

Figure 4.15 Relation between beam divergence in a symmetrical double heterostructure and both thickness of centre layer and dielectric constant step: (a) $\sin \theta_{1/2}/\delta\epsilon^{1/2}$ as a function of $\beta_0\delta\epsilon^{1/2}d$; (b) $\beta_0d \sin \theta_{1/2}$ as a function of $\beta_0d\delta\epsilon^{1/2}$

relatively simple to measure. However, it should be pointed out that there can be a considerable variation in the fraction of the total power that is contained within this angle. In Figure 4.13, for instance, the power fraction for curve A, derived from the single exponential, is 50 per cent. For curve B, derived from the double exponential, it is 65 per cent, and for curve D, derived from the cosine function, it is 78 per cent.

Let us consider how the beam width in a symmetrical double heterostructure guide, characterized by $\sin \theta_{1/2} (= \delta\epsilon^{1/2}\Phi_{1/2})$, is affected by the thickness d of the centre layer and the dielectric constant step $\delta\epsilon$. In Figure 4.15 we give normalized curves to show these dependencies (the obliquity factor is not included). Figure 4.15(a) shows a plot of $\Phi_{1/2}$ against D which, taking $\delta\epsilon$ as constant, illustrates the form of the dependence of $\sin \theta_{1/2}$ on d. Figure 4.15(b) shows a plot of $\Phi_{1/2}D$ against D which, taking d as constant, illustrates the form of the dependence of $\sin \theta_{1/2}$ on $\delta\epsilon^{1/2}$.

There is a value of d which produces a maximum in the angular width of the beam, given by $\beta_0 \delta\epsilon^{1/2} d = 3.2$. For a normal double heterostructure (30 per cent AlAs step) this corresponds to $d = 0.4 \ \mu$m and $2\theta_{1/2} \simeq 60°$. The narrowing of the beam width, which takes place as D is reduced below this value, arises from the spreading of the near field into the outer layers of the waveguide. For $D < 1.2$ ($d < 0.15 \ \mu$m and $2\theta_{1/2} < 40°$) the relation between $\sin \theta_{1/2}$ and d is almost linear. Increase of D beyond the point of maximum $\theta_{1/2}$ rapidly brings the operation into a region where higher order modes are possible. This is indicated by the dashed line in Figure 4.15(a). $\theta_{1/2}$ can be reduced by only a negligible amount from its maximum value before this region is entered.

Figure 4.15(b) indicates that $\sin \theta_{1/2}$ varies reasonably linearly with $\delta\epsilon^{1/2}$ for fixed d over most of the range where only the zero- or the first-order modes can exist. However, in the region below $D = 0.6$ (for example, $d = 0.15 \ \mu$m and $\delta\epsilon = 1.3$) $\sin \theta_{1/2}$ varies directly as $\delta\epsilon$. In this region, therefore, varying the AlAs step at the waveguide boundaries has a particularly strong influence on $\theta_{1/2}$.

The proportion of the total power output contained between $\pm\theta_{1/2}$ is shown in Figure 4.16 as a function of D.

As mentioned earlier the effective width S of the near-field intensity distribution and the normalized beamwidth in the far field $\Phi_{1/2}$ are related. Figure 4.17 shows the relation which exists in a symmetrical double heterostructure with D as the independent variable. The curve has two branches on either side of the extrema of S and $\Phi_{1/2}$. Branch I is the weakly guiding branch with D small (< 2) and branch II is the strongly guiding branch with D large (> 3). In both branches $\Phi_{1/2}$ is approximately inversely proportional to S over all except the largest values of the latter. However, for a given value of S the strongly guiding branch II exhibits a

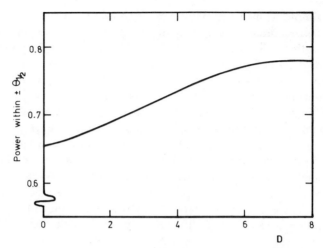

Figure 4.16   Proportion of total optical power in the output beam of symmetrical double heterostructures contained within $\pm\theta_{1/2}$ the angle between the points of half intensity as a function of width of central layer

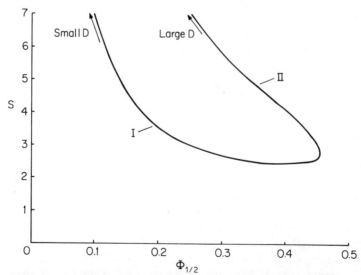

Figure 4.17   Relation between far-field beam angle and effective optical width in double heterostructure waveguide with thickness of centre layer as independent variable. Plot of $\Phi_{1/2}$ against S

far-field width $\Phi_{1/2}$ which is about 2.9 times the width for branch I. If the beam angle containing a fixed proportion of the total power is plotted instead of $\Phi_{1/2}$ then the discrepancy is less, i.e. a factor of about 2, but still appreciable. Evidently the exponential tails of the optical distribution which penetrate into the surrounding layers in the weakly guiding case make a considerable contribution to narrowing the beamwidth without broadening the near-field intensity distribution to a comparable extent.

The far-field beamwidth of a general asymmetrical heterostructure depends on the two normalized variables D and η. The behaviour predicted by equation (4.44) has not been computed over any comprehensive range of the parameters. Figure 4.18, however, shows the behaviour of a heterostructure with maximum asymmetry ($\eta = \infty$). The curve gives a relation between the normalized beam angle $\Phi_{1/2}$ and D, which applies approximately to a single heterostructure laser. The significant feature of the behaviour is the way $\Phi_{1/2}$ drops rapidly to zero as D is reduced towards the cut-off point for the waveguide. This behaviour is modified in practice as a result of optical losses, which become important in the extreme situation, near cut-off, where there is deep penetration of the optical field into one of the outer layers of the waveguide. Adams and Cross[8] have made various computations which apply in such a situation. Henshall and Whiteaway[5] have made specific computations to investigate the effect of varying the small dielectric constant step in the waveguide structure and compared this with the change in beamwidth observed in a single heterostructure as a result of varying the contribution to the dielectric constant produced by electrons in the n-type layer.

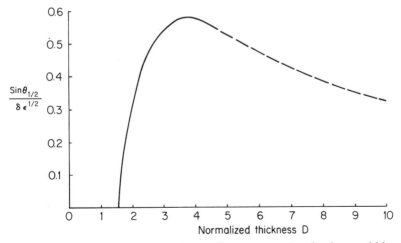

Figure 4.18   Relation between beam divergence and active layer width in single heterostructure waveguide. Plot of $\Phi_{1/2}$ against D

4.1.6   Reflectivity of the End-Face

A cleaved end-face normally fulfils the function of the end mirror in a simiconductor laser cavity. Internal reflection at the semiconductor/air interface provides sufficient feedback. In heterostructure lasers the reflection coefficient at the end-face depends to a certain extent on the mode being propagated. As indicated in Chapter 2 the reflectivity at the end-face is important in determining the threshold condition and influences the incremental efficiency. When several modes are capable of propagating in the heterostructure waveguide the relative reflectivity at the end-face is often the critical factor which favours one mode and may totally discriminate against the others.

The internal reflection of a plane wave at the boundary of a homogeneous dielectric medium obeys Fresnel's equations and the power reflection coefficient R_0 for normal reflection in a material of dielectric constant ϵ is given by

$$R_0 = \left(\frac{\varepsilon^{1/2} - 1}{\varepsilon^{1/2} + 1}\right)^2 \tag{4.46}$$

The situation when a wave guided in a dielectric guide is reflected at a normal interface is considerably more complicated. Within the centre layer of the guide the constituent plane waves propagate at some angle θ with respect to the normal at the interface. In isolation the plane waves would experience a reflection coefficient that would depend on their polarization. The reflection would be greater than R_0 if the electric vector were in the plane of the waveguide (TE modes) and less than R_0 for the perpendicular polarization (TM modes) unless θ were well beyond the Brewster angle (angle for zero reflection). However, the total field distribution of the mode also includes the exponentially decaying optical fields in the two outer layers of the waveguide. These fields, in isolation, would experience reflection which would be smaller for the TE modes and larger for the TM modes, i.e. the exact opposite of the behaviour in the centre layer. The overall reflection of the mode is an appropriate weighted average of the two contributions. It is normally dominated by the behaviour of the waves in the centre layer, but with a compensating effect from the outer layers which becomes important when the centre layer is thin.

Reinhart et al.[9] have used approximate Fourier transform methods to decompose the field of the guided wave over its total transverse distribution into plane waves with a continuous range of incident angles and obtained an estimate of the effective reflection coefficient. Ikegami[10] has used a more precise method of field matching (although still with some approximation) to give an improved result, and has applied it to derive the reflection coefficient of different transverse modes in symmetrical double heterostructures with a range of values of centre layer thickness and

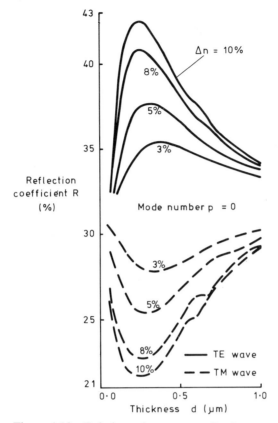

Figure 4.19 Relation between reflection co-efficient at end-face of double heterostructure waveguide and both thickness of centre layer and step in dielectric constant. Curves of R against d for various values of $\delta\epsilon$ for zero-order modes. After Ikegami[10]

dielectric constant step. Figure 4.19 shows the variation in reflection coefficient with d for various values of $\delta\epsilon$. The curves for the reflection coefficient of the zero-order TE mode are not unlike the curves for far-field beamwidth in general shape and peak for values of d which are only somewhat less than those for maximum beamwidth. For instance, for a 30 per cent AlAs step, peak reflectivity occurs for $d \simeq 0.3$ μm with a value of reflection coefficient about 20 per cent greater than that for a plane wave. For the TM mode, minimum reflectivity occurs for about the same value of d and the reflection coefficient is about 20 per cent less than that for a plane wave. The TE mode is therefore highly favoured in a heterostructure laser and is dominant in all normal circumstances.

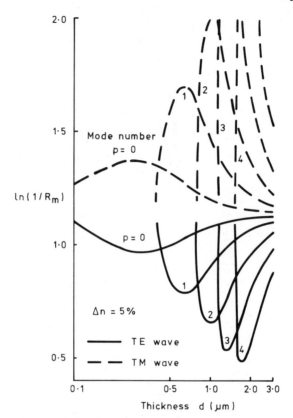

Figure 4.20 Relation between reflection coefficient at end-face of double heterostructure
waveguide and thickness of centre layer for
different transverse modes. $\delta\epsilon = 1.3$. After
Ikegami[10]

Figure 4.20 shows how the reflection coefficient, with $\delta\epsilon = 1.3$, varies
with d for a range of modes. With TE modes the higher order modes have
higher reflectivity. With increasing d the reflection coefficient of the
first-order mode overtakes that of the zero-order mode at $d = 0.4$ μm and
the reflection coefficient of the second-order mode overtakes that of the
first-order mode at $d = 0.85$ μm.

4.2   SMOOTHLY PROFILED GAIN AND DIELECTRIC GUIDES

In this section we extend the analysis of optical waveguides to cover the type
of optical guiding that occurs in stripe lasers in the plane of the junction.
There are two ways in which the necessary treatment differs from that used

for the heterostructure waveguide. First, the transverse variations in the optical properties of the medium are continuous rather than abrupt and, secondly, gain variations affect the guiding properties to an extent comparable to variations in the refractive index.

The distribution of injected carriers is the dominant factor in determining the spread of the light in stripe lasers. The injected carriers of course provide gain. They also produce a reduction in the refractive index in two separate ways. First, there is the direct free-carrier interaction with the optical wave, the so-called plasma effect the magnitude of which is proportional to the concentration of injected carriers. Secondly, there is the band-to-band interaction with the injected carriers which accompanies the gain process and whose magnitude is related by fundamental principles (the Kramers–Kroenig[11] relations) to the total dispersion of the gain spectrum. As a first approximation the gain and the refractive index can be taken as varying linearly with each other in regions where the injected carrier concentration varies. See Appendix 4 for a quantitative treatment.

The optical properties associated with the injected carriers exhibit a smooth distribution over the cross section of the stripe laser as a result of both the sideways spread of current in its passage from the contact to the active layer, and the sideways diffusion of injected carriers in the active layer. The perturbation in optical properties caused by the injected carriers is normally greatest under the centre of the stripe and dies away to zero at large distances from the centre. However, in certain circumstances (as is explained in Chapter 6, Section 6.3.2 on self-focusing) the situation is reversed as a result of a local dip in the injected carrier concentration being created at the centre of the stripe by strong stimulated recombination where the optical intensity is greatest. In both cases it is necessary for the analysis to consider a continuous distribution of the dielectric constant rather than the abrupt transitions that occur in a heterostructure waveguide.

As mentioned above the gain distribution as well as the dielectric constant distribution has a considerable influence in determining the transverse optical distribution. The standard dielectric waveguide analysis is, however, capable of dealing with the effects produced by optical gain because gain can equally well be described in terms of an imaginary component of the dielectric constant. This form has been used by Schlosser[12] for abrupt 'gain-guiding' and by Cook and Nash[13] and Hakki[14] for continuously distributed stripe-guides. It has also been used by Unger[15] in his treatment of the 'gain-guiding' situation normal to the junction in homostructure lasers. The latter treatment is equally applicable to stripe lasers. In the following sections we analyse the behaviour of wave-guides with continuous transverse distributions of complex dielectric constant where the ratio of the real and imaginary parts of the dielectric constant is fixed. This is a good approximation for a symmetrical stripe laser with a central optical filament. In Appendix 3 we extend the analysis to the case where the centres of the distributions of real and imaginary dielectric constants are no longer coincident. The results of this analysis can be used to investigate conditions where the optical filament is in unstable equilibrium at the centre of the stripe but can find a stable position at one or other side.

4.2.1   Equivalence of Gain and Imaginary Part of the Dielectric Constant

The optical gain coefficient g for a plane wave in an inverted medium forms part of an overall complex propagation coefficient of the form $(\beta + jg/2)$. (The halving of the power gain g in this expression occurs because optical field rather than power is the quantity described by the propagation coefficient.) The propagation coefficient can be considered to be proportional, in the normal way, to the square root of the dielectric constant ϵ. We must therefore postulate a complex dielectric constant ϵ in the form, say $(\epsilon_1 + j\epsilon_2)$. If we assume that $\epsilon_2 \ll \epsilon_1$ then the relation between g and ϵ is

$$g = 2 \, \text{Im}[\epsilon^{1/2}\beta_0] \simeq \frac{\epsilon_2\beta_0}{\epsilon_1^{1/2}} \tag{4.47}$$

g, or ϵ_2, may be regarded as a property of the medium which may vary from place to place in the same way as the real dielectric constant. An actual optical gain equal to the full value of g will, of course, only be observed if g is constant over a large enough region for a plane wave to be excited within it. In a guiding situation a guided wave gain g_z will be observed which is less than the maximum value of g and which, as we will show below, is related to g in an analogous way to that in which the guide wavelength is related to the plane wavelength.

4.2.2   Transverse Optical Field Distribution

To evaluate the optical distribution of the guided wave it is necessary to start with the appropriate form of Maxwell's wave equations that takes account of the continuous variation of the properties of the medium. For the analysis we take the x axis as the transverse direction in the plane of the junction and the z axis as the propagation direction. We consider the case where a heterostructure is present for confining the wave in the y direction. The polarization of the wave is determined by the geometry of the heterostructure, which in general requires that transverse E is in the x direction and transverse H in the y direction. For analysis of guiding in the x/z plane this polarization leads to the more unwieldy equations, in the same way as does the polarization associated with the TM waves in the treatment of the previous section. In this situation the exact form of

Maxwell's equations for, say, $\mathbf{H}_y$ in a region of varying ϵ, with $\mathbf{H}_y$ being the only transverse component of $\mathbf{H}$, is[2]

$$\nabla^2\mathbf{H}_y + \left(\frac{\text{grad }\epsilon}{\epsilon}\right) \times \text{curl }\mathbf{H}_y + \beta_0^2\epsilon\mathbf{H}_y = 0 \tag{4.48}$$

In weakly guiding structures (i.e. in stripe lasers of normal width) grad ϵ/ϵ may be ignored. The equations then become as simple as for the other polarization with E_y as the only transverse component of the electric field. With this approximation and for variation of ϵ only in the x direction the above equation becomes

$$-\frac{\partial^2 H_y}{\partial x^2} = \{\epsilon(x)\beta_0^2 - \beta_z^2\}H_y \tag{4.49}$$

where the variation of H_y in the z direction is of the normal sinusoidal type described by the propagation coefficient β_z. To indicate the equivalence of this equation to the similar equation (4.7) for the abrupt guide we can introduce a complex quantity q given by

$$q^2 = \epsilon(x)\beta_0^2 - \beta_z^2 \tag{4.50}$$

where q is now a function of x.

We show in Appendix 2 that we can approximately take into account the variations of ϵ in the y direction associated with the heterostructure guide by substituting the effective dielectric constant of the guided wave $\epsilon_{\text{eff}}(x)$, as given in equation (4.18), for $\epsilon(x)$ in equation (4.50). This is a good approximation when the guiding in the x direction is relatively weak. We also show in Appendix 2 that the real and imaginary variations of $\epsilon_{\text{eff}}(x)$ with respect to x follow those of ϵ with respect to x in the centre layer, but reduced by the confinement factor Γ [originally derived for gain in equation (4.28)]. We then have

$$-\frac{\partial^2 H_y}{\partial x^2} = q^2 H_y$$

$$q^2 = \epsilon_{\text{eff}}(x)\beta_0^2 - \beta_z^2 \tag{4.51}$$

Equation (4.51) can only be solved exactly for certain forms of the distribution of $\epsilon_{\text{eff}}(x)$ and hence of the function $q^2(x)$, although approximate solutions can be obtained for all forms of the distribution using the WKB method. There are two particularly convenient soluble forms of the function $q^2(x)$ which closely represent the situation in stripe lasers in appropriate conditions. The first is an inverted parabola and the second has the form $\cosh^{-2}$. The distributions are illustrated in Figure 4.21 where $\epsilon_{\text{eff}}\beta_0^2 (= q^2 + \beta_z^2)$ is plotted against x.

The parabolic distribution has been treated by Cook and Nash[13] and

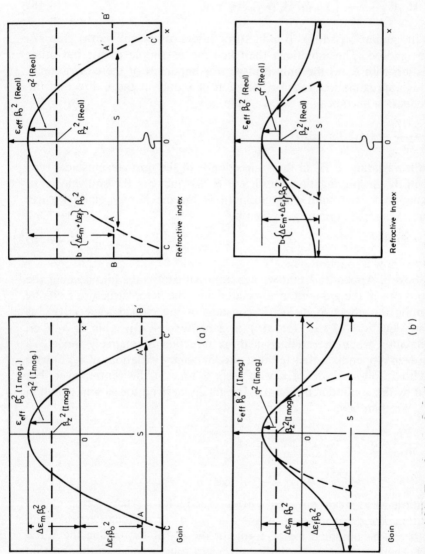

Figure 4.21 Two forms of continuous transverse distribution of dielectric constant for which exact mathematical solutions of the guided optical distribution may be found. (a) parabolic distribution, (b) $\cosh^{-1}$ distribution. Left-hand diagrams represent gain, right-hand diagrams dielectric constant

Hakki.[14] For this distribution q^2 must be expressible in the form appropriate to give the Hermite–Gaussian differential equation, as follows

$$q^2 = (a(2n + 1) - a^2x^2) \tag{4.52}$$

where a $(= a_1 + ja_2)$ is any real or complex quantity (for a localized solution a_1 must be positive), and n is the order of the transverse mode. With this substitution equation (4.51) gives Hermite–Gaussian solutions for H_y. The zero-order solution, for instance, is

$$H_y = H_{y0} \exp\left(\frac{-ax^2}{2}\right) \tag{4.53}$$

where H_{y0} is a constant; a is found by matching equation (4.50) to equation (4.52). This is only possible for some specific value of complex β_z^2.

The x variation of the complex dielectric constant required to fit this solution is illustrated in Figure 4.21(a) and is of the general form

$$\epsilon_{\text{eff}}(x) = \epsilon_1 + j\Delta\epsilon_m - (\Delta\epsilon_m + \Delta\epsilon_f)(b + j)\left(\frac{2x}{s}\right)^2 \tag{4.54}$$

b is the ratio of the real to the imaginary part of the x-dependent portion of the dielectric constant; $j\Delta\epsilon_m$ is the maximum value of the imaginary part; s is the width between the points at which the imaginary part has a value of $-\Delta\epsilon_f$; and $\Delta\epsilon_f$ may be defined arbitrarily. For a normal inverted parabolic distribution of gain $\Delta\epsilon_f$ can conveniently be taken as approximately equivalent to the loss of the unpumped laser, so that s has a value reasonably close to the width of the stripe. (It should be noted, however, that the analysis could be performed equally well with $\Delta\epsilon_f$ zero, in which case s would be the width over which the gain is positive. $\Delta\epsilon_f$ may therefore be considered as a parameter which determines the definition of s.) Under certain circumstances a non-inverted parabolic distribution of gain can occur over a limited width. This is associated with a dip being formed in the centre of the gain distribution as a result of a high local rate of stimulated emission ('hole-burning', see Chapter 6, Section 6.4.2 on self-focusing). Under such circumstances $\Delta\epsilon_f$ must be taken as negative and less than $-\Delta\epsilon_m$.

As an example we could consider the actual distribution of complex dielectric constant in a laser to be approximated by the inverted parabolic curves AA' in Figure 4.21(a) truncated by the limits of maximum absorption given by the horizontal lines AB and $A'B'$. The width s between the truncated corners is then related to the stripe width (the relation to stripe width is however not simple and is treated in detail in Chapter 6, Section 6.3). It should be noted that in the derivation of the optical distribution the parabolic distribution of dielectric constant is implicitly assumed to continue beyond the points A and A'. This discrepancy can be ignored when the optical distribution is tightly confined in the centre of the parabolic distribution and little optical field extends to the points A and A'. However, when the effective width of the optical distribution becomes greater than the distance AA' $(= s)$ the treatment is no longer satisfactory.

The alternative form for the x variation of q^2 as a $\cosh^{-2}$ function becomes useful in circumstances where the light extends more widely beyond A and A' and the saturation of the absorption at the edges of the distribution must be taken into account. The $\cosh^{-2}$ function gives a better description of this situation than does the parabolic function. The $\cosh^{-2}$ distribution has been treated by Unger.[15] To give an exact solution to equation (4.51) the $\cosh^{-2}$ term must be introduced into the expression for q^2 as follows

$$q^2 = \left(\frac{2}{s}\right)^2 \left(\frac{(u + n)(u + n + 1)}{\cosh^2(2x/s)} - u^2\right) \tag{4.55}$$

This expression applies to the nth-order transverse mode. s is the effective width of the distribution as illustrated in Figure 4.21(b) and u is any complex quantity $u_1 + ju_2$ with a positive real part. The solutions for H_y in the zero- and first-order modes are

$$\begin{aligned} H_y &= H_{y0} \cosh^{-u}\left(\frac{2x}{s}\right), & \text{for } n = 0 \\ H_y &= H_{y0} \cosh^{-u}\left(\frac{2x}{s}\right) \tanh\left(\frac{2x}{s}\right), & \text{for } n = 1, \end{aligned} \tag{4.56}$$

where H_{y0} is an appropriate constant.

As in the previous case the parameters u_1 and u_2 are found by matching equation (4.50) to equation (4.55). This imposes a specific complex value on β_z. The x variation of the complex dielectric constant in equation (4.49) that is required to fit this solution is of the general form

$$\epsilon_{\text{eff}}(x) = \epsilon_1 - j\Delta\epsilon_f + \frac{(\Delta\epsilon_m + \Delta\epsilon_f)(b + j)}{\cosh^2(2x/s)} \tag{4.57}$$

This distribution, which is illustrated in Figure 4.21(b), also has a parabolic shape close to the centre, with a peak imaginary part of $j\Delta\epsilon_m$. At large distances from the centre the imaginary part tends exponentially to $-j\Delta\epsilon_f$ with a decay constant $s/4$. This treatment can be applied particularly to stripes less than four diffusion lengths wide, although the distribution at the centre only approximates to the true distribution.

4.2.3 Analysis of Guide with Parabolic Dielectric Profile

4.2.3.1 Effective Width, Phase Front, and Beam Angle

We now treat in more detail the waveguide behaviour which results from a parabolic distribution of the complex dielectric constant. As stated above the optical distribution in the zero-order mode is of the form $\exp(-(a_1 + ja_2)x^2/2)$. Before solving for a_1 and a_2 let us consider their physical meaning.

a_1 determines the width of the Gaussian distribution. We define an effective width s_{eff} which is the distance between the points where the intensity drops to $1/e^2$ of its maximum value (the field drops to $1/e$). s_{eff} is given by

$$s_{eff} = \left(\frac{8}{a_1}\right)^{1/2} \tag{4.58}$$

The imaginary part of the exponent in the Gaussian distribution represents a relative phase delay of $a_2 x^2/2$ radians. This is parabolic with x and approximately describes a cylindical wavefront. It is convex along the propagation direction when a_2 is positive. The radius of curvature R_{int} within the waveguide is given by

$$R_{int} = \frac{\epsilon_1^{1/2}\beta_0}{a_2} \tag{4.59}$$

and the radius of curvature immediately outside the end-face of the laser is given by

$$R = \frac{\beta_0}{a_2} \tag{4.60}$$

The combination of a Gaussian intensity distribution and a cylindrical wavefront in the plane of the junction produces a Gaussian emitted beam which diverges in the far field to a greater extent than would be the case if the wavefront in the laser were plane. When a_2 is positive the beam appears to an external observer to be originating from a virtual source in the junction plane within the laser, displaced some distance z_f behind the emitting face. When a_2 is negative, as can occur in a self-focused situation (see Section 6.3.2), the beam contracts to a real source in front of the emitting face. However, in the perpendicular plane the beam emerges in both cases with a plane wavefront from the heterostructure and the waist of the near-Gaussian beam that is produced is coincident with the end-face of the laser. Hence the overall beam is astigmatic and cannot be perfectly focused using a spherical lens.

Cook and Nash[13] derive a quantitative relation between the curvature of the wavefront and the increased divergence of the emitted beam in the plane of the junction. The derivation is based only on the properties of a diffraction-limited Gaussian beam in the region of space outside the laser. The far-field beam angle θ (half angle measured to $1/e^2$ of peak intensity) is found to be related to the radius of curvature R of the wavefront emerging from the laser and its effective width s_{eff} by

$$\tan \theta = \frac{2\lambda_0}{\pi w_0}$$

$$= \tan \theta_0 \left(\left(\frac{\pi s_{eff}^2}{4R\lambda_0} \right)^2 + 1 \right)^{1/2} \tag{4.61}$$

where

$$\tan \theta_0 = \frac{2\lambda_0}{\pi s_{eff}} \tag{4.62}$$

θ_0 and w_0 are respectively the equivalent beam angle and the equivalent width that would be deduced from the actual values of w and θ if the laser were emitting a plane wavefront. Thus, θ_0 is the far-field beam angle produced by a plane distribution of width s_{eff}, w_0 is the width of a plane distribution that would give the observed far-field angle θ, and is also the width of the virtual source within the laser. Note that

$$\frac{s_{eff}}{w_0} = \frac{\tan \theta}{\tan \theta_0} \tag{4.63}$$

Using equations (4.58) and (4.59) we can express equation (4.61) for the beam angle simply in terms of a_1 and a_2 as follows

$$\frac{\tan \theta}{\tan \theta_0} = \frac{s_{eff}}{w_0} = \left(\left(\frac{a_2}{a_1} \right)^2 + 1 \right)^{1/2} \tag{4.64}$$

The distance z_f of the virtual source from the end-face of the laser is given by

$$z_f = \left(\frac{\pi s_{eff}^2}{4\lambda_0} \right) \bigg/ \left(\frac{a_2}{a_1} + \frac{a_1}{a_2} \right) \tag{4.65}$$

4.2.3.2 Determination of Parameters a_1 and a_2

We now consider how a_1 and a_2 depend on the width s and the magnitude $(\Delta\epsilon_m + \Delta\epsilon_f)$ of the complex dielectric constant distribution given in equation (4.54). Solutions for a are obtained by inserting equation (4.54) into equation (4.51) and matching the result to equation (4.52). A solution for the longitudinal propagation coefficient β_z is also obtained. For the analysis of an actual laser the initial data does not consist of a prescribed distribution of the dielectric constant and local gain but a prescribed value for the average effective optical gain of the guided wave, i.e. the gain necessary to overcome the losses and to reach threshold. We call this gain g_z. The propagation coefficient of the guided wave is complex and with the above contribution of mode gain can be represented by

$$\beta_z = \beta_{z1} + \frac{jg_z}{2} \tag{4.66}$$

where β_{z1} is some real component. To employ a more consistent notation we define an effective complex dielectric constant $\epsilon_z + j\Delta\epsilon_z$ to describe the wavelength and gain of the guided wave, given by

$$\beta_0^2(\epsilon_z + j\Delta\epsilon_z) = \left(\beta_{z1} + \frac{jg_z}{2}\right)^2 \tag{4.67}$$

Equating the various similar real and imaginary terms between equations (4.52) and (4.51), with (4.54) substituted gives

$$a_1 a_2 = \frac{2\beta_0^2(\Delta\epsilon_m + \Delta\epsilon_f)}{s^2} \tag{4.68}$$

$$a_1^2 - a_2^2 = \frac{4\beta_0^2 b(\Delta\epsilon_m + \Delta\epsilon_f)}{s^2} \quad (=2ba_1a_2) \tag{4.69}$$

$$(2n + 1)a_2 = \beta_0^2(\Delta\epsilon_m - \Delta\epsilon_z) \tag{4.70}$$

where n is the transverse mode number. Equations (4.69) and (4.68) can be solved for the ratio a_2/a_1, giving

$$\frac{a_2}{a_1} = \pm(b^2 + 1)^{1/2} - b \tag{4.71}$$

Before proceeding further with the solution we simplify the equations by introducing a characteristic width s_0, related to the threshold gain g_z as follows

$$s_0 = \frac{1}{\beta_0 \Delta\epsilon_z^{1/2}} = \frac{1}{\beta_0^{1/2} g_z^{1/2} \epsilon_1^{1/4}} \tag{4.72}$$

and a quantity B^2 given by

$$B^2 = \frac{a_2}{a_1} = \pm(b^2 + 1)^{1/2} - b \tag{4.73}$$

The characteristic width s_0 in a typical laser (length, say 300 μm with $g_z \approx 38$ cm^{-1}) is about 3.2 μm and varies as the square root of the length of the laser. Under normal conditions where the gain peaks at the centre the value of the quantity B covers the range from zero, when the real part of the dielectric constant predominates completely in creating the waveguide ($b = \infty$), through unity when the dielectric constant makes no contribution and only gain-guiding is present, up to high positive values as the distribution of real dielectric constant is inverted and an 'antiguide' is created (b negative). Under conditions where the gain has a minimum at the centre of the guide and the dielectric constant has a maximum (as occurs in a self-focused condition with b negative, see Chapter 6, Section 6.4.2.) then B^2 is negative and lies between zero and -1. $\Delta\epsilon_f$, which describes the optical losses in the unpumped part of the active region, cannot be expected to remain constant irrespective of variations in the average and peak gain of the laser. The wavelength of the peak gain decreases as the peak gain increases and the absorption of the unpumped region increases as the wavelength decreases. The result is that an increase in $\Delta\epsilon_m$ causes an increase in $\Delta\epsilon_f$. As a first approximation we take the two as being proportional to one another and introduce a quantity F given by

$$F = \frac{\Delta\epsilon_f}{\Delta\epsilon_m} + 1 \tag{4.74}$$

which we expect to remain reasonably constant as stripe width and laser length is altered.

After eliminating $\Delta\epsilon_m$ between equations (4.68) and (4.70), using equation (4.71) to eliminate a_2, and substituting the three new quantities into equations (4.72), (4.73), and (4.74), we obtain the following equation which represents a quadratic in a_1

$$s^2 = 2F\left[\frac{(2n+1)}{a_1} + \frac{1}{(Bs_0a_1)^2}\right] \tag{4.75}$$

This equation and (4.71) give the following solutions for a_1 and a_2,

$$a_1 = (2n+1)|F|\,\frac{\left\{1 + \dfrac{2}{|F|}\left(\dfrac{s}{|B|\,s_0(2n+1)}\right)^2\right\}^{1/2} \pm 1}{s^2} \tag{4.76}$$

$$a_2 = \pm\,|B|^2 a_1$$

where the negative signs of the alternative pairs are used when the gain has a minimum at the centre of the guide rather than the more normal maximum.

Using equation (4.76) we may now evaluate the width of the optical filament, the angular divergence of the emitted beam, and the position of the virtual source of the emitted beam, which have been derived in the previous section, in terms of a_1 and a_2, and in terms of the characteristics of the complex dielectric waveguide, e.g. s, F, s_0, and b.

4.2.3.3   Effective Width of Optical Distribution

First let us consider the transverse spread of the optical distribution characterized by its effective width s_{eff} to the points of $1/e^2$ relative intensity. This depends on $a_1^{-1/2}$ and is given for the zero-order ($n = 0$) mode in equation (4.58). For expressing the relation between s, s_{eff}, and various other quantities it is convenient to normalize widths to $(2n + 1)|B|s_0$. We therefore define a normalized width S of the gain distribution and a normalized width S_{eff} of the optical distribution given by

$$S = \frac{s}{(2n + 1)|B|s_0}$$

$$S_{eff} = \frac{s_{eff}}{(2n + 1)|B|s_0}$$

(4.77)

(Note that S_{eff} has a somewhat different interpretation for higher order modes where $n \neq 0$.) According to equations (4.76) and (4.58) S_{eff} is given by

$$S_{eff} = \left[\frac{8S^2}{|F| \left\{ \left(1 + \frac{2S^2}{|F|} \right)^{1/2} \pm 1 \right\}} \right]^{1/2}$$

(4.78)

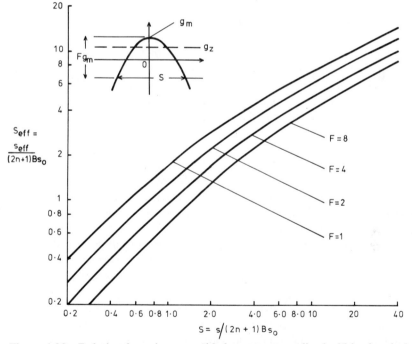

Figure 4.22 Relation for gain-waveguide between normalized width of optical distribution and normalized width of gain distribution for various proportional amounts $(F - 1)$ of optical loss at edge. of pumped region. Parabolic distribution of dielectric constant and gain with gain peaking at centre

where the negative sign of the alternative pair is used when the gain has a minimum at the centre of the guide (B^2 and F negative). Figure 4.22 shows curves of S_{eff} against S for various values of F according to this relation.

Let us consider the curve in Figure 4.22 for $F = 1$. The value of S concerned is the width between the points of zero optical gain. For $S < 1$ ($s < |B|s_0$) the effective normalized width S_{eff} of the optical distribution is larger than the width S of positive optical gain and decreases approximately linearly with S, tending to a value of $2S$ when S is small. For S greater than unity S_{eff} increases approximately as $S^{1/2}$ and becomes less than S for $S > 5$. In the latter range of S no appreciable part of the optical distribution extends to a width beyond S and into the optically lossy part of the gain distribution. At the opposite extreme of low S the optical distribution extends into the lossy wings of the gain distribution to such an extent that the gain derived from the centre region is almost entirely cancelled by the losses at the edges.

The curves in Figure 4.22 for values of F greater than unity show how the width of the filament is related to the width of the stripe when the condition at the two edges of the stripe is not one of zero gain but one of considerable optical loss. The effect of increasing the value of F is to increase the stripe width for given optical filament width in proportion to $F^{1/2}$. This follows from the assumed parabolic distribution of the gain. In fact the gain distribution in stripe lasers, which arises from the effect of current spreading and transverse diffusion on the injected carrier distribution in the active layer, is not parabolic except in the centre of the distribution. The way this affects the filament width is treated in more detail in Chapter 6 on stripe lasers, Sections 6.3 and 6.5.

4.2.3.4 *Peak Gain and Net Positive Gain*

We now consider the amount by which the optical gain varies over the width of the filament, particularly in conditions designed to produce a narrow filament. This is interesting from the point of view of both threshold current and incremental efficiency.

Consider first the effect of the gain distribution on the threshold current under conditions where the optical filament is narrow. To produce a narrow filament the gain at the centre of the stripe must be high and be closely flanked by high loss. With decreasing width of the filament still more gain is needed at the centre and the higher current density required eventually more than compensates the effect of the diminishing width of the stripe and causes the threshold current to pass through a minimum and then to start increasing again.

Secondly, consider the effect of the gain distribution on incremental efficiency. As the stripe width and the filament width are reduced the light spreads more strongly into the optically lossy outer regions. This increases the optical absorption loss and decreases the efficiency.

As the first step to analysing the above effects we investigate how the width of the optical filament is related to the excess gain supplied at the centre of the stripe and derive the associated gain profile.

Consider the ratio of the peak gain g_m at the centre of the stripe waveguide to the mode gain g_z of the guided wave. This gives a measure of the excess drive required to reach threshold compared with an infinitely wide device. The ratio can be obtained from equation (4.70), and substituting the symbols defined in equations (4.72) and (4.73) is given in terms of a_1 by

$$\frac{g_m}{g_z} = \frac{\Delta\epsilon_m}{\Delta\epsilon_z} = B^2(2n + 1)a_1 s_0^2 + 1 \tag{4.79}$$

Using equation (4.58) to express a_1 in terms of the optical width, or using equation (4.77) to express it in terms of the normalized optical width, gives the following two alternative simple expressions for g_m in the zero-order mode

$$g_m = g_z + \frac{8B^2}{\beta_0\epsilon_1^{1/2}s_{\text{eff}}^2}$$
$$= g_z\left(1 \pm \frac{8}{S_{\text{eff}}^2}\right) \tag{4.80}$$

where the negative sign of the alternative pair applies if the gain has a minimum at the centre of the stripe rather than its normal maximum.

The gain distribution that accompanies this condition, according to equations (4.54) and (4.68), is given by

$$g = \frac{g_z(\Delta\epsilon_m - 2B^2a_1^2x^2/\beta_0^2)}{\Delta\epsilon_z} \tag{4.81}$$

Using equation (4.58) to express a_1 in terms of the optical width, or using equation (4.77) to express it in terms of the normalized optical width, gives the following two alternative expressions for the gain distribution

$$g = g_z + \left(\frac{8B^2}{\beta_0\epsilon_1^{1/2}}\right)\left\{s_{\text{eff}}^{-2} - 16\left(\frac{x}{s_{\text{eff}}^2}\right)^2\right\}$$
$$= g_z\left\{1 \pm \left(\frac{8}{S_{\text{eff}}^2} - \frac{128X^2}{S_{\text{eff}}^4}\right)\right\} \tag{4.82}$$

where the negative sign of the alternative pair applies if the gain has a minimum at the centre of the stripe and where $X = x/|B|s_0$ is the normalized distance from the centre line.

The mode gain g_z of the guided wave is given by the integral over the transverse direction x of the product of the gain distribution given in equation (4.82) with the optical intensity distribution as derived from the Gaussian field distribution of equation (4.53). When B^2 is positive (gain peaking at the centre of the stripe) there is a positive and a negative contribution to this integral, the latter arising because the optical distribution extends into the region of optical loss. It is of interest to find the ratio of the total net gain (positive plus negative) to the positive part, since this indicates the proportion of the optical gain supplied by the medium which is used in amplifying the guided wave as opposed to counteracting the absorption in the adjacent optically lossy regions and can be used to derive the incremental efficiency.

Using equations (4.82) and (4.53) for the gain and optical distributions, respectively, we find that the net gain g_+ contributed to the guided wave over the region where the gain is positive is given by

$$g_+ = g_z \int_0^{[(1+\alpha^2)/2\alpha^2]^{1/2}} (1 + \alpha^2 - 2\alpha^2 y^2)\exp(-y^2)\mathrm{d}y \Big/ \int_0^\infty \exp(-y^2)\mathrm{d}y \qquad (4.83)$$

where $\alpha^2 = 8/S_{\mathrm{eff}}^2$ and $y = \alpha X$. Integrating gives

$$g_+ = g_z \left[\mathrm{erf}\left\{ \frac{(1 + S_{\mathrm{eff}}^2/8)^{1/2}}{2} \right\}^{1/2} + \left\{ \frac{4(1 + 8/S_{\mathrm{eff}}^2)^{1/2}}{\pi^{1/2} S_{\mathrm{eff}}} \right\} \exp \left\{ -\frac{1}{2}\left(1 + \frac{S_{\mathrm{eff}}^2}{8} \right) \right\} \right]$$

$$(4.84)$$

The net gain g_- (negative) contributed over the region of the optical distribution where the gain is negative can also be found by integration. More simply we may find it from the following relation

$$g_- = -(g_+ - g_z) \qquad (4.85)$$

In Figure 4.23 we show plots of g_m/g_z and g_+/g_z against S_{eff}. These two curves apply to the zero-order mode for the situation where the gain peaks at the guide centre. As a result of the normalization that we have adopted for the effective optical width in terms of $|B|S_0$ there are no variable parameters connected with either the proportion of real dielectric guiding or the average mode gain.

The curve for g_m/g_z shows how the peak threshold gain increases for lasers of given length as the width is narrowed. g_m/g_z is approximately unity when S_{eff} is large and does not increase appreciably above this value until S_{eff} is reduced below about 10. It rises to a value of 2 at $S_{\mathrm{eff}} = 2.8$, and then increases rapidly with further reduction in S_{eff}, varying in this region approximately as S_{eff}^{-2}.

Large values of g_m/g_z obviously cause an increase in the threshold current density of the laser for the filament width concerned. This effect

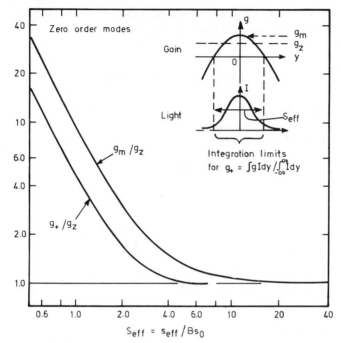

Figure 4.23 (Peak gain)/(average gain) and (net positive gain)/(average gain) for gain-waveguide as a function of normalized optical width. Parabolic distribution of dielectric constant

starts to become important when S_{eff} is less than 3. For typical values of B of around 1.5 and of s_0 of around 3.2 μm this corresponds to stripe widths of around 15 μm or less. The precise amount by which the threshold current density is increased depends also on (a) the relation between the gain and the injected carrier concentration and (b) the way the current spreads in a stripe laser between the contact and the active layer, and the particular form of transverse distribution of injected carriers that results. This behaviour is treated in detail in Chapter 6, Section 6.5.

g_+/g_z shows a dependence on S_{eff} which is generally similar to that of g_m/g_z but which is displaced by a factor of around 1.6 to lower values of S_{eff}. Hence S_{eff} can be reduced to about 1.8 before more than half the gain provided by the positive part of the gain distribution is used in counteracting the losses in the negative part of the distribution. The value of g_+/g_z is of interest not only in evaluating the external efficiency of the laser but also, as will be indicated in Section 7.4, in predicting its stability. Thus, for g_+/g_z large considerable optical power interacts with optically lossy regions of the laser. Optical pumping can take place and the gain

distribution becomes subject to the optical intensity. Hence positive
feedback effects may occur and instabilities arise.

The above results show that both the threshold current density and the
gain/loss ratio are determined by the ratio of the stripe width to the
normalization length Bs_0. The normalization length is in turn proportional to
$g_z^{-1/2}$. It is also, via B, a function of b, and in the vicinity of $b = 0$ varies
approximately as $(1 - b/2)$. Shortening the laser increases the value of g_z
and allows a given performance to be achieved with a narrower stripe.
However, the amount of real dielectric guiding has a more significant effect
on the behaviour. Positive dielectric guiding (b positive) rapidly improves
the performance of a narrow stripe and negative dielectric guiding has the
reverse effect.

4.2.3.5   Empirical Analysis of Waveguide Characteristics

The equations that we have presented can be used as a means of analysing
the behaviour of given stripe lasers and, in particular, of deriving the
relative contributions of real dielectric guiding and gain guiding from
appropriate measurements of the laser characteristics. Let us consider an
analysis of the type originally performed by Cook and Nash.[13] The
measurements required on the laser are the near-field width s_{eff}, the beam
divergence θ or the virtual width w_0 of the beam waist, and an estimate of
the characteristic length s_0. The latter can be obtained from equation
(4.72) taking the value of the mode gain g_z as $\ln(1/R)/L$. B may be
obtained from s_{eff} and w_0 or s_{eff} and $\tan \theta$ using the relation

$$B^2 = \pm \left(\left(\frac{s_{\text{eff}}}{w_0} \right)^2 - 1 \right)^{1/2} \tag{4.86}$$

$$= \pm \left(\left(\frac{\pi s_{\text{eff}} \tan \theta}{2\lambda} \right)^2 - 1 \right)^{1/2} \tag{4.87}$$

[see equation (4.64)] where the negative sign applies if the waist w_0 is
outside rather than inside the output face of the laser. The normalized width
S_{eff} of the optical distribution, as defined in equation (4.77), may then be
found using the known values of B and s_0. This allows the peak to average
gain ratio g_m/g_z and the gain to loss ratio g_+/g_- to be obtained, as given in
equations (4.80), (4.84), and (4.85) and plotted in Figure 4.22. Similarly,
the precise scale of the total transverse distribution of gain as given in
equation (4.82) can be found. To obtain the transverse distribution of the
real component of the dielectric constant from the gain distribution we use
the relation of equation (4.47) to convert gain to the imaginary component
of dielectric constant and multiply by b, where b is given in terms of B, using

equation (4.73), by

$$b = \frac{1 - B^4}{2B^2} \tag{4.88}$$

The distribution of the perturbation $\Delta\epsilon_1$ in the real component of effective dielectric constant is therefore given by

$$\Delta\epsilon_1 = \frac{b}{\beta_0^2 s_0^2}\left(1 + \frac{8B^2 s_0^2}{s_{\text{eff}}^2} - \frac{128x^2 B^2 s_0^2}{s_{\text{eff}}^4}\right) \tag{4.89}$$

4.2.4 Analysis of Guide with $\cosh^{-2}$ Dielectric Profile

We now consider the way the waveguide behaviour is altered if the transverse distribution of the dielectric constant is assumed to vary as $\cosh^{-2}(ax)$ rather than as x^2. This is a bounded distribution which flattens out at large distances from the centre line. Although the $\cosh^{-2}$ form is only one of many alternative forms of bounded distribution it is useful to consider (a) because it can be solved exactly, (b) because it approximates to the quadratic distribution for extreme values of the parameters, and (c) because it gives a good general indication of the effect of a bounded rather than an unbounded distribution.

4.2.4.1 Optical Distribution and Phase Front

The distribution of the optical field in the zero-order mode which results from the $\cosh^{-2}(2x/s)$ distribution of dielectric constant is, as given in equation (4.56), of the form $\cosh^{-(u_1 + ju_2)}(2x/s)$. As before let us consider the physical meaning of u_1 and u_2 before seeking solutions.

The expression for the optical distribution in equation (4.56) can be split up into its amplitude and phase components by writing it as follows

$$H_y = H_{y0}\cosh^{-u_1}\left(\frac{2x}{s}\right)\exp\left[-ju_2 \ln\left\{\cosh\left(\frac{2x}{s}\right)\right\}\right] \tag{4.90}$$

The amplitude distribution is therefore described by the function $\cosh^{-u_1}(2x/s)$ and the phase distribution by $-ju_2 \ln\{\cosh(2x/s)\}$.

Figure 4.24 illustrates the way the shape of the optical distribution changes as u_1 is varied. To make comparison easier s is chosen in each case to keep the effective width constant. For large u_1 (e.g. $u_1 > 10$) the shape is almost Gaussian as for a parabolic distribution of gain and the behaviour is in all respects very similar to that for the parabolic distribution. For small u_1 (e.g. $u_1 < 0.1$) the shape is close to that of a double exponential.

The effective width s_{eff} to the $1/e$ points of the amplitude distribution

$(1/e^2$ of the intensity) is given by

$$
\left.
\begin{aligned}
s_{\text{eff}} &= s \cosh^{-1}\left\{\exp\left(\frac{1}{u_1}\right)\right\} \\
&\to s\left(\frac{2}{u_1}\right)^{1/2}, \qquad \text{for } u_1 > 5 \\
&\to s(u_1^{-1} + \ln 2), \quad \text{for } u_1 < 0.5
\end{aligned}
\right\} \tag{4.91}
$$

The phase variation ϕ across the optical distribution is illustrated in Figure 4.25, where ϕ/u_2 is plotted against $2x/s$. In the centre region of x the phase variation is parabolic, as it is for the parabolic distribution of gain. However, for values of x/s greater than one-half, the variation of ϕ with x becomes more linear, the relation approaching the form of $\phi = -2u_2x/s$ for large x/s. This change in the shape of the wavefront affects the behaviour to a significant extent only if the transverse amplitude distribution is wide enough for an appreciable amplitude of optical field to remain in the region where the phase becomes linear. According to equation (4.91) this applies if u_1 is less than about 2. When u_1 is small enough (e.g. <0.5) the transverse distribution approximates to the form $\exp\{\pm(u_1 + ju_2)2x/s\}$ which consists of a vee-shaped wavefront (bow wave) falling exponentially away in amplitude in both arms from the centre of the vee.

4.2.4.2   Shape of Far-Field Distribution

The far-field beam angle of the radiated wave emitted from a laser with a $\cosh^{-2}$ profile of gain is not, in general, so simply related to the near-field pattern at the exit face as in the case of the parabolic profile of gain. However, when u_1 for the $\cosh^{-2}$ profile is large the behaviour in the two cases is very similar. The distributions of both the near- and far-fields for the $\cosh^{-2}$ gain profile then approximate very closely to the Gaussian form for the parabolic gain profile. Equation (4.91) for the effective width s_{eff} of the optical distribution in the near field when u_1 is large is exactly the equivalent of equation (4.58) for the optical width with a parabolic gain profile [$4u_1/s^2$ in (4.91) transforms to a_1 in (4.58)]. Similarly equation (4.64) for obtaining $\tan\theta$ in the far field for the parabolic gain profile can be adapted to the $\cosh^{-2}$ gain profile when u_1 is large by substituting u_2/u_1 for a_2/a_1.

As u_1 becomes smaller the analysis for the two cases becomes different. In general the Fourier transform for obtaining the far field in the case of the $\cosh^{-2}$ gain profile must be individually computed for every combination of u_1 and u_2. However, for u_1 very small the alternative exponential approximation for the near field, as given above, may be used,

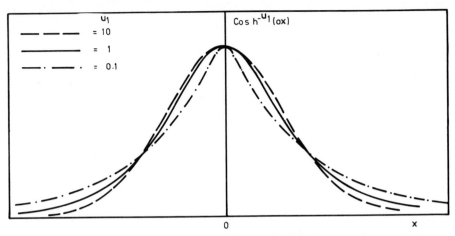

Figure 4.24 Range of shapes taken by distribution of optical field in gain-waveguide for $\cosh^{-2}$ distribution of dielectric constant

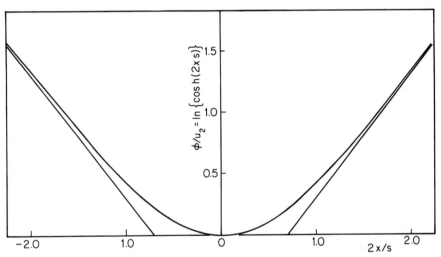

Figure 4.25 Shape of phase front for wave guided by $\cosh^{-2}$ distribution of gain and dielectric constant

and it is possible to obtain a simple result. The far-field pattern produced by this near-field distribution has, in general, two peaks symmetrically spaced about a central minimum. The far-field intensity $I(\theta)$ varies with $\sin \theta$ in the following way

$$I(\theta) = \left[\left\{ \frac{u_1}{u_2} + \left[\left(\frac{\sin \theta}{\sin \theta_0} \right)^2 - 1 \right] \frac{u_2}{u_1} \right\}^2 + 1 \right]^{-1} \tag{4.92}$$

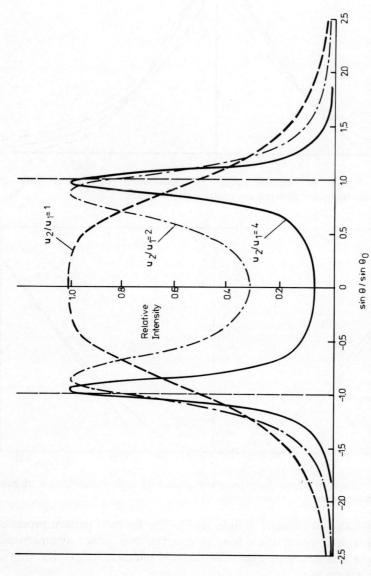

Figure 4.26 Approximate representation of twin-lobed far-field pattern of narrow gain-waveguide for various values of defocusing parameter u_2/u_1

where

$$\sin \theta_0 = \frac{2u_2}{\beta_0 s} \qquad (4.93)$$

Curves of $I(\theta)$ versus $\sin \theta / \sin \theta_0$ for $u_2/u_1 = 1$, 2, and 4 are given in Figure 4.26. For u_2/u_1 greater than unity the far-field pattern has a minimum along the axial direction, flanked by two peaks at angles to the axis lying close to $\pm\theta_0$. $\pm\theta_0$ correspond to the directions in which the two segments of the vee-shaped wavefront would emerge from the laser after refraction at the end-face and their magnitude is considered in more detail in Section 4.2.4.6. The results show, therefore, that provided the near-field distribution extends sufficiently along the two limbs of the vee (further when the vee is flatter) the two propagation directions of the vee are resolved in the far field. Increasing u_2/u_1, which is equivalent to increasing the width of the near-field distribution along the vee, increases the sharpness of the two peaks in the far field. Although the double-peaked shape is reminiscent of the far field of a first-order transverse mode the symmetry of the phase distribution is different, being symmetrical across the centre line rather than anti-symmetrical.

Computed Fourier transforms of the exact near-field distribution when u_1 is not small show that the double peaks are resolved, for $u_2 > u_1$, for values of u_1 up to about unity.

4.2.4.3   Determination of Parameters u_1 and u_2

We now consider how u_1 and u_2 depend on the width s of the distribution of gain, and the magnitude of the quantities $\Delta\epsilon_m$, $\Delta\epsilon_f$, $\Delta\epsilon_z$, and b. For convenience we put

$$\frac{\Delta\epsilon_m}{\Delta\epsilon_z} - 1 = h \qquad (4.94)$$

$$\frac{\Delta\epsilon_f}{\Delta\epsilon_m} + 1 = F \qquad (4.95)$$

and use the characteristic length s_0, as previously defined in equation (4.72) in terms of $\Delta\epsilon_z$. By analogy with the treatment for the parabolic distributions of gain we equate the various corresponding real and imaginary terms between equations (4.55) and (4.51) with (4.57) inserted. This gives

$$u_1 = \frac{(2n + 1)\{F(h + 1) - h\}}{2h} \qquad (4.96)$$

$$u_2 = \frac{[\pm\{b^2 + 1 - (2u_1 + 2n + 1)^{-2}\}^{1/2} - b](2u_1 + 2n + 1)}{2} \qquad (4.97)$$

where the negative alternative sign applies if there is a minimum of gain at the centre of the distribution and where h must satisfy the equation

$$\left(\frac{S_1}{2}\right)^4 h^4 + b\left(\frac{S_1}{2}\right)^2 Fh^3 + \left\{bF\left(\frac{S_1}{2}\right)^2 - \frac{(F^2-1)}{4} - \frac{n(n+1)}{(2n+1)^2}\right\}h^2 - \frac{F^2 h}{2}$$

$$-\frac{F^2}{4} = 0 \qquad\qquad\qquad (4.98)$$

and where S_1 measures the width of the $\cosh^{-2}$ distribution normalized to s_0 (not $|B|s_0$ as for S) given by

$$S_1 = \frac{s}{(2n+1)s_0} \qquad\qquad\qquad (4.99)$$

Equation (4.98) may alternatively be written as a relation for S_1^2 either in terms of h or in terms of u_2 and h as follows

$$S_1^2 = \frac{2F\left[\pm\left\{b^2 + 1 - \left(\frac{h}{F(h+1)(2n+1)}\right)^2\right\}^{1/2} - b\right](h+1)}{h^2} \qquad (4.100)$$

$$= \frac{4u_2}{(2n+1)h}$$

where the negative sign of the alternate pair applies if F is negative (a minimum of gain at the centre of the distribution).

The above equations have their analogues in the previous analysis for guides with a parabolic distribution of the dielectric constant. Equation (4.97) is the analogue of equation (4.71) and the two equations become identical as F (and hence u_1) tends to infinity. Bearing in mind that h and a_2 (or a_1) are closely related [e.g. substitute equation (4.94) into (4.70)] equation (4.100) can be seen to be the analogue of equation (4.75).

4.2.4.4   Effective Width of Optical Distribution

Let us consider how the $\cosh^{-2}$ gain profile alters the relationship between the widths of the gain profile and the width s_{eff} of the optical filament, as illustrated in Figure 4.22, for the parabolic profile. We will express the relationship in terms of the same quantities as previously, normalized to $|B|s_0$, namely S for the width of the gain profile and S_{eff} for the filament width. This normalization no longer gives completely generalized curves independent of B (or of b from which B is derived) because the analogue of B^2 in equation (4.97) depends slightly on the variables. However, it is still useful (a) because the curves are relatively insensitive to change of b, and (b) because it provides a direct comparison with the previous curves.

The new curves are plotted in Figure 4.27 for $b = -1$ and for various values of F. F is the quantity which determines the maximum amount of loss in the wings of the gain distribution as shown in the figure.

For wide gain distributions (S large) and for large values of F there is little difference between the filament width S_{eff} for the $\cosh^{-2}$ and for the parabolic gain profiles. This is because no appreciable optical intensity reaches the outer parts of the gain distribution where the $\cosh^{-2}$ function diverges significantly from a parabola. However, for normalized widths of the gain distribution less than 2 (e.g. < 10-μm stripe width) and for values of F less than 4 (optical loss at edge of stripe less than three times gain at centre) the two sets of curves for S_{eff} become appreciably different. The $\cosh^{-2}$ gain profile allows the optical filament to spread sideways considerably more than does the parabolic profile. This reaches an extreme for the case $F = 1$ which applies when there is no optical absorption in the region outside the stripe. The curve for $F = 1$ in Figure 4.27 shows that the corresponding width of the optical distribution is not only considerably

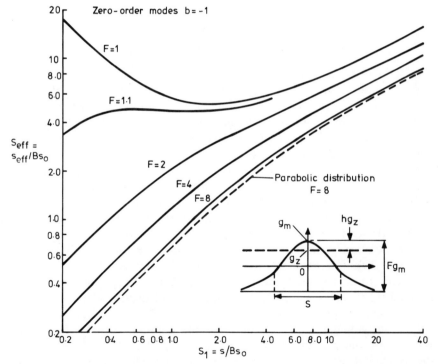

Figure 4.27 Relation between normalized width of optical distribution and normalized width of dielectric distribution in gain-waveguide for various proportional amounts $(F - 1)$ of optical loss at edge of pumped region. $\cosh^{-2}$ distribution of dielectric constant with one curve for parabolic distribution for comparison

greater than for the parabolic gain profile (see Figure 4.23) but also that after reaching a minimum for a value of S in the vicinity of unity (e.g. 5-μm stripe width) it increases rather than decreases as S is reduced below this value. This behaviour is reminiscent of that in a thin dielectric slab waveguide as the thickness is reduced, described in Section 4.1. However, it does not correspond to a condition that is likely to occur normally in lasers. The optical absorption in the outer regions of the average stripe laser is considerable, in general being greater than the gain in the central region (i.e. $F > 2$). Conditions may arise in certain circumstances with very high injected carrier concentration at the centre of the stripe, where the band-gap shrinks to such an extent that the quantum energy of the peak gain barely rises above the energy of the absorption edge in the outer regions. The losses at the edge can then be less than the gain at the centre. However, the losses must drop to less than 10 per cent of the gain at the centre $(F < 1.1)$ before the filament width will start expanding with decreasing stripe width. Thus, the curve for $F = 1.1$ in Figure 4.27 shows that the condition is only verging on expansion for as little as 10 per cent loss.

4.2.4.5 Ratio of Peak Gain to Average Gain

The ratio of peak gain to average gain for the $\cosh^{-2}$ gain profile has a dependence on the width of the gain profile and the width of the optical filament somewhat different from that for the parabolic profile. For a given width of the gain profile the peak gain at the centre of the $\cosh^{-2}$ profile is less than that for the parabolic profile as a result of its being required to compensate smaller optical losses in the wings of the distribution. For a given width of the optical filament the roles are reversed and the $\cosh^{-2}$ gain profile has the higher peak gain although the gain integrated over the width where it is positive is less because of the narrower gain distribution. The most convenient quantitative comparison between the peak gain for the two profiles is made in terms of the optical filament width, for which a simple relation has already been obtained for the parabolic profile (Figure 4.23). This comparison is illustrated in Figure 4.28 where g_m/g_z, as obtained from the analysis of Section 4.2.4.3, is plotted against the normalized filament width S_{eff} for both types of profile. Curves are shown for the $\cosh^{-2}$ profile for $b = -1$ and for $F = 1$, 1.1, 2, and 4, and compared with the universal curve for the parabolic profile. In the same way as for the relation between S_{eff} and S in Figure 4.27 there is little difference between the curves of g_m/g_z against S_{eff} for the two gain profiles provided that the optical distributions are wide and the loss in the wings of the distributions is large (large F). As before, the difference only becomes appreciable for $S < 2$ (<10-μm stripe width) and for F less than 4, and

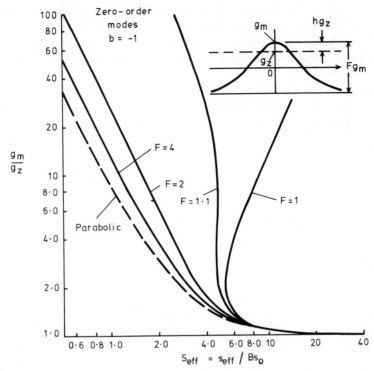

Figure 4.28 (Peak gain)/(average gain) as a function of normalized optical width in gain-waveguide for various proportional amounts of loss in unpumped region. $\cosh^{-2}$ distribution of dielectric constant with curve for parabolic distribution for comparison

again this reaches an extreme for $F = 1$. The latter characteristic is dual valued and a given filament width may be obtained either for a broad and low gain profile or for a narrow and peaked gain profile. However, as was discussed in Section 4.2.4.3, conditions where F is approximately unity are unlikely to be met in practice.

4.2.4.6 Lobes in Far-Field of Narrow Stripe Lasers

As described in Section 4.2.4.2, the far-field radiation pattern of narrow stripe lasers with a $\cosh^{-2}$ distribution of gain splits, under certain circumstances, into two separate lobes directed at equal angles on either side of the laser axis. An approximate relation for the angular distribution of the intensity is given in equation (4.92) expressed in terms of the parameter u_2/u_1 and of the angle θ_0 of the vee-shaped wavefront, itself related to u_2. Let us now consider this equation in more detail using the relations obtained in Section 4.2.4.3 for u_1 and u_2 in terms of the width s and the magnitude of the gain distribution within the laser. We will continue to use the normalized form S for the width of the gain distribution (normalized to Bs_0) since as in the other treatments this gives results which are relatively insensitive to changes in B (or b).

First let us consider the angle θ_0. We can make complete allowance for the way θ_0 varies with $\Delta\epsilon_z$ and partial allowance for the way it varies with B by expressing it in terms of a normalized quantity ϕ_0 given by

$$\phi_0 = \frac{\sin \theta_0}{B \Delta\epsilon_z^{1/2}} \tag{4.101}$$

We may then express ϕ_0 in terms of the normalized width S of the gain distribution, defined in the same way as for the parabolic distribution [$= s/Bs_0$, from equation (4.77) with $n = 0$], and the quantity u_2/B^2, using equation (4.93) for $\sin \theta_0$ and equation (4.72) for s_0, as follows

$$\phi_0 = \frac{2(u_2/B^2)}{S} \tag{4.102}$$

This is a useful form because u_2/B^2 depends predominantly on S and the derivative quantity h [defined in equation (4.94)] and barely at all on B. This can be seen by substituting $S_1^2 = B^2 S^2$ in the second version of equation (4.100) and also noting that unless u_1 is small equation (4.97) approximates to

$$\frac{u_2}{B^2} \simeq u_1 + n + \tfrac{1}{2} \tag{4.103}$$

from which it is apparent that to the degree of approximation concerned u_2 and B only appear in the conjunction u_2/B^2 and can be eliminated simultaneously.

Using equations (4.96), (4.97), and (4.98) [or (4.100)] ϕ_0 may be obtained exactly in terms of S and F with B as a relatively unimportant parameter, and hence, of course, θ_0 may also be obtained.

Before finding the way θ_0 depends on the variables, let us consider the circumstances that are necessary for the far field to exhibit twin peaks close to $\pm\theta_0$. According to Section 4.2.4.2, two conditions must be satisfied, namely $u_1 < 1$ and $u_2/u_1 > 1$.

The value of u_1 is determined mainly by F and S. Equation (4.96) shows that the minimum value of u_1, which occurs as h tends to infinity and S therefore tends to zero, is $(F - 1)/2$. Hence only if $F < 3$, i.e. if the losses at the edge of the distribution are less than twice the gain at the centre, can u_1 ever be less than unity. For $F < 3$ u_1 drops below unity as the width S of the gain distribution is reduced. According to equations (4.96), (4.97), and (4.100) the range of values of S for which u_1 is less than unity is given approximately by

$$S < \left[6\left(\frac{3}{F} - 1\right) \right]^{1/2} \tag{4.104}$$

Let us now consider the condition $u_2/u_1 > 1$. The value of u_2/u_1 is given, according to equation (4.97), approximately by

$$\frac{u_2}{u_1} \simeq B^2\left(1 + \frac{1}{2u_1}\right) \tag{4.105}$$

We are mainly concerned with circumstances where the dielectric constant distribution is either zero or produces an anti-guide. Under these conditions $B > 1$ and $u_2/u_1 > \frac{3}{2}$ when $u_1 < 1$. Hence when the first of the requisite conditions for a twin peak ($u_1 < 1$) is satisfied the second ($u_2/u_1 > 1$) is also satisfied, and equation (4.104) therefore provides a sufficient condition on its own.

Figure 4.29 shows how the normalized beam angle ϕ_0 varies with the normalized width S of the gain distribution for values of F of 1 and 2 and for b of the order of -1. $F = 1$ corresponds to no loss in the region outside the stripe and $F = 2$ corresponds to a fringe loss equal to the peak gain at the centre of the distribution. The portions of these two curves where equation (4.104) is satisfied, so that twin peaks exist and ϕ_0 can be used to find their angular separation, lie to the left of the line AB. The angle between the twin peaks increases approximately as the inverse of the width of the gain

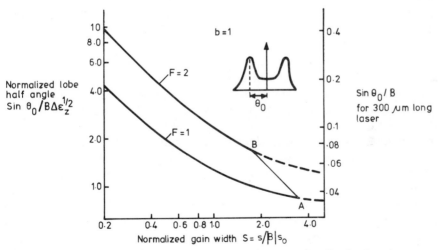

Figure 4.29 Relation between normalized width of gain distribution in narrow gain-waveguide and normalized angle from axis of lobes in far field. Proportional absorption in wings of gain distribution is variable parameters

distribution in both curves for $S < 1$, i.e. typically for stripe widths less than about 5 μm. For $F = 1$ the angle between the peaks is about half that for $F = 2$ for any particular width of the gain distribution. To indicate the magnitude of the actual angles a scale of $\sin \theta_0/B$ is given on the right-hand side of the Figure 4.29, which applies to a 300-μm long laser ($\Delta\epsilon_z \simeq 0.0018$). As an example this scale shows that a laser of 300-μm length and 3-μm width, having a typical value of $s_0 = 3.2$ μm and of $B = 1.7$ and $F = 2$ exhibits twin lobes in the far field each separated from the axis by 20°. Doubling the width of the laser would about halve the angle between the lobes, and only a little further increase in width would remove the lobes entirely.

4.2.5 Conclusions

The characteristics of a guide in which the gain varies continuously across the width from a maximum positive value at the centre to negative values at the edges and in which there is also a continuous variation of the real part of the dielectric constant can be summarized in the light of the foregoing treatment as follows.

The behaviour depends predominantly (a) on the relative contribution of the real part of the dielectric constant distribution to the waveguiding process (i.e. on the value of b), and (b) on the width of the guide. These two factors control the relative strength of the guiding. The guiding can be regarded as efficient under circumstances where no appreciable proportion of the light penetrates to optically lossy regions. Such a guide in a laser causes little increase in threshold current density and the incremental efficiency hardly deteriorates. This behaviour is associated with values of g_m/g_z (relative peak gain) and g_+/g_z (relative gain supplied to net mode gain) which are not much greater than unity. If the guiding is too weak the optical intensity extends significantly into the lossy regions flanking the guide and considerable power transfer takes place from the centre, where it is generated, to the edge, where it is absorbed. Such a power flow can be regarded as excessive when it becomes comparable with that emitted from the output faces of the laser, which occurs when $g_+/g_z > 2$.

If the real part of the dielectric profile is adequate on its own to confine the majority of the light within the gain region then satisfactory operation is assured. The preceding treatment shows, however, that the necessary conditions can still be satisfied when the contribution from the real component of dielectric constant is zero, and also even when this contribution is negative. In the latter case, however, for given gain and loss values the guide will have to be made much wider. The criterion to be satisfied can be expressed in terms of the characteristic length s_0 [see equation (4.72)] and the quantity B [see equation (4.73)] the value of which increases through unity as the real dielectric contribution b goes from positive to negative. The condition is also somewhat affected by the precise shape of the gain profile and by the apportionment between gain at the centre of the distribution and loss at the edge. However, taking the shape of the transverse distribution to lie somewhere between a parabolic and a $\cosh^{-2}$ profile gives lower reasonable limits on the width of the optical distribution (to the $1/e^2$ intensity points) of between $2Bs_0$ and $4Bs_0$ and on the effective width of the gain distribution of between Bs_0 and $2Bs_0$. These provide a value of g_+/g_z of less than 1.5, with a corresponding reabsorption of less than 30 per cent of the total power generated.

In guides much wider than these limiting values the excess of the gain supplied over the gain actually used drops to a low level. Self-absorption in the wings of the distribution is then very low, and the incremental efficiency of stimulated emission is high. However, as shown in the curve for $F = 1$ in Figure 4.22, the zero-order mode only occupies a limited proportion of the width of the gain region, and the optical gain available at the edges of the distribution is under-utilized. With increasing current there will be a tendency for the injected carrier concentration at the edges to increase, for the fringe gain therefore also to increase further and for most of the excess current to be wasted in increased spontaneous emission. Transverse diffusion of carriers limits this process to some extent, but at a certain level of increased current, which will be less the wider the laser, the first-order transverse mode reaches threshold, and other transverse modes may follow successively. The effective incremental efficiency over the whole laser width is thereby prevented from falling to a low value, but at the expense of multimode operation.

Although 'gain-guiding' can be as effective in confining the light in wide guides as guiding by a real distribution in the dielectric constant, it is accompanied by a distortion of the phase front of the wave. As shown in Section 4.2.3.1, this is sufficient to cause an appreciable broadening of the far-field beam width and to lead to astigmatic behaviour in a stripe laser.

In practice, because the amount of optical guiding, of whatever type, required in wide stripe guides is so small, the behaviour can be dominated by a variety of ancillary effects. These will be described in the section on stripe lasers.

4.3 WAVEGUIDE CHARACTERISTICS OF TRANSVERSE MODES

In this section we apply the waveguide analysis given in the two previous sections to investigate the range of possible transverse modes that may exist in both transverse planes in the laser resonator. In the plane perpendicular to the laser junction the behaviour is determined by the abrupt and relatively strong dielectric waveguide created by the heterostructure. A reasonably precise analysis may be made not only of the transverse optical distributions within the modes but also of the factors, such as mode reflectivity at the end faces (see Section 4.1.6) that determine which of the possible transverse modes predominates. In the plane parallel to the junction much weaker guiding is normally involved, except in the case of the buried heterostructure, where it is similar to that in the perpendicular direction. In the other cases the precise behaviour depends on the particular design of laser, a variety of which are described in Chapter 6. Two forms of guiding which are very frequently encountered in stripe lasers of 10–20-μm stripe width are smoothly distributed gain-guiding and smoothly distributed refractive index guiding. The former arises naturally as a result of the means used to limit the spread of injected carriers. The latter may be a deliberate part of the design but is often observed as an apparent fortuitous result of the fabrication methods, this being possible because of the small amount of refractive index change needed. To treat the behaviour of transverse modes in these circumstances it is therefore appropriate to perform the analysis for waveguides with a parabolic or $\cosh^{-2}$ distribution of both the real and complex dielectric constant.

4.3.1 Transverse Modes in a Dielectric Slab Waveguide

We first consider the behaviour of the higher order transverse modes in a dielectric slab waveguide. Such modes have multiple periodicity in the direction normal to the slab (y direction) and can occur in heterostructure lasers when the active layer is sufficiently thick. Transverse modes of rising order become guided as the thickness of the central layer is increased through certain critical values. The behaviour of the zero- and first-order transverse modes in a symmetrical double heterostructure has already been described in Section 4.1.4 where the effective width of the two modes was derived as a function of the normalized thickness D of the centre layer. Figure 4.5, in which these results are presented, shows how the zero-order mode propagates for all values of D whereas the first-order mode is not guided until D is greater than π. This cut-off value of D is an example of the general relation which can be written for the normalized critical thickness D_{crit} of the nth order mode as follows

$$D_{crit} = n\pi \; (= d_{crit}\beta_0\delta\epsilon^{1/2}) \tag{4.106}$$

where d_{crit} is the actual cut-off thickness. This relation comes from equations (4.16) and (4.15) with $\eta = 1$ and the cut-off condition that P is zero.

In the following sections we consider the intensity distribution and the lasing wavelength of the transverse modes under conditions which allow a considerable number of them to propagate.

4.3.1.1 Intensity Distribution

In Figure 4.30 we show, as an example, the intensity distribution for the three transverse modes that are capable of propagating in a structure with $D = 7$ (zero-, first- and second-order modes). The light in the higher order modes spreads to a greater extent than in the lower order modes as a result of the greater penetration of the field into the outer layers of the guide. This decreases the value of Γ so that in a laser the mode gain for given injected carrier concentration is reduced. However, except in the most extreme cases this reduction in gain is more than compensated by the increase in reflection coefficient for the higher order modes at the end-face of the laser (see Figure 4.20), so that with increasing D the highest order transverse mode normally becomes dominant quite shortly after it has come within its cut-off. This, of course, only applies to E modes. For the higher order H modes both the reflectivity and the gain are lower and hence no H modes of any order are normally excited.

4.3.1.2 Lasing Wavelength

The lasing wavelength of the transverse modes is determined by the condition that there should be an integral number of half wavelengths of the guided mode along the length of the resonator. The guide wavelength depends slightly on the transverse mode number as well as on the optical frequency, and hence the lasing wavelength differs slightly between the different transverse modes. To find the spectral separation of the transverse modes we use the relation for the axial propagation constant β_z given in the first of equations (4.7). Re-expressing this equation in terms of the normalized quantity Q, defined in equation (4.14), gives the following relation for β_z in terms of β_0 and Q

$$\beta_z = \beta_0(\epsilon_1 - Q^2\delta\epsilon)^{1/2} \qquad (4.107)$$

Using the relation $\beta_z = n\pi/L$, where n is an integer and L is the laser length, we have the following relation for the lasing wavelength λ ($= 2\pi/\beta_0$)

$$\lambda = \frac{2L}{n}(\epsilon_1 - Q^2\delta\epsilon)^{1/2} \qquad (4.108)$$

We may obtain the difference in wavelength $\Delta\lambda_{mn}$ between transverse modes m and n from equation (4.108) in terms of the appropriate values Q_m and Q_n of Q. After making allowance for the dispersion of the dielectric constant ϵ_1 by introducing a term $d(\epsilon_1^{1/2})/d\lambda$ we obtain the following relation

$$\frac{\Delta\lambda_{mn}}{\lambda} = \frac{(Q_m^2 - Q_n^2)\delta\epsilon}{2\epsilon_1^{1/2}\bar{\mu}} \qquad (4.109)$$

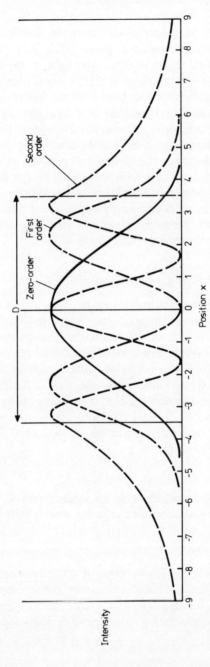

Figure 4.30   Transverse distribution of optical intensity for zero-, first- and second-order transverse modes in slab dielectric guide with $D = 7$

where $\bar{\mu}$ is the group refractive index given by

$$\bar{\mu} = \epsilon_1^{1/2} - \frac{\lambda d(\epsilon_1^{1/2})}{d\lambda} \tag{4.110}$$

This is the same effective refractive index as is used in obtaining the longitudinal mode separation (see Chapter 2, Section 2.6.1) and has a value in GaAs of about 4.5.

In Figure 4.31 we show a plot of Q^2 against D for the first eleven transverse modes in a symmetrical dielectric slab waveguide over a range up to $D = 35$ (i.e. $d = 5\,\mu m$ for a double heterostructure of average composition). These curves can be used in conjunction with equation (4.108) to obtain the relative lasing wavelengths of the various transverse modes. The curves show that, as D becomes large, the lasing wavelengths of the lower order transverse modes bunch together, giving small spectral separation, whereas the wavelengths of the highest order transverse modes are well separated.

Double heterostructure lasers are normally operated with active layer thickness corresponding to the range $D < \pi$ where only one transverse mode can exist. For wider active layers, as discussed above, lasing is predominantly in the highest order transverse mode or, close to the cut-off width, the next highest order mode. The wavelength separation between the two highest order transverse modes with equal longitudinal mode number is a few per cent in wavelength. Of course if several different

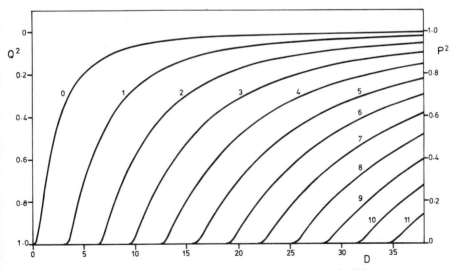

Figure 4.31 Curves to show how the lasing wavelengths of different transverse modes in dielectric slab waveguide depend upon thickness of active layer. Plot of P^2 or Q^2 against normalized thickness D for transverse modes from zero to 11

transverse modes co-exist there is no reason why they should have the same longitudinal mode number and be separated in wavelength by the above relatively large amount. The longitudinal mode number will adjust itself independently for each mode such that the wavelength of the dominant longitudinal mode lies less than the longitudinal mode separation away from the centre of the gain spectrum (i.e. within 2–5 Å, see Chapter 2, Section 2.6.1). Because the gain of different transverse modes is weighted to the different parts of the active layer where the intensity of each is strongest it is possible for the gain characteristics of the modes to differ and, say, be centred on different wavelengths. In these circumstances, for instance, two transverse modes may each be multiplied into sets of longitudinally separated members with spectral envelopes whose centres are similarly displaced in wavelength with respect to one another. Examples of this type of behaviour have been observed particularly in homojunction lasers.[16] This may arise because in these lasers there is more variation of the magnitude and spectral peak of the gain with distance from the p–n junction.

4.3.2   Transverse Modes in Smoothly Profiled Dielectric Guides

As discussed in the introduction to Section 4.3, the guiding profiles which are most appropriate for analysing transverse modes in the laser junction plane are the parabolic or $\cosh^{-2}$ profiles. We first consider the parabolic profile both of refractive index and gain. We derive the transverse intensity distribution, the lasing wavelength, and the mode gain of the different transverse modes and show how the behaviour changes as the proportion of gain-guiding increases. In the last section we briefly consider the modifications to the behaviour which arise with a $\cosh^{-2}$ profile.

4.3.2.1   Intensity Distribution in a Parabolic Guide

For a parabolic guide where the dielectric constant can be represented as varying with position x according to $\epsilon_1 - (a/\beta_0)^2 x^2$. A solution of the wave equations (4.51) and (4.52) in Section 4.2.2 give the following form for the transverse distribution of optical intensity in the nth-order mode:

$$\left| H_n(a^{1/2}x)\exp\left(\frac{-ax^2}{2}\right)\right|^2 \tag{4.111}$$

where H_n is the nth order Hermite polynomial. Examples of the lower order Hermite polynomials are

$$
\begin{aligned}
H_0(y) &= 1; & H_1(y) &= y \\
H_2(y) &= 2y^2 - 1; & H_3(y) &= y(2y^2 - 3)
\end{aligned}
\tag{4.112}
$$

For refractive index guiding the coefficient a in equation (4.111) is real. For general gain-plus-refractive-index guiding a is complex, and according to the nomenclature of Section 4.2 may be represented by $a_1(1 + jB^2)$ as defined for equation (4.52) with B^2 given in equation (4.73). When B^2 is not zero the intensity distribution $I_n(x)$, where n is the mode number, for the first four transverse modes as derived from equation (4.111) becomes

$$I_0(x) \propto \exp(-a_1x^2); \qquad I_1(x) \propto x^2 \exp(-a_1x^2)$$

$$I_2(x) \propto \{(2a_1x^2 - 1)^2 + 4a_1^2B^4x^4\} \exp(-a_1x^2) \qquad (4.113)$$

$$I_3(x) \propto x^2\{(2a_1x^2 - 3)^2 + 4a_1^2B^4x^4\} \exp(-a_1x^2)$$

Figure 4.32(a) shows the general shape of the intensity distribution of the first three transverse modes for a parabolic distribution of real refractive index obtained by putting $B^2 = 0$ in (4.113). The distributions do not differ greatly from those for the abrupt dielectric waveguide illustrated in Figure 4.30(a). In both cases the overall width of the distribution increases with mode number, although somewhat more regularly in the present case of the parabolic distribution. The major differences appear in the modes of second-order and greater where the centre lobes are less intense and obviously narrower for the parabolic distribution than for the abrupt dielectric guide.

The shape of the optical intensity distributions when a parabolic distribution of gain is added to the refractive index distribution is obtained by allowing the quantity B^2 in equation (4.113) to take the appropriate non-zero value. By this means it is possible to represent all the situations in which a negative or positive parabolic distribution of gain is combined with a negative or positive parabolic distribution of refractive index [see Section 4.2.3.2, equation (4.73)].

Let us first consider the state where there is no variation of refractive index but only a distribution of gain, peaking at the centre of the stripe. This is described by $B^2 = 1$. The zero- and first-order modes are identical in shape with those for a pure refractive index distribution, as illustrated in Figure 4.32(a). The second-order and higher order modes are different, with the inner lobes of the distribution largely suppressed. The second-order mode is illustrated in Figure 4.32(b).

Consider now the effect of adding a refractive index distribution to the gain distribution. For all combinations of refractive index and gain the shape of the optical distributions of the zero- and first-order modes remains unaltered because the quantity B^2 does not appear in the relevant relations in (4.113). Transverse modes higher than the first are, however, altered. There is a steady change in the pattern of such modes as the proportion of refractive index guiding is reduced and the proportion of gain-guiding is increased. This is continuous through the point where the

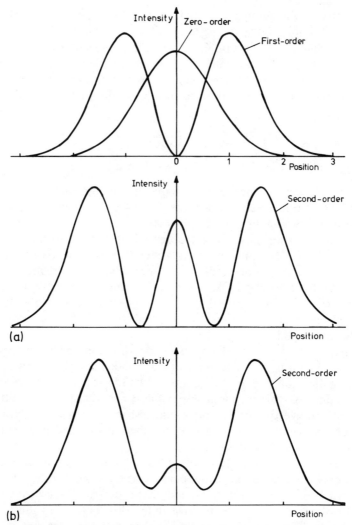

Figure 4.32 Transverse distribution of optical intensity for transverse modes of parabolic guiding profile. (a) Zero-, first- and second-order modes for parabolic dielectric guide. (b) Second-order mode for parabolic gain guide. Zero- and first-order modes are the same as in (a)

refractive index profile is inverted. The intensity of the central lobes in the optical distribution diminishes until the lobes are no longer distinguishable and the intensity close to the outer edge increases. Such a condition is similar to that which is observed along the length of a resonator with a very low end-face reflection coefficient, where the intensity builds up to a considerable value close to the two ends but is relatively small at the centre. In the present case the predominant transverse reflection of energy takes place at points close to the two intensity peaks at the sides of the distribution. As the magnitude of the gain distribution is raised to compensate the effect of an increasing anti-guiding profile of refractive index, so the height of the two outer peaks increases compared with the intensity at the centre of the distribution.

4.3.2.2   Lasing Wavelength in a Parabolic Guide

The lasing wavelength of the transverse modes in a parabolic waveguide depends on the transverse mode number in a somewhat different way from that of transverse modes in an abrupt dielectric waveguide. In order to obtain the variation of lasing wavelength we investigate the value of the guide propagation constant β_z for the different modes. Using the method adopted in Section 4.2.2 of matching the characteristic guided wave equation (4.51), with the parabolic dielectric profile of (4.54) inserted, to the mathematically soluble form in equation (4.52) we can obtain the following relation for β_z in terms of the free space propagation constant β_0 and the quantity a_1

$$\beta_z^2 = \epsilon_1 \beta_0^2 - (2n + 1)a_1 \tag{4.114}$$

where n is the transverse mode number and ϵ_1 is the real component of the dielectric constant at the centre of the parabolic distribution. The value of a_1 depends on the magnitude of the distributions of both the dielectric constant and gain, as discussed in Section 4.2.3.2. However, we can use the quantity B^2 [see equation (4.73)] to take account of the relative contributions of these two distributions, so that we may express the behaviour in terms of only one of them. We choose to do this for the dielectric constant distribution. Let a coefficient $\delta\epsilon$ be defined to describe the magnitude of the distribution in such a way that the perturbation of the dielectric constant as a function of x with respect to its value at the centre of the distribution is given by $-\delta\epsilon\, x^2$. Then by a method analogous to that used for obtaining equation (4.69) we find

$$a_1 = \frac{\beta_0 \delta\epsilon^{1/2}}{(1 - B^4)^{1/2}} \tag{4.115}$$

The laser resonance condition requires that β_z in equation (4.114) should have a particular value for a given longitudinal mode. Hence we can use the equation to find the free space propagation constant β_0, and therefore the lasing wavelength λ, for each transverse mode n of a particular longitudinal periodicity. To obtain the spacing $\delta\lambda$ between transverse modes we differentiate β_0 with respect to mode number n in equation (4.114).

Taking into account the dispersion of ϵ_1 with λ as for the case of the slab waveguide [see equations (4.109) and (4.110)] we obtain, after appropriate substitution for λ

$$\frac{\delta\lambda}{\lambda} = \frac{-a_1}{\beta_0^2 \epsilon_1^{1/2} \overline{\mu}}$$

$$= \frac{-\delta\varepsilon^{1/2}}{\beta_0 \epsilon_1^{1/2} \overline{\mu} (1 - B^4)^{1/2}}$$

(4.116)

This relation shows that there is equal wavelength separation between successive transverse modes (the spacing is independent of n) and that the separation is increased for a given dielectric profile by the effect of gain (non-zero B^2). Since the width of modes of similar transverse order depends on $a_1^{-1/2}$ [see equation (4.113)], equation (4.116) shows that varying the strength of the parabolic guide changes the wavelength separation between modes as the inverse square of the width of the corresponding optical distributions (comparing like modes).

The equality of the separation in wavelength between successive transverse modes for the parabolic guide is very different from the behaviour in an abrupt dielectric guide where the lower order transverse modes are all closely bunched (see Figure 4.31). The reason for this difference is that the lower order transverse modes in a parabolic guide are fairly closely confined near the centre of the guide, whereas in the abrupt guide all the modes, including the lower order modes, still occupy the full width of the guide. If the parabolic guide were made sufficiently weak to allow the lowest order modes to spread to an extent comparable to those in the abrupt guide, the spectral mode separation would also decrease to approximately the same value as obtained for the lower order modes in the abrupt guide.

4.3.2.3 *Mode Gain in a Parabolic Guide*

The factors that determine which transverse modes are present in the laser output are the magnitudes of the mode gain and of the end-face reflection coefficient. In weakly guiding structures, of the type that are normally encountered in the plane of the laser junction, there is little variation in the end-face reflection coefficient between different transverse modes. A far more important cause of mode discrimination is the mode gain, and modes with the highest gain are dominant. Under conditions where the local gain varies across the width of the guide the mode gain is weighted to those parts of the gain distribution where the optical intensity is a maximum and modes of different transverse order can exhibit considerable differences in mode gain.

In most laser waveguide structures the local gain varies somewhat with position across the width of the guide. In the abrupt heterostructures the gain is restricted to the centre layer and there is a region outside where the light penetrates but where the gain is zero or negative. In devices with a smooth distribution of dielectric constant there is usually also a smooth distribution of gain. This distribution may peak at the centre of the stripe; or, sufficiently beyond threshold, there may be a dip at the centre of the stripe as a result of the local higher rate of stimulated recombination. The latter effects are treated in Chapter 6, Section 6.4.2 on self-focusing. Here we only consider those distributions of gain which can satisfactorily be represented by a parabola, either inverted or otherwise.

In equation (4.79) we presented the relation between the gain g_m at the centre of the gain distribution and the net mode gain g_z for transverse mode number n. g_m/g_z depends on the magnitudes of variation of both dielectric constant and gain in the guiding profile. It can be neatly expressed in terms of the effective width s_{eff} of the optical intensity distribution in, say, the zero-order transverse mode, and the quantity B^2 [see equation (4.73)] as follows

$$\frac{g_m}{g_z} = 1 + \frac{8B^2(2n + 1)}{g_z \beta_0 \epsilon_1^{1/2} s_{eff}^2} \tag{4.117}$$

B^2 is positive for conditions where the gain peaks at the centre of the distributions and negative for conditions where the gain has a minimum at the centre.

When B^2 is positive there is discrimination against higher order modes. The discrimination depends on the magnitude of the second term on the right-hand side of equation (4.117) and becomes appreciable when this term has a value of around 0.2 for $n = 0$. The size of this term is increased both by an increase in the value of B^2 and by a reduction in the value of s_{eff}. As an example the combination of $B^2 = 1$ with $s_{eff} = 20$ μm and an average value of g_z for a 300-μm long laser gives the value of 0.2 suggested above. Because of the effect of the term B^2 a parabolic guide that is formed from a gain profile gives better selection against higher order transverse modes than does a guide formed from a profile of the dielectric constant (there is no cut-off to provide selection in a parabolic guide), and this discrimination becomes better as the transverse confinement is increased. However, this statement requires qualification when the current in the laser is increased sufficiently beyond threshold to give self-focusing effects. The resulting behaviour is treated in Chapter 6, Section 6.6.

When B^2 is negative, equation (4.13) shows that the highest order transverse modes are favoured. However, the condition imposed by negative B^2, i.e. that the gain increases from the centre outwards, cannot persist indefinitely with distance, and the point at which this distribution is truncated determines the maximum order of the transverse mode that is excited. This situation is also relevant to the analysis of the self-focused situation (see Chapter 6, Sections 6.4.2 and 6.6).

4.3.2.4 Transverse Modes of the $\cosh^{-2}$ Waveguide Profile

The $\cosh^{-2}$ profile of the dielectric constant, illustrated in Figure 4.21, approximates to an inverted parabola over its centre portion but flattens out and tends asymptotically to the horizontal at great distances from the centre. The behaviour of the modes associated with such a profile depends on the extent to which the light spreads out into the flat portion at the edges of the profile. When the guiding profile is wide and/or deep a considerable number of the lower order transverse modes are contained mainly within the approximately parabolic part of the profile. Their optical distribution is then very similar to that in the case of a true parabolic profile. The higher order transverse modes spread into the flatter part of the guiding profile. Their transverse distribution is somewhat modified as a result, and elongated in the outer regions. In contrast to the infinitely extended parabolic profile the $\cosh^{-2}$ profile exhibits a mode cut-off. Transverse modes beyond a certain order, which depends on the width and depth of the guiding profile, are no longer guided.

We illustrate in Figure 4.33 an example of the distributions of optical intensity of the zero- and first-order modes for the $\cosh^{-2}$ guiding profile under conditions that produce the behaviour that differs most from that in a parabolic guide. For such conditions the losses in the outer part of the profile must be relatively small compared with the gain at the centre and the guide size must be such as to bring the first-order mode close to cut-off. It is reasonable to compare the two transverse modes for the same mode gain, which means that the amplitude of the $\cosh^{-2}$ distribution is greater for the

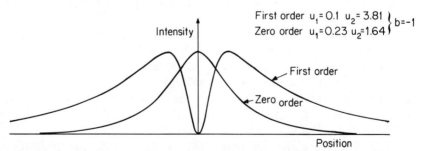

Figure 4.33 Transverse distribution of optical intensity for zero- and first-order modes for guide with $\cosh^{-2}$ gain profile and negative $\cosh^{-2}$ dielectric constant profile. Both modes have same gain and first-order mode is close to cut-off

higher order mode. If b is assumed constant this applies to both the gain and dielectric constant distribution. b is taken as -1 in the present instance, corresponding to anti-guiding. The precise details are not important, however, and the purpose of the figure is to show the greater extent to which the outer portions of the distributions spread sideways in the general conditions specified compared with a parabolic guide. In the case of the first-order mode the light spreads well beyond the two maxima. The long tails of decaying intensity for both modes constitute cross sections of outwardly angled propagating waves in a medium of reasonably low attenuation, and cannot really be regarded as part of a standing wave system. Such long tails would not exist if there were more loss in the outer regions, and the overall distributions would then differ much less from those for a parabolic guiding profile.

The way that the lasing wavelength for the transverse modes in a $\cosh^{-2}$ guiding profile depends on the mode number is different again from both the abrupt slab guide and the parabolic guide. We derive the relationship below.

We consider the behaviour in a real dielectric guide with a $\cosh^{-2}$ profile of fixed magnitude, and evaluate the propagation constant β_z in terms of the transverse mode number n. Taking the wave equation (4.51) with a dielectric constant distribution incorporated according to equation (4.57), where b is very large but $b(\Delta\epsilon_m + \Delta\epsilon_f)$ is finite and set equal to $\delta\epsilon$, and matching this equation to the mathematically soluble form in equation (4.55) gives the following expression for β_z

$$\beta_z^2 - \epsilon_1\beta_0^2 = \left(\frac{2}{s}\right)^2 u_1^2 \tag{4.118}$$

where β_0 is the free space propagation constant and u_1 is given by

$$(u_1 + n)(u_1 + n + 1) = \frac{\delta\epsilon\beta_0^2 s^2}{4} \tag{4.119}$$

and where $(\epsilon_1 + \delta\epsilon)$ is the dielectric constant at the centre of the guiding profile. These equations have a solution of the form

$$\beta_z^2 = \epsilon\beta_0^2 - \{k(2n + 1) + n^2\} \left(\frac{2}{s}\right)^2 \tag{4.120}$$

where we have put $(\epsilon_1 + \delta\epsilon) = \epsilon$ and where k is given by

$$k = \tfrac{1}{2}(1 + \delta\epsilon\beta_0^2 s^2)^{1/2} - \tfrac{1}{2} \tag{4.121}$$

Taking β_z in equation (4.120) to be a constant determined by the laser resonator, setting $\beta_0 = 2\pi/\lambda$ where λ is the lasing wavelength and defining $\delta\lambda_n$ to be the difference in wavelength between mode number n and the zero-order mode, and taking into account the dispersion of ϵ_1 with λ as for the case of the slab waveguide [see equations (4.109) and (4.110)] gives the following approximate relation for $\delta\lambda_n/\lambda$ provided that it is small

$$\frac{\delta\lambda_n}{\lambda} \simeq -\frac{n\{(1 + \delta\epsilon\beta_0^2 s^2)^{1/2} - 1\} - n^2}{2\beta_0^2 \epsilon^{1/2}\overline{\mu}} \left(\frac{2}{s}\right)^2 \tag{4.122}$$

This applies up to mode cut-off, which occurs for $n > k$.

In Figure 4.34 we show how $\delta\lambda_n$ varies with transverse mode number n according to equation (4.122). $(2\beta_0^2 \epsilon^{1/2-} \mu s^2/k^2)\ \delta\lambda_n/\lambda$ is plotted against n/k. The points corresponding to individual transverse modes in any particular situation lie on the curve in Figure 4.34 spaced out with equal intervals of $1/k$ referred to the horizontal axis. As in all cases the lasing wavelength decreases with increasing transverse mode number but in this case the wavelength separation between individual modes decreases as the mode number increases rather than increasing as for the slab guide or remaining constant as for the parabolic guide. The higher order modes are therefore closely bunched in wavelength. This behaviour can be ascribed to the greater degree, compared with the parabolic guide, by which the higher order modes spread in width with increasing mode number. In a guide where a $\cosh^{-2}$ profile of gain is also present the higher order modes have much less gain or higher loss and are not likely to be observed.

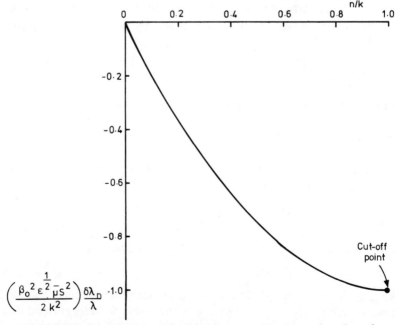

Figure 4.34   Normalized change in lasing wavelength as a function of normalized transverse mode number in $\cosh^{-2}$ dielectric waveguide

REFERENCES

1. R. E. Collins, *Field Theory of Guided Waves*, McGraw Hill, 1960.
2. D. Marcuse, *Light Transmission Optics*, Van Nostrand Reinhold Co., 1972.
3. G. A. Hockham, 'Radiation from a solid-state laser', *Electron. Lett.,* **9**, 1973, 389.
4. L. Lewin, 'Obliquity factor correction to solid state radiation patterns', *J. Appl. Phys.*, **46**, 1975, 2323.
5. G. D. Henshall and J. E. A. Whiteaway, 'Far-field emission patterns of single heterostructure GaAs Lasers', *Electron. Lett.*, **10**, 1974, 326.
6. P. A. Kirkby and G. H. B. Thompson, 'The effect of double heterojunction waveguide parameters on the far field emission pattern of lasers', *Opto-electronics.*, **4**, 1972, 323.
7. H. C. Casey, Jr, M. B. Panish, and J. L. Merz, 'Beam divergence of the emission from double heterostructure injection lasers', *J. Appl. Phys.*, **44**, 1973, 5470.
8. M. J. Adams and M. Cross, 'Electromagnetic theory of heterostructure injection laser', *Solid State Electron.*, **14**, 1971, 865.
9. F. K. Reinhart, I. Hayashi, and M. B. Panish, 'Mode reflectivity and waveguide properties of double heterostructure injection lasers', *J. Appl. Phys.*, **42**, 1971, 4466.
10. T. Ikegami, 'Reflectivity of mode at facet and oscillation mode in double heterostructure injection lasers', *J. Quantum Electron.*, QE-8, 1972, 470.
11. L. D. Landau and E. M. Lifshitz, *Electrodynamics of Continuous Media*, Pergamon Press, 1960, pp. 256–262.
12. W. O. Schlosser, 'Gain-induced modes in planar structures', *Bell System Tech. J.*, **52**, 1973, 887.
13. D. D. Cook and F. R. Nash, 'Gain-induced guiding and astigmatic output beam of GaAs lasers', *J. Appl. Phys.*, **46**, 1975, 1160.
14. B. W. Hakki, 'Striped GaAs lasers: mode size and efficiency', *J. Appl. Phys.*, **46**, 1975, 2723.
15. K. Unger, 'Modes in a semiconductor laser', *Annalen der Physik*, **19**, 1967, 64.
16. T. L. Paoli, J. E. Ripper, and T. H. Zachos, 'Resonant modes of GaAs junction Lasers II: High injection level', *J. Quantum Electron.*, QE-5, 1969, 271.

CHAPTER 5

Performance of Heterostructure Lasers

5.1 INTRODUCTION

In this chapter we review the performance capabilities of the various types of heterostructure laser. In particular we deal with the threshold current density, the incremental efficiency, the maximum power output, both for pulsed and continuous operation, and the effect of temperature on these characteristics.

Four types of heterostructure laser have been mentioned in Chapter 3 and illustrated in Figures 3.14–3.21. These comprise the single heterostructure, the double heterostructure, the large optical cavity laser (LOC), and the localized gain region (LGR) or separate confinement heterostructure (SCH) laser. The last two may be regarded as developments of the single heterostructure and the double heterostructure, respectively. In the LOC laser an additional optically confining heterojunction is placed on the weakly guiding side of the single heterostructure and in the LGR or SCH laser one or two additional optically confining heterojunctions are placed around the active layer of a narrow double heterostructure. These four types of laser differ considerably in their characteristics, and find application in various different roles.

Most of the properties of these lasers are summarized by the typical light/current characteristics of 200-μm wide broad contact devices given in Figure 5.1. These characteristics, which apply at room temperature, show the threshold currents of the lasers, their incremental efficiencies, and their peak pulsed output power capabilities. The peak power level concerned is set by the dielectric strength of the output facet of the laser which, if uncoated, suffers catastrophic damage at an optical intensity that varies with pulse length from around 10 mW cm^{-2} for pulse lengths of 50 ns down to around 1 mW cm^{-2} for d.c. operation. The maximum mean power, which is of course of considerable significance, is indicated very approximately in terms of the maximum duty cycle. The mean power capability is determined by heating, and depends on the dimensions of the laser and the efficiency of the heat sink.

240

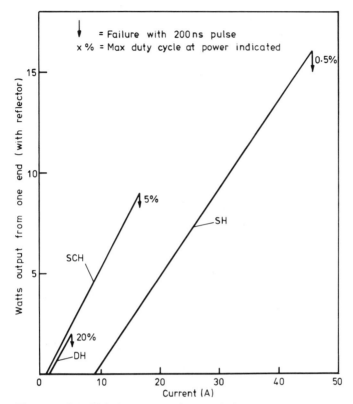

Figure 5.1 Light/current characteristics under pulsed conditions for typical examples of single heterostructure, double heterostructure, and separate confinement heterostructure lasers, showing threshold current, incremental efficiency, and peak optical output of devices 200 μm wide

The peak power capability of a semiconductor laser is determined by the breakdown strength at the output facets. These facets suffer catastrophic damage when the optical flux density passing through them exceeds a certain critical value. The safe peak power that may be taken from a laser is therefore proportional to the area over which it is spread on the facet. A convenient figure of merit for comparing devices is the peak power per unit junction width. This must hence depend on the thickness of the optical resonator and the spread of the optical intensity distribution in the direction normal to the junction. In general the threshold current density also depends reasonably linearly on the thickness of the active layer and/or the thickness of the optical resonator, particularly if the two thicknesses bear a fixed relation to one another. Hence lasers with high power output tend to have high threshold current density.

The incremental quantum efficiency of all these heterostructure lasers is high, being in the region of 50 per cent for light emitted from both ends of the device. The overall efficiency is therefore determined more by the degree to which the laser can be operated above its threshold current and, for high peak power lasers, by the voltage drop at the contacts, than by the incremental quantum efficiency.

Temperature affects the threshold current density and, to a lesser extent, the incremental quantum efficiency. Typical variations of threshold current density with temperature for two types of laser structure are illustrated in Figure 5.2.[1] The temperature dependence results from a combination of the fundamental temperature variation of the gain/current characteristic of the active layer with various other temperature-dependent mechanisms associated with the particular structures such as carrier and optical confinement. Empirically a law of the form $\exp(T/T_0)$ often applies.

5.1.1 Single and Double Heterostructure Lasers

Figure 5.1 illustrates the general tendency in the two simpler heterostructures (the single and double heterostructure) for higher peak

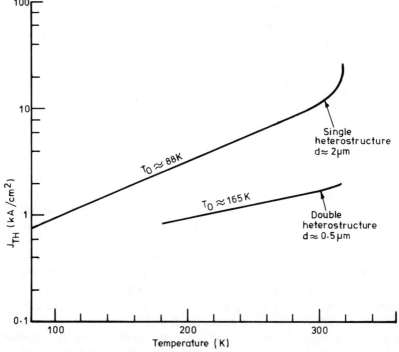

Figure 5.2 Dependence of threshold current density on temperature for single and double heterostructure lasers. Values of T_0 given for $\exp(T/T_0)$ law. After Hayashi et al.[1]

output power to be associated with higher threshold current density. The factor that links these two characteristics is the thickness of the active layer. The single heterostructure laser typically has an active layer thickness of 2 μm and a similar spread in the optical distribution. Its peak power capability with a 200 ns current pulse is about 90 W mm^{-1} and its threshold current per unit junction width is in the range 40–50 A mm^{-1} (8–10,000 A cm^{-2} for $L = 0.5$ mm). In the normal double heterostructure laser call these figures are reduced by approaching an order of magnitude. The active layer width is about 0.2 μm, the spread of the optical distribution about 0.4 μm, the peak power capability about 5–10 W mm^{-1} for a 200 ns pulse and less than 1 W mm^{-1} for continuous operation, and the threshold current is around 5 A mm^{-1} (1200 A cm^{-2} for $L = 0.4$ mm). The beam angle in the plane perpendicular to the junction is about 15–20° to the points of half intensity for the single heterostructure and about 45–55° for the normal double heterostructure. In general the behaviour of the double heterostructure can be modified considerably by varying the thickness of the active layer both below and above 0.2 μm, as will be described later. The behaviour of the single heterostructure can be varied to a much smaller extent and the range of active layer thickness that can be used is much more limited.

The temperature characteristic given in Figure 5.2 illustrates another difference between the two structures. The double heterostructure shows a steady increase of threshold with temperature, whereas for the single heterostructure there is a critical temperature above which normal operation becomes impossible. This behaviour of the single heterostructure will be treated in more detail in Section 5.2.

5.1.2 LOC Lasers

The large optical cavity (LOC) laser was proposed as a means of obtaining a high peak capability whilst eliminating the various types of critical behaviour associated with the single heterostructure laser. A wide variety of designs have been made with optical resonators ranging in thickness between 1 and 7 μm [2] and, for one device, 20 μm.[3] The LOC laser normally contains four layers in the heterostructure and uses a refractive index step at the outer optical confining heterojunction (see Figure 3.19) which is large enough to make it possible for many transverse modes to propagate. Two approaches have been adopted to discriminate against the unwanted modes. Lockwood et al.,[2] Kressel et al.,[3] and Butler[4] have investigated structures where the size of the refractive index step is made sufficiently small to considerably limit the maximum order number of the transverse modes which will propagate, even if propagation of only the zero-order mode is not achieved. Paoli et al.[5] and Hakki and Hwang[6] report structures which use large refractive index steps at the outer heterojunctions (30 per cent in AlAs content) but where the thickness of the active layer is made a sufficient proportion of the total thickness of the optical resonator to favour the zero-order mode. A selectively reflecting dielectric coating is also used to reinforce the mode discrimination.

The Lockwood and Kressel structure uses a thin active layer. It gives a threshold current density which is relatively low for the thickness of the resonator and a good temperature-independent incremental-quantum efficiency. The optical resonator can be made wide for high peak powers. However, the output beam is twin-lobed with a considerable separation between lobes. This limits the applications.

 The Paoli and Hakki structure uses a resonator of more limited thickness and has a lower peak output power. Its incremental efficiency tends to be lower but it produces a useful narrow angle output beam.

5.1.3 LGR and SCH Lasers

The laser with a localized gain region (LGR) or separate confinement heterostructure laser (SCH) differ mainly from the LOC laser in providing heterojunction barriers on both sides of the active layer (see Figures 3.20 and 3.21), and hence having the capability for near perfect confinement of injected carriers up to high temperatures. For this purpose a step in AlAs content of at least 25 per cent is required at the heterojunctions, as described in Section 3.2.1. However, because of the considerable change in refractive index that accompanies such a step in AlAs content, a strong waveguide is created unless the active layer is made very thin. To prevent any significant additional degree of optical confinement due to this cause the thickness of the active layer should not be greater than 300 Å. Such a layer may be placed at the most appropriate position within the optical resonator to aid transverse mode control without distorting the field distribution. However, because problems still remain in growing such layers reproducibly, this type of design has not yet been exploited. Two types of less ideal device have been reported. The first[7,8] is a symmetrical design in which the active layer is confined by smaller than ideal heterojunction steps (10–12 per cent AlAs), has a width of 400–1000 Å, and is placed centrally within an optical resonator the width of which is defined by outer heterojunctions with appreciable further steps in AlAs content. Because of the central placing of the active layer operation in the zero-order transverse mode is strongly favoured even under conditions where three or four transverse modes are capable of propagation. Hence the steps in composition at the outer heterojunctions can be made large enough to provide extra assistance in confining injected carriers which have surmounted the inner carrier confinement steps. Such a two-stage barrier is

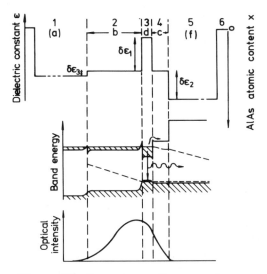

Figure 5.3 Separate confinement heterostructure with unsymmetrical optical resonator and unsymmetrical positioning of
active layer, showing relative dielectric
constant of layers, band potential under
forward bias and optical distribution of
guided wave

somewhat more susceptible to temperature changes than a single large
barrier but can perform adequately in certain situations.

The second alternative design for a high peak power LGR laser is
illustrated in Figure 5.3. In this case the optical resonator is unsymmetrical,
as in the single heterostructure laser, being limited by a large
heterojunction step on one side and a small step on the other.[9] The height
of the small step is adjusted to discriminate against higher order transverse
modes (e.g. 2 per cent steps in AlAs content). The active layer is 800 Å
wide and is confined by heterojunctions with 20 per cent steps in AlAs
content. To prevent a layer of this width having too strong a guiding effect
on the optical wave the layer must be placed close to the side of the
resonator with the large refractive index step. For optimum coupling to the
wave this distance should be adjusted so that the peak of the optical
distribution just lies at the inner edge of the active layer. Because the 20
per cent step confining the active layer is only marginally adequate for
confining electrons but adequate for confining the less mobile holes, the
direction of electron injection into the active layer is arranged, by
appropriate doping of the layers, to be outwards from the centre line of
the structure. Hence the outer large heterojunction which defines the

resonator provides an additional closely spaced heterojunction barrier for reflecting electrons which surmount the first barrier. The performance of this type of device is illustrated in Figure 5.1.

5.2   THRESHOLD CURRENT DENSITY

5.2.1   General Remarks

We have shown in the previous sections that the threshold current density in heterostructure lasers depends on three main factors. The first is the magnitude of the optical gain required. This is determined by the characteristics of the laser resonator, in particular its length, end-face reflectivity and optical loss, as summarized in equation (2.86), and its thickness. The second factor is the way the optical gain of the active layer depends on injected current density. As shown in Chapter 2, Section 2.2.7 and Section 2.6 this is determined first by the electronic properties of the semiconductor, and secondly by the confinement factor Γ. The electronic properties depend mainly on the doping level and the temperature. The confinement factor Γ is imposed by the geometrical disposition of the active layer within the light guide, as described in Chapter 4, Section 4.1.3, and summarized by equation (4.28). The third factor is concerned with the efficiency with which carriers are injected into, and confined within, the active layer. This is determined by the properties of the heterojunctions.

In most laser applications it is an advantage to have a low threshold current density, both to reduce energy dissipation and other deleterious effects, and to give a lower total operating current. For the latter purpose, of course, some sacrifice of threshold current density is allowable when it is accompanied by a reduction in total junction area. According to the factors listed above, a lower threshold current density can be obtained by eliminating the leakage of injected carriers from the active layer and by matching the gain/current characteristic of the material of the active layer most appropriately to the optical loading of the resonator. The latter item involves suitably adjusting the thickness of the gain region, and may not be possible in all laser configurations without interfering with the desired optical properties of the resonator. With the above features optimized the threshold current density depends directly on the optical loading per unit area imposed on the active layer by the optical resonator.

The optical loading imposed by the resonator is divided into a useful output component and an unwanted lossy component. Both components are proportional to the thickness of the resonator. The lossy component is additionally proportional to the resonator loss coefficient α and the output component is additionally dependent on the reflection coefficient R of the end-faces as $\ln(1/R)$ and inversely proportional to the laser length.

Reduction of the loss coefficient is always helpful for lowering threshold but a change of the other quantities also affects other aspects of the laser performance. Thus, increasing the end-face reflectivity and increasing the laser length, both of which operations reduce the threshold current density, also reduce the incremental efficiency (see Chapter 2, Section 2.7.2). Increasing the length also increases the total current. Reducing the effective thickness of the resonator increases the far-field beam angle and reduces the peak power of the output. Hence these three parameters are only available when low threshold current density is the major feature of the design. The optical loss coefficient of the resonator should, however, always be reduced as much as possible.

The loss coefficient in the resonator can be attributed to scattering losses due to non-planarity of the heterojunction interfaces, to free carrier losses, and to absorption losses in the layers adjacent to the active layer. Scattering losses become appreciable (>5 cm^{-1}) when the interface roughness at the heterojunctions reaches an r.m.s. amplitude of around 0.1 μm. Free carrier losses arise from the carriers introduced by the doping of the passive layers and from the carriers injected into the active layer. The former contributions can be limited to less than 2 cm^{-1} at the GaAs wavelength by limiting the doping to less than 5×10^{17} cm^{-3}. The latter contribution is inevitably associated with the gain process but is relatively insignificant for active layer geometries where Γ is small.

Absorption losses occur mainly in the regions surrounding the active layer, either in the adjacent layers of the heterostructure or in the part of the active layer which bounds the two edges of the laser. Of the various types of heterostructure only the single heterostructure and its derivatives can suffer appreciable absorption loss in the adjacent layers, the n-doped GaAs layer being the culprit in this instance owing to the proximity of its absorption edge to the photon energy of the laser emission. In contrast all planar-type structures with gain-guiding suffer some loss as a result of the light penetrating sideways in the plane of the junction into the adjacent unpumped regions. The magnitude of this loss is given in Section 4.2.3.4, equations (4.84) and (4.85).

The end-face reflectivity and the length of the laser cannot normally be chosen simply to minimize the threshold current density. Ideally they should be mutually adjusted, in any given circumstances, to produce the optimum overall efficiency. As indicated in Chapter 2, Section 2.7.2.2, the overall efficiency of a practical laser (taking voltage drop into account) is close to optimum when the length and reflection coefficient are adjusted first to make the laser operate at about twice threshold when it is delivering its specified output, and secondly so that the loss parameter $\alpha L/\ln(1/R)$ is reasonably close to unity. In practice short, lower power, double heterostructure lasers are often operated quite close to threshold and with a loss parameter much less than unity (a) for convenience in construction, (b) to obtain better mode control, and (c) because, without geometrical changes in the heterostructure, adjustments which reduce threshold current density can impair the match between the gain/current characteristics of the active layer and the optical loading in such a way that only a small advantage is obtained. This aspect is treated below.

The effective thickness of the optical resonator in a heterostructure laser is determined by the spread of the guided optical mode in the direction perpendicular to the junction, and has been treated in Chapter 4, Section 4.14. There is a certain minimum thickness to which the guided wave can be confined which is associated with a particular thickness of the centre layer of the heterostructure and which is inversely proportional to the square root of the step in the dielectric constant at the heterojunction boundaries. In practice the minimum effective thickness which can be achieved in (GaAl)As heterostructures is of the order of $0.25\ \mu$m. As described in Section 4.14, the far-field beam width in the direction perpendicular to the heterostructure is approximately inversely proportional to the width of the optical distribution, and hence low threshold current density obtained by this means is achieved at the expense of increased beam width.

The possibility of obtaining reduced threshold currents by matching the optical load to the gain/current characteristic of the active layer arises because gain is not directly proportional to current. To illustrate this effect we define a gain g_i, depending on J, which we call the intrinsic peak spectral gain and which is the gain experienced by a plane wave propagating entirely within a volume of the semiconductor pumped uniformly by a current per unit volume of J and with the wavelength of the plane wave centred at the peak of the gain spectrum. In this situation the confinement factor Γ is unity and according to equation (2.71), Chapter 2, g_i is given by

$$g_i = \left(\frac{\mu}{c}\right) w_{\text{stim}}(\text{max}) \tag{5.1}$$

As discussed in Chapter 2, the relation between g_i and J can be found for any particular semiconductor with some particular doping level at a given temperature. For high values of g_i, however, the effect of doping is small.

Figure 5.4 illustrates schematically the important general characteristics of the relation between g_i and J. At low gain g_i is a superlinear function of J but at sufficiently high gain it becomes a sublinear function. The ratio of gain to current density is a maximum at the point A in the figure which is where the relation changes from superlinear to sublinear. This is the optimum operating point and has an intrinsic gain and a current per unit volume which we take respectively as $g_i(\text{opt})$ and $J(\text{opt})$. We denote the ratio $g_i(\text{opt})/J(\text{opt})$ by $B(\text{opt})$.

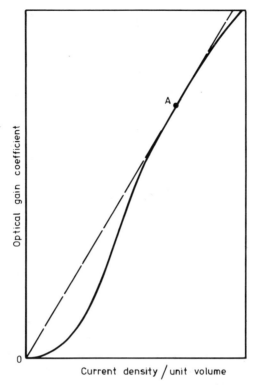

Figure 5.4 Schematic illustration of relation between intrinsic optical gain and current density over large dynamic range

To match $g_i(\text{opt})$ to the actual gain g appropriate to some particular design of laser the heterostructure geometry must be chosen so that the confinement factor Γ is given by

$$\Gamma = \frac{g}{g_i(\text{opt})} \tag{5.2}$$

As shown in Chapter 4, Section 4.13, we can express Γ in terms of the thickness d of the active layer, the effective width s of the optical distribution, and the coupling coefficient k in the form $\Gamma = kd/s$. s will, in general, be specified for the particular application. If d can be chosen independently of s, as for instance in a separate confinement heterostructure, then it should be chosen so that

$$d = \frac{(s/k)g}{g_i(\text{opt})} \tag{5.3}$$

The threshold current per unit area, say J_a, is then given by

$$J_a = \frac{(s/k)g}{B(\text{opt})} \tag{5.4}$$

This equation justifies the assertion, made at the beginning of this section, that the minimum threshold current density under best-matched conditions depends on the optical loading of the resonator. The optical loading of the resonator is proportional both to the threshold gain g and to the effective thickness s of the region occupied by the guided optical wave. The coupling factor k also enters into the relationship, but in an optimized situation for a laser of normal specification k will be found to be close to unity.

The advantage to be obtained from appropriate matching of the gain/current characteristic to the optical loading of the laser obviously depends on the degree of original mismatch. $g_i(\text{opt})$ is of the order of 500 cm^{-1} (its exact value still remains to be experimentally determined) and in normal single heterostructure or double heterostructure lasers $(s/kd)g$ is much less than this. The difference is greatest when s/kd is of the order of unity and when g is small. Such conditions are present in lasers where the optical guiding is strong (lasers with a wide active region where the light does not spread into the passive layers) and where the length of the resonator or the facet reflectivity is large. Lasers of this type would benefit particularly if the active layer could be matched to the optical load by reducing its thickness.

We now consider in more detail the relative threshold current density that can be obtained in the various types of GaAs/(GaAl)As heterostructure laser over the range of operating conditions encountered in practice. To provide a unifying element in analysing the different structures we need to use a common form for the intrinsic-gain/current-density characteristic. We choose the empirical relationship for GaAs given in curve A, Figure 5.5[9] which, although not precisely the same as that deduced theoretically by Stern,[10] provides a good fit to a variety of the better measured results. In view of Stern's theoretical analysis it is to be expected that the curved part of the characteristic close to the origin will be affected by the doping level and may therefore vary between devices. For instance, higher doping tends to increase the gain at low current density. The straight part of the characteristic is proportionately much less affected by the doping level and can be expected to be more consistent between different devices. Curve B represents more average results.

5.2.2   Double Heterostructure

We deal first with the threshold current density of the GaAs/(GaAl)As double heterostructure since it exhibits a relatively simple behaviour. Most

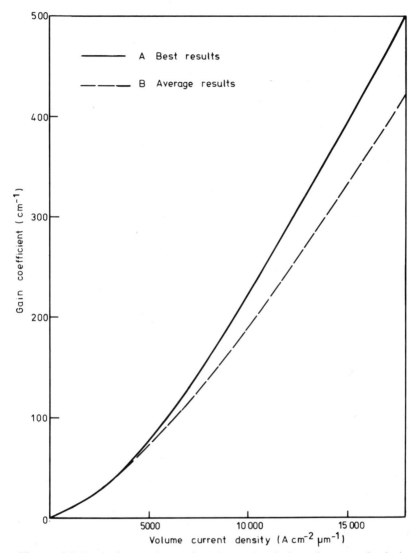

Figure 5.5 Typical experimentally observed relations between intrinsic optical gain and current density in GaAs, best and average curves given

of the characteristic features of this behaviour can be illustrated by considering how the threshold current depends on the thickness d of the active layer. For large values of d ($>0.5\,\mu$m) the behaviour is straightforward and the threshold current density is almost directly proportional to the thickness of the layer. The optical guiding in these circumstances is good so that the actual optical gain of the guided mode is little less than the intrinsic gain of the active layer, or in other words the

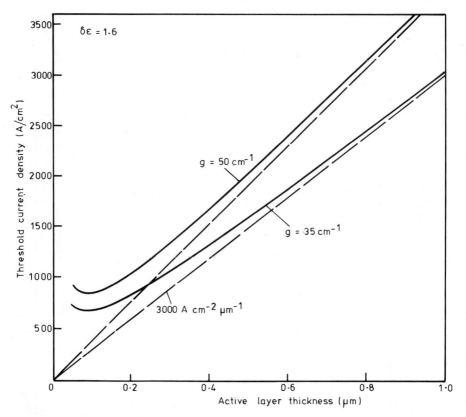

Figure 5.6   Relation between threshold current density and active layer thickness in a $Ga_{1-x}Al_x$ As/GaAs double heterostructure laser. Active layer thickness up to 1 μm with dielectric constant step of 1.6 and laser gain of 35 and 50 cm^{-1}

confinement factor Γ is close to unity. For a typical laser gain of, say, 35 cm^{-1} the threshold current density is around 3000 A cm^{-2} per μm thickness of the active layer, as indicated in Figure 5.6. The exact value depends on the doping level.

As d is reduced the effective width s of the optical distribution does not decrease in proportion, and for d less than about 0.2 μm s increases with a further reduction in d. This eventually leads to an increase in threshold current density per unit area, as indicated in Figure 5.6 and in more detail in Figure 5.7. The minimum threshold current density occurs at an appreciably smaller value of d than does minimum optical spread on account of the non-linear gain/current characteristic. The width of the minimum optical distribution that can be achieved can be considerably reduced by increasing the dielectric constant step $\delta\epsilon$ at the heterojunctions and hence a lower threshold current density can be obtained. Figure 5.7

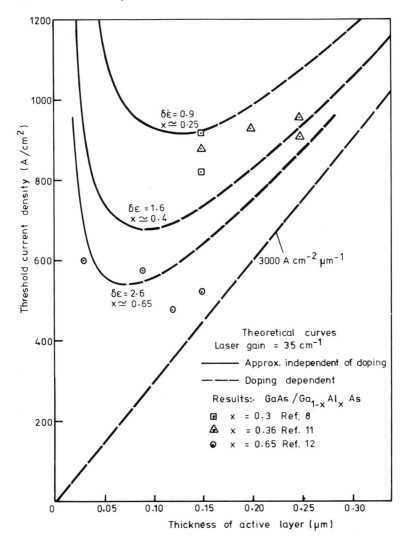

Figure 5.7 Relation between threshold current density and active layer thickness in a $Ga_{1-x}Al_x$ As/GaAs double heterostructure laser. Active layer thickness up to 0.3 μm with laser gain of 35 cm^{-1} and dielectric constant steps of 0.9, 1.6, and 2.6. Particular experimental results also shown

shows this effect. For a typical laser gain of 35 cm^{-1} the minimum in the curve of threshold current density versus d drops from 900 to 500 A cm^{-2} as the dielectric step $\delta\epsilon$ is increased from 0.9 to 2.6. These limits correspond respectively to approximately 20 and 60 per cent changes in the AlAs content across the heterojunction. The active layer thickness which gives minimum threshold current density also varies with the dielectric constant step, dropping from 0.12 to 0.07 μm as $\delta\epsilon$ is increased from 0.9 to 2.6.

The lowest threshold current density that has been experimentally observed in (GaAl)As/GaAs double heterostructure lasers has been reported by Ettenberg.[12] The results were obtained on lasers with a large step in composition at the heterojunction. The associated change in AlAs content was around 65 per cent. The lasers were of sawn cavity type, of length 400 μm, and with active layer thicknesses varying between 0.03 and 0.15 μm. The measured values of threshold current as a function of d are indicated in Figure 5.7. The lowest current density measured was

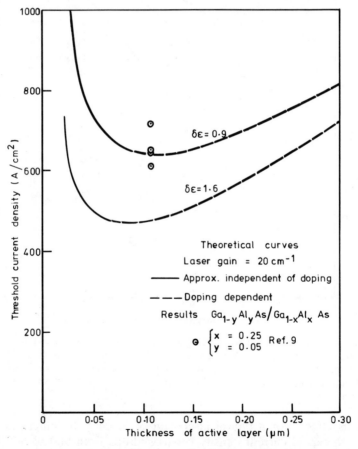

Figure 5.8 Relation between threshold current density and active layer thickness in a (GaAl)As/GaAs double heterostructure laser. As for Figure 5.7, but with laser gain of 20 cm^{-1}

475 A cm^{-2} for $d = 0.12\ \mu$m. The results are reasonably consistent with the predicted curve for $\delta\epsilon = 2.6$. Any discrepancy can probably be attributed to variations amongst individual units of the total laser gain which, with low scattering loss, might drop below the 35 cm^{-1} of the curve to a minimum value of around 30 cm^{-1}. Other experimental results[8,11] for double heterostructure lasers with smaller dielectric constant steps are also shown in Figure 5.7, and they also show reasonable agreement with the curves. It is obvious that a large AlAs content in the passive layers confers considerable benefit in threshold current density. However, this occurs at the expense of a broadened far-field beam width. For instance, the angle to the half power points for the laser with the 475 A cm^{-2} threshold was 60°.

The curves in Figure 5.8 show how the threshold in double heterostructure lasers can be reduced by reducing the laser gain to 20 cm^{-1} using, for instance, longer lasers or lasers with reflective coatings. This lowers the threshold current density for lasers of given dielectric step by about 30 per cent. The experimental results which are indicated in the figure were obtained by the author and co-workers[8] on double heterostructure lasers 500 μm long with a dielectric step of 0.9 and with an Al reflector on one end. The lowest threshold current density was 610 A cm^{-2}, associated with a far-field beam angle of 30°.

A general indication of the variation of threshold current density in double heterostructures as a function of temperature is given in Figure 5.2. The behaviour results from an interaction of several factors including (a) the fundamental variation of stimulated gain as a function of temperature, and (b) the variation of the effectiveness of the heterojunction carrier confinement barriers with temperature, as described in Chapter 3, Section 3.2.4. In many instances the temperature dependence around room temperature can be approximately described by the empirical function $\exp(T/T_0)$, where T is absolute temperature and T_0 is a constant for any given laser which may have values in the range 80–160°.

5.2.3 Single Heterostructure and Effect of Temperature

The threshold current density of the single heterostructure laser depends in a generally similar way to that of the double heterostructure on the thickness of the active layer and on the size of the dielectric constant step. The important step is the smaller of the two confining steps, i.e. the one at the p–n junction. This step is more than an order of magnitude smaller than in the double heterostructure and has therefore to be used in conjunction with an active layer which is about an order of magnitude wider. This result of the lower dielectric constant step can be put to advantage in many applications (e.g. high peak power, lower beam divergence), but there is a more inconvenient consequence which must also be taken into account. The size of the step is not much greater than the perturbation of the dielectric constant in the active layer which results from passing current through the device. Hence the strength of the waveguiding depends not only on the waveguide structure itself but also on all the other factors which affect the threshold current density. This interaction is very important in single heterostructure lasers and is discussed in detail below.

The size of the dielectric step at the p–n junction is determined mainly by the difference in electron concentration on the two sides. The electron concentration on the n-side depends on the doping but that on the p-side depends on the amount of carrier injection. The dielectric step therefore becomes smaller as the injection current is increased. Thus, any attempt to increase the gain by increasing the current density will partially be counteracted by a weakening of the optical guiding. This can have a potentially disastrous effect on the threshold, which may be simply seen as follows.

Consider the limiting condition at which real dielectric waveguiding ceases as the current density in the laser is increased. Because the unsymmetrical waveguide in a single heterostructure has a cut-off (see Chapter 4, Section 4.14 and Figure 4.8) waveguiding ceases slightly before the point where the injected carrier concentration in the active layer reaches the electron concentration of the n-passive layer and the dielectric constants of the two regions become equal. The value of the dielectric constant step at cut-off depends on the thickness d of the active layer. Hence the limiting current density depends both on the doping of the n-type region and on d. As J approaches the limiting value, the optical distribution widens and the confinement factor Γ approaches zero. A point is therefore reached, at a somewhat lower value of current density of, say, J_c, where despite the increasing intrinsic gain the overall gain of the optical wave reaches a maximum. The value of this maximum gain increases for higher n-doping or larger d and, because of the characteristics of the intrinsic gain, decreases as the temperature is raised.

When the operating condition in a single heterostructure laser lies close to this maximum value of gain then quite small changes of any of the above parameters can prevent the device operating in a dielectric guided mode, and hence can quench the lasing. A very considerable increase in current density will usually restart the lasing, but in a homojunction type of mode, where gain guiding, rather than dielectric guiding, is the controlling factor.

Experimental investigations of the effect of active layer thickness, doping level, and temperature on the threshold current density of single heterostructure lasers have been made by a number of workers.[13-16] Figure 5.9(a) and (b) shows typical plots of threshold current density J_{th} against active layer thickness at temperatures of 80 and 300 K, respectively. The

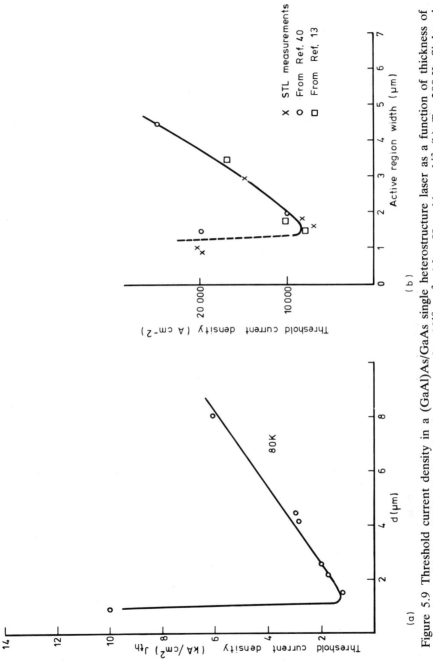

Figure 5.9 Threshold current density in a (GaAl)As/GaAs single heterostructure laser as a function of thickness of active layer. (a) $T = 80$ K. Te-doped substrate $n = 2 \times 10^{18}$ cm^{-3}. (b) $T = 300$ K. Si-doped substrates $n = 3.5$–5×10^{18} cm^{-3}. After Hayashi et al.[13]

curve in Figure 5.9(a) for results at 80 K applies for Te-doped substrates with $n = 2 \times 10^{18}$ cm^{-3} and that results at 300 K applies for Si-doped substrates with n in the range 3.5–5×10^{18} cm^{-3}. The higher substrate n-doping is necessary at 300 K to prevent waveguide breakdown.

The curves in Figure 5.9 show a general similarity to the curves for the width of the optical distribution versus the active layer thickness for a single heterostructure waveguide in Figure 4.8, Chapter 4. The threshold current density can in fact be closely linked to the width of the optical distribution. The current density is a minimum for the values of the active layer thickness, d_{min}, which give maximum optical confinement. d_{min} increases somewhat as the doping level of the n-type GaAs is reduced but in general lies around 1.5 μm. The threshold current density rises considerably as d is increased above about 2.5 μm. The way it increases depends significantly on temperature. At room temperature the threshold rapidly becomes a superlinear function of d, whereas at low temperatures it remains a linear or even a sublinear function of d. The superlinear behaviour at room temperature starts when d first exceeds the diffusion length of electrons. The region of the active layer furthest from the p–n junction is then no longer completely inverted. The optical loss that arises raises the threshold and causes the non-linearity. At low enough temperature the partially inverted region at the far side of the active layer has very much less effect because the lasing emission is produced from the deeper states in the band tail and is generated at a wavelength that is too long to be significantly absorbed. Hence the threshold current density at low temperature is much more linearly dependent on the thickness of the active layer, even when it is greater than a diffusion length. Another way of viewing this behaviour is to consider the increasing similarity between a single heterostructure laser and a homostructure laser as the thickness of the active layer of the single heterostructure laser is increased. The temperature sensitivity of the single heterostructure with wide d is therefore greater and the deterioration in threshold current is more evident at the higher temperatures.

Decreasing d first takes the threshold current density down to a minimum value and then causes it to rise rapidly again. The steepness of the branch of the associated curve below the optimum thickness can be partly attributed to the rapid way in which an unsymmetrical waveguide approaches cut-off as its dimensions are reduced (see Figure 4.8). However, the effect is enhanced because the current density rises towards its critical value of J_c. There is a reduction in the dielectric step which reinforces the result of a reduction in d and further steepens the curve. The fact that the increase in current also contributes to the breakdown in guiding can be deduced from the higher value of d at which this occurs at higher temperature where the current density is greater.

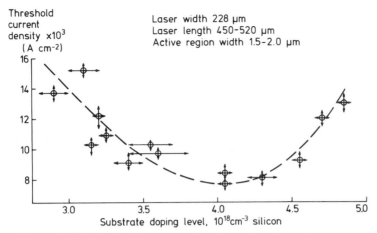

Figure 5.10 Threshold current density of a (GaAl)As/GaAs single heterostructure laser as a function of doping level of n-type layer. Active layer thickness 2 μm. After Henshall and Selway[30]

Figure 5.10 shows the effect of the doping level n of the n-type GaAs layer on the threshold current density at room temperature for single heterostructure lasers with an active layer thickness of 2 μm. The threshold current density decreases from a high value at $n = 2 \times 10^{18}$ cm^{-3} to a minimum value at $n = 4 \times 10^{18}$ cm^{-3}. This decrease can be attributed to the narrowing of the optical distribution as the waveguiding is strengthened by the increasing dielectric step at the p–n junction. Beyond an n-concentration of 4×10^{18} cm^{-3} the threshold current density increases again. This is probably a result of deep centres being generated in the material by the high impurity content, causing non-radiative recombination of the injected carriers, and taking additional current.

Figure 5.11 shows the effect of temperature on the threshold current density in single heterostructure lasers. At a critical temperature T_c and current density J_c there is a discontinuous rise which takes the threshold current to a very high value. Also, at temperatures somewhat below T_c it is possible to quench the lasing if the current is increased sufficiently above threshold. Hence an S-shaped characteristic appears on the plot, as shown in the figure. The temperature T_c depends on the doping level of the n-type layer and on the thickness of the active layer. This phenomenon is a good example of the behaviour described earlier where additional injected electrons weaken the optical guiding mechanism and cause complete cessation of lasing as J approaches J_c. The mechanism has been described by a number of authors.[14,17–19] For temperatures below T_c the current at which guiding ceases and the laser is quenched (on the backward slope of the S characteristic) becomes progressively greater than J_c as J_{th} diminishes.

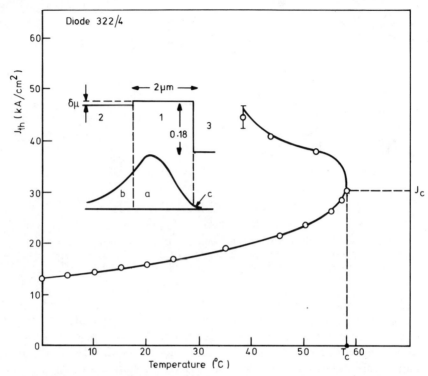

Figure 5.11 Effect of temperature on threshold current density of a (GaAl)As/GaAs single heterostructure laser

This effect occurs because that part of the current which exceeds the threshold contributes proportionately less than the remainder to increasing the injected carrier concentration.

Selway *et al.*[18] demonstrated experimentally that the anomalous increase in threshold current in the neighbourhood of T_c is in fact accompanied by a change in the waveguiding characteristics, by using observations on the variation of the far-field beamwidth with temperature. The amount by which the near field broadens as temperature is increased can be derived from these measurements and it accounts satisfactorily for the increased threshold current. The way the near-field/current characteristic interacts with the gain/current characteristics is illustrated in Figure 5.12 for a typical device. Here both the reciprocal of the confinement factor $1/\Gamma$ and the ratio of the intrinsic gain g_i to the fixed mode gain g are plotted against current density for various temperatures. Threshold occurs where the curves cross ($g_i/g = 1/\Gamma$ or $g = \Gamma g_i$). The $1/\Gamma$ curve for a particular device can be derived from the far-field measurement and the known thickness of the active layer. The intrinsic-gain-versus-current characteristic can be

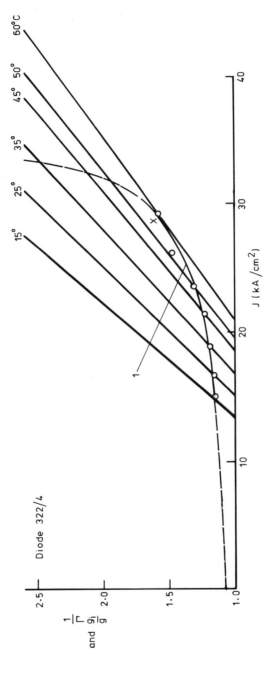

Figure 5.12 Dependence of optical loading factor and intrinsic gain at various temperatures on current density in a typical single heterostructure laser. Optical loading factor $(1/\Gamma)$ given by curve 1

estimated by extrapolating the threshold/temperature characteristic from temperatures well below the kink and from general knowledge of the characteristics of the active layer. The points of intersection of the two sets of curves can then be found to reproduce the measured thresholds over the range of temperatures near T_c. Above T_c there is no intersection between the gain curve and the $1/\Gamma$ curve, and so no guided lasing can take place.

Various curious transient effects and delay phenomena occur in single heterostructure lasers just below T_c. These can also be explained by loss of waveguiding, and are dealt with in Chapter 7, Section 7.6.

5.2.4   LGR or SCH Structures

The LGR laser design provides a means for matching the gain characteristics of the active layer to the optical load of the resonator under all conditions, and hence can in principle provide a lower threshold current density than the other types of laser. As mentioned previously this can be achieved by appropriate choice of the relative thicknesses of the carrier confinement layer and the optical confinement region (see Section 5.2.1.).

We first consider LGR structures that are designed solely to produce a low threshold current density, and compare their performance with similar 'equivalent' double heterostructures. 'Equivalent' structures will be defined as those with identical compositions of semiconductor in their outer layers. Thus, an LGR structure which is equivalent to a particular double heterostructure is obtained by splitting the active layer of the double heterostructure into three layers, the centre one of which retains the original composition and the outer pair of which have a somewhat higher bandgap. The increase in bandgap should not be too great or the light will spread unnecessarily. In (GaAl)As/GaAs devices, for instance, 12 per cent extra AlAs in the added layers is appropriate. This is adequate for confining injected carriers to the active layer when backed by appreciable additional composition steps at the outer heterojunctions. The outermost layers will have a similar composition in both types of structure. The variables of the LGR design are the dimensions of the layers, i.e. the thickness d_1 of the active layer, and the combined thickness $\Sigma_3 d$ of the three centre layers. In Figure 5.13 the threshold current density for such a structure calculated from the GaAs gain/current characteristic is plotted against the thickness of the centre layer for a structure in which $\Sigma_3 d$ is adjusted to give maximum optical confinement for each value of d_1 concerned. This is done for two values of the dielectric constant step $\delta\epsilon$ between the centre and outermost layers and for two values of the required optical gain g. Curves are also given for the equivalent double heterostructures.

(GaAl)As/GaAs LGR lasers start to show an advantage in threshold

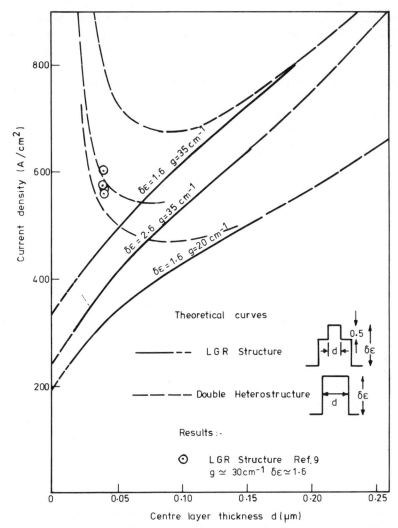

Figure 5.13 Comparison of threshold current density versus active layer thickness for (GaAl)As/GaAs LGR structures with similar relation for equivalent double heterostructures. Curves given for dielectric steps between innermost and outermost layers of 1.6 and 2.6 for laser gain of 35 cm⁻¹ and of 1.6 for laser gain of 20 cm⁻¹

current density over the equivalent double heterostructures when the thickness of the active layer is reduced below about 0.12 μm and in principle they can be expected to show a progressively increasing advantage down to an active layer thickness of around 0.02 μm. At this point the threshold current density would be less than the best value for the double heterostructure by about 40–50 per cent, ranging between 250 and 400 A cm^{-2} for the parameters considered. Devices have not yet been made with such thin layers, but the predicted performance is based on the measured levels of optical gain that have been obtained in thicker layers at the relevant very high pumping level. For even thinner layers ($<0.02\ \mu$m) the necessary pumping level would exceed the highest yet experimentally investigated. The extrapolated curves that apply to this region are shown dashed. Below some as yet unknown value of d they become inaccurate, and over-estimate the reduction in threshold. Over the range of d between the latter low value and up to about 0.15μm the active layer is operating in the linear part of the gain/current characteristic given in Figure 5.5, and the threshold current in (GaAl)As/GaAs devices is well represented by the relation (see Section 2.6.2, Chapter 2)

$$J_{\text{th}} = 4000d_1 + Bg\left(\frac{s}{k}\right) \tag{5.5}$$

where J_{th} is measured in A cm^{-2}, g in cm^{-2}, and d_1 and s in μm. s is the effective width of the optical distribution as determined by the centre three layers of the structure. B has a value of 28 A cm^{-1} μm^{-1} for the best devices and a value of around 33 A cm^{-1} μm^{-1} for average devices.

Very few experimental results are available for the range of LGR structures represented by the curves in Figure 5.13; those that are available are plotted in the figure.[8] The structures measured were not optimized for optical distribution and show results somewhat inferior to the predicted behaviour. It is not known yet to what extent inadequate carrier confinement or non-radiative recombination at heterojunction interfaces will prevent the full advantage of the structure being realized, but it is probable that performances close to the predicted curves can be achieved.

The parameter to which the threshold current is most sensitive is the threshold optical gain g, a reduction in the required gain causing a considerable decrease in threshold current. The required gain can be reduced by applying reflective coatings to one or both end-faces of the laser. The ultimate limitation is, however, the optical loss of the waveguide. If the best measured values of optical scattering and free carrier loss could be combined in one structure, and suitable reflective coatings were applied to the end-faces then the gain would be minimized and the threshold current density at room temperature in (GaAl)As/GaAs devices might well be reduced to values in the vicinity of 200 A cm^{-2}.

When LGR or separate confinement structures are designed particularly for operation at high peak power or for narrow beam widths in the plane perpendicular to the heterojunctions then a certain width must be specified for the optical distribution in the guided mode which may be considerably greater than the minimum that could be achieved. The threshold current density becomes very much a function of the value of this width and also of the optical gain required in the laser. In some structures the current density may also be increased by poor coupling to the active layer (small k) and by poor confinement of injected carriers.

The three-dimensional plot in Figure 5.14 illustrates the way that the threshold current density in LGR structures depends on the thickness of the active layer and the product of the laser gain with the effective width of the optical distribution $g(s/k)$. The contours of the constant threshold current density are shown. These are universal curves based on the gain/current characteristic of curve B in Figure 5.5. Curve B, which is slightly degraded with respect to curve A used previously, appears to give a good representation of the behaviour of average lasers rather than the best lasers of any given type. The measured performance of various actual lasers is also shown. The lasers include symmetrical SCH devices as reported by Panish et al.[7] and Thompson and Kirkby,[8] unsymmetrical SCH devices as reported by Thompson, Henshall et al.,[9] and some double heterostructure devices. The points indicate the measured values of d and the estimated values of $g(s/k)$ for each device together with a bar the length of which represents the difference between the measured threshold current density and that predicted by the plot. All the experimental results, whether on symmetrical or unsymmetrical SCH structures or on double heterostructures, show reasonable agreement with the surface that represents the predicted value of threshold current density in Figure 5.14, there being few discrepancies greater than 10 per cent.

Examination of the threshold surface in Figure 5.14 shows that it can be divided into two regions by the diagonal line OA. The contours of current density for constant d are straight lines to the right of this line [where the approximate linear equation (5.5) is applicable] as also are the contours of constant threshold current density. To the left of the line OA both sets of contours are curved. The amount of the curvature depends to some extent on the doping level of the active layer.

It is evident from Figure 5.14 that, for a given value of $g(s/k)$, a low threshold current density is obtained by choosing an active layer thickness small enough to bring the operating point well to the right of the line OA. This procedure cannot, however, be taken to extremes. Eventually, for small enough values of d, gain saturation must set in. The surface in Figure 5.14, that represents current density should therefore bend upwards at some point close enough to the right-hand edge as a result of the contours for constant d themselves curving upwards beyond a certain value of gs/kd. The region where this might happen has not yet been explored experimentally. The result obtained at point C in Figure 5.14 corresponds to the highest injected carrier concentration so far employed and is therefore the closest to gain saturation. However, there is still no

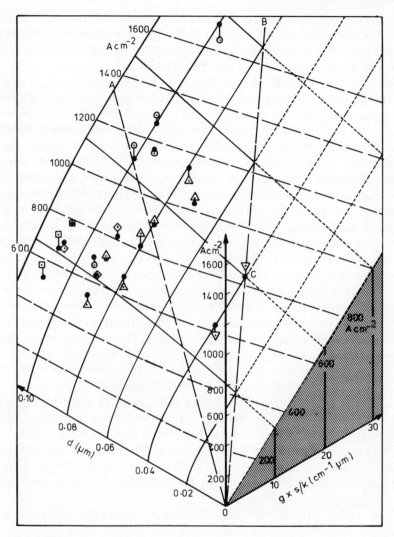

Figure 5.14 Threshold current density in (GaAl)As/GaAs LGR structures as a function of active layer thickness and product of gain and thickness of optical cavity. Contours of constant current density shown. Various experimental results also shown with extent of deviation from theoretical predictions indicated

significant sign of saturation. The part of the surface of threshold current density to the right of the line *OCB* is an extrapolation which is indicated by the dashed contours. The extent to which this region can be used for obtaining a further reduction in current density and the point at which the extrapolation becomes invalid remains to be established.

The coupling k (see Chapter 4, Section 4.1.3) of the optical distribution to the active layer has a strong effect on the threshold current density of all lasers. In symmetrical SCH structures with thin active layers the coupling for the zero-order transverse mode is excellent, since the position of the active layer coincides with the peak of the optical distribution, and $k \simeq 1$. The zero-order mode is the most strongly coupled mode, although only by a small margin compared with the higher even order modes, if the active layer thickness is large enough for those modes to propagate.

In unsymmetrical structures the coupling of the zero-order mode to the active layer depends very much on the thickness of the active layer, and if more than one transverse mode is within cut-off the coupling of the zero-order mode is in general the least. The effects of the active layer thickness on the spread of the optical distribution in the zero-order mode and on the threshold current density are illustrated by the computed curves of Figure 5.15. s and s/k are shown as functions of d for two particular unsymmetrical four-layer (GaAl)As/GaAs structures of total waveguide thickness around 0.9 and 1.3 μm, respectively.[9] The threshold current

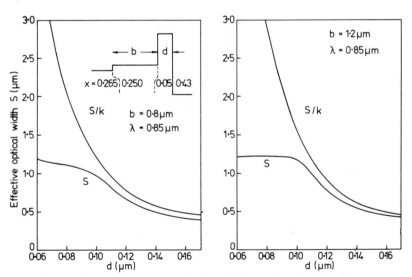

Figure 5.15 Relation between effective width s of optical distribution and optical loading s/k on active layer as a function of thickness of active layer in two typical unsymmetrical $Ga_{1-x}Al_xAs$ four-layer structures

density is linearly related to s/k [equation (5.5)]. When d is reduced below a certain value which, for the carrier confinement step of 20 per cent AlAs concerned, lies around $0.11\ \mu$m there is a rapid reduction of k and a consequent rapid increase in threshold current density. This is caused by the peak of the optical distribution moving out of the active layer into the 'b' layer. A similar behaviour occurs when the active layer does not lie right at the edge of the waveguide (five-layer structure), but the critical value of d concerned diminishes as the active layer is moved towards the centre. In both four- and five-layer unsymmetrical structures there is therefore a minimum value of d, and for given waveguide dimensions, a maximum value of s that can be used without causing an unnecessary increase in the threshold current density. All the unsymmetrical lasers,

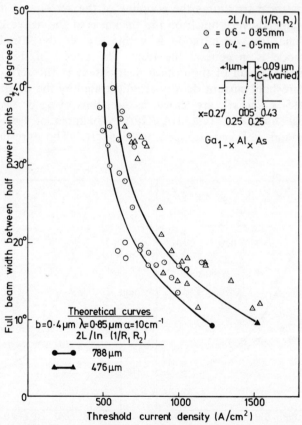

Figure 5.16 Measured relation between threshold current density in unsymmetrical five-layer structures, and far-field beam angle for different laser lengths. Theoretically derived curves also shown

whose performance is illustrated in Figure 5.14, had values of d within the acceptable range and values of k close to unity.

The width of the optical distribution in unsymmetrical five-layer structures is critically dependent upon the thickness of the active layer, which must be held within tight tolerances. However, the unsymmetrical structure offers the advantage, compared with the symmetrical structure, that for any given value of the width of the optical distribution a considerably larger value of active layer thickness may be used. This eases the demands on the LPE growth process.

For lasers operating in the zero-order transverse mode the far-field beam width perpendicular to the junction is approximately inversely proportional to the effective optical width of the guided wave, over a certain range of the parameters, as disucssed in Chapter 4, Section 4.1.5. Hence there is a close relation between the threshold current density and the far-field beamwidth. This is illustrated by the measured values of the threshold current density and beamwidth given in Figure 5.16 for two sets of unsymmetrical (GaAl)As/GaAs five-layer lasers of varying characteristics. The independent variable in these sets is the distance separating the active layer from the edge of the optical waveguide, which has a similar effect to the thickness of the active layer in determining the width of the optical distributions (as in Figure 5.15). These results apply to lasers of two different lengths, as indicated on the figure, with reflective coatings applied to the back face. Curves are also given showing the estimated threshold current density calculated using the methods described above. These results show to what extent the low threshold current density must be sacrificed in order to obtain a narrow beamwidth.

5.2.5 Temperature Sensitivity of Threshold in LGR and SCH Lasers

Poor carrier confinement in the active layer of heterostructure lasers results in an excess current which raises the threshold current density, and in particular causes it to increase in a temperature-dependent way, so that the overall temperature sensitivity of threshold is increased. As discussed in Chapter 3, leakage of injected carriers is determined by the height of the heterojunction barrier. A minimum composition change of approximately 20 per cent in AlAs is necessary at the heterojunction in double heterostructures for satisfactory performance.

In a five-layer structure designed for a wide optical distribution the situation is more complicated than in a conventional double heterostructure. First, the combination of a narrow active layer with a wide optical distribution, which demands a higher current density per unit volume of active layer, raises the injected carrier concentration by a factor of two or so, and increases the leakage by a much larger factor. This condition, of course, also applies in a double heterostructure if the active layer is narrowed in order to obtain a wide distribution of the optical field.

Secondly, the five-layer device has additional outer heterojunction barriers which also control the carrier leakage. Carriers which escape from the active layer across the first heterojunction barriers may be stopped by the second heterojunction barriers, provided the barriers are of sufficient height, and hence be confined within the optical resonator. In the double heterostructure quite a low concentration of leaking carriers causes an appreciable excess current because of the ease with which the carriers diffuse away once they have surmounted the confinement barrier, particularly if they consist of the more mobile electrons. The relatively large diffusion length of electrons allows them to spread into a volume which is an order of magnitude greater than that of the active layer so that the total recombination rate, even at low concentration, is large or, worse still if the passive layer is thin, the large diffusion length allows the electrons to spill over into the adjacent lower band-gap GaAs at an even greater rate. The second heterojunction barrier in a five-layer structure, however, confines the escaping carriers to a smaller volume where the recombination rate is much more limited provided that the barrier is spaced considerably closer to the first barrier than the 5–10 μm diffusion length of electrons. The second barrier therefore reduces the electron leakage current very significantly compared to that in a double heterostructure with a comparable first barrier. The exact effect depends on the recombination characteristics of the intermediate layer concerned, which are a function of its doping and its deep level content.

In the unsymmetrical five-layer structure only one of the outer heterojunction barriers can be made large, but it can be made as large as necessary since there are no transverse mode considerations to limit its size. It can be placed on the p-side of the active layer, where the predominant leakage due to electrons occurs, at a small distance from the active layer, Hence it provides an excellent additional leakage barrier where it is most required, and the volume into which the leaking electrons penetrate, and where they recombine, can be severely restricted.

Sufficient measurements have not yet been made on all the various five-layer structures to give a clear idea in practice of how successfully the outer heterojunction barriers can make up for poor carrier confinement at the inner heterojunctions. Judging from the threshold results given in Figure 5.14 it seems that many of the structures are satisfactory at room temperature. Measurements carried out at higher temperature to compare the performance of double heterostructures and unsymmetrical five-layer structures, both with marginal active layer confinement barriers of 20 per cent AlAs composition step, show the advantage of the additional effect of one outer heterojunction.[9]

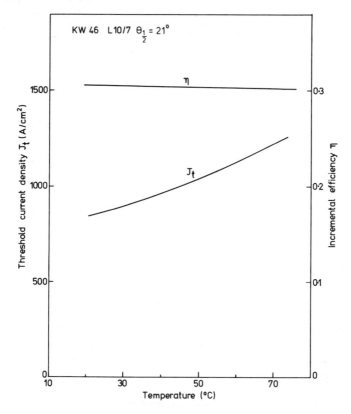

Figure 5.17 Effect of temperature on threshold current density and incremental efficiency in (GaAl)As/GaAs unsymmetrical five-layer structure

Typical results for the temperature effects in an unsymmetrical five-layer device are given in Figure 5.17. The threshold current density increases by a factor of 1.44 between 10 and 65°C and the incremental quantum efficiency barely changes. The increase in threshold is approximately the same as is found in double heterostructure lasers with good carrier confinement.

In the symmetrical five-layer laser the electrons which leak out of the active layer have a larger volume' in which to recombine than in the unsymmetrical structure, although normally a much smaller volume than in double heterostructures. The relative size of the leakage current depends on a number of factors which must be carefully considered in any particular configuration.

The extent to which the carrier recombine outside the active layer can be illustrated by the spontaneous spectrum. Figure 5.18 shows the

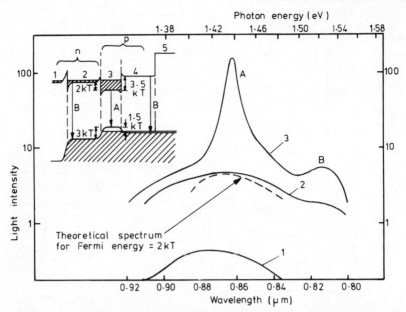

Figure 5.18 Spontaneous spectrum of symmetrical five-layer structure with marginal confinement of injected carrier in active layer measured at three different levels of current. Spectral peak observable corresponding to recombination of carriers leaking into adjacent passive layers which increases superlinearly with current

spectrum obtained for a marginal symmetrical (GaAl)As/GaAs five-layer structure by the author (0.04-μm active layer, 0.85-μm resonator, 12 per cent inner AlAs confinement step).[15] These devices showed an anomalously high threshold current for short laser length and this coincided with the appearance of the high energy component B in the spectrum. This component is attributed to the recombination of carriers which have leaked into both passive layers. It increases superlinearly with current, and hence becomes prominent quite abruptly as the required gain of the laser is increased by reducing the laser length.

However, in cases where the confinement step, the confinement factor Γ, and the resonator thickness are appropriately chosen, the outer heterojunctions can be used to reduce the leakage current to an entirely acceptable level. This may in fact be the most important way in which the five-layer concept contributes to the performance of narrow-beam, high peak power lasers. An active layer of reasonable thickness (around 0.1 μm) but rather low composition step is used to allow the light to spread appropriately, and the outermost heterojunction steps, nominally provided to set a final limit to the optical distribution, may perform a more important function in containing the electron leakage current.

5.2.6   LOC Lasers

The threshold current density in LOC lasers, and the way it depends on the various design parameters of the heterostructure, has not been investigated so extensively as that for SCH or LGR lasers. However, the results that have been obtained, allowing for the less precise confinement of the injected carriers, confirm that the same general treatment is applicable.

Lockwood and Kressel[2,3] investigated LOC devices with a range of resonator widths w varying between 1 and 7 μm, all with an active layer thickness of around 0.5 μm. The threshold current density increased with w over this range from 1500 to 8000 A cm^{-2}. Allowing for uncertainty in the effective optical width s and the coupling constant k, and assuming some leakage current, this is in reasonable agreement with the predictions of equation (5.5).

Paoli *et al.* and Hakki[5,6] investigated a structure with a 2-μm thick resonator and a 1-μm thick active layer. This gave a threshold current density of around 10,000 A cm^{-2} for a 12-μm wide stripe, which was estimated to be equivalent to about 6000 A cm^{-2} in a wide device with no current spreading. This latter figure is also in reasonable agreement with equation (5.5).

5.3   HIGH PEAK POWER

5.3.1   General Remarks

At high peak power lasers suffer from catastrophic damage to the output facet.[20–23] This occurs when the optical flux density at the output reaches a certain critical value, and it can take place virtually instantaneously during one single current pulse of appropriate length and total energy. The facet is mechanically damaged, and the effect on its reflectivity is sufficient to produce a drastic deterioration in the laser output. Figure 5.19 shows a typical example of the damage sustained by the facet. Tiny cracks and pits are formed in the vicinity of the junction, where the optical flux is greatest, and cracks or dislocations may propagate back from the damaged region into the bulk of the semiconductor.[23] The damage occurs when the electric component of the optical field at the facet reaches a certain value. Surfaces which are coated with an anti-reflective dielectric layer can withstand up to three times the emerging flux density possible with uncoated surfaces, because the considerable contribution to the total electric field from the reflected wave in the uncoated laser is then largely absent.[24]

The critical flux density depends on the semiconductor material used for making the laser and particularly its active layer. (GaIn)(AsP), for instance

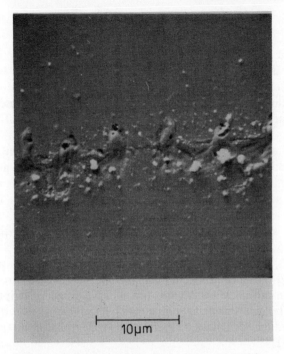

Figure 5.19 Catastrophic facet damage resulting
from excessive optical intensity

has been found to be considerably superior to GaAs.[25] The critical flux is
also appreciably greater in materials with a bandgap greater than the
photon energy of the emitted light. Thus special structures in which the
light is made to exit through a transparent region, such as the Zn diffused
window-stripe laser described in Chapter 6, can withstand considerably
higher power.[26]

The critical flux density also depends on the length of the current pulse,
on temperature and, naturally, when average values of flux are considered,
on the uniformity of the emission. It is relatively independent of duty cycle
up to the values at which steady heating becomes important. Some damage
to the laser faces can occur at power levels which are 10–20 per cent
below the levels that produce catastrophic failure. In these circumstances
cumulative degradation takes place over relatively long periods.

Eliseev[27] has discussed possible mechanisms which may cause the
catastrophic degradation and concludes that although the final damage is
caused by local heating the precise phenomenon which initiates the
temperature rise is not yet fully understood. Recent results on different
semiconductor materials and on the window-stripe laser suggest that
surface recombination plays a part in the process. The surface recombination

centres constitute such a strong sink for electron-hole pairs that the inverted state in the active layer is locally lost adjacent to the facet, and the material becomes absorbing. As the laser output is increased more carrier pairs are created in this region by absorption. The extent of the non-inverted region decreases but there is an increasing flow of carrier pairs to the surface by diffusion. As a result surface recombination and heating increase approximately as the square root of the light intensity. When the heating becomes strong enough a run-away process ensues as the bandgap diminishes and the optical absorption process becomes even stronger. At present only this latter stage of the phenomenon can be quantified with any precision.

For any particular type of junction the onset of damage, or the 'burn-off' level, is usually related to the power per unit width of the emitting junction. Because of the limit to the flux density the maximum power per millimetre of junction width depends on the extent to which the emitting area spreads in the direction perpendicular to the junction and, as we have described previously, this depends on the laser heterostructure concerned.

5.3.2 Double Heterostructure

The field distribution in double heterostructure lasers varies widely according to the dielectric waveguide parameters and the critical power is found in practice to vary accordingly. Eliseev[27] has shown that, for relatively large values of the active layer thickness d, the critical power in (GaAl)As/GaAs devices with 100 ns current pulses increases approximately linearly with d from 10 W mm^{-1} for $d = 0.5\ \mu$m to 60 W mm^{-1} for $d = 3\ \mu$m. However, devices with $d > 1\ \mu$m are not normally practical because they propagate higher order transverse modes with wide beam widths.

Kirkby and Thompson[28] have shown that for much narrower values of d it is possible to make use of the increasing size of the near-field width with decreasing d to obtain relatively high 'burn-off' power with zero-order transverse mode operation and narrow far-field beamwidth. Measurements were made on a (GaAl)As/GaAs double heterostructure with asymmetrical composition steps to exaggerate the broadening of the optical distribution as the active layer thickness was made to approach its cut-off value of $0.07\ \mu$m. When d was decreased to 0.11 μm the near-field broadened to give an effective optical width of $0.6\ \mu$m and a burn-off level of 30–40 W mm^{-1} for a 200-ns pulse length compared with 10 W mm^{-1} for wider active layers.

The above results for double heterostructures with both narrow and wide d are reasonably consistent with each other and correspond to a critical power density of around 5 MW cm^{-2} for a 200-ns current pulse.

Eliseev[24] found that the critical power P_c in double heterostructures decreased with the pulse duration time t. Over the range 30–300 ns the relation was approximately $P_c \propto t^{-1/2}$.

Chinone et al.[26] have investigated the peak power capability of 40 and 80-μm wide continuously operating stripe lasers (shallow mesa with only current confinement in the lateral direction—see Chapter 6). These lasers had a very thin active layer ($d = 0.06\ \mu$m) to give a wide near-field distribution. The measured burn-off power under continuous operation was around 5 mW/μm^{-1} in those units which were sufficiently well heat sunk not to reach saturation below this value. This corresponds to a power density of 1 MW cm^{-2} which is about one-fifth of the peak power density expected with a 200-ns pulse. Hence the $t^{1/2}$ dependence of peak power mentioned above must level off at times greater than about 5 μs.

Yonezu et al.[26] have investigated the improvement in peak power output that can be obtained from a stripe laser when the region of the active layer adjacent to the output facet is made transparent to the lasing light. This feature is incorporated in the so-called 'window-stripe' laser to which we have previously referred and which is described in Chapter 6. In a double heterostructure window-stripe laser with an active layer thickness of 0.15 μm the measured burn-off power in continuous operation for a 5 μm wide stripe was 15 mW/μm and in pulsed operation with a 100 ns pulse for a 15–20 μm wide optical filament it was 50–100 mW/μm. These figures correspond respectively to peak power densities of 3–4 and 10–20 MW cm^{-2}, which are about a factor of 4 greater than in the conventional devices.

5.3.3 Single Heterostructure

Single heterostructures can operate in a single transverse mode with much wider active layers than double heterostructures and these devices are therefore normally used when high peak powers are required. Burn-off levels are usually in the range 40–100 W cm^{-1} with 200-ns pulses. The exact value depends on the laser junction structure, but is usually higher than that of the double heterostructure with an equally thick active because of the greater penetration of the optical field into the n-layer adjacent to the active layer. Henshall and Selway[30] showed that the burn-off level was proportional to the thickness of the active layer over the range $d = 1.5$–$3.0\ \mu$m. However, it was not found very satisfactory to use active regions much thicker than 2 μm owing to increased threshold and decreased efficiency.

The part of the near-field distribution which penetrates into the n-GaAs provides useful additional power, and single heterostructures with relatively weak guiding have higher burn-off levels, provided that the guiding is not so weak that poor threshold and efficiency is encountered. For example, the use of a low n-doping level produces weaker guiding and a higher burn-off level.[30] Analysis of single heterostructure near-field distributions and burn-off levels[24] suggests a peak optical power density at the facet at failure of 5 MW cm^{-2}, more or less in agreement with results for double heterostructures.

5.3.4 SCH and LGR Lasers

The SCH and LGR lasers have at present been developed to give a peak power output intermediate between that of the double and single heterostructure lasers.

Burn-off figures are not available for the symmetrical five-layer laser, but Casey *et al.*[31] report successful operation at a power level of 22 W mm^{-1} with a pulse length of 200 ns, for a laser with $w = 1.56\ \mu$m, $d = 0.1\ \mu$m ($s = 0.65\ \mu$m).

Henshall[32] has measured the burn-off level for a variety of asymmetrical five-layer lasers for a current pulse length of 200 ns These devices differed mainly in the thickness of the active layer and of the adjacent thin p-doped layer (see Figure 5.3). This variation produces a range of effective widths to the optical distribution perpendicular to the junction, and a range of related far-field beam angles. In assessing actual devices it is more

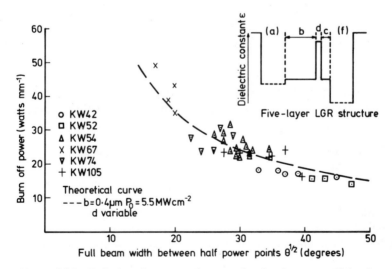

Figure 5.20 Relation between damage level of output light in W mm^{-1} and far-field beam angle in unsymmetrical (GaAl)As/GaAs five-layer structures. 200 ns pulse. Curve shows computed output power at 5.5 MW cm^{-2}. After Henshall[32]

convenient to associate the peak power with the measure far-field beam angle rather than the estimated near-field width. Figure 5.20 shows the measured results. The peak power increases as expected in inverse proportion to the far-field beam width. The curve which corresponds to a power density of 5.5 MW cm^{-2} is shown and the results are in good agreement. To obtain this consistent behaviour it was necessary to select only those lasers in which the output was reasonably uniform across the width of the junction and in which there was no evidence of internally reflected cross modes. The criterion of adequate uniformity is the absence of filaments with more than 4/3 times the average brightness, and the criterion for absence of internal modes is a good incremental efficiency for the laser length concerned.

5.3.5 LOC Lasers

The burn-off levels in LOC lasers are directly related to the thickness of the optical resonator. Kressel et al.[3] report maximum peak power levels for 100-ns pulses which increase from 40 to 160 W mm^{-1} as the combined thickness of the centre two layers is increased from 1.3 to 7 μm. The power density concerned lies around 5 MW cm^{-2} and is similar to that in the other types of lasers.

Hakki and Nash[23] obtained somewhat higher peak power density for 100-ns pulses in LOC stripe lasers with a 12-μm wide stripe and a 2-μm thick optical resonator. The results lay in the range 7–9 MW cm^{-2}. The power density concerned was the estimated peak value at the centre of the stripe, rather than an average value, and this may account for the difference.

The high burn-off levels of 160 W mm^{-1} quoted above for wide LOC lasers were obtained on devices with a double-lobed far-field pattern. This advantage has so far severely limited the application of these devices.

5.4   INCREMENTAL EFFICIENCY

5.4.1 General Remarks

The external incremental quantum efficiency η of a laser is related to the internal efficiency η_0, the resonator absorption coefficient α, the laser length l, and the end-face reflectivities R_1 and R_2 by the equation

$$\eta = \frac{\eta_0}{1 + 2\alpha L/\ln(1/R_1R_2)} \tag{5.6}$$

as derived in Chapter 2, equation (2.91). The absorption coefficient α and the internal efficiency η_0 may be derived for any particular type of laser by measurements of the external efficiency, as described in Chapter 2, Section 2.7.2.3. The values of these quantities are of considerably interest in understanding the overall behaviour.

The absorption coefficient is closely associated with the properties of the dielectric waveguide. As described in Chapter 2, Section 2.7.2.1, the overall absorption is composed of a combination of scattering losses (mainly from irregularities in the heterostructure), band-edge absorption losses (from adjacent non-inverted material), and free carrier losses. The importance of the relative contributions depends on the particular type of heterostructure.

The internal incremental efficiency is a rather imprecise concept which covers any process that diverts a proportion of the power from the lasing output in a way which is independent of current. The lasing process itself need not be taken into consideration in this context since stimulated emission is virtually 100 per cent efficient. Mechanisms which lower the internal efficiency arise as a secondary consequence of maintaining the appropriate degree of inversion as the current is increased. For instance, the concentration of carriers which are not involved, or are less strongly involved, in the lasing process may unavoidably have to be increased as the lasing output is increased. This results in additional power dissipation, either directly in the form of spontaneous emission or lattice heating from non-radiative recombination processes or indirectly as the result of additional leakage current. The non-lasing carriers may either be those which are of the incorrect energy (perhaps those which are isolated in band tails or impurity levels from the general equilibrium) or those which are located in regions of low optical intensity in the laser resonator. Provided that these carriers constitute a constant proportion of the total carrier concentration their effects can be included in the internal efficiency term. In many cases there are unintended variations of electronic gain and optical intensity across the width of the junction which lower the effective internal efficiency. In the most extreme cases the output is obviously filamentary, with the regions between the filaments taking current but not lasing and therefore leading to a severe drop in incremental efficiency.

The injected carrier concentration and the optical gain are intentionally varied over the cross section of a stripe laser. This can affect the overall efficiency of the laser in quite a complicated way. The various processes become dependent upon current, and equation (5.6) for a uniform laser is no longer applicable. The new situation which arises has been analysed by Carroll et al.[33] and is described in Chapter 7, Section 7.4, and illustrated in Figure 7.12. The light/current characteristic is no longer linear. We will not deal with this behaviour further in this section.

Measurement of the way the spontaneous emission output varies with current beyond threshold can elucidate some aspects of the 'internal efficiency'. Paoli[34] and others [35] have shown that in a stripe laser where the optical intensity is sufficiently uniform over the cross section of the active layer the spontaneous emission output is clamped beyond threshold to a fixed value over most of its spectrum. However, over the part of the spectrum where the wavelength is longer than the lasing emission, the intensity of the spontaneous emission continues to increase to some extent beyond threshold. This increase in emission detracts slightly from the lasing efficiency. In lasers where the active layer is thick enough for the intensity of the light to vary appreciably across the thickness, clamping is less effective and measurements show a considerably increase in the output of spontaneous emission over the whole spectrum beyond threshold. In this case the effect would be to decrease considerably the 'internal efficiency' of the laser.

Equation (5.6) predicts that very high incremental efficiency can be obtained from lasers which are either very short or which have end-faces with low reflectivity. It is generally observed in practice, particularly with sawn-cavity lasers, that there is a limit to which the efficiency can be improved by this means, and that if either the length or the reflectivity of the end-faces are further reduced there is an abrupt deterioration in incremental efficiency. Ettenberg et al.[36] demonstrated very clearly that this behaviour in sawn-cavity lasers is associated with the generation of trapped cavity-modes. The trapped modes propagate in the laser resonator at an angle to the axis just greater than the critical angle of 16° so that they are completely reflected from the two end-faces and partially reflected at a shallow angle from the rough sidewalls (see Figure 2.23, Chapter 2, Section 2.7.2.1). The microstructure of the sawn walls and the inverse width of the laser determine the losses of the Fabry–Perot modes. The trapped modes are suppressed when their losses exceed those of the Fabry–Perot modes. This therefore occurs when the width-to-length ratio is less than a critical value which can be increased by reducing the reflectivity of the sidewalls or increasing the reflectivity of the end-faces.

Ettenberg et al. found that for a particular type of sawn sidewall all the lasers investigated, whether double heterostructure or single heterostructure, showed the same critical behaviour. For lasers with normal cleaved facets the maximum ratio of width to length for satisfactory operation was around 0.8. Taking into account the very oblique path of the trapped cross modes this corresponded to a reflectivity of 0.005 for the sidewalls.

The reflection from the side of the laser can be reduced considerably below the above figure by forming an absorbing region at the edge of the laser using proton bombardment. By this means lasers can be operated satisfactorily with width-to-length ratios greater than unity.[32]

5.4.2 Double Heterostructures

The incremental efficiency of double heterostructure lasers depends on the doping levels of the active and passive regions and on the dielectric waveguide structure. The principle contributions to optical loss arise from free carrier absorption in both the active and passive layers of the heterostructure[37] and from optical scattering by imperfections at the heterojunctions which form the walls of the waveguide.[38] No band-edge absorption occurs because of the much higher band-gaps of the passive layers.

For normal composition steps at the heterojunction (AlAs step >20 per cent) and for active layer thicknesses greater than $0.4\ \mu$m most of the optical field is confined within the active region and the free carrier loss is determined by the carrier concentration in the active layer only. For low active-region doping levels in (GaAl)As/GaAs devices the absorption loss is found to be typically 10–$15\ \text{cm}^{-1}$. For doping levels above $10^{18}\ \text{cm}^{-3}$ the loss increases approximately linearly with doping and correlates well with the expected free carrier loss.[37] The lower limit of around 10–$15\ \text{cm}^{-1}$ is set by the absorption appropriate for the $10^{18}\ \text{cm}^{-3}$ electrons necessarily injected into the active region to give inversion. However it can be decreased if the thickness of the active layer is reduced allowing the optical field to extend into the passive layers.

The scattering loss at the heterojunction boundaries depends mainly on the mean square amplitude of the roughness of the interface and on the square of the dielectric constant step.[38] It therefore increases in importance in (GaAl)As/GaAs devices as the AlAs content in the passive layers is increased. For a typical double heterostructure the amplitude of the roughness has to be greater than $0.01\ \mu$m to give losses greater than $5\ \text{cm}^{-1}$.

Lower absorption loss and higher efficiency can be achieved in waveguide structures where more of the optical field propagates in the passive regions. By doping the passive regions at a level of, say, $2 \times 10^{17}\ \text{cm}^{-3}$, their contribution to the free carrier loss is reduced to $1\ \text{cm}^{-1}$. In double heterostructures with active layers thin enough (e.g. $<0.1\ \mu$m) to cause the optical distribution to spread appreciably into the passive layers, an absorption loss as low as $5\ \text{cm}^{-1}$ has been measured.[38] This absorption loss can be attributed in comparable parts to free carrier losses and scattering losses. The corresponding external incremental quantum efficiency is greater than 50 per cent.

5.4.3 Single Heterostructure

In a single heterostructure laser the wave penetrates significantly into the n-region. The principal optical losses are free carrier absorption in the active region and free carrier absorption with possibly some band-edge absorption in the n-region. Calculations of losses have been made by Ettenberg and Kressel.[39] Measured incremental efficiencies are usually in the range 20–40 per cent and the variation with laser length L or reflecting R can be used to determine the absorption coefficient α and the internal efficiency η_0.

Two distinct types of behaviour have been observed. For devices with heavily doped substrates a plot of reciprocal efficiency $1/\eta$ against $L/\ln(1/R)$ shows the conventional behaviour as predicted by equation (5.6), and it can be estimated that $\alpha = 20–30 \text{ cm}^{-1}$ and $\eta_0 = 50–60$ per cent. However, devices with Te-doped substrates have the unusual feature of η being approximately constant with L. In this case it must be assumed that $\alpha = 0$ or that α varies with L. This second case has been analysed by Goodwin and Selway[40] and it is concluded that α varies with L through the variation of photon energy with threshold current density; when the length is decreased the threshold current density increases and the accompanying rise in the quasi-Fermi level in the active region causes an increase in photon energy which then increases the absorption coefficieny for the part of the wave penetrating the n-GaAs region.

The reason for the difference between Si- and Te-doped material can be seen from Figure 5.21 in which the emission photon energy is plotted as a

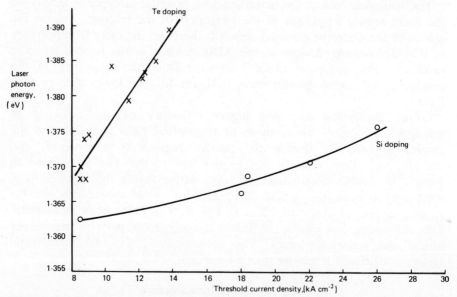

Figure 5.21 Relation between lasing photon energy and threshold current density in single heterostructure lasers. Curves shown for both Si- and Te-doped substrates with $n = 3 - 4 \times 10^{18} \text{ cm}^{-3}$ and $2.5 \times 10^{18} \text{ cm}^{-3}$, respectively

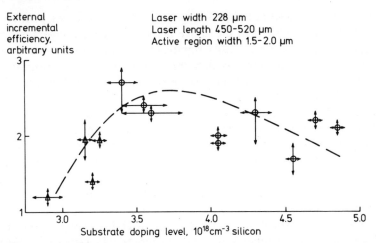

Figure 5.22 Effect of doping level of substrate on incremental efficiency in single heterostructure lasers

function of the threshold current density. The much more rapid rise of photon energy with current density in Te-doped material probably causes band-edge absorption to be more important in this case, and changes of threshold cause changes in absorption constant.

Because of problems with Ga_2Te precipitates in highly Te-doped GaAs[41] most single heterostructure lasers are made with Si-doped substrates. The effect of doping level on incremental efficiency is shown in Figure 5.22. The increase in efficiency between n-doping levels of 2.5 and 4×10^{18} cm^{-3} is thought to be due to the steadily improving waveguiding due to the variation of refractive index with electron concentration. The decrease for higher doping levels may reflect increased carrier absorption but may be mainly due to an increase in the number of crystal defects (e.g. Si precipitates) found at these very high doping levels.[42]

The variation of efficiency with active region width has been studied by Ettenberg and Kressel.[39] The efficiency decreases sharply for $d > 2.0$ μm. This behaviour is not determined by the waveguide confinement, which is good in this range, but presumably arises from absorption in unpumped parts of the active region when d exceeds the electron diffusion length. Experiments to study this effect are difficult since for a given n-doping level d can only be varied by changing the Zn concentration or the heat treatment time, either of which may affect α for other reasons.

5.4.4 SCH and LOC Lasers

In SCH or LGR lasers, as in double heterostructure lasers, free carriers and optical scattering at the heterojunctions are the main source of optical loss. The light in these lasers propagates mainly in the inner passive layers and only to a small extent in the active layer. The passive layers can have a low doping level, and so the only significant region with free carrier losses is the active layer. This layer is very thin and under these conditions it can be calculated that loss coefficients of only 2 cm^{-1} due to this cause should be observed.

The SCH laser is somewhat more subject to scattering losses than the double heterostructure laser since it contains more optical interfaces.[38] The boundary interfaces of the active layer contribute particularly to the scattering since they are located at the point where the optical field is the most intense. It is probably that a scattering loss of greater than 5 cm^{-1} is present in many of these structures. This would arise with a roughness amplitude of the order of 0.01 μm.

The measured absorption coefficients of SCH lasers vary from about 8 to 17 cm^{-1} for both symmetrical[31] and asymmetrical[32] structures. However, in spite of these rather high figures external efficiencies of over 70 per cent have been obtained in some broad contact asymmetrical devices. The length of the lasers was around 300 μm. This result was made possible because the internal efficiency approached 100 per cent. To obtain this performance it is necessary to select devices for uniform emission across the width of the junction and to suppress cross modes by creating optically absorbing stripes by proton bombardment at both edges of the laser.

LOC devices exhibit quite low optical losses, and high efficiencies can be obtained. Experimental values of up to 50 per cent have been reported and, unlike single heterostructure lasers, these are maintained up to large d values.

REFERENCES

1. I. Hayashi, M. B. Panish, and F. K. Reinhart, 'GaAs–Al$_x$Ga$_{1-x}$As double heterostructure injection lasers', *J. Appl. Phys.*, **42**, 1971, 1929.
2. H. F. Lockwood, H. Kressel, H. S. Sommers, and F. Z. Hawrylo, 'An efficient large optical cavity injection laser', *Appl. Phys. Lett.*, **17**, 1970, 499.
3. H. Kressel, H. F. Lockwood, and F. Z. Hawrylo, 'Low threshold LOC GaAs injection lasers', *Appl. Phys. Lett.*, **18**, 1971, 43.
4. J. K. Butler, 'Theory of transverse cavity mode selection in homojunction and heterojunction semiconductor laser diodes', *J. Appl. Phys.*, **42**, 1971, 4447.
5. T. L. Paoli, B. W. Hakki, and B. I. Miller, 'Zero order transverse mode operation of GaAs double heterostructure lasers with thick waveguides', *J. Appl. Phys.*, **44**, 1973, 1776.
6. B. W. Hakki and C. J. Hwang, 'Mode control in GaAs large cavity double heterostructure lasers', *J. Appl. Phys.*, **44**, 1974, 2168.
7. M. B. Panish, H. C. Casey, Jr, S. Sumski, and P. W. Foy, 'Reduction of threshold current density in GaAs–Al$_x$Ga$_{1-x}$As heterostructure lasers by separate optical and carrier confinement', *Appl. Phys. Lett.*, **22**, 1973, 590.
8. G. H. B. Thompson and P. A. Kirkby, 'Low threshold current density in

5-layer-heterostructure (GaAl)As/GaAs localized gain region injection lasers', *Electron. Lett.*, **9**, 1973, 295.

9. G. H. B. Thompson, G. D. Henshall, J. E. A. Whiteaway, and P. A. Kirkby, 'Narrow-beam five-layer (GaAl)As/GaAs heterostructure lasers with low threshold and high peak power', *J. Appl. Phys.*, **47**, 1976, 1501.

10. F. Stern, 'Gain-current relation for GaAs lasers with n-type and undoped active layers', *IEEE J. Quantum Electron.*, **QE-9**, 1972, 290.

11. J. C. Dyment, F. R. Nash, C. J. Hwang, G. A. Rozgonyi, R. L. Hartman, H. M. Marcus, and S. E. Hassko, 'Threshold reduction by the addition of P to the ternary layers of double heterostructure GaAs lasers', *Appl. Phys. Lett.*, **24**, 1974, 481.

12. M. Ettenberg, 'Very low threshold double heterojunction $Al_xGa_{1-x}As$ injection lasers', *Appl. Phys. Lett.*, **27**, 1975, 652.

13. I. Hayashi and M. B. Panish, '$GaAs-Ga_xAl_{1-x}As$ heterostructure injection lasers which exhibit low thresholds at room temperature', *J. Appl. Phys.*, **41**, 1970, 150.

14. M. T. Minden and R. Premo, 'High temperature GaAs single heterojunction laser diodes', *J. Appl. Phys.*, **45**, 1974, 4520.

15. P. R. Selway, A. R. Goodwin, and G. H. B. Thompson, 'Heterostructure injection lasers', *Festkörperprobleme*, **14**, 1974, 119.

16. P. G. Eliseev, Preprint No. 33 (in Russian), Physics Institute, Academy of Sciences of the USSR, Moscow, 1970.

17. S. Grundorfer, M. J. Adams, and B. Thomas, 'New theory of internal Q switching in semiconductor lasers', *Electron Lett.*, **10**, 1974, 354.

18. P. R. Selway, G. H. B. Thompson, G. D. Henshall, and J. E. A. Whiteaway, 'Measurement of the effect of injected carriers on the p–n refractive index step in single heterostructure diode lasers', *Electron. Lett.*, **10**, 1974, 453.

19. F. D. Nunes, N. B. Patel, and J. E. Ripper, 'A theory on long time delays and internal Q switching in GaAs junction lasers', *IEEE J. Quantum Electron.*, **QE-13**, 1977, 675.

20. C. D. Dobson and F. S. Keeble, 'The surface damage of high output gallium arsenide lasers', *Proceedings First International Symposium on GaAs* (Reading 1966), Inst. Physics and Physical Society, London, 1967, p. 68.

21. H. Kressel and H. Mierop, 'Catastrophic degradation in GaAs injection lasers', *J. Appl. Phys.*, **38**, 1967, 5419.

22. D. A. Shaw and P. R. Thornton, 'Catastrophic degradation in GaAs laser diodes', *Solid State Electron.*, **13**, 1970, 919.

23. B. W. Hakki and F. R. Nash, 'Catastrophic failure in GaAs double heterostructure injection lasers', *J. Appl. Phys.*, **45**, 1974, 3907.

24. M. Ettenberg, H. S. Sommers, H. Kressel, and H. F. Lockwood, 'Control of facet damage in GaAs laser diodes', *Appl. Phys. Lett.*, **18**, 1971, 571.

25. E. Oomura, T. Murotani, M. Ishi and W. Susaki, *Spring Meeting Appl. Phys. Soc. Japan*, 27p-W-13 1979.

26. H. O. Yonezu, M. Ueno, T. Kamejima and I. Hayashi, 'An AlGaAs window stripe laser', *IEEE J. Quantum Electron.*, **QE-15**, 1979, 775.

27. P. G. Eliseev, 'Degradation of injection lasers', *Journal of Luminescence*, **7**, 1973, 338.

28. P. A. Kirkby and G. H. B. Thompson, 'High peak power from (GaAl)As–GaAs double-heterostructure injection lasers', *Appl. Phys. Lett.*, **22**, 1973, 638.

29. N. Chinone, R. Ito, and O. Nakada, 'Limitations of power outputs from

continuously operation GaAs–Ga$_{1-x}$Al$_x$As double heterostructure lasers', *J. Appl. Phys.*, **47**, 1976, 785.

30. G. D. Henshall and P. R. Selway, 'Single heterostructure lasers for high peak power operation', *Proceeding of the Technical Programme, Electro-optics International 74 Conference*, Kiever Communications Ltd, 1974.

31. H. C. Casey, Jr, M. B. Panish, W. O. Schlosser, and T. L. Paoli, 'GaAs–Al$_x$Ga$_{1-x}$As heterostructure lasers with separate optical and carrier confinement', *J. Appl. Phys.*, **45**, 1974, 322.

32. G. D. Henshall, 'The suppression of internally circulating modes in (GaAl)As/GaAs heterostructure lasers and their effect on catastrophic degradation and efficiency', *Appl. Phys. Lett.*, **31**, 1977, 205.

33. J. E. Carroll, S. G. Eldon, and G. H. B. Thompson, 'Incremental efficiency enhancement and r.f. response of GaAs–GaAlAs double heterostructure stripe lasers', *Electron. Lett.*, **12**, 1976, 564.

34. T. L. Paoli, 'Saturation behaviour of the spontaneous emission from double heterostructure junction lasers operating high above threshold', *J. Quantum Electron.*, **QE-9**, 1972, 267.

35. P. Brosson, J. E. Ripper, and N. B. Patel, 'Variation of spontaneous emission with current in GaAs homostructure and double heterostructure injection lasers', *J. Quantum Electron.*, **QE-9**, 1972, 273.

36. M. Ettenberg, H. F. Lockwood, and H. S. Sommers, 'Radiation trapping in laser diodes', *J. Appl. Phys.*, **43**, 1972, 5047.

37. E. Pinkas, B. I. Miller, I. Hayashi, and P. W. Foy, 'GaAs–Al$_x$Ga$_{1-x}$As double heterostructure lasers—Effects of doping on lasing characteristics of GaAs', *J. Appl. Phys.*, **43**, 1972, 2827.

38. G. H. B. Thompson, P. A. Kirkby, and J. E. A. Whiteaway, 'The analysis of optical scattering in double heterostructure and five-layer heterostructure (GaAl)As/GaAs injection lasers', *J. Quantum Electron.*, **QE-11**, 1975, 481.

39. M. Ettenberg and H. Kressel, 'Dependence of threshold current density and efficiency on Fabry–Perot cavity parameters: single heterostructure (AlGa)As–GaAs laser diodes', *J. Appl. Phys.*, **43**, 1972, 1207.

40. A. R. Goodwin and P. R. Selway, 'Gain and loss processes in GaAlAs–GaAs heterostructure lasers', *IEEE J. Quantum Electron.*, **QE-6**, 1970, 285.

41. H. Kressel, H. Nelson, S. H. McFarlane, M. S. Abrahams, P. Lefur, and C. J. Buiocchi, 'Effect of substrate imperfections on GaAs injection lasers prepared by liquid-phase epitaxy', *J. Appl. Phys.*, **40**, 1969, 3587.

42. H. Kressel, H. Nelson, and F. Z. Hawrylo, 'Control of optical losses in p–n junction lasers by use of a heterojunction: theory and experiment', *J. Appl. Phys.*, **41**, 1970, 2019.

CHAPTER 6

Stripe Geometry Lasers

6.1 INTRODUCTION

The heterostructure layers in a semiconductor laser confine the light and the injected carriers in the direction perpendicular to the junction, as we have described in the previous chapters. In many laser applications an optical source is needed whose width in the plane of the junction is not a great deal larger than its thickness perpendicular to the junction. In some cases it may be required that the width be almost comparable with the thickness, although more frequently an appreciably wider source is preferred to provide a higher limiting output power. For instance, in communications applications a laser with a source width of 5–10 μm is particularly suited to the launching of light into graded index optical fibre waveguides. For dimensions of this order it is necessary to consider carefully how the injected carriers, and particularly the light, are to be confined within the desired width. We call lasers of this general configuration 'stripe lasers' and refer to the confinement of both carriers and light in the junction plane as 'lateral confinement'. In this chapter we discuss the behaviour of stripe lasers and consider the various forms of lateral confinement of light and injected carriers.

Let us first take the confinement of the light. Dielectric waveguides become much less convenient as the width of the optical filament is increased from the 0.5 μm width appropriate to a heterostructure guide up to the 5–10 μm width of the present example. For instance, consider the characteristics of a slab dielectric waveguide 10-μm wide which, in order to give a controlled lateral distribution of light, is designed to propagate only the zero-order lateral mode. The dielectric constant of the centre region of such a waveguide must be less than 0.002 greater than that outside. Two problems arise from this small step. First, the optical properties of the material concerned must be very uniform to give satisfactory performance. In a semiconductor the effect of injected carriers or even the effect of the heating due to their recombination can produce greater variations of dielectric constant than 0.002. Secondly, when the waveguide is as weak as this any disturbance has to propagate a considerable distance along the guide before a pure mode is produced, and the effect of the generation of light by the gain process alone is sufficient to upset the situation. In other words the gain introduces an imaginary component of dielectric constant, as described in Chapter 4, Section 4.2.1, which is comparable in magnitude with the step in the real dielectric constant. These various effects complicate the guiding behaviour very considerably and must be taken into careful account.

In many stripe lasers, particularly in the early designs, the light is confined to the area of the stripe without the use of a deliberate dielectric waveguide but simply by supplying optical gain only to the stripe region, leaving the outer regions in an optically lossy condition.[1-3] Photons naturally accumulate in the regions where there is gain and are removed from the regions where there is loss. Such a process was analysed in Section 4.2. It is often referred to as 'gain-guiding'. However, the light in this situation can hardly be said to be guided but rather to suffer relative attenuation (by absorption or by loss from the end-face of the laser) when it strays from the prescribed path. This mechanism can be used for discriminating against higher order transverse modes. If the laser is narrow enough in relation to its length (or if the end-faces have adequately high reflectivity) only those waves whose direction of travel lies sufficiently close to the axis to constitute the zero-order mode can traverse the whole length of the laser without excessive attenuation. It can be appreciated, however, that the guiding can only be successful if the propagation of light within the device is highly rectilinear and there are no significant optical non-uniformities, either of composition or in the dimensions of the heterostructure or as a result of injected carriers, which can deflect the optical power into the absorbing regions. Hence the stripe laser with 'gain-guiding' requires considerable care in its design and construction to operate satisfactorily in a single lateral mode.

Various designs of stripe laser have been developed in which there is a built-in two-dimensional dielectric waveguide to provide guiding in the junction plane as well as in the plane at right angles. The dielectric constant profile in the junction plane may be created in the same way as that in the direction normal to the plane, either by a change in the composition of the material,[4-6] or by a change in the doping.[7,8] The device using a change in the composition of the semiconductor is usually referred to as a 'buried heterostructure'[4] since it is typically fabricated by submerging a mesa'd rib structure under a second stage of liquid phase epitaxy. Devices which use a change in the doping level have one or more p–n junctions intersecting the active layer and are called transverse junction stripe lasers.[7]

The dielectric profile may also be produced geometrically, e.g. by increasing the thickness of the active layer, or the adjacent passive layer, over the requisite width. Such structures are called rib-loaded stripes.[9,10]

Positive guides are only useful if they give greater confinement than occurs naturally by gain-guiding. If single transverse mode operation is required, the stripe must be made narrower as the strength of the guiding is increased. Guiding by doping level or by rib-loading is suitable in the approximate width range 8–2 μm, and guiding by composition change is suitable for single mode operation in the width range 3–1 μm.

To obtain low threshold current in any stripe configuration it is desirable to prevent the injected carriers from spreading appreciably sideways, in the plane of the junction, beyond the region where the light is guided. The carriers in general spread by both conduction and diffusion. In devices where the width of the stripe is comparable with, or less than, the diffusion length of the carriers it becomes very desirable to supply potential barriers for their confinement. Hence carrier confinement, as well as optical confinement, becomes a two-dimensional problem, and methods can be used in the plane of the junction which are an extension of those used in the various types of heterostructure normal to the junction.

6.2 TYPES OF STRIPE LASER

Typical examples of the various types of stripe laser are shown in cross section in Figures 6.1–6.9. Figure 6.1 shows devices which operate simply by current confinement. In all these the current is constrained, in a variety of ways, to flow through a rectangular-shaped 'window' located in some plane in the structure which is not precisely coincident with the plane of the active layer, being displaced either upwards or downwards from it. Provided that the window is close to the active layer and the layers between the window and the active layer are of higher resistivity than the layers on the other side of the active layer, then the current does not spread greatly in its passage from the window to the active layer and the carrier confinement can be adequate. For example, it is quite practical to maintain the gain reasonably constant over the entire width of the stripe except for about 3 μm at each edge.

6.2.1 Stripe Contact Laser

The SiO_2 insulated (GaAl)As/GaAs stripe laser, which was the original design of stripe contact laser as reported by Dyment,[1,2] is illustrated in Figure 6.1(a). The design is straightforward but a few particular points require consideration. The top p-layers of the heterostructure are normally relatively low doped (e.g. 5×10^{17} cm^{-3}) to reduce current spreading and a capping layer of GaAs is used for contacting purposes [it being difficult to

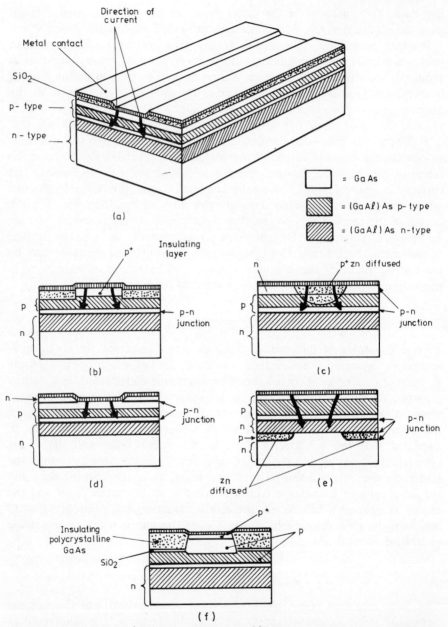

Figure 6.1   Different configurations of stripe geometry laser using 'current confinement window'. (a) Oxide-insulated stripe contact laser, (b) shallow mesa stripe laser. Lasers with reverse biased p–n junction isolation, (c) Zn-diffused planar stripe laser, (d) hetero-isolation stripe laser, (e) striped-substrate laser, (f) embedded-stripe laser with MBE top layer

make a good contact to (GaAl)As]. After the SiO_2 is applied the stripe window is opened up by a photolithographic process. The p-side contact (e.g. Au on top of Cr or Ti) is normally evaporated without alloying in order to avoid strain which, for (GaAl)As/GaAs devices, is particularly deleterious to laser life. However, to obtain low resistance without alloying, it is necessary to dope the p-region highly. This can be achieved without increasing the current spreading by making a shallow diffusion of Zn through the SiO_2 window. As in all designs of stripe contact lasers the stripe width must be chosen appropriately in conjunction with the laser length and the layer thicknesses to give single transverse mode operation.

Figure 6.1 (b)–(f), illustrates various other methods which have been used to produce a 'current window' in the structure. Figure 6.1(b) shows a shallow mesa design in which the capping layer of GaAs is etched away outside the stripe.[11,12] This layer can be highly doped since it does not contribute to current spreading in the final structure, and there is no need for a subsequent Zn diffusion. The insulating layer may be either a separately applied layer (of SiO_2 or phosphosilicate) or it may consist of a native oxide formed *in situ* by, say, anodization. Figure 6.1(c) shows a design in which the current block is provided by a reverse biased p–n junction[13]—the so-called planar stripe laser. The capping layer of GaAs is grown n-type and the current window is created by diffusing Zn through the appropriate area to make contact with the p-(GaAl)As layer beneath. This device has also been made by the diffusion of S into a p-type capping layer to create n-type regions outside the stripe[14,15] (internally-striped laser, not illustrated). The devices shown in Figure 6.1(d) and (e) also use a reverse biased p–n junction to block the current. Device (d) is similar to device (c) except that the current window is created by locally removing the n-type capping layer rather than diffusing Zn through it.[16] In device (e) the reverse biased p–n junction is located below the active layer rather than above it (striped substrate laser) and is formed before the heterostructure is grown by appropriate Zn diffusion of the substrate.[17] Devices have also been made with reverse biased junctions both below and above the active layer.[18] Finally, the device illustrated in Figure 6.1(f) (embedded stripe laser) has the insulating layer applied directly to the p-(GaAl)As. A window is opened up and contact is made to the exposed area by the growth of GaAs by molecular beam epitaxy.[19] The MBE layer also grows across the insulating region, but in a polycrystalline form. The finished structure is, therefore, planar.

6.2.2 Proton Bombarded and Oxygen Implanted Stripe Lasers

The stripe laser structure illustrated in Figure 6.2(a) also operates by current confinement but differs from those in Figure 6.1 in that the

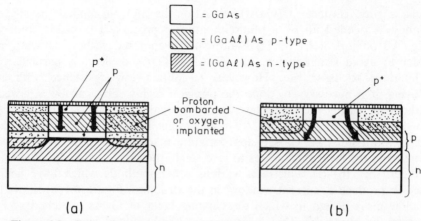

Figure 6.2 Stripe lasers using semi-insulating regions for current confinement produced by proton-bombardment or oxygen-implantation. (a) Deep
bombarded or implanted stripe, (b) shallow bombarded or implanted stripe

confinement extends right to the active layer. In this structure regions of
high resistivity are created in the semiconductor either by proton
bombardment,[3] or by oxygen implantation,[20] and are used to define the
boundaries of the stripe. Current therefore only flows into the active layer
in the untreated region of the stripe. However, the semi-insulating regions
do not provide confinement barriers to the minority carriers actually
injected into the active layer. A proportion of these diffuse sideways into
the insulating regions, taking majority carriers with them, where they
recombine. Proton bombardment creates a large number of non-radiative
recombination centres but does not greatly reduce the carrier mobility.[21]
Hence carrier pairs flow transversely with considerable velocity to the
semi-insulating interface where their concentration is reduced to a low
level. The effective current loss thus caused, particularly for devices less
than two diffusion lengths wide, can be appreciably greater than that in the
current window type of stripe laser. Oxygen implantation, on the other
hand, tends in certain circumstances greatly to reduce the carrier mobility
without much increasing the recombination rate.[20] Hence transverse carrier
diffusion is restricted at the boundary interface and the effective loss of
current is considerably less than in the proton bombarded stripe, and less
even than in a good current window stripe.

If the high resistivity region in either of these types of device does not
extend right down to the active layer, as illustrated in Figure 6.2(b), the
behaviour is very similar to the current window type of stripe, and the
current spreading is also similar.

6.2.3 Buried Heterostructure Stripe Laser

In the buried heterostructure laser a filament of narrow bandgap material is entirely embedded in wider bandgap material. This filament produces both a strongly guiding dielectric waveguide and also a region in which the injected carriers are confined by potential barriers on four sides. Figure 6.3(a) shows a cross section of the (GaAl)As/GaAs structure as originally reported by Tsukada.[4] This device is fabricated by growing a double heterostructure slice, masking a stripe region, etching down through all the layers to the substrate (exposing Al-free material for easy regrowth) and then, with a second stage of liquid phase epitaxy, filling in all the material

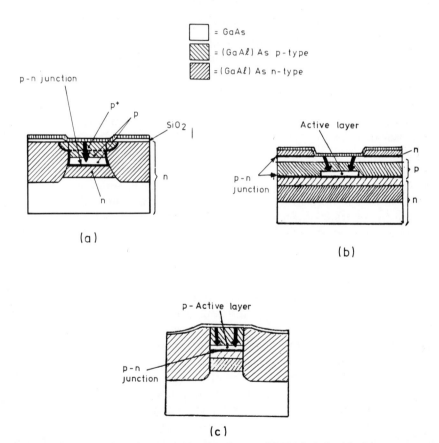

Figure 6.3 Buried heterostructure stripe lasers. (a) Buried double heterostructure. (b) Strip-buried-heterostructure. Contains additional waveguide layer extending right across structure. (c) Buried optical guide. Waveguide layer is truncated by second growth

removed with a single layer of n-type (GaAl)As. Contact is finally made to the isolated p-type (GaAl)As above the active layer by diffusing Zn down from the surface through an appropriate window of SiO_2, and then evaporating a metal layer. The p–n junction formed by the growth and the diffusion is bounded on both sides by (GaAl)As except where it lies adjacent to the active layer. Injection current is selectively diverted from the part of the p–n junction entirely in (GaAl)As, because of its higher reverse potential, and channelled into the part adjacent to the active layer. The buried heterostructure has been demonstrated to operate very successfully when the width of the active layer in the junction plane is as small as 1 μm. Higher order lateral modes appear when the width is greater than 1.5 μm.

A shortcoming of the simple buried heterostructure is that it must be made very narrow in order to operate in a single lateral mode. In principle reducing the AlAs content of the infilling material that forms the lateral boundaries of the guide, and hence increasing its dielectric constant, could be used to reduce the strength of the waveguide to any degree desired, and hence allow the width of the laser to be increased to any size. The snag here is that the degree of confinement, when it is small, depends sensitively on the thickness of the active layer, since this thickness plays a major part in determining the effective dielectric constant of the centre region. Too much reduction of the outer AlAs content could, for instance, result in the production of an anti-waveguide. Tsang et al.[22] have used an ingenious modification of the design to overcome this problem. They have developed a four-layer separate confinement buried heterostructure which they called a strip-buried-heterostructure. In this structure, illustrated in Figure 6.3(b), the new layer forms the bulk of the optical cavity. It is not truncated laterally by the second stage of epitaxial growth, but extends right across the structure. Only the relatively thin active layer above it is so truncated. The lateral waveguide that results is therefore confined mainly to the new layer over the width of the region where it is loaded by the active layer. The degree of lateral waveguiding in this structure can be arranged to be small, by using a thin active layer, without running into the possibility that it may be lost entirely. Such structures have been demonstrated to operate in a single lateral mode up to widths of at least 4 μm—almost three times the width of the conventional buried heterostructure.

Figure 6.3(c) illustrates a buried structure which is intermediate between the simple buried heterostructure of Figure 6.3(a) and the strip device of Figure 6.3(b) and is called a buried-optical-guide structure.[23] It also employs the four-layer separate-confinement structure of the strip device, but the etching prior to regrowth is taken below the level of the additional layer so that the whole structure is bounded by higher band-gap lower refractive index material. By choosing the band-gap of the regrown layer to be only a little greater than that of the additional waveguide layer the lateral waveguide may be made relatively weak and almost as wide as that in the strip-buried-structure without generating the first order lateral mode. Similarly the maximum power that can be extracted will only be a little less than for the strip-buried-structure. In principle the lateral confinement of carriers should be somewhat superior to that in the strip-buried device. In both devices some injection of holes takes place into the additional layer particularly at higher temperatures because of the relatively low heterojunction barrier, but in the present device these holes are prevented from diffusing laterally because of the two bounding heterojunctions to somewhat higher band-gap material. The device will operate in a single lateral mode up to a width of about 3 μm with a threshold current of around 20 mA and can give a maximum optical output from one facet of more than 10 mW.

Alternative methods of fabricating the buried heterostructure laser have been investigated which do not require two stages of liquid phase epitaxy. The devices which are produced are the etched buried heterostructure of Burnham and Scifres[5] and the channelled substrate laser described by Kirkby et al.[6] They both make use of a particular property of liquid phase epitaxy growth which enables it to fill grooves before growing on flat surfaces. It is possible, starting with a grooved substrate, to alternate the growth of continuous layers of (GaAl)As and discontinuous layers of GaAs in such a way as to embed an isolated filament of GaAs in the (GaAl)As. The cross section of such a structure, as investigated by Kirkby, is illustrated in Figure 6.4. It is not easy to make the filament of GaAs as narrow as in a conventional buried heterostructure and a width of about 10 μm was used. This allows the propagation of a range of lateral modes, the number and characteristics of which are predictable from the geometry of the guide. Discrimination against the unwanted modes may be provided by positioning a narrow stripe contact centrally above the GaAs filament.

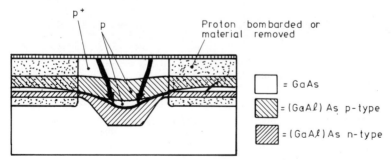

Figure 6.4   Buried heterostructure stripe laser grown on channelled substrate

This produces a gain distribution that favours the zero order mode and allows an appreciable power to be extracted before the higher order modes are generated. The structure reported by Burnham and Scifres[5] had a narrower active region (3 μm) and required no special means to give the zero order mode. The narrow structure was achieved at the expense of a discontinuous first (GaAl)As layer, which opened up a path for current leakage between the second (GaAl)As layer and the substrate and led to a high threshold current. However with further development to overcome their present deficiencies these structures should offer a performance comparable to that of the buried heterostructure and at the same time be simpler to fabricate.

6.2.4 p–n Confinement Structures

The p–n junction, where the n-region is sufficiently highly doped, provides a useful means of injecting or confining electrons to the p-region, and by virtue of the dielectric constant difference reported in Chapter 3, Section 3.2.4, of guiding light in the p-region. These characteristics have been very successfully exploited in the single heterostructure laser. They also have potential in stripe lasers for providing optical confinement and some carrier confinement in the plane of the active layer, with the possible advantage over the buried heterostructure that much wider stripe widths can be used without the danger of generating higher order lateral modes.

An early attempt was made to use these characteristics in the transverse-junction-stripe laser reported by Namizaki.[7,24] In this device, illustrated in Figure 6.5, the current flows transversely through the centre

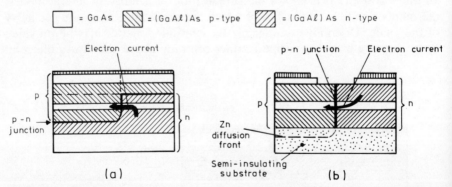

Figure 6.5 Transverse homojunction stripe lasers formed by diffusion of Zn into appropriate heterostructures. (a) With grown-in p–n junction in upper passive layer and with Zn diffusion terminating in lower passive layer giving p–n junction extending over whole width. (b) With heterostructure grown on semi-insulating substrate where Zn diffusion terminates, leaving only a vertical p–n junction and producing a structure which requires two top contacts

layer of a double heterostructure from a Zn-diffused region into an n-type active region. The active stripe is defined by the intersection of the p–n homojunction and the GaAs/(GaAl)As double heterostructure. This forms a region only about 1-μm square, and c.w. threshold currents as low as 10 mA have been obtained at room temperature.[25] The behaviour in general is consistent with a homojunction mechanism, including a temperature dependence of threshold which varies as T^3.

Two different methods have been used in this structure to channel the majority of the recombination current through the active layer. These are illustrated respectively in Figure 6.5(a) and (b). The early devices exploited the difference between the I/V characteristics of p–n junctions in GaAs and (GaAl)As. Because of the greater band-gap the current at fixed voltage through a p–n junction in (GaAl)As is reduced by a factor of $\exp(-\Delta E/kT)$ compared with that in GaAs, where ΔE is the difference in band-gap. The p–n junction in the structure is therefore arranged to run through (GaAl)As except where it crosses the active layer. The tortuous path which it follows is imposed by the presence of a top GaAs layer for contacting purposes. In the later structure, illustrated in Figure 6.5(b), a semi-insulating substrate is used so that only the vertical section of the p–n junction remains. Leakage current is considerably less in this arrangement. Both the p- and n-contacts are applied to the top surface. They are separated by an etched groove, aligned with the p–n junction. The GaAs contacting layer is also removed at the bottom of this groove, where otherwise additional injection current would flow which would shunt the lasing p–n junction.

A device which in principle is superior to the transverse homojunction laser is the transverse single heterostructure laser, also proposed by Namizaki,[7,26] and illustrated in Figure 6.6. This device requires a second stage of liquid phase epitaxy in its construction, similar to that used for the buried heterostructure laser, to grow the Zn doped (GaAl)As regions. Owing to problems with the interface of the second growth this device has not yet given a threshold current of less than 200 mA, although in principle it should be possible to reduce it to below 10 mA.

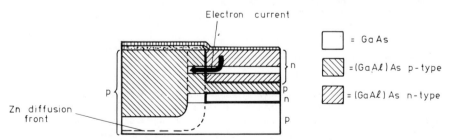

Figure 6.6   Transverse single heterostructure stripe laser

A device which is easier to construct than the transverse single heterostructure laser but should give comparable performance is the twin transverse junction (TTJ) or deep Zn-diffused laser. This has been investigated by Yonezu *et al.*[8] in the form illustrated in Figure 6.7(a), and by the author and co-workers[27] in the form shown in Figure 6.7(b). In its geometrical configuration the TTJ laser can be said to consist of two back-to-back transverse homojunction lasers with the p-side butted together. However, in operation it much more closely resembles two back-to-back transverse single heterojuction lasers. Carriers accumulate in the p-region with no net flow across the plane of symmetry, as if there were a confinement barrier at this point. There is good optical confinement between the two junctions. The lowest order lateral mode is symmetrical, with a maximum of optical intensity at the centre, and has no cut-off as the

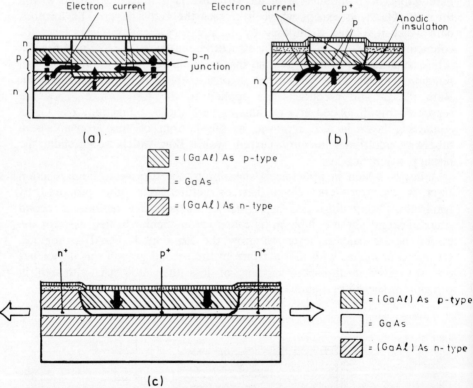

Figure 6.7 Twin transverse junction stripe lasers. (a) With p–n junction present over whole width and penetrating lower passive layer in central region, (b) with p–n junction localized under stripe and coincident with active layer boundary in centre region. (c) Longitudinal section of window-stripe laser, showing passive 'window' sections next to facets. Cross-section same as for (b)

width of the p-region is reduced. In this respect it differs from the lowest mode of the single heterostructure. The anti-symmetrical first-order mode in the TTJ structure is precisely equivalent to that in a pair of back-to-back single heterostructures, having a zero of optical intensity at the plane of symmetry, as if it were a waveguide boundary. However, provided that the width is chosen correctly, the twin transverse junction laser should operate in the zero-order mode only. A threshold current as low as 25 mA has been obtained at room temperature.[27]

The TTJ laser may either be constructed with the electrons being injected only through the two transverse junctions, as in Figure 6.7(a), or with the main injection taking place normal to the heterostructure over the whole width of the active layer, as in Figure 6.7(b). The difference depends on whether the segment of the p–n junction which joins the two transverse junctions lies within the higher band-gap material [see Figure 6.7(a)] when little current will flow through it, or whether it borders the active layer [see Figure 6.7(b)] when it will contribute its full complement of injection current. Intermediate behaviour occurs when the junction lies within a distance of around 0.1 μm from the active layer, the exact distance depending on the size of the heterojunction step.

The performance of the two structures differs little if the width of the stripe is less than 1–1.5 diffusion lengths. If the width is greater then the injected carrier concentration in structure (a) is no longer uniform but falls away appreciably from the edges to the centre. This increases the threshold current density in a way reminiscent of the behaviour in a single heterostructure with wide d. Also, the presence of higher gain at the edges tends to favour the first-order mode. In extreme cases, particularly where the waveguiding is weak or the device is not exactly symmetrical in composition and injection, two separate relatively uncoupled filaments may be produced close to the respective junctions, rather than a properly behaved first-order mode.

The TTJ structure is normally made by diffusion of Zn into the appropriate heterostructure. In this case structure (a) is the easier to make since the tolerance on diffusion depth is much greater. The device could be made by the diffusion of an n-type dopant down into an appropriate heterostructure only in those regions outside the desired stripe.[14] In this case both types of structure would be equally easy to make, although there might be considerable technical problems with the diffusion.

The TTJ structure can be very conveniently modified to make a high power laser whose emitting facets are less susceptible to damage by intense optical flux. As mentioned in Chapter 5, Section 5.3.2, damage of the facet by large optical fields can be attributed, at least in part, to absorption of a part of the lasing light close to the facet. The free carriers generated by the absorption recombine in the states at the surface and produce intense local heating. In the TTJ laser the n-doped part of the active layer has a relatively low absorption for the lasing emission that is generated in the p-type region, particularly if it is doped to greater than $2 \times 10^{18} \, \text{cm}^{-3}$. Hence in order to provide a non-absorbing region adjacent to the active layer it is only necessary to prevent the Zn diffused region from extending right up to the two end facets. A longitudinal section of such a stripe structure is illustrated in Figure 6.7(c). Typically the total length is 250 μm and the transparent regions are 50 μm long. Yonezu et al.[28] have fabricated this structure which they call the window-stripe laser and shown that it will handle four or five times greater power than conventional structures.

6.2.5 Rib Stripe Lasers

A rib structure can provide lateral optical confinement in stripe lasers. A waveguide is formed by locally stepping up the thickness of either the active layer or, in certain circumstances, the passive layers of the heterostructure. Any change in the dimensions of the individual layers which decreases the guide wavelength is equivalent to an increase in dielectric constant and can be used in the same way for creating a waveguide. Two types of geometry have proved suitable for this purpose. The first, reported by Lee et al.,[9] and called a 'rib-waveguide' stripe, uses a change in the thickness of the active layer and is illustrated in Figure 6.8(a) and an alternative version[27] in Figure 6.8(b). The second, uses a change in the thickness of the passive layer. To cause this change in thickness to react strongly on the light the passive layer is backed up, in the area where it is thinned, by a material of different refractive index, normally considerably lower. Figure 6.9 shows a variety of such structures. In the structure of Figure 6.9(a), reported by Kawaguchi and Kawakami[10]

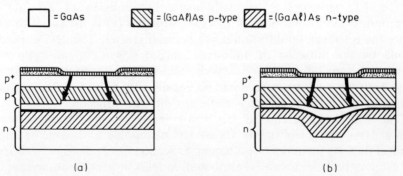

Figure 6.8   Rib-waveguide stripe lasers. (a) Fabricated by two stages of epitaxy, (b) fabricated by single stage of epitaxy on channelled substrate

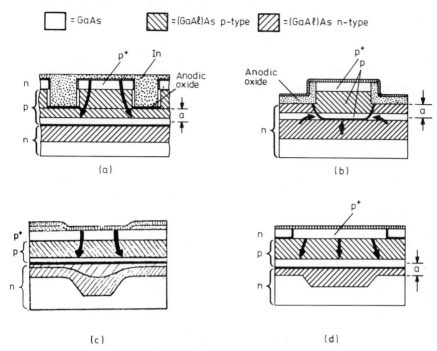

Figure 6.9   Passive-rib-loaded stripe lasers. (a) Basic structure. (b) With twin transverse p–n junctions added for lateral carrier confinement. (c) Plano-convex-waveguide-stripe. (d) Channelled substrate planar stripe

and called a strip-loaded waveguide, the upper passive layer is partially removed in the region outside the stripe. The structure in Figure 6.9(b) is similar in principle to the previous one except for the location of the p–n junction. Figure 6.9(c) shows a four layer structure, in which it is the variation in thickness of the layer of intermediate composition beneath the active layer that provides the lateral guide. This structure was first reported by Furuse et al.[30] under the name of a plano-convex waveguide stripe. The final structure (Figure 6.9(d)) differs somewhat from the others in Figure 6.9 in that the passive layer whose thickness is varied (the lower passive layer in this instance) is backed on its remote side by GaAs material which has a higher refractive index than the passive layer and is optically lossy. The operation of this device is therefore somewhat different from the others, as will be described below. This structure was first described by Aiki et al.[31] and is called a 'channelled-substrate-planar' stripe.

The main purpose of introducing the waveguide in these structures is to stabilize the position of the optical filament. This helps in producing a linear light/current characteristic, as is described in Section 6.6.2. The guide must be strong enough to fulfill this function but not so strong as to cause the generation of more than one lateral mode. This combination of properties becomes more difficult to achieve as the stripe width increases because the minimum guiding strength that can excite the first-order mode diminishes rapidly and the margin between this and the weaker guiding strength that stabilizes the light characteristic falls and may disappear completely. In the laser it is not, however, essential that the higher order lateral modes should not propagate, but only that their gain should be sufficiently less than that of the zero-order mode such that they are not generated. Discrimination in favour of the zero-order mode may be improved by suitably tailoring the lateral distribution of gain and loss. The gain should be enhanced at the centre of the guide where the zero-order mode has its highest intensity, and reduced at the edges where the intensity of the higher order modes is greater. Such a distribution of gain tends to be provided naturally in stripe lasers by the lateral spreading of current and by injected carrier diffusion. In some waveguide structures the natural discrimination can be augmented by the properties of the waveguide and this may confer considerable benefits in marginal situations. Let us therefore consider the various rib-structures in terms of both the strength of dielectric guiding that they can conveniently provide and in terms of any additional mode discrimination that they can confer.

In the rib-waveguide laser the step in the thickness of the active layer has a strong effect on the guiding and the rib height must be small to prevent higher order modes being generated. For instance, the combination of a 0.05-μm high rib with a 0.5-μm thickness of the active layer has been found to give a single lateral mode for 5-μm rib width.[9] Theoretical analysis shows that in order to prevent the propagation of higher order modes as the rib is widened the rib height must be reduced as the inverse square of its width, and that if the thickness of the active layer is reduced the rib height must be reduced more than in proportion.[9] Some latitude is allowable because of the mode discrimination referred to above, but even so fabrication of satisfactory structures becomes increasingly difficult as the width is increased above 5 μm or as the active layer thickness is reduced below 0.5 μm.

In the passive-rib loaded laser the interaction between the rib and the active layer is attenuated by the intervening thickness of passive layer. In the structures shown in Figure 6.9(a) and (b) the distance a between the centre line of the active layer and the free surface of the passive layer is the main variable that determines the strength of the guiding, largely irrespective of the thickness of the active layer. Typically, to prevent propagation of higher order modes with a rib 4-μm wide, a should have a value of about 0.5 μm and should be increased by about 0.1 μm each time the width is doubled.

In the plano-convex waveguide stripe the strength of the lateral guiding depends on the dimensions and relative compositions of the active layer and the additional layer that forms the optical resonator. In general the guiding becomes stronger the more the light spreads out into the additional layer. In practice single lateral mode operation can be obtained up to widths of at least 4 μm.

In the channelled substrate planar stripe conditions are reasonably similar to those in the passive rib-loaded structures although here the distance a is measured downwards to the substrate. In this case, however, not only is the real part of the effective dielectric constant affected by the thinning of the passive layer but also a loss component is introduced. Hence the lateral dielectric waveguide is complex.

The loss, which is of course restricted to the region outside the main lateral waveguide, is in principle beneficial because it interacts more strongly with the higher order lateral modes and hence adds to the mode discrimination in favour of the zero-order mode. The strength of the waveguide may therefore be increased considerably above the cut-off value of the first-order mode and the filament position in the zero-order mode may be stabilized to a greater extent. In practice these advantages seem to be realized and the structure gives a wide dynamic range for single-mode operation with good linearity in the light/current characteristic.

The constructional methods for the various structures differ considerably. The rib-waveguide laser may be fabricated in two ways by methods which are similar to those described in Section 6.2.3 for the buried heterostructure laser. The first method [see Figure 6.8(a)] involves the use of two stages of liquid phase epitaxy. The heterostructure is first grown up to the active layer. The rib is formed by appropriate photolithographic etching techniques and then the remaining layers of the heterostructure are grown on top.[9] In the second method[27] [see Figure 6.8(b)] the whole structure is grown in one stage on a grooved substrate, as described in Section 6.2.3. In this case conditions are adjusted so that the active layer is thickened up over the groove but is otherwise continuous.

The passive-rib-loaded structure is fabricated by a controlled photolithographic etching procedure after the heterostructure has been grown in a conventional manner. The plano-convex waveguide stripe and the channelled substrate planar structure are grown on a grooved substrate in a very similar manner to the structure in Figure 6.8(b) but the conditions are chosen[31] such that the passive layer or layers first grow preferentially in the groove and finally leave a plane interface over the whole surface of the slice when, in the case of the channelled substrate planar structure, the thickness outside the groove is still small (e.g. 0.3 μm).

These devices may use the same current confinement methods as in a

normal stripe laser. Figure 6.8(a) and (b) show the use of suitable windows
in an insulating layer aligned with the location of the rib in the active
layer. Figure 6.9(a) shows the use of a shallow mesa for the rib-loaded
structure, Figure 6.9(c) again shows the use of suitable windows in an
insulating layer and Figure 6.9(d) shows the use of Zn-diffusion through a
GaAs contacting layer of opposite doping type (n-type) for the channelled
substrate planar stripe. Where the rib is narrow such methods are wasteful
of current density. In the passive-rib-loaded structure it is, in principle,
possible to combine the concept of a rib guide with the layout of the
twin-transverse-junction laser to give a composite guiding action in
conjunction with reasonable carrier confinement. This is illustrated in
Figure 6.9(b). Such a device should combine the advantages of both
designs but has so far not been successfully produced.

6.2.6 Double-Stripe Laser

The change in refractive index produced in a semiconductor by injected
electrons can also be used for creating an optical waveguide in a stripe
laser. Because the electrons reduce the refractive index, as described in
Section 6.4.2 of this chapter, the effect in a normal current- confinement
stripe laser is the exact opposite of what is required and an anti-waveguide
is produced with the lowest refractive index at the centre. However by
using the double stripe geometry illustrated in Figure 6.10, with the two
stripes sufficiently separated to produce a dip in the injected carrier
concentration at the midway point between them, it is possible to create a
dielectric waveguide of the necessary strength. The strength of this guide
must be carefully gauged so that it provides adequate guiding for the zero
order lateral mode but is insufficient to support the first order mode, which
would otherwise be favoured by a gain distribution with a minimum at the
centre. By optimising the spacing and the width of the stripes Kirkby *et
al*.[32] have reported satisfactory operation in a zero order transverse mode
up to a power of 5–10 mW.

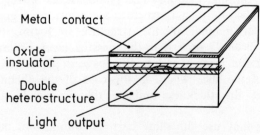

Figure 6.10   Double stripe laser

6.3   CARRIER CONFINEMENT IN STRIPE LASERS

We consider the lateral confinement of carriers in stripe lasers before we deal with the lateral confinement of light, because in the considerable number of stripe laser designs where there is no deliberate optical waveguide the lateral distribution of injected carriers also determines the width of the optical distribution.

6.3.1   Methods of Carrier Confinement

Because the cross section of the active layer of a typical stripe laser is much wider than it is thick it is less essential to provide carrier confinement in the lateral direction than it is to provide it in the perpendicular direction by the use of a heterostructure. However, as the stripe width is narrowed the situation changes. Edge leakage first becomes evident, in simple stripe lasers with no positive carrier confinement barriers, at stripe widths of around 30 μm and at 10 μm it can account for more than half the total current. Some positive confinement becomes very worthwhile for widths below 10 μm, and for widths below 2 μm strong confinement by heterostructure barriers is appropriate.

Four methods of carrier confinement are used in stripe lasers. In the first method, where an insulator is suitably disposed near the active layer, the current flows mainly into the centre region of the device and is constricted at the edges. The injected carrier concentration distributes itself approximately in proportion to the current. The effectiveness of this method depends on the resistivity and geometry of the layers.

In the second method, employed in deep proton and oxygen implanted lasers, the course of the current flow is completely determined by the geometry of the semi-insulating regions [see Figure 6.2(a)] so that the entire current is directed to injecting carriers into the prescribed section of the active layer. However, once the carriers are injected they are capable of diffusing sideways, and can enter the semi-insulating regions without restriction. Here they can, in general, recombine at an enhanced rate. The lateral distribution of minority carriers in the p-type active layer along the direction parallel to the junction is illustrated by the band diagram in Figure 6.11(a). Minority electrons injected across the p–n junction, as indicated by the vertical arrow, flow down the concentration gradient in the p-type material into the semi-insulating regions on either side. The confining barrier for majority holes that exists in equilibrium conditions at the semi-insulating region boundary is largely removed by the net negative charge injected into the region so that holes flow in at an equal rate to the electrons and take part in the recombination. The diffusion process intercepts a substantial proportion of the injection current which flows into the active layer within a diffusion length of the stripe edge.

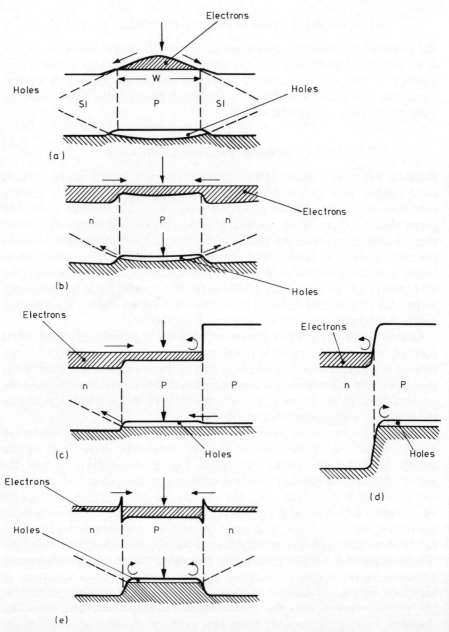

Figure 6.11   Band diagrams showing effectiveness of carrier confinement in various types of stripe laser. (a) Deep proton bombarded and oxygen implanted lasers, (b) twin transverse junction laser, (c) transverse single heterojunction laser, (d) barrier to by-pass injection of carriers in structures (b), (c), and (e) provided by p–n junction in passive layer, (e) buried heterostructure laser

The third method of carrier confinement is by a transverse p–n junction barrier. This is used both in the twin transverse junction laser and in the transverse single heterojunction laser. The band structure in the active layer parallel to the main heterostructure is illustrated for the twin transverse junction laser in Figure 6.10(b) and for the transverse single heterojunction laser in Figure 6.10(c). The main electron current that is injected directly into the active layer across the heterojunction and the compensating hole current are indicated by the vertical arrows. The p–n junction or junctions which traverse the active layer act as reasonable confinement barriers for majority holes and as additional sources of injection of minority electrons. They perform the same function as in an orthodox single heterostructure laser and require heavy n-doping to do this most effectively. However, since electron injection can take place into the n-side from the adjacent wider band-gap n-layer the high n-doping is not so essential as in the normal single heterostructure. Since the p–n junction must be continuous through the cross section of the structure it must traverse the higher band-gap layers of the heterostructure outside the stripe section. In this region it presents a useful block to the flow of shunt current, as indicated in Figure 6.11(d). With the same voltage applied as in the active layer a considerable potential barrier remains which reduces the injection current by several orders of magnitude.

The fourth method of carrier confinement is by the use of a heterojunction, as employed in the buried heterostructure laser of Figure 6.3. In this structure identical methods are used for carrier confinement in the two transverse directions, and the overall confinement efficiency approaches 100 per cent. The distribution of carriers in the plane parallel to the main heterostructure is illustrated in Figure 6.11(e). The transverse heterojunctions at both edges provide good confinement of holes in the central region and also an additional source for electron injection.

6.3.2 Current Spreading in Stripe Contact Lasers

The current spreading in a stripe laser, as it affects the threshold current and the incremental efficiency, is a complex process in which the behaviour both underneath and outside the stripe contact must be taken into consideration. Also, in practice the distinction between current spreading and transverse diffusion becomes somewhat blurred in processes which take place in the active layer. Various simplified approaches can be made. One such treatment has been presented by D'Asaro[33] and Dumke[34] which deals particularly with the edge leakage current that flows sideways in the active layer outside the area of the stripe. A simple linearized analysis allows the total leakage current and its transverse distribution outside the stripe to be obtained in terms of the characteristics of the p–n junction and

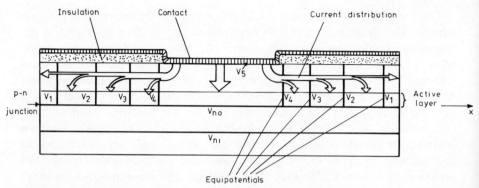

Figure 6.12 Simplified diagram of equipotentials and current distribution between contact and active layer in stripe contact laser

the resistivity and thickness of the heterostructure layers. This serves as a useful introduction to the general problem of transverse carrier flow in stripe lasers. However, a further question which must be answered is: from which part of the region under the stripe is the leakage current drawn? For instance, if it comes from the edges of the stripe the effect on the carrier distribution at the centre of the stripe is minimal and the threshold current density remains the same. Only the width of the lasing filament is reduced. To investigate this aspect of the problem the derivation of the external leakage current must be followed by an analysis of the carrier distribution under the stripe.

For the present purpose the potential distribution over the cross section of the laser in the layers adjacent to the contact (or 'current window') is assumed to take the simple form illustrated in Figure 6.12. (For comparison a more exact representation of the potential distribution, both inside and outside the contact, is given in Figure 6.13.) The n-side boundary of the active layer is assumed to be a plane of equipotential V_{n0}. This is a reasonable assumption when the conductivity of the n-passive layer is relatively high, which is normal. The equipotentials in the thin layer on the p-side (V_1, etc.) are taken to be perpendicular to the p–n junction in the region outside the contact, with purely transverse current flow. The analysis of the lateral distribution of the voltage outside the contact is then reduced to the solution of a one-dimensional differential equation relating the voltage gradient alone the x direction to the current taken by the p–n junction as follows

$$\frac{\mathrm{d}^2 V}{\mathrm{d}x^2} = \left(\frac{J_0}{gt}\right) \exp\left(\frac{eV}{nkT}\right) \tag{6.1}$$

where g is the conductivity of the p-layer (average conductivity if more

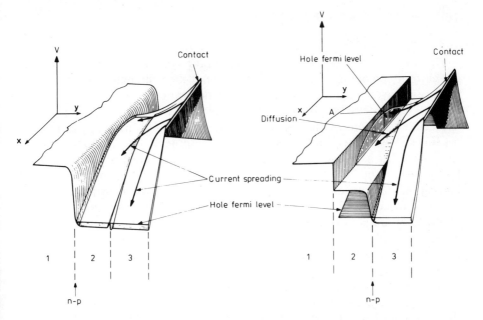

(a) p-doped active layer (b) n-doped active layer

Figure 6.13   Three-dimensional representation of valence band potential and hole Fermi level in stripe contact laser over region between contact and n-passive layer. (a) p-doped active layer, (b) n-doped active layer

than one p-layer), t is the combined thickness of the p-layers (including the active layer if p-doped), V is the voltage on the p-side of the active layer at position x measured with respect to the voltage at $x = 0$, J_0 is the current density per unit area at $x = 0$, and $\exp(eV/nkT)$ gives the relative current/voltage dependence of the laser junction below threshold. Solving this equation shows that the current density J through the active layer drops off with distance x from the edge of the contact according to the relation

$$J = 2 \frac{J_0}{(x/l_s + 2^{1/2})^2} \qquad (6.2)$$

where l_s is a spreading length given by

$$l_s = \left(\frac{gtnkT}{J_0 e}\right)^{1/2} \qquad (6.3)$$

As an example for typical values of $t = 2 \ \mu\text{m}$, $J_0 = 2 \times 10^3 \ \text{A cm}^{-2}$, $g = 10^2 \ \text{mho cm}^{-1}$, and $nkT/e = 0.03$, l_s has a value of about $5 \ \mu\text{m}$. The total current per unit length J_{fringe} which flows into the fringe region on both sides of the stripe is given by

$$J_{\text{fringe}} = 2.2^{1/2} l_s J_0 \tag{6.4}$$

When the active layer is of the same doping type as the layers in which the current spreading occurs (normally p-type) then the majority carriers in the active layer must also be included in determining the total transverse current. The interaction between the passive and active layer can be better appreciated by considering the potential distribution in more detail. Figure 6.13(a) shows a three-dimensional plot of the potential distribution around the contact in both the passive layer and the active layer as a function of both the x and y co-ordinates. The potential on the n-side of the heterojunction barrier, also illustrated, is assumed to be constant over the lateral x direction. The potential of both the valence band and the hole Fermi level are shown. For ease of presentation the Fermi level is taken as being located in the valence band. It is continuous across the heterojunction which divides the p-passive and active layers. The potential gradient which drives holes sideways in the two regions is hence very similar in the two layers, and only differs as a result of the injected component of holes in the active region. Where this component is small the same ohmic treatment for transverse flow is appropriate in both layers. Otherwise allowance must be made for the greater transverse flow which occurs in the centre region of the active layer where the hole concentration is greater. In the ideal model electrons do not contribute to the transverse flow since the electron quasi-Fermi level is clamped by the equipotential on the n-side of the p–n junction and is flat across the region. In practice, owing to voltage dropped in the n-layers, there would be some variation in potential on the n-side, which would tend to drive the injected electrons against their concentration gradient towards the centre of the stripe.

Measurements show that the value of the spreading length l_s is of the order of 2–5 μm, which means that half the current leaks out sideways in stripes of around 10-μm width.

6.3.3 Carrier Loss by Diffusion

The lateral spreading of current in stripe lasers occurs in the active layer as well as in the passive layer adjacent to the contact. If the active layer is of the same doping type as the passive layer (usually p-type) then, as mentioned in the previous section, the current spreading takes place by the same ohmic process as in the p-passive layer [see Figure 6.13(a)]. However, if the carriers are injected in appreciable concentration into the active layer, as occurs if the active layer doping is low or of the opposite type to the passive layer, then the movement of injected carriers takes place by diffusion.

Figure 6.13(b) shows a plot of the x/y distribution of potential in a stripe contact laser with an n-doped active layer under the combined effect of current spreading in the p-passive layer and diffusion of holes in the active layer. Since the Fermi level for holes is still continuous between the two layers the two processes interact. The combined behaviour is treated in Section 6.3.4.

In stripe lasers where deep proton bombardment or oxygen implantation has produced an insulating region intersecting the active layer, diffusion provides the only mechanism for the lateral flow of carriers; the diffusion is ambipolar if both types of carrier are present in equal concentrations. Hakki[21] has investigated this behaviour in both shallow and deep proton bombarded lasers. In the shallow bombarded lasers concerned, the observed distribution of carriers (as deduced from measurements of spontaneous emission) is consistent with a diffusion length of 6 μm, both within and outside the stripe. In the deep proton bombarded devices the characteristics of the active layer at the edge of the stripe are changed by the bombardment and in particular the carrier recombination time is reduced. This produces a high recombination velocity for carriers and reduces their concentration at the boundary to around 25 per cent of their peak concentration at the centre of the stripe. Blum et al.[20] have investigated the behaviour in deep oxygen implanted lasers. The dominant effect of the oxygen is to reduce the carrier mobility rather than the recombination time, thereby reducing the lateral flow of carriers and maintaining a higher concentration under the stripe.

The diffusion profile of the injected carriers, both within and outside the region where the injection current flows, has been analysed by Hakki.[21] In the general case it is necessary to take into account the different values of the diffusion constant and the diffusion length in the central and outer regions, which we represent respectively D_1, l_1 and D_2, l_2, and in particular the ratio $D_1 l_2/D_2 l_1$ which we represent by ζ. ζ is unity when the active layer characteristics are uniform. The carrier concentration n is given as a function of position x from the centre line of the stripe, of width w, by

$$n = n_0\left(1 - A \cosh\left(\frac{x}{l_1}\right)\right), \quad \text{for } -\frac{w}{2} < x < \frac{w}{2}$$

$$n = n_0 B \exp\left(\frac{-x}{l_2}\right), \quad \text{for } x < -\frac{w}{2} \text{ and } \frac{w}{2} < x \tag{6.5}$$

where n_0 is the injected carrier concentration which would be produced by the input current density J if there were no sideways diffusion. The coefficients A and B are given by

$$A = \left\{\cosh\left(\frac{w}{2l_1}\right) + \zeta \sinh\left(\frac{w}{2l_1}\right)\right\}^{-1}$$

$$A = \exp\left(\frac{-w}{2l}\right), \quad \text{when } \zeta = 1$$

$$B = A\,\zeta \sinh\left(\frac{w}{2l_1}\right) \exp\left(\frac{w}{2l_2}\right) \tag{6.6}$$

$$B = \sinh\left(\frac{w}{2l}\right), \quad \text{when } \zeta = 1$$

with

$$\zeta = \frac{D_1 l_2}{D_2 l_1} = \frac{(D_1/\tau_1)^{1/2}}{(D_2/\tau_2)^{1/2}}$$

Various profiles of injected carrier concentration are illustrated in Figure 6.14 for different values of $w/2l_1$ and ζ. The profiles given in (a), (b) and (c) apply for $\zeta = 1$ and show the effect of varying the stripe width (or the diffusion length). When the stripe is wider than about five diffusion lengths the distribution of carrier concentration over the centre region of the stripe is very flat and the maximum concentration at the centre line approaches within 10 per cent of the value in a broad contact laser at the same current density. Under such circumstances [see Figure 6.14(c)] the carrier concentration at the edge of the stripe rises to approximately $\zeta/(1 + \zeta)$ of its value at the centre. The total current per unit width which is lost by sideways diffusion corresponds to that flowing into a width of the stripe which is a fraction $2/(1 + \zeta)$ of the diffusion length under the stripe. This value of effective width is about half of that calculated for current spreading in equation (6.4) (depending on the exact value of ζ).

The current lost at the edges of the stripe causes a considerable lowering of the injected carrier concentration within a diffusion length of the edge but a much smaller lowering at the centre, particularly for stripe widths greater than four diffusion lengths. Therefore, provided the lasing filament is confined to the centre region of the stripe the lost current at the edge has little effect on the threshold current density of the wider lasers. In this instance, therefore, the previously derived treatment of D'Asaro and Dumke is not applicable although, as will be described later, circumstances arise in which the lost current in wider lasers becomes important.

When the stripe is less than a few diffusion lengths wide [see Figure 6.14(a)] the peak carrier concentration at the centre of the stripe drops considerably below the value n_0 for a wide stripe, and continues to diminish as the stripe width is further reduced. The height of the peak is also affected by the value of ζ, and this dependence becomes increasingly significant as the width of the stripe is narrowed.

Figure 6.14(d) and (e) show the carrier concentration profiles for $w/l_1 = 2$ and for values of ζ of both 0.25 and 4. Hakki has found that ζ is

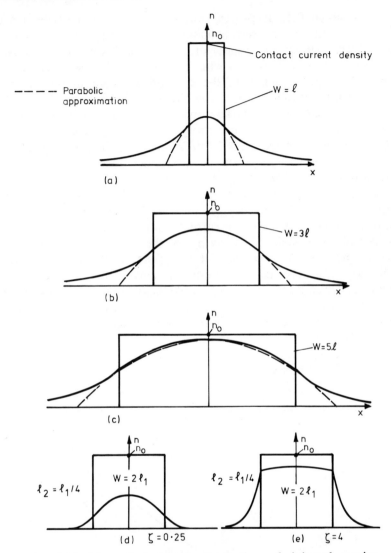

Figure 6.14 Theoretical lateral distribution of injected carrier concentration or non-lasing recombination current density in stripe lasers with uniform injection current density across width of contact. Profiles determined by diffusion. (a), (b), and (c) material uniform within and outside stripe and width of stripe varying from one to five diffusion lengths. (d) Example of deep proton bombarded stripe laser. Diffusion length outside stripe reduced by factor of 4 owing to reduction in τ. Stripe width equal to two internal diffusion lengths. (e) Example of deep oxygen implanted stripe laser. Diffusion length reduced by factor of 4 outside stripe owing to reduction in diffusion coefficient. Stripe width equal to two internal diffusion lengths

reduced to about 0.25 in proton bombarded lasers as a result of a large reduction in the carrier recombination time in the proton bombarded regions.[21] In contrast the results of Blum *et al.*[20] for oxygen implanted lasers are reasonably consistent with a value of ζ of 4 (see Section 6.5.2), indicating a large reduction in the diffusion constant in the bombarded region with little change in the recombination rate. Figure 6.14(d) and (e) show that the peak of the carrier concentration distribution is appreciably increased for $\zeta = 4$ compared with $\zeta = 1$ and appreciably reduced for $\zeta = 0.25$. When the stripe width is further narrowed to less than about one diffusion length the height of the peak becomes directly proportional to ζ. These results show that deep proton bombarded lasers with $\zeta = 0.25$ become relatively unsatisfactory for stripe widths of less than about 1.5 diffusion lengths, whereas oxygen implnated lasers with $\zeta = 4$ become particularly suitable in respect of current confinement.

To describe the peak value, say n_m, of the carrier concentration at the centre of the stripe it is convenient to define an effective width w_0 over which the imput current I, if perfectly constrained, would produce a uniform carrier concentration of n_m. In the case where the characteristics of the active layer are uniform across the width ($\zeta = 1$), which is approximately true in the majority of stripe lasers, then according to equations (6.5) and (6.6) w_0 is given by

$$w_0 = \frac{w}{1 - \exp(-w/2l)} \tag{6.7}$$

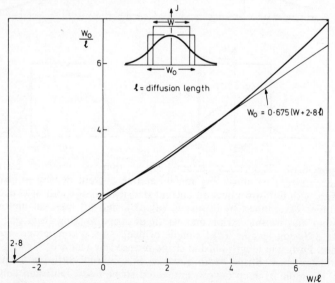

Figure 6.15 Effective stripe width which relates current density at centre of stripe to current supplied under conditions of lateral carrier diffusion

w_0/l is plotted as a function of w/l in Figure 6.15. The curve approximates to a straight line over the interval $0.5 < w/l < 5$ with a gradient of approximately 0.7 and a negative intercept on the w/l axis of approximately 2.8. This is a useful relation which will be used in Section 6.5 on threshold current.

6.3.4 Current Spreading and Diffusion Under Contact

There is a close analogy between transverse diffusion, treated in Section 6.3.3, and current spreading, treated in Section 6.3.2. Indeed, when the change in voltage which drives the transverse current is small compared with kT, equation (6.1) can be written precisely as a diffusion equation with $\exp(eV/nkT)$ in the right-hand side replaced by $(1 + eV/nkT)$. The potential diagrams in Figure 6.13 also illustrate the similarity. In any situation where current spreading and transverse diffusion occur in combination it is reasonable, as an approximation, to treat the two processes as one and modify the values of the diffusion constants appropriately. The behaviour under the contact is generally of most significance since this is where the light in most stripe lasers is mainly concentrated (see next section). It is the region where the smallest changes in voltage occur and hence where the replacement of $\exp(eV/nkT)$ by its linear approximation causes the least inaccuracy.

Up to this point the transverse flow of carriers has been treated in the same one-dimensional manner both underneath and outside the contact. Underneath the contact this is a very considerable approximation and it is less true for current flow in the passive layer than it is for diffusion in the active layer. The conditions under the contact differ from those outside in that the direction of major current flow is normal (y direction) rather than parallel (x direction) to the junction. Any variation in voltage at the junction causes a change in the voltage drop between the junction and the contact and hence, in addition to inducing some lateral current flow, changes the current density normal to the junction. This new factor affects the transverse distribution of injected carriers. By introducing a further tendency to stabilize the carrier concentration it has the effect of reducing the effective diffusion length. An analysis of this behaviour can be made as follows.

The quantity to be fixed will be the external applied voltage, which we will take equal to that required to drive some particular current density J_0 through a broad contact laser. The potential distribution around the contact is illustrated in Figure 6.16. The current density normal to the contact is equal to $g\partial V/\partial y$, where g is the conductivity of the medium concerned. As an approximation a change V of the voltage from its original value at the junction changes the current density by $-gV/t$, where t

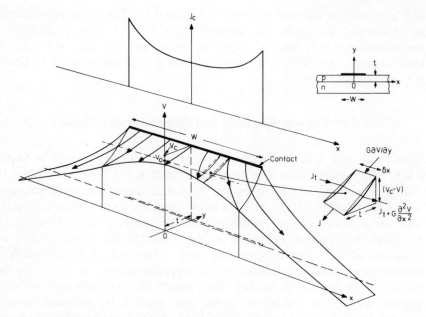

Figure 6.16 Diagram of potential distribution around contact in stripe laser, illustrating method used for analysis of current distribution

is the thickness of the layer separating the contact and the junction. However, in a situation where second derivatives of voltage are important it is necessary to take into account variations of $\partial V/\partial y$ over the thickness t. A more accurate approximation of the variation of V with y can be obtained by investigation of the two-dimensional flow of current beneath the contact. Current continuity imposes a relation between the y and x variations of potential. Accordingly, we can use as the basis for a more accurate analysis an approximation for the second derivative of potential in the transverse x direction. We take $\partial^2 V/\partial x^2$ to increase linearly with distance between the contact and the junction with a value of zero at the contact (the true relation is sinusoidal) so that

$$\frac{\partial^2 V}{\partial x^2} = \left(\frac{\mathrm{d}^2 V}{\mathrm{d}x^2}\right)_{\text{junction}}\left(1 - \frac{y}{t}\right) \tag{6.8}$$

where $y = 0$ at the junction and t at the contact. Integrating equation (6.8) with respect to y and multiplying by g to obtain the total divergence of the x component of current (per unit length); setting this equal to the difference between the contact current density J_c and the current density J injected into the active layer; using the current continuity relation $(\partial^2 V/\partial x^2 + \partial^2 V/\partial y^2 = 0)$ to obtain $\partial^2 V/\partial y^2$ from (6.8) and, by integration with respect to y, $\partial V/\partial y$ and V in terms of y and d^2V/dx^2 at the junction; equating $g\partial V/\partial y$ at $y = 0$ to J, and measuring junction voltage V with respect to the voltage drop tJ_0/g that would exist between the contact and the junction in a uniform laser at threshold current density J_0; gives the following two equations for J_c and J from which the third for J_c can be deduced

$$J_c - J = - \left(\frac{gt}{2}\right)\frac{d^2V}{dx^2} \tag{6.9a}$$

$$J - J_0 = \frac{-gV}{t} + \left(\frac{gt}{3}\right)\frac{d^2V}{dx^2} \tag{6.9b}$$

$$J_c - J_0 = \frac{-gV}{t} - \left(\frac{gt}{6}\right)\frac{d^2V}{dx^2} \tag{6.9c}$$

We may express the excess current $J - J_0$ across the junction in terms of the excess voltage V at the junction, using the approximate junction characteristics and allowing in the process for any transverse diffusion of carriers in the active layer of thickness d. This gives

$$J - J_0 = \frac{J_0 eV}{nkT} - n_0 de\mu \frac{d^2V}{dx^2} \tag{6.9d}$$

where n_0 is the average injected carrier concentration and μ is the mobility. Substitution into equation (6.9b) gives the following differential equation to replace equation (6.1)

$$\left(\frac{gt}{3} + n_0 de\mu\right)\frac{d^2V}{dx^2} - \frac{gV}{t} = \frac{J_0 eV}{nkT} \tag{6.10}$$

This equation also has the form of a diffusion equation, and associated with it is an effective diffusion or spreading length which we will call l_{eff}. The value of l_{eff} obtained by solving this equation is given by

$$l_{eff} = \left\{\frac{l_s^2/3 + l_D^2}{1 + l_s^2/t^2}\right\}^{1/2} \tag{6.11}$$

where l_D is the diffusion length in the active layer and l_s is the spreading length as given in equation (6.3). When the contact is not closely coupled to the active layer ($t^2 > l_s^2$) the effective diffusion length l_{eff} given by the above equation is somewhat greater than the larger of the two lengths $l_s/3^{1/2}$ and l_D. Closer coupling of the contact reduces the effective diffusion length until eventually it tends either to $t/3^{1/2}$ if current spreading is dominant ($l_s > l_D$), or to the larger value of $t(l_D/l_s)$ if diffusion is dominant ($l_D > l_s$). In both cases the proximity of the contact very much reduces the effective diffusion length. It should be noted that the condition for close coupling of the contact is that the voltage drop between the contact and the active layer, including any incremental contact impedance, should be considerably less than nkT, i.e. less than 40–80 mV.

When the contact is closely coupled to the active layer the current density supplied by the contact is no longer uniformly equal to J_0 over the whole area. According to equations (6.9) and (6.3) using $d^2V/dx^2 = V/l_{eff}^2$, the additional current density $(J_c - J_0)$ drawn from the contact is given in terms of the increase in junction current J_0eV/nkT at additional junction voltage V by

$$J_c - J_0 = \frac{-\rho J_0 eV}{nkT}, \quad \text{where } \rho = l_s^2 \left\{ \frac{1}{t^2} + \frac{1}{6\,l_{eff}^2} \right\} \tag{6.12}$$

which must be integrated over x to obtain the increase in total current drawn from the contact per unit length of stripe. This additional current must be taken into account when obtaining the effective width w_0, so that equation (6.7) becomes

$$w_0 = \frac{w + \rho \int_{-w/2}^{w/2} (1 - J/J_0)dx}{1 - A}$$

$$= \frac{w + 2\rho l_{eff} A \, \sinh(w/2 l_{eff})}{1 - A} \tag{6.13}$$

Figure 6.17 shows a typical distribution of the contact current density and the junction current density under conditions where the contact is closely coupled. This distribution applies to the particular case where the diffusion length under the stripe is half that outside ($\zeta = 2$) and one-eighth of the stripe width, and where $\rho = 3$. The voltage dropped in these circumstances between the contact and the active layer would be $nkT/3$,

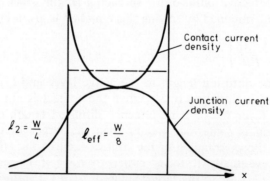

Figure 6.17 Example of lateral distribution of junction current density and contact current density under circumstances where contact is closely coupled to active layer

e.g. 15 mV. The figure shows that the junction current density at the centre of the stripe is very nearly equal to the contact current density at the same position, and that extra current that flows is confined almost entirely to the two ears of additional current density at each edge of the stripe.

Some care must be used in deriving the value of ζ used in equation (6.6) for determining A in the above equation. If diffusion is dominant $(l_D \gg l_s)$ then it is given straightforwardly by

$$\zeta = \left(1 + \frac{l_s^2}{t^2}\right)^{1/2} \left(\frac{D_1 \tau_2}{D_2 \tau_1}\right)^{1/2} \tag{6.14}$$

where D_1, D_2, τ_1, and τ_2 are diffusion constants and recombination times for the active layer within and outside the stripe, respectively. If current spreading into the passive layer is dominant it must be noted that outside the stripe the transverse current flow is $\sqrt{2}$ times what it would be if l_s were a true diffusion length [see equation (6.4)]. Hence

$$\zeta = \left\{\frac{1 + l_s^2/t_1^2}{6}\right\}^{1/2} \left(\frac{t_1}{t_2}\right)^{1/2} \tag{6.15}$$

allowing for a possible change in the thickness of the passive layer from a value of t_1 under the stripe to t_2 outside.

6.3.5 Carrier Confinement in the Buried Heterostructure

In the buried heterostructure laser the functions of channelling the current to the active region and confining the injected carriers within the same region are combined in one structure. This is illustrated in the three-dimensional diagram of the band structure over the cross section of the laser in Figure 6.18. The x and y axes in this figure represent the two transverse directions in the laser structure, as indicated in the inset. The vertical axis represents energy, as in the standard one-dimensional band diagram. The cross section of the active GaAs region, where the band-gap is smaller, is indicated on the diagram. This is surrounded on its four sides by material of higher band-gap, providing a complete heterojunction confinement barrier.

Holes can be injected from the p-(GaAl)As region into the active region from one side in the structure illustrated, and electrons can be injected from the n-(GaAl)As region into the active region from three sides. Abrupt heterojunctions cause potential spikes to appear at the band discontinuity, and the electrons must tunnel through the spikes in the course of injection, as described in Chapter 3. These spikes, which form a three-sided barrier in the present example, are illustrated in the figure. They do not, however, represent a significant barrier to current flow and

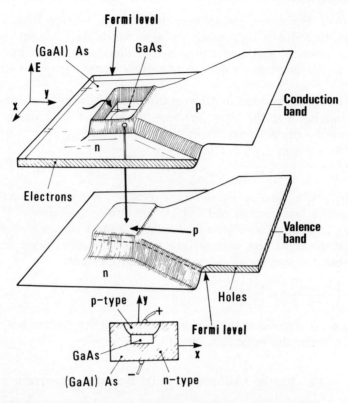

Figure 6.18   Three-dimensional plot of band potentials and Fermi levels over cross section of buried heterostructure laser to illustrate carrier injection and confinement processes

are not present if the heterojunctions are graded over a few hundred ångströms.

The electron and hole Fermi levels are indicated on the diagram as flat planes which extend from the respective injecting contacts, as quasi-Fermi levels, through into the active region. The condition illustrated applies when the driving voltage is sufficient to raise the concentration of the carriers injected into the active region, both holes and electrons, above that of the adjacent injecting regions. This constitutes carrier accumulation. The recombination path of electrons and holes in the active region is indicated by the vertical arrow.

The pair of p–n junction barriers in the (GaAl)As, which funnel the hole current into the active region, are illustrated lying at an angle to the layer structure. They present a potential barrier against the direct injection of holes into the n-(GaAl)As region and electrons into the p-(GaAl)As region. If these barriers are sufficiently close to the active region for the effect of ohmic potential gradients to be neglected, then they are equal in height to the heterojunction barriers surrounding the active layer and are equally effective in preventing the passage of minority carriers.

In practice the buried heterostructure can give very good carrier confinement. This is indicated by the excellent results which have been achieved, with measured threshold current as low as 7 mA in devices of 1.5-μm width and 300-μm length with an active layer thickness of 0.2 μm.[4] The corresponding threshold current denisty is comparable to that in a broad contact laser.

6.3.6 Carrier Confinement in Twin Transverse Junction Lasers

Figure 6.19 shows a three-dimensional plot of the band structure illustrating carrier confinement over the cross section of a twin transverse junction laser. This is a similar plot to that shown in Figure 6.18 for the buried heterostructure. The active region is contained in the centre layer of GaAs, and is confined laterally by the two p-n junctions. Holes are injected into one side of the active region from the p-(GaAl)As layer across the heterojuction boundary. Electrons are injected from the n-(GaAl)As layer mainly across the heterojunction in the layout illustrated to the right. If the junction is abrupt the electrons have to tunnel through a barrier produced by a potential spike which accompanies the band discontinuity. Some electrons are, however, injected transversely across the p–n junctions. A small proportion of holes are lost by injection in the opposite direction across this junction, which depends, as in the single heterostructure, on the n-doping level concerned. An alternative structure can be made in which, as indicated to the left of Figure 6.19, the p–n junction is completed in the n-(GaAl)As region rather than lying along the heterojunction boundary of the active layer. In these circumstances all the electron injection must take place across the two p–n junctions in the GaAs layer. The parts of the p–n junction barriers which are angled back in the (GaAl)As perform the same function of channelling the hole current to the active layer as they do in the buried heterostructe.

6.4   OPTICAL CONFINEMENT IN STRIPE LASERS

Three processes are important in considering optical confinement in stripe lasers: dielectric waveguiding, so-called gain-guiding, and self-focusing. Dielectric guiding follows the principles that have already been treated for heterostructures and will not be pursued further. Gain-guiding has a particularly significant bearing on the behaviour of conventional stripe lasers and a physical description of the process is presented to supplement

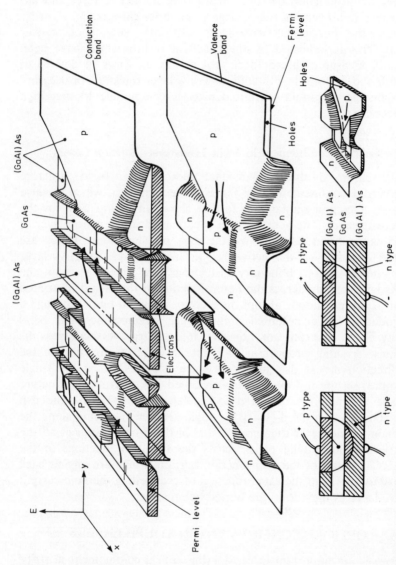

Figure 6.19 Three dimensional plot of band potentials and Fermi levels over cross section of twin transverse junction stripe laser to illustrate carrier injection and confinement processes. Main diagram shows central portion of p–n junction located at active layer boundary. Diagram at left shows central portion of p–n junction located in passive layer. Inset diagram at bottom right shows underside of valence band

the theoretical treatment given in Section 4.2. Self-focusing effects associated with the interaction of light and injected carriers which have been tentatively suggested in the past[35,36] have recently been shown also to contribute significantly to the behaviour of stripe lasers.[37] A theoretical treatment of such processes is also given.

6.4.1   Gain-Guiding

This section attempts to interpret in more physical terms the theoretical treatment of gain-guiding given in Section 4.2 and tries to establish the fundamental principles which lie at the basis of the behaviour. Two models of the gain guide, one with abrupt steps between the gain and loss regions and one where the gain/loss characteristic is continuously graded over the laser cross section, illustrate slightly different aspects of the phenomenon.

6.4.1.1   *Abrupt Steps between Gain and Loss*

Figure 6.20 gives a perspective illustration of a typical two-dimensional wave which is generated in a gain-guiding situation, where an elongated region of uniform gain is surrounded by regions which are either transparent or optically lossy. The overall wave motion creates a herring-bone pattern. The spreading V-shaped waves in the outer transparent or lossy regions are linked together at their apex in the gain region by curved sections of the wavefront where the driving power is applied. The outer waves die away in amplitude with distance from the guide axis, and fan out like the wake from a ship.

Energy is propagated in the direction normal to the wavefronts. In the centre strip the majority of the power flux is directed along the axis of the guide. A proportion, however, moves out to the edges of the guide and is fed into the diverging waves in the 'wake'. The magnitude of the proportion which leaks out determines the dissipation of the structure, and the effectiveness of the gain-guiding.

The way the diverging waves die away with distance from the axis controls the transverse spread of the light, and may be regarded as an indication of how well the light is confined. This behaviour resembles in one respect that in the slab dielectric waveguide described in Chapter 4 section 4.1.3—viz. that the optical field decreases exponentially in the outward direction—but differs from it in that this field is associated with an outward propagating wave rather than with a constant-phase evanescent decay. Accordingly the lateral propagation constant has a real part, which we call p_1, and an imaginary part which we call jp_2. p_2 is the equivalent of the decay constant p defined for the slab waveguide in Section 4.1.2. The optical intensity therefore decays in the lateral direction according to

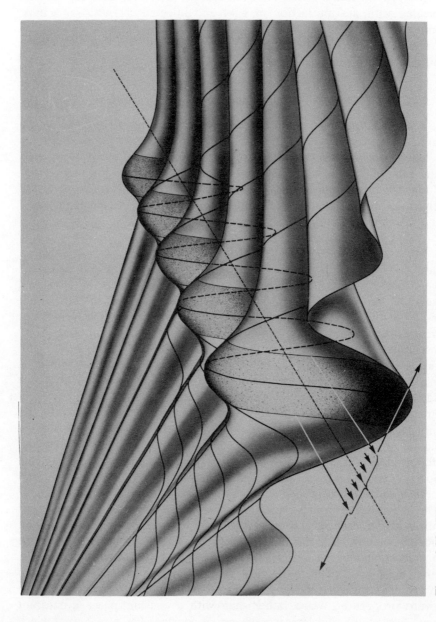

Figure 6.20 Three-dimensional representation of the field distribution of a propagating gain-guided mode in a stripe geometry laser

$\exp(\pm 2p_2 x)$. Figure 6.21 gives a geometrical representation of how the lateral decay is related to the gain along the axis (gain coefficient g_z), the angle θ between the axis of the laser and the propagation direction of the diverging waves in the outer region, and the loss coefficient of the diverging wave. The equation on which Figure 6.21 is based is that relating the transverse propagation constant $(p_1 + jp_2)$, the longitudinal propagation

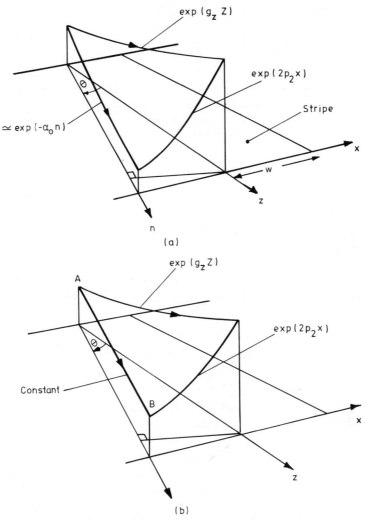

Figure 6.21 Optical intensity distributions to show relation between longitudinal gain coefficient, lateral decay coefficient, and emergent angle of leaky waves in gain-guided mode of stripe laser. (a) Region external to stripe is lossy, (b) region external to stripe is transparent

constant $(\beta_z + jg_z/2)$, and the plane wave propagation constant $(\mu\beta_0 - j\alpha_0/2)$ which, by an extension of equation (4.6) to complex quantities, is given by

$$(p_1 + jp_2)^2 = \left(\mu\beta_0 - \frac{j\alpha_0}{2}\right)^2 - \left(\beta_z + \frac{jg_z}{2}\right)^2 \tag{6.16}$$

where μ is the refractive index and $\beta_0 = 2\pi/\lambda$. θ is related to p_1 by

$$\sin\theta \simeq \frac{p_1}{\mu\beta_0} \tag{6.17}$$

Equating the real and imaginary parts in equation (6.16) shows that the only approximation in the representation of Figure 6.21 is in ascribing the same attenuation constant α_0 to the diverging waves as is applicable to plane waves in the same region. This is a good approximation provided the transverse decay constant is small compared with the plane wave propagation constant in the material. From Figure 6.21(a) it can be seen that the transverse decay constant is given approximately by

$$2p_2 \simeq \frac{g_z + \alpha_0}{\sin\theta} \tag{6.18}$$

The angle θ is very important in determing the transverse decay constant, and when it is small the confinement is good. θ is itself determined by the way the waves inside the gain region are refracted as they emerge across the boundary. This depends, according to the normal laws of refraction, on the refractive index difference between the two regions and the angle of propagation of the waves in the centre region. If the waves in the centre region were to propagate precisely along the axis then, according to Snell's law, the angle θ of the emerging refracted waves would be given by

$$\sin\theta = \text{real part of } \left(\frac{2\delta\mu}{\mu}\right)^{1/2}$$

where $\delta\mu$ is the amount by which the external refractive index is greater than the refractive index in the gain region. Exact analysis shows that to satisfy the boundary conditions the waves in the centre region propagate at a slight angle to the axis. This does not, however, increase θ by more than a factor of 2.

The refractive index difference between the centre and outer regions is composed of a real contribution due to injected electrons and an imaginary contribution due to the difference between the central gain and the outer loss. The real contribution is of the order of 0.002, which on its own gives a value of $\sin\theta$ of the order of 0.03. The imaginary contribution, taking a gain coefficient g_0 and a loss coefficient α_0, has a value $j(g_0 + \alpha_0)/2\beta_0$. [See, for example, equation (4.35) in Chapter 4, Section 4.2.1 for the equivalent dielectric constant.] For a typical case $[(g_0 + \alpha_0) = 150 \text{ cm}^{-1}]$ we find

$\delta\mu = 0.001$j, giving a value of sin θ only a little smaller at 0.02 than that suggested for the real part of the refractive index. Putting these values back into equation (6.18) and taking a value of $(g_z + \alpha_0)$ of 100 cm^{-1} gives a transverse decay length of the order of a few microns.

It should be noticed that even if the outer medium is lossless there is still a lateral fall-off in intensity which arises only from the axial gain g_z. This is illustrated in Figure 6.21(b). Consider the arbitrary point B on the diverging wave, where the intensity is considerably diminished with respect to the peak. This has originated, by wave propagation with no attenuation, from the point A far back in the gain region where the intensity is relatively low because it has not yet experienced the amplification in the intervening length. Increasing the amplification reduces this contribution to the lateral spread, but the effect is partially offset by an increase in θ, so that the overall relationship between lateral spread and gain has the approximate form of an inverse square root.

Although this model gives a good indication of the reason why the optical intensity falls off so rapidly in the tranverse direction outside the central gain region it is not so suitable for indicating the actual amplitude of the diverging waves at the point where they are generated adjacent to the gain region. This is determined to a considerable extent by the distribution of the optical intensity within the gain region itself and by the way it falls off between the centre and the edge. A treatment which is more useful in this respect can be based on the model analysed mathematically in Section 4.2 where it is assumed that the gain varies uniformly over the transverse section. This model will therefore be used to explain the way the loss in the wings of the optical distribution is determined by the width of the region of gain.

6.4.1.2 Continuous Gain/Loss Profile

In a more realistic model of the stripe laser the gain varies continuously across the transverse section, peaking at the centre and falling away to a region of loss at the edges. This gain distribution is accompanied by a similar continuous variation of the refractive index, but with a minimum value at the centre, giving a distribution that tends to spread the wave rather than confine it. This situation has been analysed theoretically in Section 4.2 for a parabolic variation of the parameters. Here we attempt to give a descriptive treatment.

In the distributed model there are no abrupt boundaries between regions of gain and loss that can give rise to specific reflections, and there is no positive source of optical confinement. The spread of the lasing mode is determined largely by diffraction, augmented by anti-focusing effects associated with the refractive index profile. The amount of diffraction is related to the width of the beam. The width of the beam can be taken to be not much greater than the width of the gain region (in certain circumstances, as explained below, it can be considerably less). The way that such a beam would spread by diffraction in the absence of gain can be estimated using reasonable assumptions for the shape of its intensity distribution and the curvature of the wavefront. The proportion of the beam which spreads outside the gain region in propagating along the length of the laser can then be regarded as a measure of the diffraction loss and can be used as a criterion for the performance of the stripe laser.

We assume the transverse intensity distribution to be Gaussian, which is shown to be true in Section 4.2 for a parabolic gain profile, and set its width, to the $1/e^2$ points of intensity, equal to s_{eff}. Initially assume the wavefront to be plane. Such a source produces a far-field distribution which is also Gaussian with an angular half width $\theta_{1/2}$ (measured between the centre line and the direction where the intensity is reduced by $1/e^2$) given by

$$\sin \theta_{1/2} = \frac{2\lambda}{\pi \mu s_{eff}} \tag{6.19}$$

where μ is the refractive index. The effective width of the beam at a distance L from the source is $2L \sin \theta_{1/2}$ (provided L is large enough to make this appreciably greater than s_{eff}). A convenient criterion of a beam which is adequately directional for laser operation, and which will not cause an unacceptable rise in threshold, is that it should not spread to more than double its size over the length L of the laser. On this basis equation (6.19) shows that the minimum allowable value of the optical width is given by

$$(s_{eff})_{min} = \left(\frac{2L\lambda}{\pi \mu}\right)^{1/2} \tag{6.20}$$

For a laser of length, say 300 μm this equation indicates that the beam width should be at least 7 μm. This result is reasonably consistent with that obtained by the analysis of Section 4.2. For instance, if the effective width just satisfies equation (6.20) then equation (4.80) in Section 4.2 shows that the peak intrinsic gain at the centre of the gain distribution at threshold is about 2.5 times the actual gain g_z imparted to the laser mode. This will be taken here as the acceptable limit although, in any particular design of laser, characteristics other than threshold current density could affect the issue.

The total light generated in the lasing mode of the stripe laser does not, of course, diverge as it propagates from one end of the resonator to the other. The transverse optical distribution settles to such a form, along the whole length of the laser, that the effect of the gain distribution in enhancing the centre and attenuating the edges of the optical distribution just counteracts the spreading effect of diffraction, and the wave propagates along the laser axis unchanged in shape but with the necessary amplification. The treatment of Section 4.2 shows that the equilibrium optical distribution is Gaussian but that wavefront is curved. If there is no refractive index profile to cause anti-focusing then the equilibrium distribution corresponds precisely, in both shape and curvature of wavefront, to that in a Gaussian beam at the point in the transition region between the near and far field where the beam has expanded by a factor of $2^{1/2}$, compared with its width at the waist. A Gaussian beam is illustrated in Figure 6.22, and the point concerned is indicated by z_0. The angle $\theta_{1/2}$ at which the beam diverges at this point is a factor of $1/2^{1/2}$ less than the final diffraction angle but precisely equal to the angle given in terms of s_{eff} in equation (6.19). Hence no adjustment need be made to equation (6.20) to take account of the curvature of the wavefront. If a refractive index profile that causes anti-focusing is present the curvature of the wavefront for a given beamwidth is increased. This increases the value of $\sin \theta_{1/2}$ or alternatively means that for given diffraction loss a larger beam width must be used. The minimum acceptable value of s_{eff} is then greater than that given by equation (6.20) and it is necessary to use the exact theory given in Section 4.2 to find its value.

The width of the beam in a stripe laser is determined by the width of the gain profile and the magnitude of the diffraction. If the width of the optical distribution is small the diffraction loss is large and the majority of the gain is taken up in counteracting this loss rather than in imparting overall amplification to the wave.

In a precise treatment of the gain/loss equilibrium the diffraction loss is

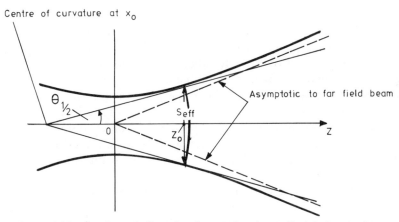

Figure 6.22 Section of Gaussian beam showing cylindrical wavefront at z_0 which is 'frozen' in gain-guided mode

an unsatisfactory quantity because it requires the definition of a boundary which the escaping energy must cross before it is defined as a loss. Instead, we consider absorption loss. This is a reasonable alternative since all the optical flux that escapes from the gain region by diffraction is eventually absorbed in the surrounding lossy regions (or emitted from the end of the laser). The magnitude per unit length of this loss can be obtained by an appropriate integration of the product of optical intensity and loss coefficient in the lossy region.

To produce a net amplification of the wave, the gain contribution over the width of the stripe where the gain is positive must be greater than the loss contribution over the remaining width where the gain is negative. Expressed more precisely this requires that the integral of the (optical intensity) gain product in the centre region be greater than that of the (optical intensity) loss product in the outer regions. This condition can in principle be reached in all reasonable circumstances, however narrow the gain region, by sufficient increase in the current density. If increasing the current density only increased the gain in the centre region and left the losses unaltered in the outer regions then the laser would operate with a relatively large penetration of the optical field into the outer regions. However, at a fixed wavelength the maximum optical gain that can be obtained is normally considerably less in magnitude than the loss which exists under unpumped conditions. If the necessary increase in gain required to reach threshold of the narrow stripe is large it is mainly available at a shorter wavelength, closer to the band-edge, and hence the losses in the unpumped regions are larger. The penetration of the light into the lossy regions is therefore reduced. The treatment of Section 4.2, equation (4.82), shows that when the gain and loss profile can be approximated to a parabola the maximum distance the light can penetrate into the lossy region is such that the effective optical width s_{eff}, measured to the $1/e^2$ points, is twice the width of the region where the gain is positive. The losses then exactly compensate the gain. The corresponding distribution of gain and optical intensity are illustrated in Figure 6.23(a).

A different situation arises when the gain region is wide. The diffraction loss of the laser mode is small and the lasing emission is generated over a width where the gain barely exceeds the end losses of the laser. Because of the curvature at the peak of the gain profile this can correspond to only a fraction of the width over which the gain is positive, as is shown by equation (4.78) in Section 4.2. This behaviour is illustrated in Figure 6.23(b).

The situation becomes more complicated, however, as the laser is driven harder, because then the gain profile is affected by the stimulated emission, and its shape changes. This results eventually in higher order lateral modes reaching threshold and broadening the total emission. Also, a change in

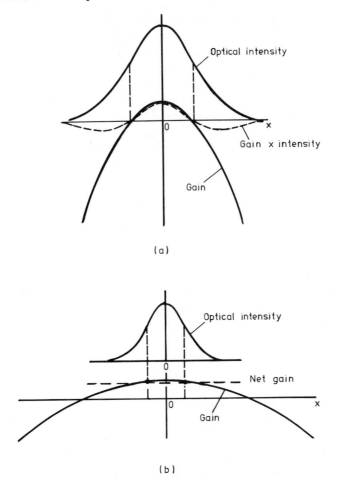

Figure 6.23 Corresponding distributions of gain and optical intensity in gain-guided modes. (a) Narrow gain distribution, (b) wide gain distribution

gain profile implies a change in the injected electron concentration and hence a change in the electronic contribution to the refractive index. This is the cause of self-focusing which is treated in the next section.

6.4.2 Self-focusing

Self-focusing is a phenomenon in which the lasing beam interacts with the medium through which it propagates in such a way as to provide its own optical waveguide. This process involves strong positive feedback and tends to be unstable. In the present instance it is rendered even more unstable because of the nature of the interaction with the semiconductor. The rise in refractive index which creates the waveguide is produced by a drop in the injected electron concentration in the active layer of the laser. This drop occurs in the region of the optical filament because of the high local rate of stimulated recombination. It is, of course, accompanied by a decrease in the value of the optical gain coefficient. Hence the filament finds itself in a region of relatively high refractive index and low gain, surrounded on both sides by regions of higher gain. The stability of the situation is determined amongst other things by the physical extent of the higher gain regions. If these regions are sufficiently wide then, with little further increase in current, further filaments will be excited within them. The filaments are initiated in a gain-guided mode, but immediately become subject to self-focusing and are then indistinguishable from the original filament. This makes the behaviour in a wide laser relatively complicated. However, in a sufficiently narrow laser the behaviour is simpler. The regions of higher gain bordering the filament are not then wide enough to support either a gain-guided mode or a higher order transverse mode within the original filament and it is possible to obtain a stable zero-order self-focused filament over an appreciable range of current.

Various workers have investigated the phenomenon of self-focusing[35,36,38] in broad semiconductor lasers and recently it has been demonstrated in practice to contribute significantly to the behaviour of stripe lasers.[37] In this section we present a theoretical analysis of the behaviour, first as an artificially isolated phenomenon in a wide laser, and secondly in the more realistic situation in a stripe laser.

Injected electrons lower the refractive index of the active layer of the laser by two separate interactions. The first is the free-carrier–plasma interaction, which can be precisely calculated[35] in terms of velocity imparted to the electrons by the alternating optical field. The second is the result of the gain process itself. Gain or loss processes with a pronounced spectral variation make a contribution to the refractive index of the material which can be deduced, according to the Kramers–Kroenig relations, from fundamental principles. The injected electrons cause a reduction in this component of refractive index in the process of supplying optical gain, by shifting the absorption edge of the semiconductor to a slightly higher photon energy. This produces an additional effect that is comparable with the plasma interaction.[36] Both effects are treated in more detail in Appendix 4. The change in refractive index seems to be approximately proportional to the current flowing.[38,39]

To calculate the degree of self-focusing we need to know the effect on the injected carrier concentration of the increased recombination rate in the laser filament.

The excess rate of carrier recombination produced by stimulated emission depends on both the phonton density ϕ and the carrier concentration n. No matter what the photon density may be, the stimulated recombination drops to zero at the injected carrier concentration n_0 which gives zero gain. If we take the stimulated recombination rate as being proportional to the excess carrier concentration beyond some value n_t which is the concentration for transparency, and include the effect of carrier diffusion, then we may write the following rate equation for determining the carrier concentration n[36]

$$J = \frac{n}{\tau} + \frac{(\phi/\phi_0)(n - n_t)}{\tau} + D \operatorname{div} n \tag{6.21}$$

where J is the electron current per unit volume, D is the diffusion constant of the electrons, τ is the spontaneous recombination time, and $\phi/\phi_0\tau$ is the stimulated recombination constant, with ϕ_0 defined in such a way that when $\phi = \phi_0$ the total incremental carrier recombination rate is twice that due to spontaneous emission alone. If we ignore the diffusion of electrons this gives the following expression for the injected carrier concentration in terms of the light intensity and the current

$$n = N - \frac{(N - n_t)(\phi/\phi_0)}{(1 + \phi/\phi_0)} \tag{6.22}$$

where N is the carrier concentration that would be produced by the current J in the absence of stimulated recombination. Equation (6.22) shows that the injected carrier concentration varies in approximately the opposite way to the light, and that when ϕ is considerably less than ϕ_0 (up to about 10–15 per cent above threshold) the relationship is almost linear, the change δn in n being approximately proportional to $-\phi$.

As a result of a combination of the above effects a self-focused lasing filament can be established. This is illustrated in Figure 6.24. The greater intensity of light at the centre of the filament reduces the injected carrier concentration according to equation (6.22), increases the refractive index, and provides the dielectric waveguide that is necessary to contain the filament. In general such a situation is not stable because the injected carrier concentration outside the filament rises to a level considerably higher than the threshold concentration in a uniform laser. In theory further filaments should form until the region of high optical gain which separates them is too narrow for any more filaments to be initiated by a gain-guiding process. In practice such behaviour has not been observed in broad Fabry–Perot lasers due to competing interactions, but it has been found when an external cavity is used to stabilize the condition.[60] Self-focusing behaviour has also been observed in stripe lasers of width appropriate to support only one self-focused filament.[37,38]

The width of the filament depends on the amount the laser is driven

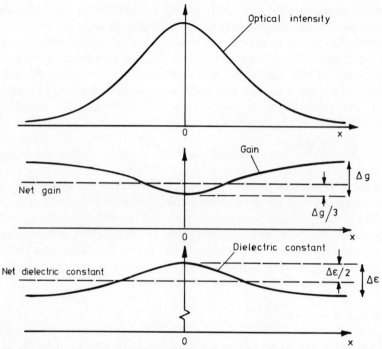

Figure 6.24 Distribution of optical intensity, gain, and dielectric constant for idealized self-focused filament

above threshold. As the current is increased the relative variation of the injected carrier concentration increases, the optical guiding becomes stronger, and the filament contracts in width. The behaviour was analysed theoretically by the author.[36] A simplified treatment is presented here.

6.4.2.1 Analysis in Broad Lasers

In the regime where there is a linear relation between the optical intensity and the injected carrier concentration $(I < 1.15\,I_{th})$ and the refractive index and the injected carrier concentration the refractive index distribution generated in the filament must be the exact equivalent of the light intensity distribution. The only refractive index profile where this is possible, namely the $\cosh^{-2}(2x/s)$ distribution, is analysed in Section 4.2. In general this produces an optical intensity distribution of the form $\cosh^{-2u}$ $(2x/s)$, see equation (4.56). u is in general complex $(= u_1 + ju_2)$. When u_1 is equal to unity the distributions of refractive index and optical intensity are of the same form, as illustrated in Figure 6.24. The imaginary component u_2 is associated with the phase of the optical distribution. According to equation (4.97) it is given in the present instance by $u_2 \simeq -2/3b$ where $1/b$ is the ratio of the imaginary component (gain component) to the real component of the dielectric constant perturbation. Using equations (4.51), (4.55), and (4.57) it is possible to show that if the total amplitude of the variation of the real part of the dielectric constant is $\Delta\epsilon$ then the effective width s_{eff} of the filament to the $1/e$ points of intensity is given by

$$s_{\text{eff}} = \frac{1.08\lambda(2 - (\tfrac{2}{3}b)^2)^{1/2}}{\pi\Delta\epsilon^{1/2}} \tag{6.23}$$

(The quantity $(2/3b)^2$ was omitted from the original analysis[36].) Equations (4.51), (4.55), and (4.57) can also be used to show that the amount by which the carrier concentration at the centre of the filament falls below the threshold concentration in a uniform laser is 50 per cent of the amount by which the carrier concentration far from the filament (no stimulated recombination) exceeds this value (assuming operation close to threshold). Hence

$$\Delta\epsilon \simeq 1.5\left(\frac{J}{J_{\text{th}}} - 1\right)\Delta\epsilon_{\text{th}} \tag{6.24}$$

where $\Delta\epsilon_{\text{th}}$ is the perturbation in the dielectric constant produced by the carrier concentration injected at threshold in a uniform laser. Hence the filament width is given in terms of current, up to around 10–15 per cent above threshold by

$$s_{\text{eff}} = \frac{1.08\, s_0}{(J/J_{\text{th}} - 1)^{1/2}}$$

where

$$s_0 = \frac{\lambda(2 - (\tfrac{2}{3}b)^2)^{1/2}(\tfrac{2}{3})^{1/2}}{\pi\Delta\epsilon_{\text{th}}^{1/2}} \tag{6.25}$$

The value of $\Delta\epsilon_{\text{th}}$ is not precisely known, but a reasonable estimate is 0.04. Inserting this in equation (6.24), and putting $b = -1$, gives $s_0 = 1.418\ \mu\text{m}$ and $s_{\text{eff}} \simeq 5\ \mu\text{m}$, for operation at a current 10 per cent above threshold.

The more complete treatment of self-focusing[36] shows that the filament width does not continue decreasing as fast as is given by equation (6.25) when the current is increased beyond about 10 per cent above threshold. This happens because the injected carrier concentration at the centre of the filament starts to decrease more slowly as it approaches its minimum limiting value (the transparency point).

Diffusion processes, which have been ignored so far, cause minority carriers to move in towards the centre of the filament. These counteract the local depletion and reduce the magnitude of the refractive index variation. The filament broadens and the total current supplied to it increases. It has been shown[36] that the effect on the width of the filament can be approximately allowed for in equation (6.25) by substituting $s_{eff}/(2l/s_{eff} + 1)^{1/2}$ for s_{eff} in the left-hand side where l is the diffusion length.

6.4.2.2   Analysis of Self-Focusing for Stripe Lasers

In stripe lasers a single zero-order self-focused filament can form at the centre of the stripe and continue to exist in a stable form over a considerable range of current. The self-focusing action has to counteract an initial carrier distribution which has a peak at the centre of the stripe, as given by equation (6.6), and is the exact reverse of what is finally produced. As the current is increased above threshold the current taken by the lasing flattens the peak, as shown in Figure 6.25(a) and initially there may be a slight increase in the width of the optical distribution. However, after a sufficient increase in current, and provided the stripe is not too narrow (e.g. $>10 \mu m$), the curvature at the peak of the carrier distribution becomes inverted and self-focusing starts, as shown in Figure 6.25(b). This improves the optical guiding and the filament contracts in width. The optical losses also become less and the injected carrier concentration at the centre of the distribution can therefore dip appreciably below the level in the neighbouring regions before the gain drops below the lower level now required. This means that the current available for stimulated emission increases and that a greater optical output is produced than in the previous condition.

However, as the drive current is further increased the filament continues to narrow, and the inward diffusion of injected carriers is insufficient to prevent the carrier concentration in the two peaks which border the filament from increasing in height. This diverts current from the lasing emission and reduces the incremental efficiency. The effect of the self-focused operation on the light/current characteristic is therefore to enhance the output in the current range over which the focusing is first initiated but to follow this with a region of reduced slope where the filament narrows and the spontaneous output increases. Eventually a first-order mode is produced.

An exact analysis of self-focusing in stripe lasers requires computational methods[40,41] but, following Kirkby et al.,[37] it is possible to make an approximate analysis by relatively simple methods which satisfactorily illustrate the general principles. There are three phenomena that must be taken into consideration, namely the injected carrier distribution, the stimulated emission distribution, and the optical distribution. These all mutually interact. The optical distribution depends on the waveguide produced by the carrier distribution. The distribution of stimulated emission depends on both the optical distribution and the gain distribution,

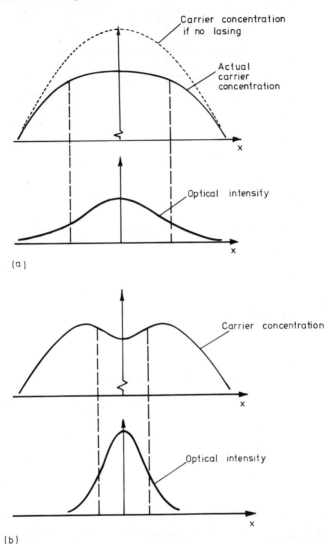

Figure 6.25 Distribution of carrier concentration and optical intensity in stripe laser at currents appreciably above threshold. (a) Gain-guiding situation, (b) self-focused situation

the latter produced by the carrier distribution. The carrier distribution depends on the injection current, the stimulated emission and spontaneous emission, and the extent of carrier diffusion and current spreading. The problem of the analysis is to obtain a self-consistent solution taking all these interactions into account.

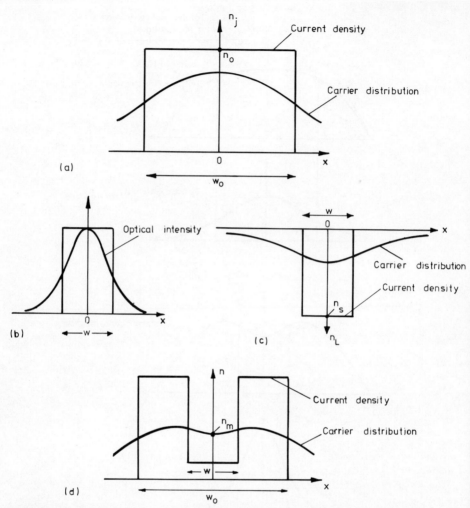

Figure 6.26   Diagrammatic representation of the way the injected current from the contact in a stripe laser and the stimulated recombination current combine to produce a diffused injected carrier profile which gives self-focusing. (a) Current density injected at contact and corresponding contribution to carrier distribution, (b) distribution of optical intensity of lasing filament, (c) current density removed by stimulated emission and corresponding contribution to carrier distribution, (d) net non-lasing injection current density and actual carrier distribution

One way of entering into this circle of interdependence is to take a simple approximation for the distribution of stimulated emission. The simplest is a rectangular distribution to which we attribute some particular width w, to be evaluated later. The carrier distribution can then be calculated in terms of the distribution of stimulated emission, the known distribution of injection current, and the diffusion and current spreading properties of the system. Current spreading in the passive layers can in general be considered in combination with diffusion, as indicated in Section 6.3.3, and an effective diffusion length can be defined.

Figure 6.26 indicates the stages necessary for deriving the carrier distribution under the above circumstances. We can take the net current causing injection of carriers into the active layer to be the difference between the actual injection current and the stimulated emission current. We assume that the distribution of the current injected by the contact is rectangular. This distribution and the carrier distribution that results after diffusion, in the absence of lasing, is shown in Figure 6.26(a). The distribution of the intensity of the lasing filament is shown in Figure 6.26(b). The distribution of stimulated emission (or stimulated recombination current density), that we have assumed to be rectangular, is taken here to have the same effective width w as the filament, as shown in Figure 6.26(c). The rectangular approximation is acceptable when the width of the optical filament is not much greater than a diffusion length. The negative injection current due to stimulated emission would, on its own, produce the carrier distribution shown in Figure 6.26(c). The actual final injected carrier distribution that is produced is the sum of the two individual distributions in Figures 6.26(a) and (c). This applies because the diffusion equations are linear in carrier concentration. The total injected current density and the final distribution of injected carriers are illustrated in Figure 6.26(d).

Close positioning of the contact and the active layer slightly modifies the behaviour. The treatment of Section 6.3.4 shows that when the voltage drop between the contact and the active layer is less than kT the local current density drawn from the contact in the region of the dip in injected carrier concentration increases, giving a higher rate of stimulated emission. The consequence is that a greater intensity of lasing emission is required to produce a given degree of self-focusing.

We will be particularly concerned with the region in the centre of the injected carrier distribution where the lasing filament is located. Here the carrier distribution is approximately parabolic either of normal curvature when the lasing output is low, as in Figure 6.25(a), or inverted when the output is greater, as in Figure 6.25(b). The parabolic distribution of injected carriers provides a gain-cum-refractive index guide whose properties are known (as analysed in Section 4.2) and which supports a Gaussian distribution of optical intensity. The Gaussian distribution of light stimulates a recombination current which also has an approximately Gaussian distribution (only approximately because the optical gain also varies across the width). For self-consistency we must match this approximately Gaussian current distribution as well as possible to the

originally assumed rectangular distribution. A suitable method is to equate
the peak values and the areas of the stimulated emission distribution and
the rectangular current distribution. We must also stipulate that the
magnitude and shape of the gain and dielectric constant profile associated
with the carrier distribution is consistent with the width and the overall
mode gain of the optical filament. These conditions provide three
equations from which the lasing current, the width of the filament, and the
carrier concentration at the centre of the distribution may be found in
terms of the current supplied, provided the diffusion length, the relation
between the injected carrier concentration, and gain and the relation
between refractive index and gain are known. The equations are derived in
the following section.

(a) *Theoretical derivation.* Let a current density of $(n_0/\tau)d$ carriers cm^{-2}
s^{-1} be supplied at the contact whose width is w_0. (τ is the spontaneous
recombination time and d is the thickness of the active layer.) The
resulting contribution n_J to the carrier distribution has the following form over
the width w_0

$$n_J = n_0\left(1 - A\cosh\left(\frac{x}{l}\right)\right); \qquad A = \exp\left(\frac{-w_0}{2l}\right) \tag{6.26}$$

as given in equation (6.5). l is the effective diffusion length. The
distribution is illustrated in Figure 6.26(a).

Let a current density of $(\rho + 1)(n_s/\tau)d$ be removed by the lasing filament
over width w, of which $\rho(n_s/\tau)d$ is supplied directly by the contact (due to its
proximity; ρ depends on the geometry as explained in Section 6.3.4) and
$(n_s/\tau)d$ is extracted from the original rectangular distribution of injected
current. The resulting contribution n_L to the carrier distribution over the
width w is given by the similar relation

$$n_L = n_s\left(1 - a\cosh\left(\frac{x}{l}\right)\right); \qquad a = \exp\left(\frac{-w}{2l}\right) \tag{6.27}$$

This distribution is illustrated in Figure 6.26(c).

The combined distribution obtained by subtracting the contribution in
equation (6.27) from that in equations (6.26) is illustrated in Figure
6.26(d). The carrier concentration n_m at the centre of this distribution is
given by

$$n_m = (1 - A)n_0 - (1 - a)n_s \tag{6.28}$$

The distribution of optical gain over the width of the lasing filament
must be consistent with that required for guiding the wave, and be in the
form given in equation (4.82), Section 4.2, on gain-guiding, as follows

$$g = g_z\left\{1 + \frac{8B^2s_0^2}{s_{eff}^2}\left(1 - \frac{16x^2}{s_{eff}^2}\right)\right\} \tag{6.29}$$

where we may put $s_{eff} = (8/\pi)^{1/2}w$. The relation between the gain g and the carrier concentration n has the form $g \propto (n - n_t)$ where n_t is the injected concentration necessary to produce transparency. We will take n_{th} as the concentration necessary to give threshold gain, i.e. the gain that equals the end and scattering losses of the laser.

Some care is necessary in specifying both n_t and n_{th}. The gain/carrier concentration characteristic cannot be assumed to be invariant. Different characteristics exist for different optical wavelengths which give different values of n_t and different values of n_{th} for a given value of gain coefficient. These characteristics are illustrated in Figure 6.30, Section 6.5.1. The characteristic which is appropriate for any particular circumstances is that which produces the maximum mode gain for the particular cross section of filament concerned. The product of the local gain and the local optical intensity must be integrated over the width of the filament and then maximized with respect to wavelength. Because the wavelength of peak gain shifts as the peak gain increases the local gain cannot lie at its spectral maximum over the whole width of the filament. However, it is reasonable to assume that there will be two symmetrically disposed points on either side of the centre line of the filament where the local gain lies at its spectral peak. This does not occur at the centre of the filament because there would then be a rapid variation in gain from the centre outwards which would not give the most favourable situation [see Figure 6.31(a)]. Analysis shows that if the individual gain/carrier concentration characteristics are straight lines of varying slope which touch a curved envelope then the wavelength which maximizes the local gain at the point where it lies half way between the gain g_m at the centre (which may be a maximum or a minimum) and the average gain g_z also maximizes the average gain. This effect is illustrated for $g_m < g_z$ in Figure 6.31(b). The general effect of this behaviour is slightly to increase n_{th} and reduce n_t in the self-focused case (minimum gain at the centre) and to increase n_{th} and increase n_t in the gain-guided case, both with respect to the behaviour in a broad laser.

Taking the gain/carrier concentration characteristic to be linear the gain distribution produced by the combined carrier distribution of Figure 6.26(d) varies according to a hyperbolic cosine within the width w, and in a more complicated way outside, whereas the distribution analysed in Section 4.2.3.4, equation (4.82), is parabolic. As a reasonable approximation we will match the parabola to the actual distribution at the central point $x = 0$, and at the points $x = \pm s_{eff}/4$ ($= \pm w/\sqrt{2\pi}$) which are determined by the width of the filament itself and correspond to the points where the local gain is equal to the mode gain of the filament, by putting $n_L + n_J = n_m$ at $x = 0$ and $= n_{th}$ at $x = w/\sqrt{2\pi}$. This is a slightly superior approximation to that used by Kirkby et al.[37] who matched the value and curvature of the two curves at $x = 0$. Then, using $n_m/n_{th} - 1 = (g_m/g_z - 1)(1 - n_t/n_{th})$ we obtain the following equations

$$\frac{n_m}{n_{th}} - 1 = \frac{\pi B^2 s_0^2 (1 - n_t/n_{th})}{w^2} \tag{6.30}$$

from equation (6.29) with $g = g_m$ at $x = 0$ and

$$\frac{n_m}{n_{th}} - 1 = \left(\frac{An_0}{n_{th}} - \frac{an_s}{n_{th}}\right)\left(\cosh\left(\frac{w}{\sqrt{2\pi l}}\right) - 1\right) \tag{6.31}$$

by matching the parabolic and hyperbolic cosine distributions as suggested above. s_0 in equation (6.30) is the characteristic gain-guide length ($= (\lambda/2\pi g_z \epsilon^{1/2})^{1/2}$) as defined in equation (4.72), and B is the anti-focusing parameter as defined in equation (4.73). By taking the two solutions for B^2 ($= \{\pm(b^2 + 1) - b\}$ where b is the ratio of real to imaginary dielectric constant associated with the injected carriers and is negative) the equations may be applied either to the self-focused situation ($0 > B^2 > -1$) or to the gain-guide situation ($B^2 > 1$).

Equations (6.28), (6.30), and (6.31) can be solved explicitly for the light output L per unit junction area in photons per second ($= (\rho n_s/\tau)d$) and the current density J ($= (n_0/\tau)d$) both in terms of the filament width. The two quantities are expressed as proportions of the threshold current density J_{th0} ($= (n_{th}/\tau)d$) of a similar but wide laser. Hence curves can be plotted of the light-current characteristic and the filament-width-versus-current characteristic for appropriate values of the parameters. When $\rho = 0$ the relations are

$$\frac{J}{J_{th0}} = \frac{a[1 - \{(1-a)/(\cosh(w/\sqrt{2\pi l}) - 1) - 1\}\pi B_0^2/w^2]}{a - A} \tag{6.32}$$

and

$$\frac{L}{J_{th0}} = \left(\frac{w}{w_0}\right)\frac{(1 - A)J/J_{th0} - (1 + \pi B_0^2/w^2)}{1 - a} \tag{6.33}$$

where we have incorporated a characteristic length B_0 given by the following equation. (Since B_0 may be imaginary it will also be referred to in terms of its modulus s_1, also given below):

$$B_0^2 = B^2\left(1 - \frac{J_t}{J_{tho}}\right)s_0^2; \qquad s_1 = |B_0| \tag{6.34}$$

We may regard the normalized filament width w/s_1 as being the independent variable in these equations. There are then only two additional parameters to consider, namely the normalized stripe width w_0/s_1 and the normalized diffusion length l/s_1. This relatively simple dependence makes it easier to compare the general functional form of the theory, even if not the quantitative details, with the observed behaviour of stripe lasers.

(b) *Results of theoretical treatment.* The theoretical treatment described above gives the light output and the filament width as a function of the current. These relations are illustrated respectively in Figure 6.27(a) and (b) for three different stripe widths and for particular values of the diffusion length and the other relevant parameters. The values concerned are given in the figure caption.

Let us first consider the light/current characteristics given in Figure 6.27(a) and compare the behaviour for the different stripe widths. To the degree of approximation of the theoretical treatment two disconnected curves are produced in each instance. One of the curves has the shape of a conventional lasing characteristic in which the light increases with current approximately linearly beyond threshold. The mode concerned is gain-guided and the lasing filament occupies most of the width of the gain region. The second curve is hairpin shaped and applies to the self-focused mode. This curve needs careful consideration.

In the self-focused mode a minimum amount of light is required to sustain the operation, and this is indicated by the presence of a minimum in the characteristic. The light level must be sufficient to create an inversion of curvature around the peak of the injected carrier concentration [see Figure 6.25(b)]. Once self-focused operation is initiated the light increases with current along the lower branch of the hairpin with an incremental efficiency less than that for the gain-guided characteristic. The upper branch of the hairpin is unstable and any disturbance causes the operating point to relax back to the lower branch.

Comparing the light/current characteristics for different stripe widths shows that the amount of light required to create self-focused operation increases as the width of the stripe decreases, and the corresponding current also increases. The physical explanation is linked with the increasing curvature around the peak of the injected carrier distribution, which becomes more difficult to invert for the narrower stripes.

The theory is not exact enough to show how the self-focused operation is triggered as current is increased. Triggering can only arise if the gain guide and the self-focused curves are continuous, joined by a loop connecting the near parallel dotted lines in the figure. Such continuity would certainly occur in the case of wider stripes, where sufficiently strong excitation of the gain-guide mode would cause inversion of the carrier concentration peak and give a continuous change between the two forms of operation. For very wide guides the reverse slope section of the hairpin characteristic of the self-focus mode would disappear completely and a smooth transition between gain-guiding and self-focused operation would occur. For narrower stripes the reverse slope section would remain giving some current hysteresis in the initiation of self-focusing. For very narrow stripes the self-focused branch of the characteristic would become inaccessible and incapable of excitation by any continuous increase in current.

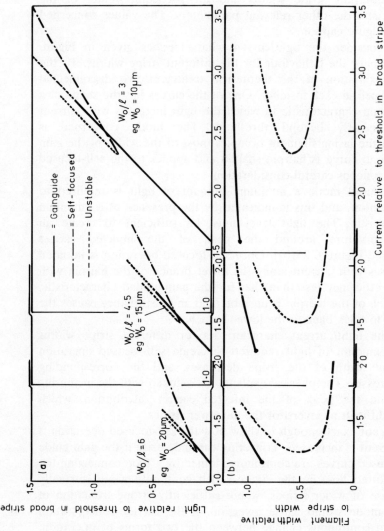

Figure 6.27 Comparison of theoretical results for gain-guided and self-focused modes in stripe lasers, obtained using simplified model to take account of effect of stimulated recombination on injected carrier distributions. (a) Light/current characteristics, with stripe width as a variable parameter. (b) Relative optical filament width versus current, with stripe width as a variable parameter. Calculated for $b = -1.875$, $l/s_0 = 2.5$, and for $w_0/l = 3$, 4.5, and 6. These values apply, for instance, for $l = 3.3 \mu m$, laser length $= 350 \mu m$, $\lambda = 0.87 \mu m$, $1 - J_t/J_{th} = 0.15$, and for stripe widths of 10, 15, and 20 μm

Figure 6.27(b) shows how the width of the filament varies with current for the different stripe widths. As before, there are two curves which are discontinuous in this approximate treatment, relating to the gain-guided and the self-focused modes, respectively. For the gain-guided mode there is little change in the width of the filament with current. The filament width for the self-focused mode on the stable part of its characteristic is

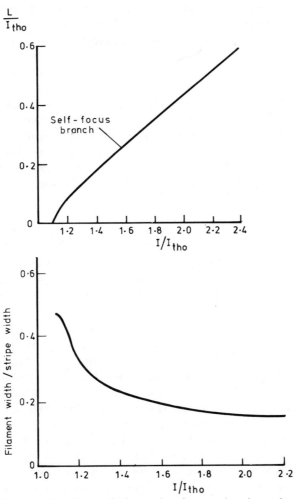

Figure 6.28 Theoretical results for modes in stripe lasers with built-in dielectric waveguide. Light output and relative optical filament width given as a function of current. Curves show smooth transition from gain-guided to self-focused mode. Calculated for $b = -1.5$, $l/s_0 = 3$, and $w_0/l = 6$

considerably less than that of the gain-guided mode, particularly when the stripe width is large. As current is increased above the self-focus threshold the filament narrows. This is the main cause of the reduced incremental efficiency in self-focused operation.

Figure 6.28 shows how the theoretical behaviour of the light/current characteristic and the filament width changes in the presence of a positive dielectric guide. The dielectric guide gives a smooth initiation of self-focusing, as was discussed above, and would occur naturally in the case of wider stripes if a more accurate theoretical analysis were applied. The smooth transition to self-focusing is accompanied by a smooth collapse in the width of the filament. The necessary analysis is an extension of that given in the previous section and the reader is referred to reference (54).

The above treatment shows in a general way how the width of the lasing filament can change with current drive, as a result of self-focusing effects, and indicates that such an effect can show discontinuities in the light/current characteristic which tend to be suppressed in the presence of an additional dielectric waveguide. This subject will be taken up again in Section 6.6.2 on non-linearity in the light/current characteristic, where theory and observation will be compared and additional instabilities in the self-focusing process will be investigated.

6.5 THRESHOLD CURRENT IN STRIPE LASERS

This section deals with the threshold current of stripe lasers that have no deliberate optical or carrier confinement in the lateral direction. The treatment applies to those lasers in which the width of the lasing filament is determined by the natural distribution of injected carriers which results from lateral current spreading and carrier diffusion.

In general the threshold current of a laser at a given temperature depends on its length and reflection coefficient, on its width, and on the thickness of its active layer. The dependence on length, reflection coefficient, and active layer thickness are relatively unaffected by the particular configuration of stripe concerned except when it becomes very narrow. Some brief remarks are given in Section 6.5.3 on the effect of length and reflection coefficient in stripe lasers. For the effect of the active layer thickness the reader should refer to the general treatment given in Chapter 5 which applies adequately to all types of laser. The particular type of stripe configuration is, however, much more important in considering the dependence of threshold current on stripe width. The threshold current density, which in wide lasers can be taken as independent of width, starts to increase for narrow stripes. The major part of this section is concerned with the analysis of this aspect of the behaviour.

Lateral current spreading and carrier diffusion, and the particular gain guide that results, play an important part in determining the threshold current density versus width relation in stripe lasers. These features of the behaviour have been treated separately in previous sections (Section 6.3 for the injected carrier profiles and Sections 4.2 and 6.4 for the gain guide). In the present section we combine the effects and obtain their total effect on threshold current.

The increase in threshold current density that results as the stripe width is decreased can be helpfully divided into two parts. One part can be attributed solely to the effect of the sideways spreading of the injected carriers. Carrier spreading lowers the peak concentration of carriers at the centre of the stripe below the value that would apply in a broad contact laser at the same current density. The current density flowing into the stripe must be increased to counteract this effect. The second part of the current increase can be attributed to the effect of the gain-guiding process which determines how far the filament spreads from the centre line of the stripe. Because the filament spreads into regions of lower gain the net modal gain is somewhat less than the peak value of the gain at the centre. Hence to reach threshold the current density must be further increased so that the net gain reaches the same value as in broad laser, and in the process the peak gain will exceed that value by an appropriate amount which increases as the laser gets narrower.

The major effect on threshold current in all except the narrowest stripe lasers comes from the first of the above mechanisms—the lateral spreading of carriers—and hence to a first approximation the increase in threshold can be estimated ignoring the second mechanism. Two ways of treating the lateral spreading of carriers have been suggested. D'Asaro[33] and Dumke[34] have shown that there is an effective lateral leakage current that flows out of the edge of a stripe laser, as described in Section 6.3.2, which corresponds to the current which would flow through some particular additional width of stripe at the current density supplied by the contact. The implication is that this represents an additional current which must be added to the normal current flowing into the stripe to give the increased value of the threshold. Hakki,[21,42] on the other hand, as described in Section 6.3.3, has treated the situation in terms of the conditions existing near the centre of the stripe. The distribution of injected carriers around the central peak is assumed to be determined by diffusion processes only, and the magnitude of the peak concentration can be obtained in terms of the diffusion constant. To the degree of approximation being considered the condition at threshold requires the peak gain to assume some specific value, reasonably independent of the stripe width (provided that it is not too narrow), and the additional current required to attain this condition increases as the stripe becomes narrower. This component of current is, however, always less than the leakage current. The reason is that such a current is only required to make good the carrier concentration at the centre of the stripe and not that at the edges. The leakage current in these conditions is deflected from the active layer and drawn away at the expense of the outer sections of the stripe.

Circumstances can arise, however, when the full leakage component of current must be supplied. To demonstrate this we must take into account the interaction between the potential distribution at the stripe contact and the distribution of injected carrier concentration in the active layer, as described in Section 6.3.4. This interaction causes additional current density to be drawn from the edges of the stripe which, under extreme circumstances, can account for the whole of the additional transverse leakage current postulated by Dumke and D'Asaro. However, in general the additional current drawn from the stripe is small and the behaviour approximates more closely to the lateral diffusion model of Hakki. It is still useful to represent the effect of current spreading in terms of an apparent increase in stripe width, the increase having to account for the additional current necessary to maintain the injected carrier concentration at the centre of the stripe at the level that would exist without current spreading, on the basis of a fixed effective value of current density. In the diffusion model, however, the increase in apparent width is not a constant but decreases as the stripe width is increased.

In narrower stripe lasers (e.g. $<15~\mu\mathrm{m}$) the second part of the threshold increase which, as described above, depends on the gain-guiding process at the centre of the stripe, becomes more important. Various parameters affect the behaviour. However, they can all be lumped together into a single parameter which we will call the characteristic gain-guide width s_1. The threshold increase depends on the ratio of the actual stripe width to the gain-guide width, becoming greater as the stripe width gets smaller. For example, a stripe laser of width $2s_1$ requires twice the current density at the centre of the stripe than is necessary in a very wide laser.

The treatment presented in the following sections describes the range of circumstances in which the threshold versus stripe width relation can be represented by a carrier-diffusion plus gain-guiding model, using in most instances only the two variable parameters mentioned above, namely the effective diffusion length and the characteristic gain-guide width.

6.5.1 Theoretical Analysis of the Threshold Current

The first stages in the investigation of the threshold current behaviour comprise the evaluation of the carrier distribution in the active layer beneath the stripe and the analysis of the gain-guiding action which takes place as a result of this distribution. In the process the following factors must be taken into account.

(a) The thickness, resistivity, and diffusion characteristics of the passiive and active layers both under and outside the stripe.

(b) The effect of the potential at the contact in modifying the carrier distribution beneath the stripe and in causing variation in the contact current density.

(c) The dependence of the gain in the active layer on the injected carrier concentration at the wavelength which maximizes the overall gain.

(d) The perturbation of refractive index produced by the injected carrier distribution, as discussed in Section 6.4.2.

In the following section we present a general treatment of the dependence of the threshold current on stripe width in stripe lasers. This treatment takes into account the effect of the contact potential and current spreading on the distribution of injected carriers, and the effect of the refractive index variations associated with the injected carriers on the gain-guiding.

In cases where the potential of the contact has little influence on the behaviour (appreciable series resistance) and where the distribution of carriers can be considered to be determined mainly by diffusion, with a constant value of the effective diffusion length, the relation between threshold current and stripe width can be expressed in a simple approximate form which depends on only two parameters, namely the effective diffusion length l_{eff} and the characteristic gain-guide width s_1. The latter parameter is combined from three more basic parameters, namely the average coefficient of modal gain in the laser resonator (which depends on the length and end-face reflectivity), the relative slope of the gain/current characteristic at fixed wavelength, and the ration of the change in refractive index to the change in gain produced by the injected carriers. The treatment is consistent with that used for self-focusing in Section 6.4.2. By reasonable choice of the two variable parameters most of the published values of the threshold current of stripe lasers as a function of stripe width can be satisfactorily fitted to the theoretical curve.

In cases where the contact equipotential lies close to the active layer, or where the current spreading effects are as significant or more significant than the diffusion processes, or where the lateral diffusion length cannot be regarded as constant over the width of the device, then it is not possible to obtain such a simple general expression for the variation of threshold current with stripe width. To indicate how much the behaviour is modified under these circumstances, curves are presented for specific instances. It will be apparent that the change from lateral diffusion to current spreading only has significant effect for narrow stripe widths. The effect of the proximity of the contact equipotential, on the other hand, is more significant at greater stripe widths, where the analysis shows that the additional leakage current postulated by Dumke and D'Asaro is indeed drawn straight from the contact when it is sufficiently close to the active layer. The theoretical treatment of the case where the diffusion lengths differ under and outside the stripe gives particularly interesting results. This treatment applies to deep proton bombarded and oxygen implanted stripe lasers. These two different fabrication methods produce lasers with very different observed behaviour. The theoretical curves show how these differences arise and give a good fit to the experimental results.

6.5.1.1   Distribution of Carrier Concentration and Gain

The analysis of threshold current in stripe lasers is commenced by finding the precise way in which the injected carrier concentration is distributed beneath the stripe. This determines the lateral distribution of optical gain which in turn determines the lateral distribution of optical intensity in the lasing mode. The interaction between the gain distribution and the optical distribution determines the average optical gain for the lasing mode. The average optical gain at threshold must equal the resonator losses and this criterion is fed back to provide the solution for the absolute magnitude of the threshold concentration of injected carriers, and hence the input current. The first stage in the analysis is to determine the relation between the injected carrier distribution and the optical distribution of the lasing mode.

The distribution of carrier concentration for a stripe of width w and with an effective transverse diffusion length of l_{eff} is given in equation (6.5), Section 6.3.3, as

$$n = n_0\left\{1 - A\,\cosh\left(\frac{x}{l_{\text{eff}}}\right)\right\}$$ (6.35)

with

$$A = \left\{\cosh\left(\frac{w}{2l_{\text{eff}}}\right) + \zeta\,\sinh\left(\frac{w}{2l_{\text{eff}}}\right)\right\}^{-1}$$

$$= \exp\left(\frac{-w}{2l_{\text{eff}}}\right), \quad \text{for } \zeta = 1$$ (6.36)

n_0 is the carrier concentration that would be injected if the contact were infinitely wide $(n_0/\tau)d$ being the corresponding current density (d is the active layer thickness and τ is the recombination time in the active layer). ζ is a measure of the change in lateral transport properties of the carriers between the regions under and outside the stripe, as given in equation (6.6). Such a difference can arise directly as a result of the presence of the contact itself [see equations (6.14) and (6.15)], but more particularly it can be caused by processes which selectively interfere with the different regions, such as proton bombardment. The effective transverse diffusion length l_{eff} results, as described in Section 6.3.4, from the combined effects of transverse diffusion in the active layer, current spreading in the passive layer, and the proximity of the contact.

To obtain the local value of the optical gain g from the injected carrier concentration n we assume that the gain is proportional to $n - n_t$, where n_t is the carrier concentration which produces transparency at the wavelength concerned. We are interested in general in the amount the gain g varies from its average value, which is equal to the threshold gain g_z. It can be useful to express the behaviour in terms of the injected carrier concentration that gives a gain g_z at the wavelength concerned, which we will denote as n_{th}. (n_{th} is of the same order as the injected carrier concentration required at threshold in a broad contact laser, but need not be precisely the same because of a possible change in wavelength.) The wavelength of stripe lasers adjusts itself to maximize the average optical gain which is not necessarily the same as maximizing the gain at the average carrier concentration. This point is taken up again in Section 6.5.1.3. In terms of n_{th} the relative gain increment $(g/g_z - 1)$ is given by

$$\left(\frac{g}{g_z} - 1\right) = \frac{n/n_{th} - 1}{\beta} \tag{6.37}$$

where β is a constant somewhat less than unity given by

$$\beta = 1 - \frac{n_t}{n_{th}} \tag{6.38}$$

We can then substitute equation (6.37) into equation (6.35) to find the gain distribution.

6.5.1.2 Filament Width as a Function of Stripe Width

To obtain the filament width s_{eff} (to the $1/e^2$ intensity points) in terms of the gain distribution we use equation (4.82), Section 4.2, which gives the parabolic distribution of gain g that will sustain a filament of the prescribed width. This equation for g in terms of x, with s_{eff} as a parameter, can be written

$$\frac{g - g_z}{g_z} = 8(Bs_0)^2 \left\{ s_{eff}^{-2} - 16\left(\frac{x}{s_{eff}^2}\right)^2 \right\} \tag{6.39}$$

where s_0 is the characteristic gain-guide length $(= (\lambda/2\pi g_z \epsilon^{1/2})^{1/2})$ as defined in equation (4.72) and B $(= \{\pm(b^2 + 1) - b\}^{1/2})$ is the anti-focusing parameter, as defined in equation (4.73).

The gain distribution which we derived in the previous section [equation (6.35) combined with equation (6.37)] is in the form of a hyperbolic cosine rather than a parabola. However, we approximate it to the parabola of the above equation by fitting it at three points, namely the central peak and the points on each side where $g = g_z$. This approximation underestimates the gain when it is greater than average and overestimates it when it is less than average. Hence it gives the least mean error. Matching the two distributions gives the following two equations for n_0/n_{th} and s_{eff} in terms of A

$$\frac{(1 - A)n_0}{n_{th}} = 1 + \frac{8s_1^2}{s_{eff}^2} \tag{6.40a}$$

$$= 1 + A\left(\frac{n_0}{n_{th}}\right)\left\{\cosh\left(\frac{s_{eff}}{4l_{eff}}\right) - 1\right\} \tag{6.40b}$$

where

$$s_1 = \beta^{1/2}Bs_0 = \left[\frac{\beta\{(b^2 + 1)^{1/2} - b\}}{\beta_0\epsilon_1^{1/2}g_z}\right]^{1/2} \tag{6.41}$$

s_1 is the useful guiding parameter that we described in the introduction to Section 6.5 and called the characteristic gain-guide width.

Although there is no analytic solution to these equations for s_{eff} in terms of A there is a simple solution for A, and hence w, in terms of s_{eff}. For convenience we write this relation in terms of a normalized filament width x, a normalized stripe width w', and a normalized diffusion length l' all expressed in terms of the characteristic gain-guide width s_1 and given by

$$x = \frac{s_{eff}}{s_1}; \qquad l' = \frac{l_{eff}}{s_1}$$

$$w' = \frac{w}{s_1} \tag{6.42}$$

The required solution is

$$A = \left[1 + \left(1 + \frac{x^2}{8}\right)\left\{\cosh\left(\frac{x}{4l'}\right) - 1\right\}\right]^{-1} \tag{6.43}$$

The normalized stripe width w' can then be obtained in terms of A, according to equation (6.36) by

$$w' = 2l' \ln\left[\frac{1/A + (1/A^2 + \zeta^2 - 1)^{1/2}}{1 + \zeta}\right] \tag{6.44}$$

$$= 2l' \ln\left(\frac{1}{A}\right), \quad \text{when } \zeta = 1$$

These relations give a series of curves of normalized optical filament with x against normalized stripe width w', with normalized diffusion length l' and ζ as variable parameters. An example is shown in Figure 6.29 of a set of

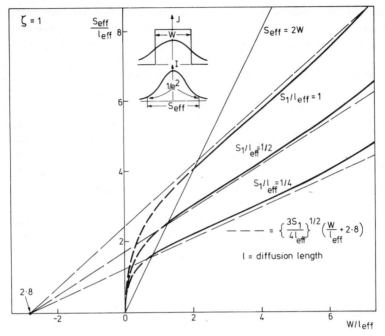

Figure 6.29 Theoretical relation between filament width and stripe width in gain-guided modes in a stripe laser with diffusion length as a parameter

curves of s_{eff}/l_{eff} (i.e. x/l') against w/l_{eff} (i.e. w'/l') for various values of l' with $\zeta = 1$ (i.e. applying when there is no discontinuity in the carrier transport characteristics at the edge of the stripe). Over the range of w'/l' from 1 to 6 the curves can be fitted quite well by straight lines (as pointed out in one instance by Hakki[42]) which have the approximate form

$$s_{eff} \simeq A_1 \left(\frac{\beta^{1/2} B s_0}{l_{eff}} \right)^{1/2} (w + B_1 l_{eff}) \tag{6.45}$$

where A_1 and B_1 are reasonably independent of l' but depend on ζ. For $\zeta = 1$, $A_1 \simeq (3/4)^{1/2}$ and $B_1 \simeq 2.8$.

Examination of the curves for $\zeta = 1$ shows that the filament width measured to the $1/e$ intensity points ($1/\sqrt{2}$ of that measured to the $1/e^2$ points) is of the order of the stripe width, being somewhat greater for narrow stripes and somewhat less for broad stripes, the difference in both instances being somewhat more marked when the diffusion length is greater. The division between 'broad' and 'narrow' occurs at a stripe width of around $4s_1$. The curves for other values of ζ are reasonably similar but with the filament width tending to increase with ζ.

The above analysis of filament width provides all the information necessary to derive the threshold current density of the stripe provided that the current can be assumed to be uniform over the width of the contact. (See Section 6.3.4 for the conditions at the contact which give uniform current density.) The threshold current density is equal to $n_0 d/\tau$ and can be obtained from equation (6.40a) in terms of s_{eff}, A, and n_{th}. We may obtain an exact solution in terms of the filament width s_{eff}, using equation (6.43) for A and deriving the stripe width from equation (6.44). This is satisfactory for plotting general curves of threshold current density against stripe width. For the more practically useful procedure of deriving the threshold current density for a given stripe width we can obtain an approximate result using equation (6.34) for s_{eff} in terms of stripe width and equation (6.36) for A. For this purpose it may be helpful to rewrite equation (6.40a) to give the threshold current I of the stripe laser in terms of the current that would flow if the current density were equal to the threshold value in a broad laser, say I_{th}, and in terms of the effective current-spreading width w_0 given in equation (6.13) and which tends to $w/(1 - A)$ for uniform current density. We then obtain

$$\frac{I}{I_{th}} = \left(\frac{w}{w_0}\right)\left(1 + \frac{8s_1^2}{s_{eff}^2}\right) \tag{6.46}$$

The expression on the right-hand side of equation (6.46) splits the increase in threshold current into current spreading effects, contained in the first parentheses, and gain-guiding effects, contained in the second parentheses, as postulated in the introduction to Section 6.5.

Equation (6.46) can be extended to cover lasers with close-coupled contacts, where additional current is drawn as a result of alterations in voltage associated with the injected carrier profile, by using the exact form for w_0 in equation (6.13). The appropriate modified diffusion length, as given in equation (6.11), must then be used in equations (6.42) and (6.45).

6.5.1.3   Maximization of Net Spectral Gain

The relation between the gain coefficient g and the carrier concentration n in equations (6.37) and (6.38) which includes the parameters n_{th} and β has been applied on the assumption that these quantities do not vary appreciably as the stripe width is varied. However, the situation is complicated by the fact that the gain coefficient depends on the wavelength. β and n_{th} are normally defined at the wavelength corresponding to the spectral peak of the gain, but the wavelength of the spectral peak varies with the magnitude of the gain. Hence care must be exercised in the definition of β and n_{th} under conditions where the gain varies considerably over the width of the optical filament.

Figure 6.30, based on Stern's curves,[44] shows schematically how the gain coefficient g depends on the current density (or carrier concentration) for different values of the wavelength. The envelope curve for g_{max} is also given. At low values of gain the loci for individual wavelengths are reasonably linear with carrier concentration, whereas the envelope locus has appreciable curvature concave upwards). At higher values of gain the position is reversed with the individual loci being curved (convex upwards) whereas the envelope locus is reasonably straight. The loci for the shorter wavelengths are steeper than those for the longer wavelengths, exhibiting greater loss at low injected carrier concentration and greater gain at higher injected carrier concentration. Hence for any given profile of injected carrier concentration in a stripe laser the distribution of gain varies with wavelength.

Such a variation of gain is illustrated in Figure 6.31(a). Over the centre part of the wavelength spectrum the peak gain at the centre of the gain

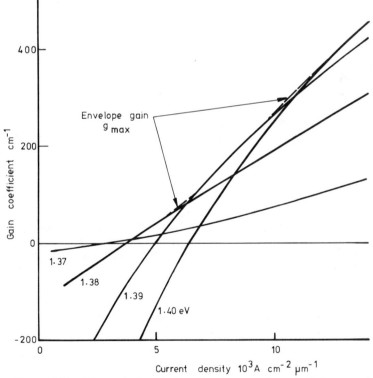

Figure 6.30 Theoretical relation between gain coefficient and current density in GaAs with photon energy as a variable parameter (after Stern [44])

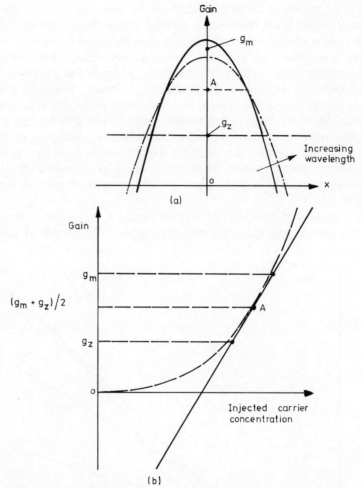

Figure 6.31   Maximization of net spectral gain in stripe laser.
(a) Gain distribution as a function of wavelength for fixed carrier
distribution, (b) gain/current characteristic which maximizes net
gain

distribution diminishes and the width of the distribution broadens as the
wavelength increases. There is a certain wavelength that gives highest net
gain which is intermediate between that which gives highest peak gain and
that which gives the widest region with gain greater than g_z.

Figure 6.31(b) illustrates the gain characteristic associated with the
wavelength which gives highest net gain. Analysis shows that if the
individual wavelength characteristics are straight and the envelope
characteristic has constant curvature then the optimum characteristic

touches the envelope characteristic at a value of gain which is approximately the mean between the net gain g_z and the peak gain g_m. To obtain the value of β in equation (6.38) we need to know the slope of the characteristic and its intersection with the horizontal axis. If the laser operation is in the region where the envelope characteristic is curved, then β decreases and n_{th} increases as the stripe is reduced in width and the threshold analysis becomes complicated. However, if the operation is on the straight part of the envelope characteristic then β and n_{th} are nominally not affected by the stripe width. Because the individual wavelength characteristic is somewhat curved there will be some interaction but this can probably be ignored down to very narrow stripe widths.

6.5.1.4 Effective Spreading Width

The spreading of carriers by diffusion and other processes is treated in Sections 6.3.3. and 6.3.4. Various complications can arise in the general case but the behaviour is particularly simple when diffusion is the dominant process, when there are no changes in transport properties between the regions under and outside the stripe, and when the contact is decoupled from the active layer. The effective spreading width w_0 [that represents current spreading in equation (6.46) for the threshold current] is then given by the expression in equation (6.7), Section 6.3.3 which, as described in that section and illustrated in Figure 6.14, can be satisfactorily represented by the approximate linear relation

$$w_0 \simeq 0.7(w + 2.8l_{eff}) \tag{6.47}$$

over the range $0.5 < w/l_{eff} < 5$. This equation is particularly convenient since the variable $(w + 2.8l_{eff})$ is very similar to that in equation (6.45) for the filament width, and in most cases can be taken as identical. This convenient circumstance allows a very simple general expression for the threshold current to be obtained, as described in the next section, which can easily be applied whatever the values of the parameters.

In the general case, where the previous conditions are not satisfied, the effective spreading width w_0 is given, according to equations (6.13) and (6.6), by the more complicated expression

$$w_0 = \frac{w\{\cosh(w/2l_{eff}) + \zeta \sinh(w/2l_{eff})\} + 2l_{eff}\rho \sinh(w/2l_{eff})}{\cosh(w/2l_{eff}) + \zeta \sinh(w/2l_{eff}) - 1} \tag{6.48}$$

where

$$\rho = l_s^2\{1/t^2 + 1/6l_{eff}^2\} \tag{6.49}$$

$$= \frac{nkT}{\delta V} \text{ [using equation (6.3) and ignoring } l_{eff}^{-2}]$$

δV being the voltage dropped between the contact and the active layer in an equivalent broad contact laser at threshold. The expression given above corresponds to that given by Hakki,[21] except for the additional term involving ρ which takes into account the effect of the proximity of the contact.

Curves of w_0/l against w/l are given in Figure 6.32 to illustrate the effect on current spreading both of reducing the value of ζ, and of increasing the value of ρ with the corresponding increase in ζ. Curve A is plotted for $\zeta = 0.25$ and the values of w_0 and w are given relative to the diffusion length beneath the stripe. This curve, for example, applies approximately for a deep proton bombarded laser. Curve B is plotted for $\rho = 99$, $\zeta = 10$, and in this instance the values of w_0 and w are given relative to the diffusion length outside the stripe rather than to the greatly reduced diffusion length beneath the stripe. This curve applies when the contact is positioned very close to the active layer. Curve C, provided for comparison, is the standard curve for a uniform laser given in Figure 6.15. Curve A shows a situation where the current spreading rapidly increases as

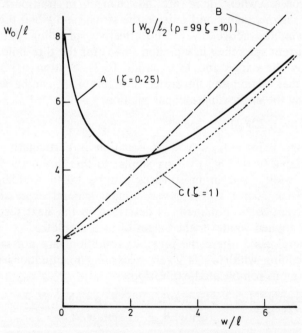

Figure 6.32 Dependence on stripe width of current required in stripe laser to maintain constant carrier concentration at centre of active layer as a result of lateral diffusion. Plotted in terms of effective width w_0, with ζ and ρ as parameters (determined by proximity of contact)

the stripe width drops below two diffusion lengths. Curve B, on the other hand, gives increased current loss for wide stripes and closely represents the situation described by D'Asaro[33] and Dumke[34] where the effective width is approximately two diffusion lengths greater than the actual width.

6.5.1.5 Simple Threshold-Current/Width Relation for Lasers with Diffusion Induced Carrier Profile

We now complete the solution for the threshold current of a stripe laser for the simple case $\zeta = 1$, $\rho \simeq 0$. Substituting the approximate expression for filament width [equation (6.45)] and the approximate expression for the current spreading width w_0 [equation (6.47)] into equation (6.46) gives the threshold current density in terms of the stripe width w and the other quantities. The resulting relation is most conveniently expressed in terms of another effective stripe width w_{eff} which can be used in conjunction with the threshold current density of a very broad stripe laser and the actual length of the stripe to obtain the threshold current of the actual stripe laser. If we assume n_{th} and β are constant then w_{eff} is given by

$$w_{\mathrm{eff}} = 0.7w + 1.95l_{\mathrm{eff}} + \frac{7.47s_1 l_{\mathrm{eff}}}{w + 2.8l_{\mathrm{eff}}}$$

or   (6.50)

$$w_{\mathrm{eff}} = 0.7s_2\left(y + \frac{8}{y}\right)$$

where

$$y = \frac{w + B_1 l_{\mathrm{eff}}}{s_2}\,; \qquad B_1 \simeq 2.8$$

and   (6.51)

$$s_2 = \left(\frac{4l_{\mathrm{eff}}s_1}{3}\right)^{1/2}$$

with s_1 as given in equation (6.41).

Equation (6.50) is a rough approximation, which is reasonably valid over the range of stripe widths between $0.5l_{\mathrm{eff}}$ and $5l_{\mathrm{eff}}$, and when the carrier transport properties do not change between the region under the stripe and the region outside. It provides a useful means of analysing the relevant experimental results and of sorting out the contributions of the various parameters, particularly when backed up by other independent experimental evidence.

Figure 6.33(a) gives, as an example, a plot of w_{eff} in equation (6.50) against w for a typical case where $l_{\mathrm{eff}} = 4\ \mu\mathrm{m}$ and $s_1 = 2\ \mu\mathrm{m}$. Also

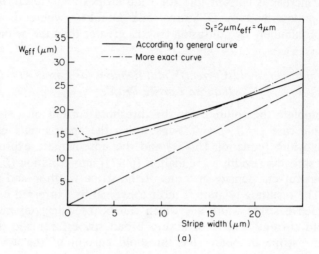

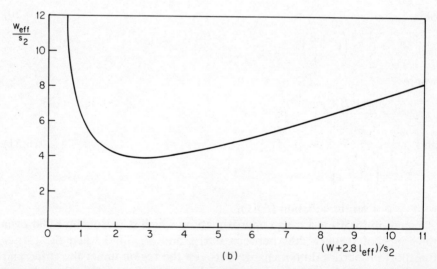

Figure 6.33 Specific and general theoretical curves relating threshold current to stripe width for stripe lasers with no change in current spreading properties between regions under and outside stripe. Plotted in terms of effective stripe width w_{eff} (a) Specific curve for case where $l_{eff} = 4\ \mu$m and $s_1 = 2\ \mu$m. (b) General curve showing relation between w_{eff}/s_2 and $(w + 2.8l_{eff})/s_2$

illustrated is the 'exact' curve which applies for these values as calculated using equations (6.43), (6.44), and (6.7). It can be seen that the approximate curve represents the 'exact' curve reasonably well. It should also be noted that in the region where the curves diverge at narrow stripe widths, the 'exact' curve is no longer reliable because the optical filament spreads appreciably outside the stripe.

Figure 6.33(b) gives a more general plot of the normalized effective stripe width w_{eff}/s_2 in equation (6.51) against the quantity $(w + 2.8\,l_{eff})/s_2$. This is a generalized relationship which can be used for any values of s_2 and l_{eff}. To provide a direct plot of w_{eff}/s_2 against the normalized stripe width w/s_2 the horizontal scale should be shifted to the right by the quantity $2.8\,l_{eff}/s_2$.

In general the approximate curve, in conjuction with the shift of axis to allow for the diffusion length, provides a reasonably universal relation between w_{eff} and w for any pair of values of the parameters s_2 and l_{eff} which is satisfactory over the range of validity for w/l_{eff} quoted above. The extent to which this curve can be used in describing experimental results is treated in Section 6.5.2.

6.5.1.6   Limitations of the Simple Width Relation

Let us now consider the ways in which the simple expression for the threshold current versus width in equation (6.50) may be modified in stripe lasers where either $\zeta \neq 1$ or $\rho \neq 0$. According to equations (6.14) and (6.15), ζ can differ from unity because of differences in the layer geometry, and the mobility and the diffusion length of carriers between the regions under and outside the stripe. It can differ somewhat from unity when current spreading rather than diffusion is the dominant carrier transport mechanism. It can also differ from unity because of a non-zero value of ρ [see equation (6.12)]. ρ differs from zero when the equipotential at the contact lies sufficiently close to the active layer.

The largest alteration occurs when the diffusion lengths under and outside the stripe differ appreciably as a result of changes in the recombination time or the diffusion constant of the injected carriers. These are produced, for example, by deep proton bombardment or by oxygen implantation. Hakki[21] found that the major effect of proton bombardment was to lower the recombination time in the bombarded region, reducing the value of ζ to as little as 0.25. Conversely Blum et al.[20] found that in deep oxygen implanted lasers the main effect of the oxygen was to decrease the diffusion constant in the implanted region, giving a value of ζ greater than unity. The result of these changes is to modify the threshold current width relation very considerably, particularly as a result of the change in the effective current spreading width w_0. Typical curves that result are illustrated in Figure 6.36 for values of ζ of 0.25, 1 and 4, and for a value of l_{eff}/s_1 in the centre region of 2 (denoted by l_1'). These curves are discussed and compared with experiment in Section 6.5.2.

In the situation where current spreading rather than diffusion is dominant but where the effect of the contact need not be taken into account ζ assumes a value somewhat less than unity. This is because the fringe leakage due to current spreading is $2^{1/2}$ times greater than would result from diffusion under similar circumstances [compare equation (6.4) for current spreading with the equivalent diffusion relation.] As a result we may put $\zeta = 1/2^{1/2}$. Such a condition would apply if the main cause of lateral current flow were the majority carriers in the p-doped active layer and if the p-passive layer had sufficient resistivity to largely isolate the active layer from the effects of the contact.

The threshold-versus-width relation for $\zeta = 1/2^{1/2}$ is illustrated in Figure 6.34 by a curve of w_{eff} against w for the case $l_1' = l_1/s_1 = 2$, l_1 being the effective diffusion length in the central region. The curve for $\zeta = 1$, $\rho_1' = 2$ is also given. The change in ζ has its main effect for stripe widths less than 2.5 diffusion lengths. For a stripe width of one diffusion length there is an approximate 20 per cent increase in threshold current. However, the bulk of

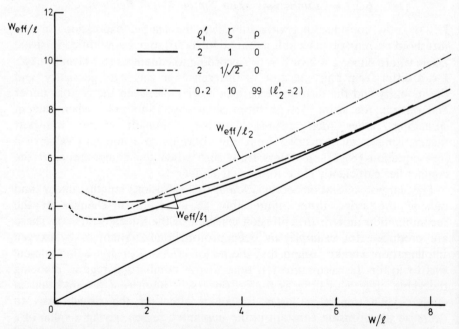

Figure 6.34 Curves showing calculated effect of current spreading and calculated effect of contact proximity on threshold current of stripe lasers. Plotted in terms of w_{eff}/l. Comparison curve for simple diffusion-controlled behaviour also given ($\zeta = 1$)

the discrepancy between the two curves can be removed by taking a modified value of the diffusion length in the case $\zeta = 1/2^{1/2}$ which is about 20 per cent greater than the true diffusion length. This brings the two curves very close together for stripe widths down to about one diffusion length. Hence it is not likely that in practice the effect of current spreading will be distinguishable from the effect of lateral diffusion by the functional form of the threshold versus width characteristics.

When the contact of the stripe laser lies sufficiently close to the active layer, with no resistive layer in between, it exerts an appreciable effect on the injected distribution via the effective diffusion length, as given in equation (6.11), and the value of ζ as given in equation (6.14) and (6.15), and also results in additional current being drawn from the contact edge so that the effective spreading width w_0 is modified according to equation (6.13).

As an example we take an extreme case where the additional current ratio ρ has a value of 99 and ζ is 10, which corresponds to a very closely coupled contact with diffusion being the dominant spreading mechanism, With layers of normal resistivity this would apply, for instance, if the contact were separated by less than 0.1 μm from the active layer (quite impracticable, however, for a real laser). Figure 6.34 gives a curve of threshold against width (w_{eff}/l against w/l) for this condition and for $l_2' = 2$ where $l_2' = l_2/s_1$. l_2 is the diffusion length outside the stripe. It is chosen for the normalization of w_{eff} and w rather than l_1 (now very small) because it facilitates comparison with the other results. This curve diverges more from the standard curve ($\zeta = 1$, $\rho = 0$, also shown in the figure) as the stripe width is increased. For stripe widths greater than about three diffusion lengths w_{eff} is about two diffusion lengths greater than the stripe width w. This corresponds to the presence of a fixed amount of additional leakage current as postulated by Dumke and D'Asaro. Less extreme conditions contribute a smaller amount of additional current. For instance, it is only necessary to raise the value of ρ to about 4 to obtain half the above limiting value of additional current. For layers of normal resistivity this corresponds to placing a good contact within about 2 μm of the active layer. Somewhat paradoxically, therefore, a good contact placed close to the active layer causes some increase in threshold in the wider stripes. This is accompanied by a more obvious increase in filament width because of the flatter distribution of the injected carrier concentration.

Let us attempt to modify expression (6.50) for the case of a closely coupled contact with current spreading rather than diffusion being the important transverse transport mechanism. We replace 0.7 w by w and we replace l_{eff} by $2^{1/2}l_s$. We can make no simple substitution for the final gain-guide term, but the curve in Figure 6.34 suggests that this is much smaller than in the previous case. We therefore end up, as a reasonable approximation down to stripe widths of 8–10 μm, with

$$w_{eff} = w + 2^{3/2}l_s \tag{6.52}$$

which is the relation originally postulated by Dumke and D'Asaro. The performance of any actual device is likely to lie somewhere between the results given by the above equation and equation (6.50).

6.5.2 Measured Results on Threshold Current Versus Width

The section describes the experimental results which have been reported on the threshold current and its variation with stripe width for a variety of types of stripe laser, The observed performance of the 'current window' types of stripe laser is compared with the simple approximate theoretical relation derived in Section 6.5.1.5. Some justification is advanced for the particular values of the parameters which must be chosen to give a good fit between theory and measurement. The significant ways in which the measured performance of deep proton bombarded and oxygen implanted lasers differ from the previous types of stripe laser and from each other are described. Their behaviour is related to curves obtained from the more elaborate theoretical treatment described in Section 6.5.1.6, in which allowance is made for differences in transport properties of the injected carriers beneath and outside the stripe.

The results of threshold current versus width measurements on 'current window' types of stripe lasers are given in Figure 6.35. This shows a plot of w_{eff} against w for a variety of stripes reported by various workers. These include the internally striped S-diffused lasers of Takusagawa et al.,[14] the MBE embedded stripe lasers of Lee and Cho,[19] the planar stripe lasers of Yonezu et al.,[13] the striped substrate lasers of Burnham and Scifres,[17] and the shallow proton bombarded stripe lasers of Dyment et al.[45] and Rossi et al.,[46] each type comprising devices of various lengths. It is interesting to note the similarity that exists in the performance of a large range of devices, and particularly of the three sets of devices that give the least increase in threshold current density compared with broad contact lasers. The similarity in the latter instance applies despite a considerable variation between different devices in the thickness and doping level of the active layer (0.18–0.4 μm in the thickness of the active layer and doping between 10^{17} cm^{-3} n-type and 5×10^{17} cm^{-3} p-type). The common factor between the best results is probably that in these lasers the passive layers contribute little extra current spreading beyond that already occurring in the active layer (including diffusion) by virtue of the low doping of the relevant layers and their total thickness of 1 μm or less.

We also show two theoretical curves in Figure 6.35 based on the approximate equation (6.50) which give a good fit with the measured

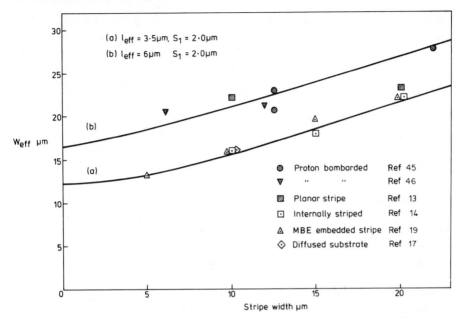

Figure 6.35   Observed value of effective width w_{eff} (derived from threshold current density), for various types of stripe laser with 'current window', plotted against stripe width. Theoretical curves for $s_1 = 2\ \mu\text{m}$, and diffusion lengths of 3.5 and 6 μm, also given

results using appropriate values of the parameters l_{eff} and s_1. The theoretical curves (a) and (b) apply respectively for effective diffusion lengths of 3.5 and 6 μm and for a value of the characteristic gain guide width s_1 of 2 μm in both curves. The fit to the measured points is excellent for curve (a) and satisfactory for curve (b). However, it is not possible on the basis of the measured points alone to make an unambiguous best-fit choice of both the parameters, since over a certain range any increase in l_{eff} if largely compensated by a decrease in s_1. The ambiguity could be resolved by independent measurements of the diffusion length or the filament width in the individual cases. However, some help can be provided by a theoretical estimate of the likely value of s_1.

The relation for s_1 is given in equation (6.41). In addition to precisely known quantities s_1 depends on B and β. B, as derived from the measurements of Kirkby et al.,[37] is of the order of 1.5, although it may vary somewhat between devices as a result of changes in the active layer thickness and doping level. β is not very accurately known. According to the transient measurements reported in Chapter 7, β has a typical value of 0.2. The results of Kirkby et al. suggest a smaller value of the order of 0.05. Doping level and active layer thickness could also affect the value of

β somewhat. Combining all the above estimates gives a value of s_1 in the range 1.2–2.4 μm. The value of 2 μm used for fitting the measured results in consistent with the above rough estimate. The fact that there is no evidence in the measured results for much variation in s_1 (including the results on deep proton bombarded and oxygen implanted lasers to be described below) is encouraging since there are no obvious differences between the devices involved likely to cause a large variation.

Although s_1 can be expected to vary somewhat between lasers of different length and the contribution to s_1 from B and β can be expected to be somewhat dependent on the thickness and doping level of the active layer, it seems reasonable to conclude from these results that the predominant cause for variations in w_{eff}/w in actual devices is due to variations in the effective diffusion length l_{eff}. Variations in the thickness and doping level of the p-passive layer probably constitute the major factors controlling l_{eff} although variations in the doping level of the active layer when they reach a level comparable with the concentration of minority carriers injected at threshold must also be taken into consideration.

We now deal with stripe lasers in which there is a change in the properties of the semiconductor across the boundary edge of the stripe. First let us consider the observed performance characteristics of these lasers. Figure 6.36 shows the measured values of w_{eff} versus w for deep proton bombarded lasers as obtained by Dyment et al.[45] and Rossi et al.[46] and for deep oxygen implanted lasers obtained by Blum et al.[20] Measurements on shallow proton bombarded lasers by the first two sets of workers are also included for comparison. The results show that the deep bombardment and deep implantation produce lasers with significantly different performance from each other as well as from the control group. Deep proton bombardment causes an appreciable increase in w_{eff} and in threshold current, which becomes rapidly greater as the stripe width is reduced below 10 μm. In contrast the deep oxygen implantation causes an appreciable reduction in w_{eff} below that of the control group, also particularly for widths less than 10 μm. It therefore seems that the latter form of fabrication would be particularly suitable for narrow stripes.

Theoretical curves of w_{eff} against w are also given in Figure 6.36. Values of ζ considerably differing from unity are used to obtain these curves which require an exact solution of equations (6.40), (6.43), and (6.44). By examination of the transverse distribution of injected carriers in deep proton bombarded lasers Hakki deduced a value of ζ of around 0.25 for these lasers which he could attribute to a 25 times increase in the recombination rate and an 0.7 times reduction in the diffusion constant in the bombarded region. We have therefore used $\zeta = 0.25$ in the theoretical curve, curve (a) in Figure 6.36. By taking $s_1 = 2$ μm, as previously, and

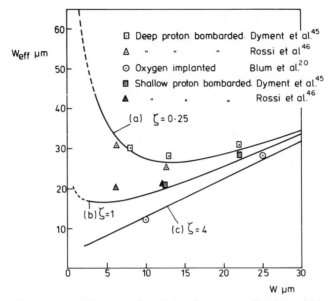

Figure 6.36 Theoretical relation between effective width w_{eff} (derived from threshold current density) and actual width of stripe lasers with various values of ζ and with $l' = 2$ (i.e. transport properties differ under and outside stripe). Measured results for both deep and shallow proton bombarded and oxygen implanted lasers also shown, taking $s_1 = 2$ μm and diffusion length $= 5$ μm

adjusting l_{eff} to around 5 μm a good fit is obtained to the two separate sets of results for w_{eff} against w in deep proton bombarded lasers.

Theoretical curves (b) and (c) use the same values of s_1 and l_{eff} while ζ is varied. Curve (b) with $\zeta = 1$ gives a reasonable fit to both sets of results for the shallow proton bombarded lasers and curve (c) with $\zeta = 4$ gives a good fit to the results for the deep oxygen implanted lasters. In the case of the deep oxygen implanted lasers Blum et al.[20] have also measured the lateral profile of injected carrier concentration, although they have not interpreted it in the same detail as Hakki. However, a value of around 4 appears to be consistent with their carrier profiles as well as giving a satisfactory fit to the w_{eff} versus w results. This large value of ζ must arise from a considerable reduction in the diffusion constant in the implanted region, by a factor of around one-twentieth, or less if there is any accompanying increase in the recombination rate. This provides the desirable feature of confining the injected carriers to the width of the stripe without introducing any appreciable recombination at the edges.

6.5.3   Effect of Laser Length on Threshold Current

In this section we consider the effect of the length of stripe lasers on the threshold current. We make an approximate theoretical analysis of the behaviour and compare the results with the rather limited number of experimental observations that have been made.

Although the threshold current density in all lasers rises as the length is decreased the total threshold current normally falls. This is another example of the general rule established in connection with the thickness of the active layer, i.e. that reducing the volume of the active layer increases its effectiveness. The approximate methods that have been applied previously for deducing the threshold current density can be applied to deriving the relationship between threshold current and laser length, but caution must be exercised in extrapolating the results to very short lasers (e.g. 50 μm and less) because of the very high current density involved. The associated values of optical gain can easily exceed the presently explored range, particularly in narrow stripes where the peak gain at the centre of the stripe is considerably greater than the average mode gain. Also, the high density of heat generation in short lasers may impose practical limitations in providing an adequate heat sink. Measurements that have been carried out by Steventon et al.[47] on proton bombarded lasers with widths in the range 5–15 μm seem to indicate, however, that no significant anomalies occur down to the shortest lengths investigated of around 50 μm and that the heat sinking also remains adequate.

In carrying out a theoretical derivation of the variation of threshold current with laser length there are various simplifying assumptions which it is convenient to make. The parameter which depends particularly on laser length is the threshold optical gain, and the relation for gain versus current density therefore forms the basis of the analysis. As indicated in Figure 6.30, there are various gain/current curves for different wavelengths, together with an overall optimized curve. To a first approximation the optimized curve will be taken as straight and the fixed wavelength curves will also be taken as straight and parallel to the first curve over the important but limited range close to where they touch the first curve. In spite of the considerable curvature that exists at the lower end of the optimized gain curve (see, for instance, Figure 5.5) the above approximation is not excessively drastic because the magnitude of the gain in the transverse distribution in most stripe lasers is mainly concentrated in the range greater than 100 cm^{-1} as a result of both the large peak near the centre of the stripe and the value of the Γ confinement factor which in an average heterostructure is appreciably less than unity (see Chapter 4, Section 4.1.3). In this range of gain the optimized gain/current-density characteristic of Figure 5.5 is reasonably straight.

A suitable approximation for the gain/current-density characteristic in the linear range is given in Chapter 5, equation (5.5). Using this expression with $B = 33$ A cm^{-1} μm^{-1} we find the following relation for the threshold current I_{th} in mA of an average stripe laser of length L, active layer thickness d, effective thickness of optical distribution s, coupling constant k, and effective width w_{eff}

$$I_{th} = w_{eff}\left[0.04dL + 3.3\left\{\frac{\ln(1/R_1R_2)}{2} + \alpha L\right\}\frac{s}{k}\right] \text{ mA} \qquad (6.53)$$

where w_{eff}, d, L, and s are measured in microns, αL is dimensionless, and R_1 and R_2 are the reflection coefficients at the two ends of the laser.

In addition to its explicit dependence on L in equation (6.53) I_{th} is also affected by the variation of the effective stripe width w_{eff} with L. w_{eff} varies because the strength of the gain guide increases in the shorter lasers as a result of the higher injected carrier concentration. The more significant changes occur in narrower lasers. When the stripe is less than a diffusion length wide the values of the quantities in equation (6.51) for w_{eff} are such that the term $(y + 8/y)$ lies close to its minimum and is reasonably invariant and w_{eff} is thus approximately proportional to s_2 or, using equation (6.41), approximately proportional to $g_z^{-1/4}$ and therefore $L^{1/4}$. This is a relatively weak dependence which becomes even weaker as the stripe is broadened.

As an example we illustrate in Figure 6.37 the calculated dependence of threshold current on laser length for stripes of 4 and 8 μm width, where the thickness of the active layer is 0.2 μm, the effective diffusion length of injected carriers is 4 μm, and the characteristic gain-guide width s_1 is 2 μm for $L = 400$ μm. These values of L and s_1 were found appropriate in the previous section. The full curves in Figure 6.37 are obtained by taking into account the variation of w_{eff} with L. The dashed curves are calculated for a fixed value of w_{eff} appropriate to $L = 400$ μm. The two sets of curves do not diverge appreciably except for the shortest lasers.

In general the plots on Figure 6.37 are reasonably straight lines which head in a direction to intercept the vertical axis at a finite value of current for zero laser length. It is interesting to consider the individual plots in terms of values of their intercepts and their gradients. Let us consider the magnitude $I_{th}(0)$ of the intercept for the approximate solutions (e.g. *OA* and *OB* in Figure 6.37). Putting $L = 0$ in equation (6.53) we find

$$I_{th}(0) = 1.65w_{eff}\left(\frac{s}{k}\right)\ln\left(\frac{1}{R_1R_2}\right) \text{ mA} \qquad (6.54)$$

where w_{eff} and (s/k) are measured in microns. For a normal double ended laser with cleaved end-faces ($R_1 = R_2 = 0.32$) the above relation gives a threshold current of 1.9 mA μm^{-1} effective width of the stripe. For a laser

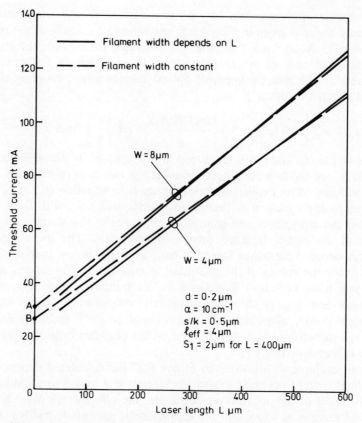

Figure 6.37 Calculated relation between threshold current and laser length in typical stripe laser. Curves given for 4- and 8-μm wide stripes making allowance for variation of effective width with laser length. Plots also given for constant effective width

with a perfect reflector at one end the threshold current is reduced to about 1 mA μm^{-1} effective width. These results are independent of the thickness of the active layer and the value of the absorption coefficient. The latter characteristics only influence the way the threshold increases with laser length.

The gradient of the approximate plots of Figure 6.37 measured in mA per 100 μm length, is given in terms of d and α by

$$\frac{dI_{th}}{dL} = w_{eff}\left\{4d + 0.033\left(\frac{s}{k}\right)\alpha\right\} \quad \text{mA per 100 } \mu\text{m} \tag{6.55}$$

where w_{eff}, d, and (s/k) are measured as before in microns and α is measured in cm^{-1}. In general the active layer thickness makes a greater contribution to the gradient than does the absorption coefficient. For typical values of the absorption coefficient of 10 cm^{-1} and (s/k) of $0.5 \, \mu\text{m}$ the optical losses in the laser contribute a gradient of 0.16 mA of threshold current per $100 \, \mu\text{m}$ of laser length per micron of effective stripe width. In comparison, an active layer with a typical thickness of $0.2 \, \mu\text{m}$ contributes about 0.8 mA of threshold current per $100 \, \mu\text{m}$ length per micron effective width. The sum of both these contributions for $100 \, \mu\text{m}$ length is still considerably less than the effective driving current of the laser (the zero length intercept). In most cases if the laser length is $100 \, \mu\text{m}$ or below, the threshold current will not be more than about 50 per cent greater than the minimum obtainable for the effective width concerned, and even in the worst cases (0.5-μm thick active layer) it will not be more than about twice the above value. However, in particularly narrow lasers (e.g. $< 2 \, \mu\text{m}$) the increase of slope due to the effect of varying w_{eff} must be taken into account.

Some of the lowest threshold currents obtained in normal (GaAl)As/ GaAs stripe lasers with short cavities have been reported by Steventon et al.[47] The lowest value achieved was 28 mA for a 50-μm long shallow proton bombard laser of $5 \, \mu\text{m}$ width. The relative results for lasers of different lengths and different widths agreed well with a calculation of the type presented above. Ettenberg and Lockwood[48] have investigated the effect of applying a reflective coating to one end of the laser and obtained a threshold current as low as 33 mA for a 150-μm long oxide-insulated stripe laser of $12 \, \mu\text{m}$ width.

6.6 LIGHT/CURRENT CHARACTERISTICS IN STRIPE LASERS

Stripe lasers with no lateral confinement of light do not in general produce entirely linear light/current characteristics. Their behaviour cannot be described as simply as that of broad contact lasers whose incremental efficiency is determined, as given in equation (2.38), Chapter 2, by internal optical absorption or scattering and by a loosely defined but constant internal efficiency term η_0. Although optical absorption remains an important factor in determining the output power of stripe lasers, and is indeed usually greater than that in broad contact lasers because of the part played by the partially pumped parts of the active layer at the edges of the stripe, the incremental efficiency of stripe lasers also depends strongly on the extent to which the optical filament fills the total width of the stripe. If the filament is narrower than the stripe the regions of the active layer towards the edge of the stripe contribute only spontaneous emission to the output and no lasing and so the incremental efficiency is reduced.

Both the above factors can give rise to non-linearities in the light/current characteristic. First, we must consider the optical absorption contributed by the fringe regions of the active layer which is not constant but decreases with drive because the absorption process pumps the material into a less absorbing state. Hence the incremental efficiency increases as the laser is driven harder. Secondly, we must consider the variation of the filament width which is determined by guiding processes associated with the injected carriers. Such a variation is particularly evident when a higher order lateral mode starts to be generated. Changes in the width of the filament and, in some circumstances, in its axial position can produce a very considerable non-linearity in the light/current characteristics, as detailed in Section 6.6.2.

6.6.1   Effect of Edge Absorption on Incremental Efficiency

We deal first with the effect of the optical absorption in the partially pumped region at the edges of the stripe on the incremental efficiency in stripe lasers. This has been studied by Hakki[42] in a gain-guided situation. From the standard equation for incremental efficiency given in Chapter 2 [equation (2.38)] it is evident that the contribution, say η_α to the incremental efficiency due to edge losses in the stripe is given by the ratio of the gain coefficient g_z necessary to overcome end losses in the laser to the total gain coefficient g_+ contributed by the centre region of the stripe where the gain is positive.

In Chapter 4, Section 4.2.3.4, an expression was obtained [equation (4.84)] for g_+ in a parabolic gain-guided situation in terms of g_z and of the normalized effective width of the filament S_{eff}/Bs_0. g_+/g_z, which is plotted in Figure 4.23, is equal to $1/\eta_\alpha$. Equation (4.84), from which this plot is derived, is similar to that obtained by Hakki except that the anti-guiding effect contributed by the distribution of the real component of refractive index has also been included via the term B. We first need an expression for S_{eff} in terms of the stripe width. We can obtain this from our approximate equation (6.45), using s_2 as defined in (6.51), as follows

$$S_{eff} = \frac{s_{eff}}{Bs_0} \simeq \beta^{1/2}(w + 2.8l_{eff})/s_2 \tag{6.56}$$

This equation in conjunction with equation (4.84) therefore allows us to obtain the incremental efficiency η_α of a stripe laser due to edge absorption in terms of its width w and β, l_{eff}, and s_2.

Figure 6.38 shows, as an example, η_α plotted against w for the value of s_1 and the two alternative values of l_{eff} which were found appropriate for matching the theoretical curves and measured results on the threshold current given in Figure 6.35, and for the value of β (=0.14) which is compatible both with the above values and the estimated values of B and

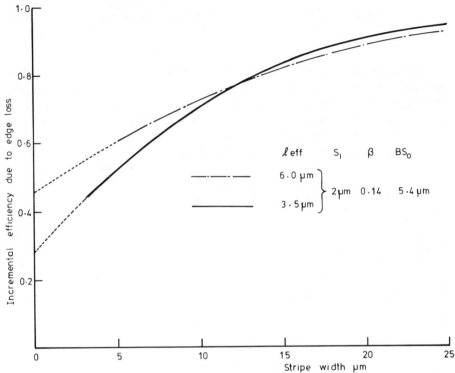

Figure 6.38 Theoretical relation between incremental efficiency due to edge loss and stripe width in 'current window' type of stripe lasers with $s_1 = 2 \, \mu m$ and diffusion lengths of 6 or 3.5 μm (the same as for Figure 6.35)

s_0. The curves show that η_α does not drop below 70 per cent for stripe widths greater than 10 μm and that it is not greatly affected in this range by the value of the diffusion constant. Below a width of 10 μm a shorter diffusion length results in a somewhat lower efficiency. The analysis is not, however, reliable for stripe widths less than about one diffusion length, where the curves are shown dotted.

The factors that exert the major effect on the incremental efficiency are (a) the degree of anti-focusing introduced into the gain-guiding process, as measured by the parameter B, and (b) the effects which increase the losses in the fringe of the filament, such as particularly any increase in the relative slope $1/\beta$ of the gain/current characteristic. Both these factors may depend to some extent on the doping level of the active layer, but there is not sufficient information available to predict their precise behaviour. Experimental results are at present confused by non-linear behaviour, which is treated in the next section. Further work needs to be done on this subject.

6.6.2   Non-linearity of Light/Current Characteristics

6.6.2.1   Observed Non-linearity

In current confined stripe lasers (proton bombarded, stripe contact etc.) it has been generally found that the light/current characteristics beyond threshold are non-linear. The non-linearity is greatest when the width of the stripe lies between 10 and 20 μm. A variety of light/current characteristics are observed in this range, typical examples of which are illustrated in Figure 6.39. In most cases some form of 'kink' occurs at an output level of between 2 and 10 mW. This consists of a point of inflexion where the output may temporarily level-off or even fall. The best lasers however exhibit only a fairly small reduction in slope efficiency at this output.

The level of output at which the kink occurs depends on the width of the stripe. Dixon *et al.*[49] have observed that reducing the width of shallow proton bombarded stripe lasers from 12 μm to 8 μm prevents the appearance of kinks in the normal operating range of current. Kobayashi[50] has shown that the power level at which the first kink occurs in planar

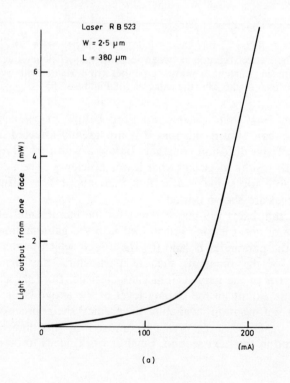

(a)

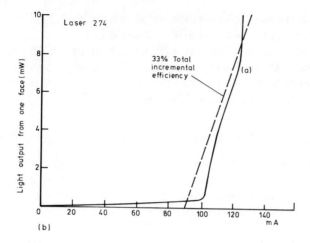

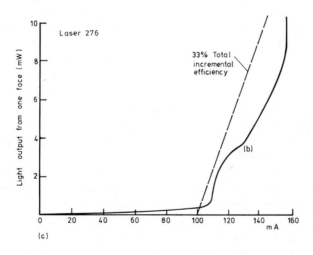

Figure 6.39 Measured light/current characteristics for stripe lasers of various widths showing (a) smooth curvature for 2.5 μm width, (b) S-shaped characteristic for 20 μm width, and (c) kinked characteristic for 20 μm width

stripe lasers increases rapidly as the stripe is narrowed, from around 2 mW at 10 μm width up to over 100 mW at 2 μm width.

As the width of the laser is increased beyond 25–35 μm the kinks straighten out and eventually disappear. The device then gives a linear increase of light with current, but the lateral mode content of the output increases steadily as the laser is driven harder.

6.6.2.2   Shifts in Near-Field Distribution

Several workers[49–52] have observed that the kinking in the lasers of intermediate width is associated with changes in the near-field distribution of the output. Figure 6.40 (a), (b), and (c) shows various ways in which the near field can evolve as the current is increased, associated respectively with the light/current characteristics of Figure 6.39(a), (b), and (c). The set of near-field distributions in Figure 6.40(a) illustrate the smooth increase in the single mode output of a well-behaved narrow (<5 μm) stripe laser, with no kinks in its light/current characteristic. The near-field distributions in Figure 6.40(b) illustrate the behaviour of a 'good' broader stripe laser (10–20 μm) with a relatively minor kink in the light/current characteristic. As the current is first increased beyond threshold, the output is confined to the zero-order lateral mode only. When threshold is first exceeded the peak of the optical distribution increases rapidly with current. This corresponds to the region in the light/current characteristic where the slope efficiency is high. With further current increase the peak increases more slowly and the width of the distribution narrows. This corresponds to the region of decreased slope efficiency. The next stage occurs when the first-order lateral mode starts to be generated. The near-field distribution broadens and then starts to split into two individual peaks. At this point a kink in the light/current characteristic occurs (point a in Figure 6.39(b)). Beyond this point the total output again starts to increase rapidly.

The less well-behaved broader stripe lasers show a variety of responses. However, in many devices a fairly typical succession of events is observed as the current is raised above threshold. This is illustrated in Figure 6.40(c). The output close to threshold appears to be confined to a single lateral mode, in the same way as for the previous lasers, and initially increases steeply with current. Further increase of current causes the peak of the optical distribution to move steadily away from the centre line of the stripe, and this is accompanied by a more obvious saturation in the light/current characteristic than in the previous 'good' lasers. The saturation is followed by a kink (point b in Figure 6.39 (c) and a subsequent considerable increase in slope efficiency. This is not associated with the generation of an identifiable higher order mode, as previously, but with a snap back of the optical distribution closer to the centre line of the stripe.

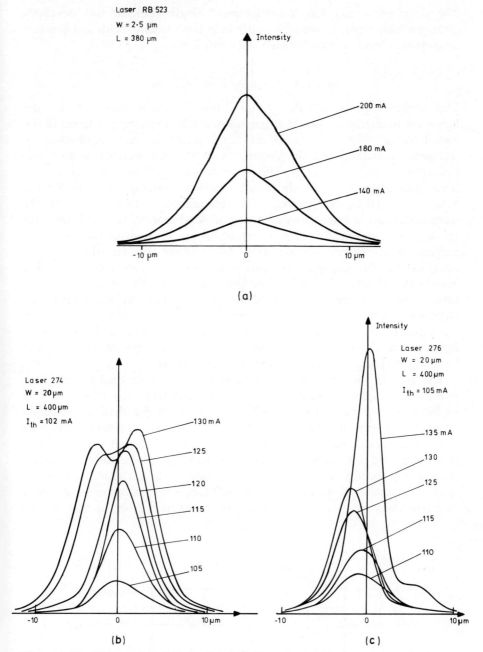

Figure 6.40   Measured evolution of near-field patterns with current in stripe lasers of various widths, showing (a) 2.5-μm wide stripe, (b) 'well-behaved' 20-μm wide stripe, and (c) 20-μm wide stripe with 'kinked' light/current characteristic

The distribution still has a predominant single peak, is not obviously distinguishable from the original distribution close to threshold, and also has a comparable and reasonably high slope efficiency.

6.6.2.3   Cause of Non-linearity

The major aspects of the various non-linearities observed in the light/current characteristics of stripe lasers can be explained in terms of the 'hole-burning' effect produced on the injected carrier distribution by stimulated emission, and the distortions of the distributions of gain and dielectric constant that result. This combination of phenomena has already been invoked in the analysis of self-focusing in stripe lasers in Section 6.4.2. We extend the concepts in the present section, in a mainly qualitative way, to cover a wider range of non-linearity. We deal first with the way in which higher order lateral modes are successively excited as the current is increased, accompanied by a point of inflexion on the light/current characteristic as each new mode is generated. We then investigate asymmetrical solutions and show how the filament may be driven away from the centre line of the stripe even in conditions where the structure itself has negligible asymmetry. Such a shift is naturally accompanied by a saturation, or in certain circumstances a dip, in the light/current characteristic because of the deterioration in the coupling between the lasing filament and the injected carriers.

The kink in the light/current characteristic shown in Figure 6.39(b) at point a is a typical feature of wide stripe lasers when the threshold of a higher order lateral mode is reached. In stripes wider than the example given such points may be repeated several times as successive transitions occur to modes of increasing order. Just before each higher order mode is generated, the interaction between the existing mode and the carrier distribution becomes considerable. In the case of the zero-order mode this interaction causes a strong degree of self-focusing which can be deduced experimentally from the characteristics of the emitted beam. It may also be

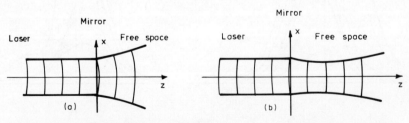

Figure 6.41   Beam width and shape of wavefront in guided mode within laser and in emitted beam outside laser. (a) 10-μm wide stripe, (b) 20-μm wide stripe. (From Kirkby et al.[37])

observed directly, both for the zero and higher order modes, using spontaneous emission as a measure of the carrier concentration.

Figure 6.41 shows how the emitted beam for the zero-order mode is affected by self-focusing. Without self-focusing the beam diverges from the output face of the laser as shown in Figure 6.41(a), appearing to emanate from a waist within the device. With self-focusing the beam is emitted with a converging wavefront, as shown in Figure 6.41(b), and forms a waist external to the laser. The position and width of this waist can be used to deduce the approximate gain and dielectric constant distribution in the self-focused waveguide (see Chapter 4, Section 4.2.3.5). Typical results are shown in Figure 6.42 where the pair of distributions are compared for gain-guided operation in a 10-μm wide stripe [part (a) of the figure] and for self-focused operation in a 20-μm wide stripe [part (b) of the figure]. In the self-focused operation at the output level concerned there is a considerable dip in the centre of the gain distribution.[37]

Figure 6.43 illustrates the interaction between the lasing emission and the carriers directly in terms of the distribution of the intensity of the spontaneous emission from the laser end-face. Provided only the shorter wavelength end of the spontaneous spectrum is detected, where the self-absorption is greater and the optical system needs to provide little depth of focus inside the laser, this measurement gives an adequately resolved picture of the distribution of injected carriers. Examples are given in Figure 6.43 of spontaneous emission distributions for lasers of four

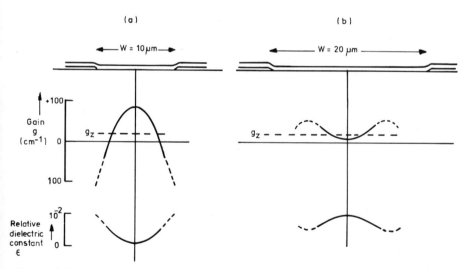

Figure 6.42 Measured lateral distribution of gain coefficient and dielectric constant in stripe contact lasers. (a) 10-μm stripe width, (b) 20-μm stripe width. (From Kirkby et al.[37])

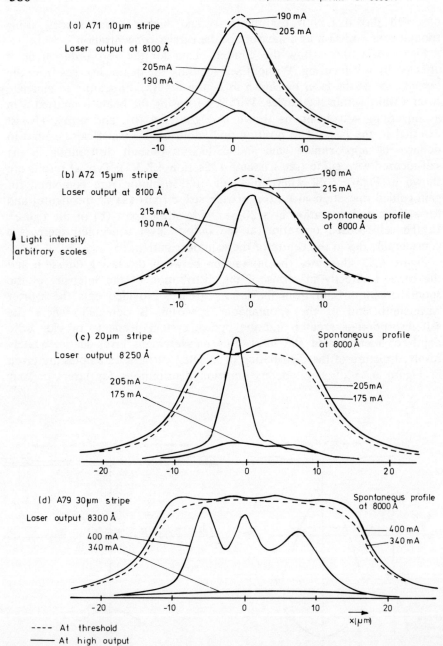

Figure 6.43 The effect of the intensity of laser emission on the profiles of spontaneous emission in stripe lasers of various widths. Distribution of lasing emission and spontaneous emission at low and high lasing output for (a) 10-μm wide stripe, (b) 15-μm wide stripe, (c) 20-μm wide stripe, and (d) 30-μm wide stripe. (From Kirkby et al.[37])

different widths between 10 and 30 μm.[37] The distribution of lasing emission is also shown. The figure shows that the increase in stimulated emission as the current is raised above threshold causes some change in the shape of the distribution of injected carriers in all four cases. For the narrow stripes (10–15 μm) there is only a small flattening of the peak of the carrier distribution, as shown in Figure 6.43 (a) and (b). For stripes in the width range of 15–20 μm the effect is more pronounced [see Figure 6.43(c)]. Increasing the current beyond threshold first causes a dip to form in the centre of the carrier distribution. Considerable peaks may grow on the two separated shoulders before they, in turn, are flattened (not shown here) by the creation of a higher-order mode. For stripes which are wider than 20 μm the effect produced on the shape of the carrier distribution by increasing the current is less pronounced [see Figure 6.43(d)]. A whole series of troughs and peaks are formed successively in the carrier distribution as the order of the predominant mode increases with rising current, but individual distributions exist over a current range too small for them to become pronounced.

The lasing output and the spontaneous emission output are complementary so that the slope efficiency of the lasing falls in a current range where the total spontaneous output is increasing and vice versa. Hence we can relate the distributions of spontaneous emission in Figure 6.43 in a qualitative way to the non-linearities in the light/current characteristic.

Consider first the behaviour of the narrow lasers in Figure 6.43(a) and (b). There is some decrease in the total spontaneous output beyond threshold, but this soon stabilizes. The accompanying laser output therefore shows some enhancement of efficiency just beyond threshold but thereafter the light increases reasonably linearly with current. For lasers in the width range 15–20 μm [see Figure 6.43(c)] the dip that appears in the spontaneous distribution owing to the onset of self-focusing causes a considerable initial enhancement of slope efficiency. This is followed by a reduction of slope efficiency as the two ears of the distribution grow, leading to a subsequent increase as the first-order mode reaches its threshold and the ears are flattened. For broader lasers [Figure 6.43(d)] the effects on the light/current characteristic becomes less and less pronounced because only small dips and peaks may be formed in the distribution of spontaneous emission before each new lateral mode passes its threshold.

For the pattern of dips and peaks in the carrier distribution to form smoothly and symmetrically across the width of the stripe it is necessary for a stabilizing influence to be present, such as a weak dielectric waveguide. This creates the 'nucleating point' for hole-burning to start, not only providing a positive location to the pattern but also encouraging the dips in the injected carrier concentration to form more easily.

A variety of phenomena are capable of producing weak waveguides in stripe lasers. The most universal is the non-uniform distribution of temperature created by the heat evolution in the region of the active layer under the stripe. Buus[41] has made an exact numerical analysis of hole-burning and shown that it does not occur in the typical circumstances investigated unless a waveguide is present and that the calculated temperature distribution is sufficient to produce such a waveguide.

Another phenomenon that can create a waveguide is the strain that is generated in the semiconductor as a result of the particular processes used to fabricate the stripe. Compression in GaAs reduces the refractrive index and the distribution of compression that is produced under the contact window of an oxide insulated stripe when the oxide itself is under compressive stress produces a significant waveguiding effect. Such a behaviour has been demonstrated and analysed by Kirkby et al.[53] Fortuitous effects of fabrication of this type exert a very considerable effect on the performance of a number of different stripe designs.

6.6.2.4 Asymmetrical Filaments and Non-linearity

To investigate the full degree of non-linearity that may exist in the light current characteristic of stripe lasers when the gain distribution is distorted by the stimulated emission (as illustrated in Figure 6.39(c)) it is necessary to take into account the possibility of the filament not lying along the centre line of the stripe. This does not imply asymmetry in the laser itself, but simply that the symmetrical state may be in a condition of unstable equilibrium. This cannot be identified if the model is denied the necessary degree of freedom to allow equilibrium to be lost in one or other transverse direction.

The characteristic of the semiconductor that makes it possible for the filament to settle in an off-centre position is the property of the injected carriers in providing a perturbation of the dielectric constant which is of opposite sign to the perturbation of gain. Consider the distribution of gain and dielectric constant illustrated for typical stripes in Figure 6.42. In the gain-guided distribution (a) the filament normally centres at the point of peak gain. However, the dielectric constant distribution is such that any light which strays to one side encounters an increasing value of the dielectric constant and is hence deflected increasingly away from the axis. It does not seem unreasonable to conjecture that under certain circumstances a filament might find a stable position off centre where the outward-turning nature of the wavefront would be restrained by the stimulated emission interaction from pulling the filament entirely out of the central gain region that supplies it with its source of photons.

In the self-focused condition (b) the filament normally centres on the peak of the distribution of dielectric constant. By the same reasoning as presented above there might be a more favourable disposition in which the filament would lie off centre, drawing its photons strongly from the region of higher gain at one side, whilst being prevented from further displacement by the deflection of its wavefront towards the centre of the stripe on its other side.

Guiding situations with the general characteristics suggested above can be shown to be theoretically capable of being generated in stripe lasers either by approximate analysis[54] or by exact numerical computation for specific instances[55]. In the Appendix A.3 we present an approximate analysis of the waveguiding which occurs in the general type of dielectric distribution that can be created by unsymmetrical 'hole-burning'. In the rest of this section we show how this analysis can be applied to understanding the behaviour of the lasers and to formulating criteria for lasing to be symmetrical, with consequent suppression of non-linearity in the light/current characteristics.

Figure 6.44 shows a typical way in which the gain distribution and the distribution of dielectric constant might vary in a stripe laser as the current is increased beyond threshold. This behaviour is based on a model proposed in the Appendix as a good representation of a range of actual devices, where the guiding action is produced both by the injected carriers, with their associated distributions of gain and dielectric constant, and also by the additional effect of a built-in dielectric waveguide, the magnitude of whose distribution of dielectric constant may be adjusted to match the observed behaviour. Asymmetry may be introduced into the model by allowing the centre of the built-in waveguide to be slightly displaced from the centres of the injected carrier distribution, as shown in Figure 6.44(a). However, in the analysis that follows we only treat the symmetrical structure.

Figure 6.44(a) shows the condition at threshold with an inverted parabolic distribution of gain and, for the strength of built-in waveguide concerned, also an inverted parabolic distribution of dielectric constant. The latter is the result of choosing the strength of the built-in waveguide in this instance to be just greater than that of the dielectric anti-waveguide produced by the injected carriers.

Figures 6.44(b), (c) and (d) show the conditions as the current is increased above threshold and the gain and dielectric constant profiles are distorted by the effect of stimulated recombination on the carrier distribution. The filament first moves steadily sideways and the general asymmetry increases. Eventually, when a strong hole-burning effect takes over, the resultant intense self-focusing brings the filament once again back to the centre.

The detailed analysis presented in Appendix 3 shows that the centre of

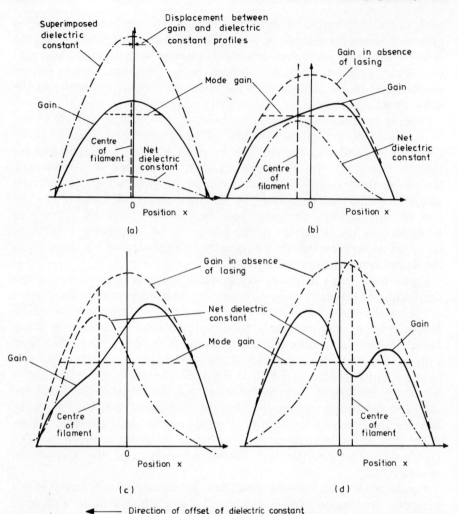

Figure 6.44 Theoretical succession of gain and dielectric constant distributions in asymmetrical stripe lasers as current is increased, progressing from gain-guiding to self-focused conditions. (a) Gain-guide mode close to threshold, (b) and (c) gain-guide mode with gain profile distorted by stimulated emission, (d) self-focused mode

the filament, once it lies off-centre, must be located at a point where there is a certain specific relation between the lateral gradients of the gain and dielectric constant profiles, and that the relation between these gradients depends on the curvature of the profiles. For instance, when the gain profile slopes linearly from one side of the filament to the other the filament is located precisely at the peak of the dielectric profile, as it would be in the absence of gain. When the gain profile is convex upwards but generally sloping in one direction the filament is located where the dielectric profile has a slope opposite to the slope of the gain. When the gain profile is concave upwards the filament is located where both profiles have the same direction of slope. Overall relations of this type, which are expressed quantitatively in Appendix 3, provide one of the conditions for determining the filament position. The second condition results from the requirement that at the centre of the stimulated emission distribution the gain profile should have approximately the same slope as the gain profile that would have existed in the absence of lasing. This is another way of saying that maximum depression of the gain profile occurs close to this point. As a further approximation we may take the centre of the stimulated emission distribution as being at the centre of the optical filament, although in a more accurate treatment[54] the former would be displaced slightly from the latter in the direction of increasing gain. Using the above two conditions we now proceed to find the particular curvature of the gain profile that is consistent with the filament being displaced from the centre of the stripe.

Let the centre of the filament be located at $x = 0$. Let the centre of the injected carrier distribution and the centre of the built-in waveguide be located at $x = x_0$, giving a filament displacement of $-x_0$.

Let $\delta\epsilon_f$ be the incremental complex dielectric constant due to injected free carriers at threshold. If it has an inverted parabolic distribution and if the ratio of the real to the imaginary (gain) component is b (normally a negative quantity) then it can be represented by

$$\delta\epsilon_f = -A(b + j)(x - x_0)^2 \tag{6.57}$$

where A is a real constant, and where $\delta\epsilon_f$ is measured with respect to the value at the peak of the distribution.

Let $\delta\epsilon_\gamma$ be the incremental dielectric constant of the built-in waveguide which will also be taken to have an inverted parabolic distribution. We can define its amplitude in terms of the amplitude of the imaginary component of the dielectric constant due to the injected carrier concentration at threshold using a proportionality constant γ such that the waveguide distribution is given by

$$\delta\epsilon_\gamma = -\gamma A(x - x_0)^2 \tag{6.58}$$

Let $\delta\epsilon_\rho$ be the incremental complex dielectric constant due to the injected carriers in the presence of lasing at a current ρ times the threshold current. According to the approximation suggested above we assume that the x distribution of this quantity has the same gradient at $x = 0$ as the (hypothetical) gradient of the same quantity in the absence of lasing, i.e. of $\rho\delta\epsilon_f$, the gradient being $-2A(b + j)\rho x_0$ according to (6.57). The distribution will be altered from its shape in the absence of lasing as a result of the 'hole-burning' effect but will still be approximately parabolic in the centre region. We introduce the coefficient k to describe the new parabolic coefficient as a proportion of the old and hence write the x distribution of $\delta\epsilon_p$ as

$$\delta\epsilon_p = -A(b + j)(kx^2 - 2\rho x_0 x) + \text{constant} \qquad (6.59)$$

As the light output increases k decreases below unity, eventually becoming negative when real hole-burning starts. We consider how the value of k affects the guiding, and in particular find the specific value of k which is compatible with a non-zero value of x_0 and allows the filament to shift from a central position.

To find this value of k we can match the total dielectric distribution given by summing equations (6.58) and (6.59) to the necessary form to give guiding with non-zero x_0 as presented in equation (A3.5) in Appendix 3. Equating the ratios of the real and imaginary coefficients of x in the two distributions and expressing the result in terms of the parameters a_1 and a_2 in equation (A3.5) gives

$$\frac{a_2}{a_1} = -b - \frac{\gamma}{\rho} \qquad (6.60)$$

Performing the same operation with the coefficients of x^2 gives

$$\frac{\{1 - (a_2/a_1)^2\}}{2(a_2/a_1)} = b + \frac{\gamma}{k} \qquad (6.61)$$

Eliminating a_2/a_1 between these two equations gives the following expression for the specific value of k in the asymmetric region of operation, which we will represent by k_{as}

$$k_{as} = \frac{2\gamma(-b - \gamma/\rho)}{b^2 + 1 - (\gamma/\rho)^2} \qquad (6.62)$$

The value of k_{as} describes the amount of flattening that must occur across the top of the gain profile before the filament starts to move off centre, one way or the other. Of course as the filament shifts from the centre line more current is required in order to raise the carrier concentration at the centre of the filament to the value originally existing at the centre of the stripe. However, in the process the intensity of the filament, which must adjust itself to maintain the same degree of flattening of the gain profile, does not increase much. This accounts for the accompanying non-linearity in the light/current characteristic.

In order to find the light output and the current input associated with any particular value of k and of the filament displacement x_0 it is necessary to carry out an analysis of the type described in Section 6.4.2 on self-focusing in a stripe laser. The analysis in the present case follows the same course, starting with an approximation for the distribution of stimulated emission. The stimulated emission is regarded as a sink of current that can be combined with the injection current to provide the driving term in a diffusion equation the solution of which gives the injected carrier distribution. The associated gain and dielectric distribution guides a filament the width of which must be made consistent with the starting distribution of stimulated emission. The only differences from the previous treatment are that a built-in waveguide is postulated and that offset guiding characteristics are used rather than the original symmetrical ones. Details of this calculation are given in reference (54).

Figure 6.45 shows a typical shape for the light/current characteristic of a device calculated according to the above methods where the strength of the

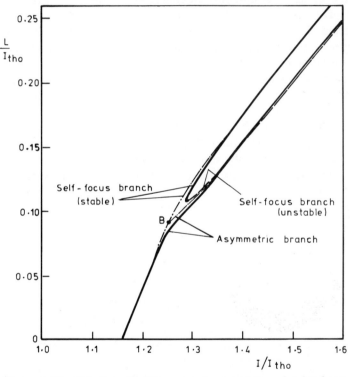

Figure 6.45 Calculated light/current characteristics of stripe laser with moderate built-in dielectric waveguide. Waveguide just fails to compensate anti-guide due to injected carriers at threshold. Applies to stripe width of five diffusion lengths (e.g. 25 μm). $w_0/l = 5$, $l/s_0 = 3$, $b = -2$, $\gamma = 1.67$.
—·—·— Structure with perfect symmetry
———— Centres of built-in guide and gain profile 0.02l apart

dielectric guide has been chosen to be just greater in magnitude than the negative dielectric distribution introduced by the injected carriers at threshold. The heavy lines correspond to a device with a certain amount of in-built asymmetry whereas the dashed lines refer to a symmetrical device. There are two branches to the characteristic. First, there is the gain-guide branch which is continuous from threshold up to high currents. A kink occurs in this branch in the region of point B, where the filament starts to move off sideways. Secondly, there is the self-focus branch which is in the form of a hairpin loop and only the upper branch of which is stable.

The calculated displacement of the filament corresponding to the light/current characteristic of Figure 6.45 is plotted as a function of current in .Figure 6.46. As before the full line refers to the device with some built-in asymmetry and the dashed line to a device with almost zero asymmetry. As for the light/current characteristic there are two branches to this plot. The gain-guide branch gives a filament position which starts to deviate from the centre of the stripe close to the point B. The self-focus branch has a section where the filament is offset in the oppostie direction to the gain-guide branch, but this is unstable. Stable operation occurs with a near central filament position. Although this self-focus branch apparently carries on the behaviour of the symmetrically placed gain-guide filament from point B up to higher currents, there is no continuity between the two solutions. The way in which the curve is traced with current increase is centrally from O to B and then off to one side. The centralized position of the self-focus branch is only accessible after some break up of the whole mode pattern, such as might occur if a first-order mode were transiently

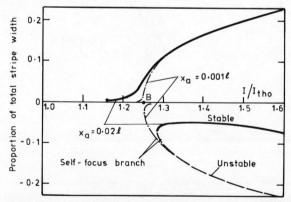

Figure 6.46 Calculated displacement of filament from centre line of laser as a function of current with offset x_a of built-in waveguide as a parameter. Applies to stripe width of five diffusion lengths (e.g. 25 μm). $w_0/l = 5$, $l/s_0 = 3$, $b = -2$. $\gamma = 1.67$

generated. First-order modes may exist above a certain value of the current but they have not been taken into consideration in this plot.

There are two ways of preventing the occurrence of asymmetric operation in the operating range of the laser. The first is to prevent the degree of flattening or hole-burning in the gain distribution from attaining the value k_{as} at which filament displacement starts. The second is to lower k_{as}, preferably to large negative values, such that a greater degree of hole-burning may be tolerated before filament displacement starts.

The first of the above objectives can be achieved by narrowing the stripe. The general principle involved is demonstrated in the treatment of self-focusing given in Section 6.4.2, where it is shown that to flatten the profile of the injected carrier concentration and then to create a dip requires a very marked increase in stimulated recombination as the width of the stripe is reduced to less than a few diffusion or spreading lengths. The analysis in Section 6.4.2 applies in the absence of a waveguide but the general behaviour remains similar when a built-in waveguide is introduced, as in the present instance. A weakening of the flattening effect defers the asymmetric operation to higher currents.

The second of the above objectives, lowering k_{as}, can be achieved by increasing the strength of the built-in waveguide. The coefficient γ provides a measure of this strength and equation (6.62) relates k_{as} to γ. k_{as} first increases with γ, then falls through zero and becomes increasingly negative, reaches $-\infty$ and turns finally to large positive values. A negative value of k_{as} means that a dip must be created in the carrier distribution before asymmetric operation starts. When k_{as} passes through $-\infty$ asymmetric operation becomes impossible. We represent the critical value of γ for which this occurs by γ_c. γ_c, according to equation (6.62), is approximately given by

$$\gamma_c = \rho(b^2 + 1)^{1/2} \tag{6.63}$$

A more accurate analysis[54] shows that γ_c lies in the range

$$(b^2 + 1)^{1/2} < \gamma_c < \rho(b^2 + 1)^{1/2} \tag{6.64}$$

This condition states that, for avoiding asymmetrical operation, the strength of the built-in waveguide should be made somewhat greater than the anti-guide created by the injected carriers in the absence of lasing, although the calculation is not very definite as to whether the anti-guide concerned should be measured at threshold current or at the highest current at which the laser is required to operate.

Hole-burning in the injected carrier distribution can therefore be prevented from introducing filament instability by the presence of a sufficiently strong built-in dielectric waveguide but it still eventually leads to the generation of higher order lateral modes. Some scope is however available to suppress this effect. The simplest approach is to delay the onset of hole-burning by reducing the stripe width in relation to the spreading length of the injected carriers. Another approach is to adjust the overall waveguide to give maximum discrimination against the higher order lateral modes. One possible way of increasing the discrimination is to limit the width of the built-in waveguide so that it is no greater than the effective width of the zero-order optical filament, which in general means that it is considerably narrower than the effective width of the injected carrier distribution. A second possibility is to, incorporate into the built-in waveguide at the edges a considerable amount of optical loss in a position where it selectively couples to the higher order transverse modes.

The channelled substrate planar laser[31] [see Figure 6.9(c)] uses both the above methods of mode discrimination. The width of the waveguide produced by the channel is considerably narrower than the 'current window' used for limiting the spread of the injected carrier distribution. Also, the guide is designed to introduce optical loss outside the main guiding region. The combination of these two properties has been experimentally found to give the desired result with good linearity of the light/current characteristic over a large dynamic range of currrent with no shift in the filament position and no generation of higher order lateral modes. Some computer simulations of specific structures give further backing to this finding.[55]

6.7   SUMMARY OF STRIPE LASER CHARACTERISTICS

The important performance characteristics of the currently reported stripe lasers are summarized in Table 6.1. The quantities presented are the stripe width, the typical threshold current, the range of output power (from one end) over which a reasonably linear single transverse mode output can be maintained, the filament width, and the far-field beam width.

6.7.1   Lasers with Current Confinement Window

The first group of devices in Table 6.1 are of the 'current confinement window' type of construction. They comprise (1) oxide-insulated stripe contact devices (2) planar Zn-diffused devices (3) shallow proton-bombarded stripes and (4) deep oxygen-implanted stripes (see Figure 6.1 and 6.2). In general the properties of these devices depend mainly on the stripe width, the length and the amount of current spreading (determined by the layer resistivities, etc.) and only differ incidentally between the different designs. The deep oxygen implanted device is somewhat exceptional in its current spreading properties and is discussed in more detail at the end of this section.

Table 6.1 Performance characteristics of (GaAl)As/GaAs stripe lasers

	Width (μm)	I_{th} (mA)	Peak power or current (Single mode no kinks)	Beam Angle (∥) (to 1/e points) (degrees)	Near-field width (∥) (to 1/e points) (μm)	Ref.
1. Stripe contact	20	90–180	3–5 mW	5	6	37, 53
	2.5	50–100	20 mW	30–40	6–8	58
2. Planar stripe	10	100–125	5 mW	5	7	13
	2.5	95	50 mW	20–40		50
3. Proton-bombarded	12	100	2 mW	10		3
	8	40–100	5–9 mW			49, 56
	5	30–60				47
4. Oxygen-implanted	12.5	150				20
5. Double stripe	8	40–90	5 mW	6–9	4	32
6. Rib-waveguide	5	(500)	$2 \times I_{th}$		4	9
7. Passive-strip-loaded waveguide	4	90–130	$5 \times I_{th}$	20		10
	8		$3 \times I_{th}$	10		
8. Plano-convex waveguide	2 (groove)	40–50	$3 \times I_{th}$	10	4	30
9. Channelled-substrate-planar stripe	4	40–90	$3 \times I_{th}$	20	4	31
	8		$2 \times I_{th}$	10		
10. Transverse junction	—	15–30	$4 \times I_{th}$	16	2	24, 25, 26
11. Twin transverse junction	4	25–50	$2 \times I_{th}$	10	4	27
12. Zn-diffused window-stripe	5	40–70	$6 \times I_{th}$		5	28
13. Buried heterostructure	1.5	5–10	$7 \times I_{th}$	30	1.5	4
14. Buried optical guide	2–4	20–30	>20 mW	25	2–4	23
15. Strip-buried heterostructure	5	(90)	$9 \times I_{th}$	10	5	22, 59

The threshold current of these devices is determined mainly by the parameters listed above. In general it lies in the range 50–150 mA. The lowest values have been obtained in devices of between 5 and 10 μm width which were also either particularly short of particularly limited in current spreading. For instance, shallow proton-bombarded devices with low conductivity in the p-passive layer have given threshold currents as low as 45 mA for normal length devices (380 μm)[56] and 28 mA for a length of 50 μm.[47]

The linearity of the light/current characteristic in these devices is a second important feature which depends on stripe width, or more precisely the ratio of the stripe width to the characteristic length for current spreading. There is an awkard range of widths, which for devices with average current spreading lies between about 10 and 20 μm, where the light/current characteristic shows non-linearities and kinks which appear at output levels between about 2 and 5 mW. If the devices are very symmetrical or have some weak form of waveguide present (e.g. a thermal or strain waveguide) then the kinks are relatively minor and simply signal the appearance of a higher order transverse mode. In such favourable circumstances the devices may operate in a single longitudinal mode, certainly up to the kink. When there is no weak waveguide present the kinks are in general much more severe. They usually signal a more drastic change in the field pattern than in the previous case, such as a sideways shift of the lasing filament, and are frequently accompanied by temporal instability and self-pulsing. The spectrum does not then normally consist of a single longitudinal mode but of a broad and irregular set of many modes.

In contrast to the wider stripes, devices with stripe widths up to between 3 and 5 μm give smooth light/current characteristics up to very much higher power. They have, however, a rather poorly defined threshold, with the spontaneous emission merging much more gradually into stimulated emission.[50] Lasing takes place in a number of longitudinal modes spread over a spectrum which narrows somewhat as the current is increased but usually has a width of around 20 Å. This behaviour is a natural consequence of the small cross-sectional area of the laser, which minimizes the distinction in spatial coherence between the lasing and the spontaneous output (see Section 2.6.3). The distinction is made even weaker by the leaky nature of the guided lasing mode in narrow stripes and the curvature in the wavefront.

The filament width of the zero-order mode in current confinement lasers tends to be greater than the stripe width for stripes of less than 8 μm width and less than the stripe width for wider stripes. It can seldom be made to exceed about 10 μm in broad stripes without the generation of higher order lateral modes, probably as a result of self-focusing effects.[37]

In the majority of the current confinement type of lasers the far-field

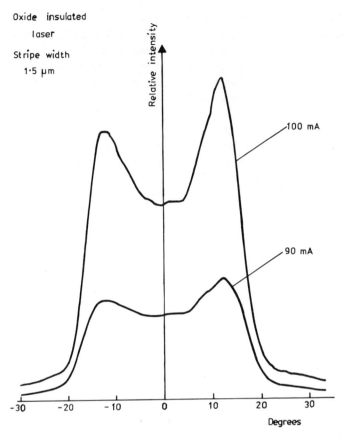

Figure 6.47   Far-field pattern of narrow stripe laser (1.5 μm wide)

pattern in the plane of the junction is about 7° wide to the points of half intensity. However, for devices with stripe width in the range 2.5–5 μm it is considerably wider and tends to exhibit a pair of lobes,[50] as shown in Figure 6.47. The lobes arise directly from the radiation leakage at the edges of the gain-guide which, in narrow stripes, gives rise to spreading V-shaped plane waves within the laser as illustrated in Figure 6.20. An approximate theoretical derivation of this phenomenon is given in Chapter 4, Section 4.2.4.6. There it is shown that the lobes appear when the width of the gain region is reduced below a certain critical value, and that further reduction in width increases the relative intensity of the lobes and increases the angle between them. Asbeck et al.[57] have observed that driving the laser further beyond threshold also increases the intensity of the lobes and that this is accompanied by a broadening of the near-field distribution. By carrying out a more detailed theoretical analysis (along the lines of that described for self-focusing effects in wider stripe lasers in Section 6.4.2.2) and using self-consistent computation of the carrier and optical distributions in the presence of stimulated emission, Asbeck *et al.* have shown that this behaviour can be satisfactorily explained by gain-guide theory.

Stripe lasers in the width range 2.5–5 μm differ in one further respect from the wider stripes. They respond differently to current modulation. In Chapter 7, Section 7.3 it is shown that in general a modulation resonance exists in a laser which exhibits itself as a transient oscillation when a step-function of current is applied. In narrow stripe lasers the poorly defined nature of the threshold means that the device may be driven considerably above the nominal threshold but still operate in a condition where spontaneous emission is the major source of the output. Under

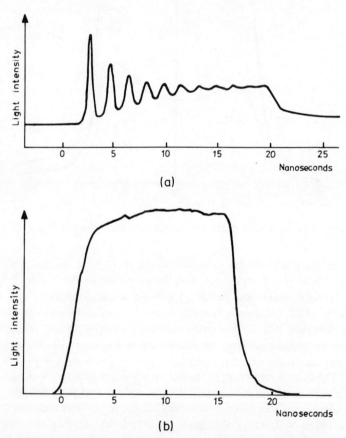

Figure 6.48 Transient response of stripe lasers to step in current. (a) Laser of normal width (10–20 μm), (b) narrow stripe laser (3.0 μm)

these circumstances the transient oscillation is not seen[45] and the time response resembles more closely that in a light-emitting diode with an exponential-like approach to the final output. The two types of response are compared in Figure 6.48.

The last device in the first group of lasers in Table 6.1 is the deep oxygen implanted stripe laser. This differs somewhat from the previous stripes in that a certain amount of carrier confinement is provided as a result of the low mobility in the oxygen doped regions. As explained in Section 6.5 and illustrated in Figure 6.36 this type of structure is particularly suitable for suppressing the lateral diffusion of carriers and hence providing low threshold current in narrow stripes of less than 10 μm width. The threshold current actually obtained and indicated in Table 6.1 for 12 μm wide lasers is not a particularly low. However, this appears to be an unfortunate property of the few heterostructure slices actually investigated, as instanced by the high threshold current density of the corresponsing broad contact lasers, and does not necessarily indicate the performance that would be obtained from narrow stripes with optimized slices.

6.7.2 Lasers with Additional Optical Confinement

The second group of stripe lasers in Table 6.1 comprises those designs in which an additional degree of lateral optical confinement is provided but where there is no deleberate means of lateral carrier confinement. The double stripe,[32] item 5 in the list, uses the distribution of injected carrier concentration to create the waveguide (see Section 6.2.6 and Figure 6.10). The remainder of devices in this group use the geometry of the layer structure (see Section 6.2.5 and Figures 6.8 and 6.9). The thickness of either the active layer or of one of the passive layers is varied over the cross-section. These devices include (6) the rib-waveguide laser,[9] (7) the passive-strip-loaded-waveguide laser,[10] (8) the plano-convex waveguide stripe,[30] and (9) the channelled substrate planar stripe.[31]

The threshold current of most of these devices is much the same and lies in the range 40–90 mA. The double stripe achieves its lowest values in short devices (100–150 μm). The thin active layer in both the plano-convex-waveguide structure (0.1 μm) and in the 40 mA threshold channelled-substrate-planar stripe (0.04–0.15 μm) contributes to the low threshold of these devices. A relatively large threshold is quoted for the rib-waveguide laser (500 mA) but this arises from the relatively broad top contact that was used in the prototype devices to overcome registration problems. The threshold current observed in the passive-strip-loaded lasers is also somewhat higher than expected, being around 100 mA for 250 μm long devices of 4–8 μm width. These however were early results.

In order to obtain linear operation over a considerable dynamic range the guide strength must be chosen in conjuction with the gain distribution to stabilize the zero order mode but to prevent the generation of the first order mode. All the devices are made relatively narrow for this reason (4–8 μm). The double stripe is at a disadvantage however in that the gain distribution, which cannot be chosen independently of the refractive index distribution, is unfavourable for maintaining single mode operation up to high powers, and limits the range to 5–10 mW. In the other devices the top contact is made appreciably wider than the waveguide to give uniform gain over the width of the filament. Then, by careful control of the layer dimensions, single transverse mode operation can be achieved with good linearity up to currents of three or even five times threshold. The devices all provide a single longitudinal mode in at least part of this range.

The width of the near-field to the $1/e$ points in most of the devices is of the order of 4 μm, being comparable with or smaller than the waveguide width. The far-field patterns in the junction plane are in general narrower than for normal stripe lasers of similar width. In the case of the passive strip-loaded waveguide and the channelled-substrate-planar stripe the reported far-field was not as narrow as would be expected from a perfectly guided wave. It is possible that the results are somewhat variable and depend on the precise details of fabrication.

6.7.3   Lasers with both Optical and Carrier Confinement

The third group of stripe lasers in Table 6.1 have lateral confinement of both the optical and the carrier distributions. There are two categories of device, those with p–n junctions and those with heterojunctions for the confining barriers. We take the p–n junction devices first.

The transverse junction stripe laser[7,24] (item 10 in the table) may be said to provide a one-sided lateral confinement of holes at the p–n junction but little lateral optical confinement from the asymmetrical refractive index distribution. However, the relative performance is good. Threshold currents as low as 15 mA have been measured with single transverse mode operation up to at least four times threshold. These devices also provide a single longitudinal mode. The filament width is about 2 μm and the far-field beam width is about 16°. Modulation of these devices does not excite the normal ringing resonance. This behaviour is similar to that in narrow stripe lasers and can probably be ascribed to the small cross-sectional area of the filament and the consequent significant interaction of the spontaneous emission with the lasing output.

The twin transverse junction laser[27] and the deep Zn-diffused window-stripe laser,[28] items 11 and 12 in table 6.1, are similar in general concept (see Section 6.2.4) and both provide lateral optical confinement of holes to the same region. Provided the width of the stripe is appropriately chosen in terms of the n- and p-doping (normally around 4–6 μm) these devices show single transverse mode and single longitudinal mode operation over a considerable current range. The threshold current in 4 μm wide twin transverse junction devices lies in the range 25–50 mA depending on length. In the window stripe lasers it is somewhat greater due to the higher p-doping and the window sections.

The buried heterostructure,[4] item 13 in Table 6.1, provides strong lateral confinement of light and excellent lateral confinement of injected carriers. The threshold current is very low with best figures of around 5 mA. For stripes not wider than 1.5 μm, single transverse mode operation can be obtained over a current range up to at least seven times threshold. The device also gives a single longitudinal mode. The filament width closely matches the stripe width and the far-field pattern is accordingly relatively wide at around 18°. The small output aperture limits the c.w. output power to around 1 mW.

The buried-optical-guide laser[23], item 14 in Table 6.1, is a variation on the buried heterostructure designed to give a greater output power (see Section 6.2.3). It contains a separate confinement heterostructure with one extra layer next to the active layer for spreading the light in the direction normal to the junction. This results also in a somewhat weaker guide in the lateral direction so that the stripe may be slightly wider than in the simple buried heterostructure (2–4 μm). The threshold current is correspondingly greater than in the buried heterostructure, lying around 20–30 mA. The pulsed catastrophic failure limit is also raised in comparison to the buried heterostructure to 25–30 mW per μm stripe width, and the device will provide 10 mW of CW power without degradation. The strip-buried heterostructure, item 15 in Table 6.1, is another four layer variation of the buried heterostructure which allows the device to be made even wider without generation of the first order lateral mode, i.e. 5 μm or greater (see Section 6.2.3). The threshold current for good 5 μm wide devices is expected to lie around 40 mA since 60–80 mA has been obtained in 10 μm wide devices[59] although at present the best quoted figure for 5 μm wide devices is 90 mA.[22] The far-field beam angle for 5 μm wide devices is 10° parallel to the junction and 30° perpendicular. The device will operate pulsed up to about nine times threshold without change of the far-field pattern, and up to twice threshold in a single longitudinal mode. The catastrophic failure limit is about 40 mW per micron stripe width.

REFERENCES

1. J. C. Dyment, 'Hermite–gaussian mode patterns in GaAs junction lasers,' *Appl. Phys. Lett.*, **10**, 1967, 84.

2. J. E. Ripper, J. C. Dyment, L. A. D'Asaro, and T. L. Poole, 'Stripe-geometry double heterostructure junction lasers: mode structure and CW operation above room temperature', *Appl. Phys. Lett.*, **18**, 1971, 155.

3. J. C. Dyment, L. A. D'Asaro, J. C. North, B. I. Miller, and J. E. Ripper, 'Proton bombardment formation of stripe geometry heterostructure lasers for 300 K CW operation', *Proc. IEEE(Lett.).*, **60**, 1972, 726.

4. T. Tsukada, 'GaAs–Ga$_{1-x}$Al$_x$As buried-heterostructure injection lasers', *J. Appl. Phys.*, **45**, 1974, 4899.

5. R. D. Burnham and D. R. Scifres, 'Etched buried heterostructure GaAs/Ga$_{1-x}$Al$_x$As injection lasers', *Appl. Phys. Lett.*, **27**, 1975, 510.

6. P. A. Kirkby and G. H. B. Thompson, 'Channelled substrate buried heterostructure GaAs–(GaAl)As injection lasers', *J. Appl. Phys.*, **47**, 1976, 4578.

7. H. Namizaki, H. Kan, M. Ishii, and A. Ito, 'Transverse-junction stripe-geometry double heterostructure lasers with very low threshold current', *J. Appl. Phys.*, **45**, 1974, 2785.

8. H. Yonezu *et al.*, 'New stripe geometry laser with high quality lasing characteristics by horizontal mode stabilization—a refractive index guiding with Zn doping', *Japan J. Appl. Phys.*, **16**, 1977, 209.

9. T. P. Lee, C. A. Burrus, B. I. Miller, and R. A. Logan, 'Al$_x$Ga$_{1-x}$As double heterostructure rib-waveguide injection laser', *IEEE J. Quantum Electron.*, **QE–11**, 1975, 432.

10. H. Kawaguchi and T. Kawakami, 'Transverse mode control in an injection laser by a strip loaded waveguide', *IEEE J. Quantum Electron*, **QE–13**, 1977, 556.

11. T. Tsukada, R. Ito, H. Nakashima, and O. Nakada, 'Mesa-stripe geometry double—heterostructure injection lasers', *IEEE J. Quantum Electron.*, **QE–9**, 1973, 356.

12. S. Iida and Y. Watanabe, 'Spectral characteristics and inhomogeneities near active regions of DH (GaAl)As–GaAs lasers with stripe geometry', *Japan J. Appl. Phys.*, **13**, 1974, 1249.

13. H. Yonezu, I. Sakuma, K. Kobayashi, T. Kamejima, M. Ueno, and Y. Nannichi, 'A GaAs–Al$_x$Ga$_{1-x}$As double heterostructure planar stripe laser', *Japan J. Appl. Phys.*, **12**, 1973, 1585.

14. M. Takusagawa, H. Nishi, S. Osaka, M. Morimoto, H. Imai, H. Takanashi, and T. Misugi, 'A new sulphur-diffused stripe-geometry D.H. laser', *Proc. Electron. Devices Conf.*, Washington, 1975.

15. H. Nishi, H. Kuwahara, K. Hanamitsu, M. Takusagawa, and T. Kudo, 'A semiconductor laser with a flat frequency response up to 2 GHz', 1977 Int. Conf. on Integrated Optics Tokyo, July 18–20, *IECE and IEE (Japan). Techanical Digest*, 73.

16. K. Itoh, M. Inoue, and I. Teramoto, 'New heteroisolation stripe-geometry visible-light-emitting lasers', *IEEE J. Quantum Electron.*, **QE-11**, 1975, 421.

17. R. D. Burnham, D. R. Scifres, J. C. Tramontana, and A. S. Alimonda, 'Striped substrate double-heterostructure lasers', *IEEE J. Quantum Electron.*, **QE-11**, 1975, 418.

18. W. T. Tsang and R. A. Logan, 'Lateral current confinement by reverse biased junctions in GaAs–AlGaAs DH lasers', *Appl. Phys. Lett.*, **30**, 1977, 538.

19. T. P. Lee and A. Y. Cho, 'Single-transverse-mode injection lasers with embedded stripe layer grown by molecular beam epitaxy', *Appl. Phys. Lett.*, **29**, 1976, 164.

20. J. M. Blum *et al.*, 'Oxygen-implanted double-heterojunction GaAs/GaAlAs injection lasers', *IEEE J. Quantum Electron.*, **QE-11**, 1975, 413.

21. B. W. Hakki, 'Carrier and gain spatial profiles in GaAs stripe geometry lasers', *J. Appl. Phys.*, **44**, 1973, 5021.
22. W. T. Tsang, R. A. Logan, and M. Ilegems, 'High power fundamental-transverse-mode strip buried heterostructure lasers with linear light-current characteristics', *Appl. Phys. Lett.*, **32**, 1978, 311.
23. N. Chinone, K. Saito, R. Ito, K. Aiki and N. Shige, 'Highly efficient (GaAl) As buried heterostructure lasers with buried optical guide', *Appl. Phys. Lett.*, **35**, 1979, 513.
24. H. Namizaki, 'Transverse-junction-stripe lasers with a GaAs p–n homojunction', *IEEE J. Quantum Electron.*, **QE-11**, 1975, 427.
25. W. Susaki, E. Oomura, K. Ikeda, M. Ishii, and K. Shirakata, 'Single mode oscillation characteristics of long lived AlGaAs TJS lasers', 3rd European Conference on Optical Communication, Sept. 1977, *Conference Proceedings*, VDE Verlag GmbH, p. 123.
26. W. Susaki, T. Tanaka, H. Kan, and M. Ishii, 'New structures of (GaAl)As lateral injection lasers for low threshold and single mode operation', *IEEE J. Quantum Electron.*, **QE-13**, 1977, 587.
27. G. H. B. Thompson, D. F. Lovelace and S. E. H. Turley, 'Deep Zn-diffused (GaAl)As heterostructure stripe laser with twin transverse junctions for low threshold and kink-free light characteristics', *IEEE J. Quantum Electron.*, **QE-15**, 1979, 772.
28. H. Yonezu, M. Ueno, T. Kamejima and I. Hayashi, 'An AlGaAs window structure laser', *IEEE J. Quantum Electron.*, **QE-15**, 1979, 775.
29. D. Botez, L. Figueroa, and S. Wang, 'Optically pumped GaAs/GaAlAs half ring laser fabricated by LPE over chemically etched channels', *Appl. Phys. Lett.*, **29**, 1976, 502.
30. T. Furuse, I. Sakuma, Y. Ide, K. Nishida and F. Saito, 'Transverse mode stabilized AlGaAs DH laser having a built-in plano-convex waveguide', Proceedings of Optical Communication Conference, Amsterdam, Sept. 17–19, 1979.
31. K. Aiki, M. Nakamura, T. Kuroda, J. Umeda, R. Ito, N. Chinone, and M. Maeda, 'Transverse mode stabilised $Al_xGa_{1-x}As$ injection lasers with channelled-substrate-planar structures', *IEEE J. Quantum Electron.*, **JQE-14**, 1978, 89.
32. P. A. Kirkby, 'Double stripe laser', IEE and IoP Conference on Semiconductor Lasers and their Applications, Cardiff, 31 March—1 April 1977, post deadline paper.
33. L. A. D'Asaro, 'Advances in GaAs junction lasers with stripe geometry', *J. Luminescence*, **7**, 1973, 502
34. W. P. Dumke, 'Current thresholds in stripe contact lasers', *Solid State Electron.*, **16**, 1973, 1279.
35. A. K. Jonscher and M. H. Boyle, 'The flow of carriers and its effect on the spatial distribution of radiation from injection lasers', *Proceedings of IPPS Symposium on GaAs*, Reading, 1966, p. 78.
36. G. H. B. Thompson, 'A theory for filamentation in semiconductor lasers including the dependence of dielectric constant on injected carrier density', *Opto-electronics*, **4**, 1972, 257.
37. P. A. Kirkby, A. R. Goodwin, G. H. B. Thompson, and P. R. Selway, 'Observations of self-focusing in stripe geometry semiconductor lasers and the development of a comprehensive model of their operation', *IEEE J. Quantum Electron.*, **QE-13**, 1977, 705.
38. M. R. Matthews, R. B. Dyott, and W. P. Carling, 'Filaments as optical waveguides in gallium arsenide lasers', *Electron. Lett.*, **8**, 1972, 570.

39. P. R. Selway, G. H. B. Thompson, G. D. Henshall, and J. E. A. Whiteaway, 'Measurement of the effect of injected carriers on the p–n refractive index step in single heterostructure diode lasers', *Electron. Lett.*, **10**, 1974, 453.

40. B. W. Hakki, 'GaAs double heterostructure lasing behaviour along the junction plane', *J. Appl. Phys.*, **46**, 1975, 292.

41. J. Buus, 'A model for the static properties of DH lasers', *IEEE J. Quantum Electron.*, **QE-15**, 1979, 734.

42. B. W. Hakki, 'Striped GaAs lasers: Mode size and efficiency', *J. Appl. Phys.*, **46**, 1975, 2723.

43. D. D. Cook and F. R. Nash, 'Gain-induced guiding and astigmatic output beam of GaAs lasers', *J. Appl. Phys.*, **46**, 1975, 1660.

44. F. Stern, 'Calculated spectral dependence of gain in excited GaAs', *J. Appl. Phys.*, **47**, 1976, 5382.

45. J. C. Dyment, C. J. Hwang, and A. R. Hartman, Unpublished results quoted in reference (19).

46. J. Rossi and J. P. Donelly, 'Experimental observations on proton bombarded GaAs double-heterostructure stripe-geometry lasers', unpublished, 1976.

47. A. G. Steventon, P. Fiddyment, D. H. Newman, and J. M. Tinkler, 'Low threshold current proton-isolated (GaAl)As DH lasers', 3rd European Conference on Optical Communications, September 1977, *Conference Proceedings*, VDE-Verlag GmbH, p. 126.

48. M. Ettenberg and H. F. Lockwood, 'Low threshold, high efficiency, CW $Al_xGa_{1-x}As$ injection lasers', 1977 IEEE Device Research Conference Cornell University, Ithaca, New York; *Abstracts of Papers*, p. 29.

49. R. W. Dixon, F. R. Nash, R. L. Hartman, and R. T. Hepplewhite, 'Improved light-output linearity in stripe geometry double-heterostructure $Al_xGa_{1-x}As$ lasers', *Appl. Phys. Lett.*, **29**, 1976, 372.

50. T. Kobayashi, H. Kawaguchi, and Y. Furukawa, 'Lasing characteristics of very narrow planar stripe lasers', *Japan J. Appl. Phys.*, **16**, 1977, 601.

51. T. L. Paoli, 'Non linearities in the emission characteristics of stripe geometry $Al_{1-x}Ga_xAs$ double-heterostructure junction lasers', *IEEE J. Quantum Electron.*, **QE-12**, 1976, 770.

52. W. Kobayashi, R. Lang, H. Yonezu, I. Sakuma, and I. Hayashi, 'Horizontal mode deformation and anomalous lasing properties of stripe geometry injection lasers—experiment', *Japan J. Appl. Phys.*, **16**, 1977, 207.

53. P. A. Kirkby, P. R. Selway, and L. D. Westbrook, 'Photo-elastic waveguides and their effect on stripe geometry $GaAs/Ga_{1-x}Al_xAs$ lasers', *J. Appl. Phys.*, **50**, 1979, 4567.

54. G. H. B. Thompson, D. F. Lovelace, and S. E. H. Turley, 'Kinks in the light/current characteristics and near-field shifts in (GaAl)As heterostructure stripe lasers and their explanation by the effect of self-focusing on a built-in optical waveguide', *Solid State and Electron Devices*, **2**, 1978, 12.

55. R. Lang, 'Lateral mode instability and its stabilization in stripe geometry injection lasers', *IEEE J. Quantum Electron.*, **QE-15**, 1979, 718.

56. J. C. Bouley, Ph. Delpech, J. Charil, G. Chaminant, J. Landreau, and J. P. Noblanc, 'Low-current proton-bombarded (GaAl)As double-heterostructure lasers', *Appl. Phys. Lett.*, **33**, 1978, 327.

57. P. M. Asbeck, D. A. Cammack, J. J. Daniele and V. Klebanoff, 'Lateral mode behaviour in narrow stripe lasers', *IEEE J. Quantum Electron.*, **QE-15**, 1979, 727.

58. A. R. Goodwin, A. W. Davis, P. A. Kirkby, R. E. Epworth and R. G. Plumb, 'Narrow stripe semiconductor laser for improved performance of optical

communication systems', Proceedings Optical Communication Conference, Amsterdam, Sept. 17–19, 1979.

59. W. T. Tsang, R. A. Logan and J. P. van der Ziel, 'Low-current-threshold strip-buried-heterostructure lasers with self-aligned current injection stripes', *Appl. Phys. Lett.*, **34**, 1979, 644.

60. H. J. Bachert, A. P. Bogatov and P. G. Eliseev, 'Mode deformation in an injection laser due to the self-focusing effect and its relation with nonlinearity of the output characteristic', *Sov. J. Quantum Electron.*, **8**, 1978, 346.

CHAPTER 7

Dynamic Response of Lasers

In this chapter we deal with both the transient and the modulation responses of semiconductor lasers. The response of the laser to a varying current input is of considerable practical significance, since variation of current provides a convenient means of modulating the laser for applications such as communications and range-finding. The response to a varying optical input would be of comparable practical significance if lasers were to be seriously considered for use as optical amplifiers. However, in addition to any direct significance that the optical response may have it is also relevant in determining the noise modulation of the laser output; the optical input concerned then being the fluctuations in the spontaneous and stimulated processes within the laser resonator. We consider the transient and modulation responses to both types of input and use the results later in a treatment of laser noise and stability.

The small-signal modulation of lasers can be analysed in considerable detail. The mechanism involves an interaction between the injected electron population and the photon population which in most lasers exhibits resonance at a certain modulation frequency. A simple theoretical analysis can be used to explain most of the behaviour. Only three properties of the laser are involved, namely the lifetime of the injected carriers, the lifetime of the photons in the resonator, and a factor that describes the relative steepness of the gain/current characteristic. The analysis is presented in the first part of this chapter.

The modulation behaviour observed in actual lasers, particularly stripe lasers, shows various small but significant departures from the simple theory. To explain these it is necessary to take into account three additional factors, namely carrier diffusion, optical pumping, and spontaneous emission. Carrier diffusion in the direction transverse to the laser axis plays an important role when a narrow filament of light is generated in a region of reasonably uniform injected current density. The diffusion tends to damp transient oscillations in the laser output. Optical pumping is important in the complementary situation where the injected

402

carriers are confined in a small width and the light spreads to a greater extent into the adjacent optically lossy regions. This may lead to instability in the laser output. Spontaneous emission must be taken into consideration at currents not too far beyond threshold. The laser output may then be regarded as amplified spontaneous emission, and the degree of amplification affects the modulation behaviour. Such effects are particularly evident in lasers of small crosssection where the contribution of spontaneous emission to each lasing mode represents a larger proportion of the total current.

We give a theoretical analysis of all three of these factors.

The transient behaviour of lasers is in general very closely related to the modulation response. For instance, the small-signal modulation resonance which occurs in most lasers is closely associated with the transient ringing response which is observed when a step function of current is applied. However, the interactions in a semiconductor laser are non-linear and these must be taken into account particularly in treating the large transient oscillations which follow switch-on. For this analysis it is not only necessary to consider in detail the amplitude variation of the total intensity of all the laser modes in the initial stages of switch-on, where spontaneous emission is an important factor, but it is also necessary to take into account how the spectral distribution of the laser modes varies with time. We describe and analyse both types of behaviour.

Single heterostructure lasers sometimes show a specific form of slow transient behaviour which is made more noticeable by the positive feedback associated with the perturbing effect of injected carriers on the heterostructure waveguide (see Section 5.2.3). We show that, in these circumstances, otherwise unimportant heating or saturable absorption effects which may have relatively long time constants can control the switch-on behaviour, and long switch-on delay times may be observed.

7.1   PHYSICAL MODEL OF THE TRANSIENT RESPONSE

Semiconductor lasers respond much more rapidly to changes in the pump power than do other types of laser. They can be modulated directly and efficiently by the pump current to produce pulses at bit rates of up to 1–2 Gbits s⁻¹ in a manner which is very suitable for application to communication systems.[1-3] This is a consequence of the short time constant associated with the carrier injection and also of the high volume excitation rate which allows a small optical cavity to be used. However, current modulation is a complicated process which involves both the carrier and photon population. There are a variety of factors which contribute to the behaviour and which can be adjusted to optimize the response, to minimize delays, to suppress ringing, and to prevent excessive spectral broadening.

To appreciate the way these factors interact let us first consider a physical model of the process involved.

In a light-emitting diode, or in a laser below threshold, the output of spontaneous emission depends only on the injected carrier concentration, and the output intensity responds to an increase in current with a time constant determined mainly by the carrier recombination time. In a laser spontaneous emission normally produces a relatively insignificant output of light. The main output derives from stimulated emission, and the way the output intensity responds to a current step involves the interaction between the photon population in the cavity and the fraction of injected carriers that are in excess of the equilibrium threshold concentration. Hence the time constants associated with both the carriers and the photons are concerned in the process.

To analyse the effect of a change in the drive current in a laser it is therefore necessary to trace the resulting changes in the concentrations of both the injected carriers and the photons in the resonator. The initial effect of raising the current is, as in the light-emitting diode, to cause the injected carrier concentration to start increasing. Also, as in the light-emitting diode, the local rate of light emission increases as the carrier concentration increases. However, the predominant mechanism of light emission is different since in the laser there is a stimulated component the intensity of which depends on the photon population. A further point of difference is that in the laser a distinction must be made between the rate of light emission into the laser resonator and the rate of light output from the end-faces of the resonator. The output from the end-faces depends not on the rate of generation of photons but on the size of the photon population which has accumulated in the resonator. The rise in photon population lags behind the increase in generation rate, and this delay, although small, is significant in the response mechanism since it determines the way the photons supply feedback to the stimulated emission. In spite of the fact that the laser response proceeds in two stages, a stage of electron accumulation followed by a stage of photon accumulation, the overall speed of response is more rapid than that in a light-emitting diode. This is because the photon lifetime in the resonator is short—about 5 ps. The photon population can therefore rise extremely rapidly proportionately to its initial value, immediately enhancing the stimulated emission rate and hence speeding up the response to the injected carrier concentration.

The strong two-way interaction between the populations of injected carriers and photons and the phase delay associated with the accumulation time of the photons gives rise to a tendency to oscillation. The stored energy of the system can swing between the two populations with a natural resonance frequency which depends on particular circumstances but is normally in the vicinity of 1 GHz. Little damping is supplied by the optical resonator, since under lasing conditions its Q is very large, and the main contribution to damping comes from the spontaneous recombination time of the carriers, giving a decay time of the order of 5.ns. The resonance manifests itself as a transient oscillation during laser switching and also as an enhancement of the modulation response to a small sinusoidal current in the relevant frequency range.

The way these various processes follow one another during the switching-on of a laser is illustrated in Figure 7.1. The curves show the response of both the photon and the injected carrier populations. The former is shown on a logarithmic scale so that the behaviour at the start of the switch-on is easier to see. When a step function of current is applied which takes the current beyond threshold there is a delay in the optical response as the injected carrier concentration rises to a level just beyond the threshold level. Up to this level there is a negligible lasing emission. The length of the delay depends on the previous current drive, the carrier recombination time, and the amount of current overdrive associated with the step function. For switching from zero current to normal operating levels the delay, as will be shown below, is of the order of two to three times the recombination time of the carriers, i.e. 6–10 ns. When the threshold concentration of injected carriers is exceeded at the end of the delay period the true switch-on starts and the lasing emission grows from the spontaneous level in an exponential-like way with time, rising to its full output over a time whose extent depends on the photon lifetime in the resonator, on the injected carrier recombination time, and on the degree of current overdrive. This switch-on time is, in practice, of the order of a few hundred picoseconds.

The injected carrier concentration rises significantly above its equilibrium level during the switch-on process, and this also causes the photon population to exceed its equilibrium level at the end of the first phase of switch-on and serves to excite the transient oscillation mentioned above. This behaviour is illustrated in Figure 7.1.

The spectrum of the lasing emission after switch-on also evolves with time, as shown in Figure 7.1. It does this in a way which is not particularly related to the transient behaviour of the total intensity. The initial spectrum of spontaneous emission which triggers the laser action is spread over a bandwidth of several hundred ångströms and is separated by the laser cavity into a large number of rudimentary modes. During the course of the switch-on a considerably number of these modes adjacent to the eventual lasing mode experience temporary amplification. In the initial period of the switch on, while the main mode is growing, they increase in magnitude, but more slowly than the main mode, in such a way as to produce a constantly narrowing overall linewidth. The linewidth continues to narrow consistently, even during the period where the main mode is in

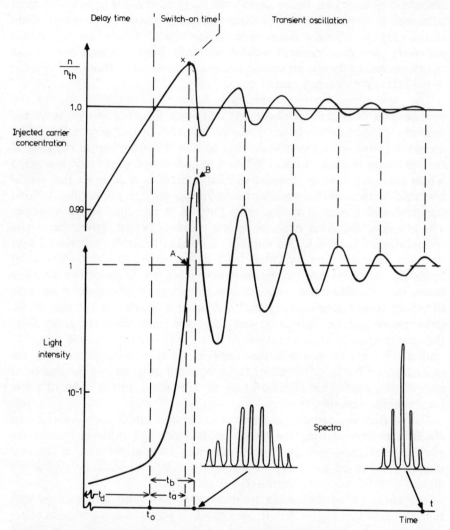

Figure 7.1 Time dependence of photon population density and injected carrier concentration during switch-on of a semiconductor laser. Delay time t_d corresponds to rise of injected carrier concentration to threshold value n_{th}. Switch-on time t_a is that required to first raise photon population to final steady state value and is also approximately that to raise injected carrier concentration to highest point. Transient oscillation becomes sinusoidal as it decays with carrier concentration variation advanced in phase by approximately a quarter cycle compared with photon density. Evolution of longitudinal mode spectrum shown with number of modes decreasing with time

transient oscillation. In this period the satellite modes are also in transient oscillation, but on average they steadily diminish in amplitude with respect to the main mode. In practice up to 15 ns can elapse before the mode spectrum of the laser approaches close to its c.w. form, which in uniform lasers with sufficient output normally consists of one dominant mode.

The natural resonance of the electron and photon populations also affects the sinusoidal modulation and the noise characteristics of the laser. The response of the laser to sinusoidal modulation of the current varies little with frequency over most of the frequency range up to resonance, but experiences an enhancement at the resonance frequency itself by a factor of up to 5 or 10, thereafter rapidly dying away. Photon quantum noise and electron shot noise are similarly enhanced in the resonance band.

Under circumstances where the light and the optical gain are not uniformly distributed in the laser cavity, either in the longitudinal or, more particularly, in the transverse direction, the Q of the resonance may be enhanced to the extent that instability can arise, and a continuous spiking response be produced. This is most likely to occur if the photon density is high in regions where the optical gain is negative. The behaviour may be explained in terms of a Q switching process, in which the injected carriers continue to accumulate until the photon emission is sufficient to bleach (or saturate) the absorption where the gain is negative. Feedback is then suddenly increased and a spike of stimulated emission is produced which is sufficient to entirely dissipate the inverted population and leave the laser in an extinguished condition. The cycle of events is then repeated and an infinite train of pulses results.

When the cross-sectional area of the optical filament is small (e.g. $<1-2\ \mu m^2$) the laser does not exhibit the electron/photon resonance or the ringing response until the current is raised by a certain appropriate amount above threshold. As explained in Chapter 2, Section 2.7.3, spontaneous emission is the controlling factor in the output of such lasers up to a current appreciably above the nominal threshold, being much larger in comparison with the drive current than in lasers of larger cross section. This follows because the spontaneous contribution per mode at threshold is reasonably independent of laser volume while the total drive current is closely related to the volume. Lasers with a relatively large contribution of spontaneous emission per mode operate as amplifiers rather than oscillators, emitting in a super-radiant rather than a lasing mode. This behaviour is particularly evident over a considerable current range in narrow stripe lasers, where the absolute as well as the relative magnitude of the spontaneous emission output per mode increases with reducing width because of the increasing current density required to produce gain-guiding. In the super-radiant regime the transient response is mainly determined by the behaviour of the spontaneous emission and its speed is related to the spontaneous recombination time. There is no positive feedback from the photon to the electron population to produce resonance in ringing.

7.2   DELAY TIME

The delay time t_d will be taken, somewhat arbitrarily, as that part of the response of the laser to a step in current that is concerned with raising the injected carrier concentration to the lasing level. The delay time is determined by the carrier rather than the photon lifetime. The standard analysis, as first carried out by Konnerth,[4] applies to most lasers, except some single heterostructure devices where the threshold condition is time dependent. The results depend slightly on the carrier recombination law assumed. We give the analysis below.

At the moment of switch-on we take the particle current density per unit volume to be stepped up from an initial value of J_1, less than the threshold value of J_{th}, to a final value J_0 greater than threshold. (The J's are defined as particle currents per unit volume rather than the more conventional current per unit area to save continually repeating the unnecessary symbols of electronic charge and thickness of the active layer.) The carrier concentration is thereby raised steadily from its starting value, say n_1, to a value which instantaneously just surpasses the threshold value of n_{th} before finally settling back to this value in steady state operation. t_d is defined as the time to raise n from n_1 to n_{th}. For convenience we define a carrier recombination time τ_{th} at threshold given by

$$\tau_{th} = \frac{n_{th}}{J_{th}} \tag{7.1}$$

not necessarily requiring τ_{th} to be independent of n_{th} (to take into account possible non-linear recombination). Initially we will, however, take the case of a highly doped active layer and assume a linear recombination rate so that τ_{th} is constant $(= \tau)$. We then write the rate equation for carrier accumulation as

$$\frac{dn}{dt} = \frac{n_0 - n}{\tau} \tag{7.2}$$

where, for convenience, we have put $J_0 = n_0/\tau$. The solution for this equation for the interval t_d which elapses between $n = n_1$ and $n = n_{th}$ is

$$\frac{t_d}{\tau} = \ln \left\{ \frac{1 - n_1/n_0}{1 - n_{th}/n_0} \right\}$$

$$= \ln \left\{ \frac{1 - J_1/J_0}{1 - J_{th}/J_0} \right\} \tag{7.3}$$

This equation ignores the time associated with charging the depletion layer capacitance which may be significant in the case of switch-on from zero current.

Secondly, we consider the case of an undoped active layer where the recombination rate is taken as the product of the (equal) electron and hole concentrations. The rate equation becomes

$$\frac{dn}{dt} = \beta(n_0^2 - n^2) \tag{7.4}$$

where β is the recombination constant and n_0 is now defined so that $\beta n_0^2 = J_0$ is the injection current density. The solution for t_d is[5]

$$
\begin{aligned}
t_d &= \left(\frac{1}{\beta n_0}\right)\left(\tanh^{-1}\left(\frac{n_{th}}{n_0}\right) - \tanh^{-1}\left(\frac{n_1}{n_0}\right)\right) \\
&= \tau_{th}\left(\frac{J_{th}}{J_0}\right)^{1/2}\left(\tanh^{-1}\left(\frac{J_{th}}{J_0}\right)^{1/2} - \tanh^{-1}\left(\frac{J_1}{J_0}\right)^{1/2}\right)
\end{aligned} \tag{7.5}
$$

The relationships for t_d given by equation (7.3) for linear recombination and equation (7.5) for quadratic recombination differ appreciably in the general case. Figure 7.2 shows the plot of t_d/τ against $\ln (J_0 - J_{th})/J_0$ according to the two relationships for $J_1 = 0$. These curves indicate that as J_0 becomes large compared with J_{th} the two relations become similar.

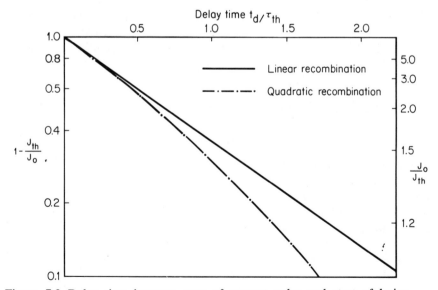

Figure 7.2 Delay time between start of current pulse and start of lasing emission as a function of drive current in laser. Curves shown applying to both linear and quadratic recombination of the injected carriers

Ripper[6] has shown that this applies generally, whatever the recombination law. The argument runs as follows. Equations (7.2) and (7.4) may both be represented approximately by

$$\frac{dn}{dt} \simeq J_0 \tag{7.6}$$

when J_0 is large compared with n/τ and the recombination rate can therefore be ignored compared with the injection rate. The delay time with J_1 zero is then given by

$$t_d \simeq \tau_{th}\left(\frac{J_{th}}{J_0}\right) \tag{7.7}$$

This relation is useful for obtaining the time constant τ_{th} from the delay time at high currents for a laser of unknown recombination characteristics. The recombination law may then be deduced by determining whether τ_{th} depends on J_{th} from measurements of other similar lasers but with different threshold current density (as a result of a change in length of facet reflectivity). Namizaki *et al.*[7] have carried out such an investigation on a set of double heterostructure lasers and found that the parabolic recombination law was applicable in the particular instance concerned.

In practice τ_{th} is of the order of 3–5 ns. For switching from zero current to, say, a current 33 per cent above threshold the particular form of the recombination does not affect the delay greatly and equations (7.3) and (7.5) give delay times respectively of $1.4\tau_{th}$ and $1.14\tau_{th}$. For switching from an initial current 95 per cent of threshold to the same final current 33 per cent above threshold the delay time is very much reduced. For linear recombination the delay is $0.14\tau_{th}$ and for quadratic recombination it is half this.

7.3   PHOTON/ELECTRON RESONANCE AND MODULATION

7.3.1   Rate Equations

To analyse the resonance interaction between injected carriers and photons in a semiconductor laser it is first necessary to write down the rate equations which determine the time variation of the concentration of the two species. Because the equations are non-linear it is only possible to obtain simple results when the time dependence consists of a small oscillation superimposed on the steady state behaviour. Initially we assume that the concentration of injected carriers is uniform throughout the active region of the laser, both in the steady state and in the oscillatory condition, leaving to Section 7.5 consideration of the considerable modifications which may arise if this is not so. In the treatment which follows we reproduce the principles of the original analysis by Ikegami and Suematsu.[8]

We consider first the rate equation for photons, distinguishing between the photon density in the different modes and providing individual relations for each mode. This separate consideration is particularly necessary in the multimode situations that arise when the contribution of spontaneous emission is appreciable, such as the switch-on of lasing (Section 7.5) and the behaviour of lasers that are operated close enough to threshold for spontaneous emission to induce many modes (Section 7.3.3). However, for the analysis of small oscillations in the normal laser it is in general sufficient to lump together the output of all the modes (Section 7.3.2).

Let the photon density per unit effective volume of the optical resonator for longitudinal mode number m and transverse mode number q be ϕ_{mq}. We will assume that the active material occupies the full length of the resonator but only a portion of its cross section. To obtain the average stimulated emission density into mode mq we use equation (2.23), Chapter 2, for the stimulated emission density per unit bandwidth in terms of the photon density per unit bandwidth. We integrate both sides over the resonator volume, then divide by the spectral density of modes in the resonator and by its volume. This gives

$$r_{stim}(mq) = \Gamma_q \phi_{mq} w_{stim}(h\nu) \tag{7.8}$$

where Γ_q is the confinement factor. The subscript q is inserted to take account of the possible variation of Γ with transverse mode number.

We define the rate of loss of photons from the cavity by end emission and absorption in terms of a lifetime which we denote by σ. (Several authors use the symbol τ_p for this lifetime, but our notation without subscript will be more convenient in the treatment that follows.) Equation (2.103) in Chapter 2 gives the following expression for σ in terms of the laser length and the facet reflectivity

$$\frac{1}{\sigma} = \left(\frac{c}{\mu}\right)\left(\alpha + \frac{\ln(1/R_1 R_2)}{2L}\right) \tag{7.9}$$

σ is typically of the order of 3–5 ps. It is reasonable to assume that σ does not depend on longitudinal mode number, but possibly varies with transverse mode number. We use $\sigma = \sigma_q$ for transverse mode number q.

To avoid confusing the effect of transverse mode number and the effect of optical frequency on w_{stim} it is convenient to number the longitudinal modes in each of the transverse mode sets according to their optical frequency rather than the number of nodes they contain, taking $m = 0$ for the modes closest to the centre of the gain spectrum and numbering both positive and negative. This ensures that modes in different transverse sets with the same longitudinal mode number have virtually the same optical frequency.

When the injected carrier concentration is uniform over the laser width we find that w_{stim} in equation (7.8) depends only on optical frequency (i.e.

on m and is independent of transverse mode number. Any variation of coupling is taken up in Γ_q. We absorb the two contributions in one symbol G_{mq} which we define by

$$\Gamma_q \, w_{\text{stim}}(q, h\nu) = G_{mq} \tag{7.10}$$

This applies satisfactorily in wide lasers. However, in narrow stripe lasers, where the injected carrier concentration is not uniform and is affected differently by the different lateral modes, it is not possible to define a single average value of w_{stim} which applies to all the modes. In some circumstances the effective values of w_{stim} for the different low order lateral modes may originate from such spatially separated locations as to be almost independent of one another. Caution must therefore be exercised in applying the q variation in equation (7.10).

The average rate of spontaneous emission per unit volume into mode mq can be obtained by the same methods as for $r_{\text{stim}}(mq)$ from equation (2.26), Chapter 2, and is $\Gamma_q w_{\text{spon}}(mq)/V$, where V is the volume of the resonator. We will denote this expression by δ_{mq}.

The rate equation for photons in mode mq is obtained by relating the accumulation rate of photons per unit volume to the stimulated emission rate plus the spontaneous emission rate plus any input photon flux of, say, F_{mq} per unit volume, less the absorption and loss rate. This gives

$$\frac{\mathrm{d}\phi_{mq}}{\mathrm{d}t} - \phi_{mq}\left(G_{mq} - \frac{1}{\sigma_q}\right) - \delta_{mq} = F_{mq} \tag{7.11}$$

Under conditions where the injected carrier concentration can be taken as uniform throughout the laser volume the rate equation for the carrier concentration n is given in terms of the stimulated recombination associated with all the modes, the spontaneous and non-radiative recombination with time constant τ, and an input particle current J per unit volume of the optical resonator, as

$$\frac{\mathrm{d}n}{\mathrm{d}t} + \frac{n}{\tau} + \Sigma_{mq}\phi_{mq}G_{mq} = J \tag{7.12}$$

(J is defined as a particle current per unit volume rather than the more conventional current per unit area to save continually repeating the unnecessary symbols of electronic charge and thickness of the optical resonator.) G_{mq} in equations (7.11) and (7.12) is measured at fixed optical frequency; the frequency of the mode concerned. G_{mq} increases approximately linearly with injected carrier concentration n over the small range normally involved in the solution of equations (7.11) and (7.12). The form of its precise variation with n can be judged from the plots of gain against current density J in Figure 6.30, taking J as proportional to n^2.

Equations (7.11) and (7.12) represent an oscillatory system. In the general case the oscillations are not sinusoidal. This arises because the equations are non-linear in ϕ and n, effectively containing a product of the two quantities in the terms $\phi_{mq}G_{mq}$. For small deviations from equilibrium the equations become approximately linear so that the oscillations are sinusoidal. We consider this approximation below. In Section 7.5 we consider an alternative approximation which can be applied to the switch-on process.

To make the small-oscillation analysis of equations (7.11) and (7.12) it is convenient to separate the photon population, the injected carrier population, the current, and any input photon flux into steady state and oscillatory components. Accordingly we put

$$\phi_{mq} = \phi_{mq0} + \phi_{mq1}; \qquad J = J_0 + J_1$$
$$n = n_0 + n_1; \qquad F_{mq} = F_{mq0} + F_{mq1} \tag{7.13}$$

where the terms with subscript zero are the steady state components and those with subscript one are small oscillatory components. We can then write the following rate equations for the small oscillatory components

$$\frac{d\phi_{mq1}}{dt} + \frac{\phi_{mq1}\epsilon_{mq}}{\sigma_q} - \phi_{mq0}G'_{mq}n_1 = F_{mq1} \tag{7.14}$$

$$\frac{dn_1}{dt} + n_1\left(\frac{1}{\tau} + \Sigma\phi_{mq0}G'_{mq}\right) + \Sigma G_{mq}\phi_{mq1} = J_1 \tag{7.15}$$

where we have ignored any contribution of spontaneous emission resulting from the additional carrier concentration n_1 in the photon rate equations and where

$$\epsilon_{mq} = 1 - \sigma_q G_{mq} \quad \text{and} \quad G'_{mq} = \frac{dG_{mq}}{dn}$$

$$= \frac{1}{\tau}\frac{dG_{mq}}{dJ} \tag{7.16}$$

with $1/\tau = dJ/dn$. [Note that τ does not equal τ_{th} in equation (7.1) if the recombination is not linear.]

The relations between the steady state components give the following expression for the total photon density if the optical inputs F_{mq0} and δ_{mq} can be ignored compared with the output

$$\Sigma\phi_{mq0} \simeq \sigma(J_0 - J_{th}), \quad \text{with } G_{mq} \simeq \frac{1}{\sigma} \text{ and } \epsilon_{mq} = 0 \tag{7.17}$$

where we have neglected the variation of σ with q. When the optical inputs cannot be ignored the photon density is obtained from a solution of the simultaneous equations represented by

$$\phi_{mq0} = \frac{\sigma_q(\delta_{mq} + F_{mq0})}{\epsilon_{mq}}$$

$$\Sigma G_{mq}\phi_{mq0} = J_0 - \frac{n_0}{\tau}$$

(7.18)

where G_{mq} and ϵ_{mq} depend on n_0.

Equations (7.14) and (7.15) for the oscillatory components can be treated in two different ways depending on the level of the lasing output with respect to the spontaneous emission into the laser mode. At high steady state output level we can put $\epsilon_{mq} \simeq 0$ and the treatment becomes particularly simple. In these circumstances the photon loss term, the second term in the photon rate equation (7.14), is almost zero. This happens because the photon loss from the end of the resonator is almost entirely compensated by the stimulated emission, and the result is that the resonator exerts negligible damping on any oscillation in the photon population. The only overall damping on the system results from interaction with the electron population with a time constant equal to the injected carrier recombination time. There is therefore a relatively high Q resonance. This is analysed in the next section.

At low steady state output levels a very different situation can arise. In these circumstances the high rate of photon loss from the optical resonator is no longer exactly balanced by stimulated emission. With even a small relative imbalance the net absolute photon loss rate becomes large, easily exceeding the carrier loss rate by spontaneous recombination, and increasing the net damping rate of the whole system. Very considerably effects on the overall damping can be produced at current levels which are still sufficiently above threshold to give a laser output predominantly in the form of stimulated emission. Under appropriate circumstances, particularly when the cross section of the laser is small, a condition of critical damping may be achieved at current levels corresponding to normal operation of the laser. This behaviour is analysed in Section 7.3.3.

For large amplitude oscillations in the photon population, equations (7.14) and (7.15) cannot be simply analysed. Various authors have obtained numerical solutions for specific relations between injected current density and gain.[9-11] These show that as the amplitude of the photon oscillation increases the peaks become more spiky, the troughs flatten, and the resonance frequency decreases. Harth[12] has shown that under these circumstances the logarithm of the photon concentration shows a much more sinusoidal oscillation than the concentration itself, and has analysed the effect on the resonance frequency. This topic will, however, not be pursued further here, and we refer readers who require more information to the original publication.

7.3.2 Small Oscillations in a Single Mode Laser

In this section we investigate the solution of the combined photon and carrier rate equations for small oscillations, associated with either a small modulation signal or a state of transient decay. We obtain the modulation efficiency, the resonance frequency, and the damping constant. The variable parameter is the d.c. component of the current drive to the laser. The spatial distribution of light and injected carriers is taken as uniform in this treatment. The very significant effect of a non-uniform spatial distribution is treated in Section 7.5.

Let us first consider small oscillations in a laser with a single transverse and single longitudinal mode using the rate equations (7.14) and (7.15) derived in the previous section. Equation (7.14) then comprises only one equation with $m = q = 0$. Also, according to the treatment in Section 2.8.3 [equation (2.125)] single mode operation only occurs when ϵ is less than $1/M^2$, where $2M$ is the total number of potential longitudinal modes in the width of the gain spectrum. For lasers larger than the normal minimum length of 150 μm this gives $\epsilon < 10^{-3}$. It is then justifiable to ignore the term in ϵ in the photon rate equation (7.14) (the criterion is $\epsilon < \sigma\omega \simeq 10^{-2}$). We then eliminate either the carrier concentration or the photon concentration from the equations to obtain a resonance relation for the other quantity. Dropping the subscripts m and q in considering the zero-order mode we obtain the following resonance equation for the photon concentration ϕ_1

$$\frac{d^2\phi_1}{dt^2} + \left(\frac{1}{\tau} + \phi_0 G'\right)\frac{d\phi_1}{dt} + \phi_0 GG'\phi_1 = \frac{dF_1}{dt} + \left(\frac{1}{\tau} + \phi_0 G'\right)F_1 + \phi_0 G'J_1$$

(7.19)

Provided that the lasing ouput is not too small (too close to threshold) we can use the approximate steady state equations (7.17) to express ϕ_0 and G simply in terms of better known quantities. To substitute for the remaining unknown G', we need to know the gain/current characteristic. For a linear gain/current characteristic similar to that in equation (2.76) we have

$$G = \frac{J - J_t}{\sigma\beta J_{th}}$$

with

$$\beta = 1 - \frac{J_t}{J_{th}}$$

(7.20)

and hence using equation (7.16)

$$G' = \frac{1}{\beta \sigma \tau J_{th}} \tag{7.21}$$

The modulated output flux P_1 in photons per second per unit volume of the optical resonator $(= \phi_1/\sigma)$ at angular frequency ω can then be written in terms of the modulated photon and current input as follows

$$P_1 = \frac{\sigma^{-1}(j\omega + 1/\tau_1)F_1 + \omega_0^2 J_1}{-\omega^2 + j\omega/\tau_1 + \omega_0^2} \tag{7.22}$$

where the resonance angular frequency ω_0 and the damping time constant τ_1 are given by

$$\omega_0^2 = \phi_0 G G' = \frac{J/J_{th} - 1}{\beta \sigma \tau} \tag{7.23}$$

$$\frac{1}{\tau_1} = \frac{1}{\tau} + \frac{J/J_{th} - 1}{\beta \tau} \tag{7.24}$$

We can obtain the magnification factor relating the modulated light output P_1 to both the modulated current and the modulated light input from equation (7.22). The magnification factor at the resonance frequency for a current input J_1 is given by

$$\left| \frac{P_1}{J_1} \right| = \omega_0 \tau_1 = \left(\frac{\tau}{\sigma} \right)^{1/2} \left\{ \frac{\xi^{1/2}}{1 + \xi} \right\} \tag{7.25}$$

where

$$\xi = \frac{J/J_{th} - 1}{\beta} \tag{7.26}$$

This has a maximum value of $(\tau/\sigma)^{1/2}/2$ at the current for which $\zeta = 1$, i.e. of around 15 at a current about 20 per cent above threshold. (Such a high value is not often observed in practice for reasons to be explained in Section 7.3.4).

The magnification factor determining the ratio of the modulated light output to the modulated light input increases as the d.c. current is lowered towards threshold. Its magnitude is given by

$$\frac{P_1}{F_1} = \left\{ \left(\frac{\tau_1}{\sigma} \right)^2 + \frac{1}{(\omega_0 \sigma)^2} \right\}^{1/2}$$

$$\simeq \frac{\tau/\sigma}{1 + \xi} \tag{7.27}$$

The magnification is much greater than that for the current; about 30 times for the typical value of τ/σ of 10^3. For currents closer to threshold

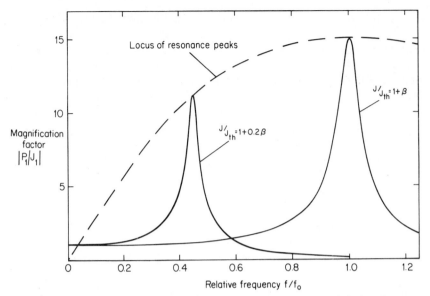

Figure 7.3 Theoretical plot of modulation response versus modulation frequency for broad laser. Magnification factor relative to zero frequency response plotted in terms of relative frequency f/f_0, where $f_0 = [2\pi(\sigma\tau)^{1/2}]^{-1}$ Curves given for two different values of the drive current. Also, a curve representing locus of peak magnification factor at resonance versus resonance frequency with current as the independent variable

than correspond to $\zeta = \sigma/\tau$ there is no resonance and the maximum magnification occurs at zero frequency. Equation (7.22) gives a magnification of $1/\zeta$ for this condition. However, the treatment becomes inappropriate at these low outputs, as a result of the approximation used in deriving equation (7.19) of equating the gain to the loss, and the magnification at low levels can never become greater than the ratio of the total d.c. output to the total spontaneous emission input into the lasing modes.

Figure 7.3 illustrates the resonance response of the system to current modulation according to equation (7.21) $|P_1/J_1|$ is plotted against normalized frequency f/f_0, where

$$f_0 = \frac{1}{2\pi(\sigma\tau)^{1/2}}$$

(typically 1.3 GHz) for two values of the excess current above threshold given by $\zeta = 0.2$ and 1. The locus of the peak of the resonance over the range of resonance frequencies from $f = 0$ to $f = 1.2\,f_0$ is also shown.

The resonance has a substantial peak even at currents of only 5 or 10 per cent above threshold, the range which in average circumstances corresponds to $\zeta = 0.2$. The maximum magnification factor, at a current 25–50 per cent above threshold (depending on the value of β), is 15. The maximum magnification observed in practice is normally somewhat less than this as a result of various effects, predominant among which are damping by carrier diffusion under conditions of non-uniform injected carrier concentration, see Section 7.4, and in certain instances damping by spontaneous emission effects, as described in the next section.

We can also use equation (7.22) to obtain the characteristic of the small-signal transient solution. Under these conditions the input signals F_1 and J_1 are taken as zero and the modulated output power P_1 is of the form

$$P_1 \propto \exp\left[\left(j\omega_{tr} - \frac{1}{\tau_{tr}}\right)t\right] \tag{7.28}$$

where ω_{tr} is the angular frequency of the transient and τ_{tr} is the envelope decay time of the transient. These two quantities are obtained by putting the denominator of the expression in (7.22) equal to zero and solving for complex ω. This gives

$$\omega_{tr} = \left(\omega_0^2 - \frac{1}{4\tau_1^2}\right)^{1/2} \tag{7.29}$$

$$\tau_{tr} = 2\tau_1 \tag{7.30}$$

provided that $\omega_0^2 > 1/4\tau_1^2$ (i.e. not too low a current), with ω_0 and τ_1 given by equations (7.23) and (7.24). Hence at normal currents the transient frequency differs little from the modulation resonance frequency and the transient decay time is twice the recombination time (spontaneous plus stimulated) of the injected carriers.

7.3.3 Small Oscillation near Threshold in Multimode Lasers

We now consider the way that small oscillations behave when the output level of the laser is not large enough for the contribution from spontaneous emission to be ignored. In these circumstances the photon loss from the resonator by end-emission and optical absorption is not entirely compensated by stimulated gain. The net deficit is, of course, made good under steady state conditions by the contribution from spontaneous emission, but it provides an additional damping load on the system which must be taken into account when considering the transient oscillations. The criterion that determines when this additional damping is important is evident from the photon rate equation (7.14) An appreciable contribution to the time derivative of the photon population must be provided by the photon loss rate—the second term in the equation. This requires that the feedback deficit term ϵ_{mq} should approach the value $\sigma\omega$ (normally about

10^{-2}). In lasers of normal length (>50 μm) such a value of ϵ_{mq} is large enough to cause the laser spectrum to be spread over a number of longitudinal modes. A multimode analysis is therefore necessary, similar to that presented in Section 2.8.3, Chapter 2, for the steady state situation. In general there will be enough modes present such that the total output can be integrated over the envelope spectrum, as in the steady state treatment, rather than being summed over individual modes. A self-consistent model can then be built up by ascribing a spectral dependence to ϵ_{mq} which determines both the steady state distribution of intensity amongst the modes as well as their respective contributions to the damping coefficient.

The modifications which must be made to the previous treatment are all concerned with the photon rate equation (7.14), the steady state distribution of photon population amongst the various modes, given in equation (7.18), and the expression for ϵ_{mq} and gain in equation (7.16). For simplicity we consider only the distribution of photons among the longitudinal modes, assuming that a single lateral mode is present in all cases ($q = 0$). We treat the case where the modulated input is in the form of current only and there is no external optical input, either steady state or modulated (F_{mq0} and $F_{mq1} = 0$). We neglect variations of the spontaneous emission rate δ_m and the gain derivative G'_m over the width of the lasing spectrum and allocate them constant values of δ and G', respectively. The only spectral variation that we consider is the variation of ϵ_m, which represents the relative proportion of the resonator loss which is not compensated by gain. To calculate the latter quantity we take the spectral distribution of gain to be in the shape of an inverted parabola. The form of the parabola is more conveniently related to mode number m rather than to wavelength, with m taken as zero for the central mode. The gain G_m for mode number m is then given in terms of the photon time constant σ by

$$G_m = \left(\frac{1}{\sigma}\right)(1 - \epsilon_0)\left(1 - \left(\frac{m}{M}\right)^2\right) \tag{7.31}$$

where $2M$ is the total number of modes over which the gain is positive and ϵ_0 determines the excess of loss over gain at the centre of the spectrum and depends on the current drive. ϵ_m is then, according to equation (7.16) (with subscript q suppressed), given approximately by

$$\epsilon_m \simeq \epsilon_0 + \left(\frac{m}{M}\right)^2 \tag{7.32}$$

for ϵ_0 small. We insert the above value of ϵ_m into equation (7.18) (with subscript q suppressed) to obtain the steady photon density ϕ_{m0} in the various longitudinal modes. ϕ_{m0} is required since it also enters into the photon rate equation.

The photon rate equation (7.14) (with subscript q suppresssed) gives the following relation between the modulated photon population ϕ_{m1} in mode m at angular frequency ω and the modulated carried concentration n_1

$$\phi_{m1} = \frac{(G'\phi_{m0})n_1 + F_m}{j\omega(1 - j\epsilon_m/\sigma\omega)} \tag{7.33}$$

We substitute for ϕ_{m0} using equation (7.18) and then sum this equation over the contributions from all the modes and approximate to the sum using an integral over m. The integral gives the approximate total modulated component of the photon concentration, which we write as ϕ_1. It is a good approximation to the true sum provided that there are at least several modes with more than half the intensity of the main mode. We can simplify the expression by writing it in terms of the value of the total steady state photon population $\Sigma\phi_{m0}$, which we call ϕ_0, obtained by integrating equation (7.18) over m. We obtain

$$\phi_1 = G'\phi_0 \left\{ 1 - \frac{1}{(j\alpha + 1)^{1/2}} \right\} \frac{n_1}{j\omega} \tag{7.34}$$

where

$$\alpha = \frac{\sigma\omega}{\epsilon_0} = \frac{\omega\phi_0^2}{\pi^2 M^2 \delta^2 \sigma}$$

$$\phi_0 = \frac{\sigma\pi M\delta}{\epsilon_0^{1/2}} \tag{7.35}$$

Eliminating n_1 between equation (7.34) and the carrier rate equation (7.15) (with subscript q suppressed) and taking ϵ to be small compared with unity so that we can put $G_{mq} \approx 1/\sigma$ in the last term in the latter equation, gives a photon resonance equation analogous to equation (7.22). From this equation we can obtain the output photon flux P_1, in photons per second per unit volume of the optical resonator, at angular frequency ω in terms of the drive current J_1 as follows

$$P_1 = \frac{(A + jB)\omega_0^2 J_1}{-\omega^2 + j(\omega/\tau_1 + B\omega_0^2) + A\omega_0^2} \tag{7.36}$$

where

$$(A + jB) = \left(1 - \frac{1}{(j\alpha + 1)^{1/2}} \right) \tag{7.37}$$

and where ω_0 and τ_1 are in this case more appropriately given in terms of P_0, the steady state output photon flux per unit volume, rather than current as in equations (7.23) and (7.24), by

$$\omega_0^2 = \frac{P_0}{J_{th}\beta\sigma\tau}$$

$$\frac{1}{\tau_1} = \frac{1}{\tau} + \frac{P_0}{J_{th}\beta\tau} \tag{7.38}$$

Equations (7.36) and (7.37) differ from the original resonance equation (7.22) by the presence of the new term α and the two derivative quantities A and B. When α is large $A \simeq 1$ and $B \simeq 0$ and the behaviour is unaltered from that described by the original equation. If α decreases then A also decreases below unity and B increases from zero. The effect of the reduction in A is to reduce the resonance frequency somewhat below the value ω_0 obtained in the previous analysis. The much more important effect of the increase in B is to increase the damping of the resonance and decrease the magnification factor of the modulation.

Let us consider the values of α that are likely to be encountered in practice and identify the factors upon which they depend. The important parameters in the expression for α in equation (7.35) are the total output power per unit volume ϕ_0/σ, which we denote by P_0, and the spontaneous input per unit volume per mode δ. We set the latter equal to J_{th}/N, where N is the total number of modes in the laser resonator over the bandwith of the spontaneous emission including all possible transverse modes (in the same way as used in the mode analysis in Section 2.8.3, Chapter 2). Substituting this into equation (7.35) produces an N/M term. In Chapter 2, equation (2.140), we showed that N/M is approximately given in terms of the cross-sectional area of the laser ws by

$$\frac{N}{M} \simeq \frac{8\pi\mu^2 ws}{\lambda^2} \tag{7.39}$$

where we have taken the widths of the gain spectrum and the spontaneous spectrum to be approximately equal so that the term B in equation (2.88) is unity.

Substituting (7.39) into (7.35) gives for α

$$\alpha = \left(\frac{8\mu^2 ws}{\lambda^2}\right)^2 \sigma\omega\left(\frac{P_0}{J_{th}}\right)^2$$

$$\alpha \simeq \left\{\frac{720(ws)^2}{\beta^{1/2}}\right\} \left(\frac{P_0}{J_{th}}\right)^{2.5} \left(\frac{\omega}{\omega_0}\right) \tag{7.40}$$

for $\lambda = 0.85 \ \mu m$, $\sigma/\tau = 0.001$, $\mu^2 = 13$, and with w and s measured in microns.

Equation (7.40) shows that the important parameters which determine the value of α and the amount of additional damping are the cross-sectional area of the laser and the proportion by which the current is raised above threshold. Decreasing both of these quantities increases the damping of the modulation resonance.

In Figure (7.4) we show some calculated results which illustrate the effect on the modulation efficiency versus frequency characteristic of varying the cross-sectional area of the laser. Curves are given for lasers operated at currents of both 10 and 30 per cent above threshold. The value of β is 0.3. For operation at 10 per cent above threshold the magnification factor at the peak of the resonance starts to drop appreciably for cross-sectional areas of less than 5 μm^2. For an area of 1 μm^2 the peak is reduced to about one-eighth of its original value and for an area of 0.5 μm^2 the resonance peak is entirely removed. For operation at 30 per cent above threshold [see Figure 7.4(b)] a similar behaviour is obtained but with all the cross-sectional areas concerned being smaller by a factor of four. Hence little additional damping is produced in this case until the cross-section is reduced to approaching 1 μm^2. The removal of the resonance is achieved in both cases for a value of α of approximately 2 at a frequency of ω_0.

The curves in Figure 7.4 are also labelled with the number of longitudinal modes present in each instance with intensities not less than half that of the centre mode. These figures apply to lasers of 250 μm length, the number of modes concerned being directly proportional to laser length. Around ten longitudinal modes are present in 250-μm lasers when the cross section is reduced sufficiently to eliminate the resonance.

It is necessary to make one important qualifying statement about the use of the curves in Figure 7.4. The cross-sectional area of the laser resonator, which constitutes the main variable parameter for these curves, is in many cases difficult to define with any precision. In particular, in stripe lasers where gain-guiding is the main factor controlling the width of the optical distribution in the plane of the junction (see Chapter 6, Section 6.4), there are no obvious edges to the resonator. It is not in general satisfactory to take the width of the resonator as equal to the effective width of the lateral distribution of lasing emission, because only a small central part of this distribution is subject to significant feedback by reflection from the ends of the resonator. The remainder of the distribution can be ascribed to emergent leaky waves propagating obliquely away from the lasing region. As an analogy, in the axial rather than the transverse dimension, the optical intensity of the output waves in the region beyond the end-faces of the laser does not form part of the stored energy of the resonator. The problem of defining the exact width in a stripe laser to which the light is effectively confined has not yet been treated rigorously. As a first approximation it is probably adequate to take the effective width as being that which, if the propagating mode had a plane wavefront rather than its actual cylindrical wavefront, would give the same far-field beam angle as that actually observed in the junction plane. This width is equal to the apparent width of the waist as observed by focusing the astigmatic output to a plane within the laser (see Chapter 4, Section 4.2.3). Since the far-field pattern of narrow stripe lasers with gain-guiding is relatively wide the appropriate resonator width defined in this way is relatively narrow (e.g. around 1–2 μm).

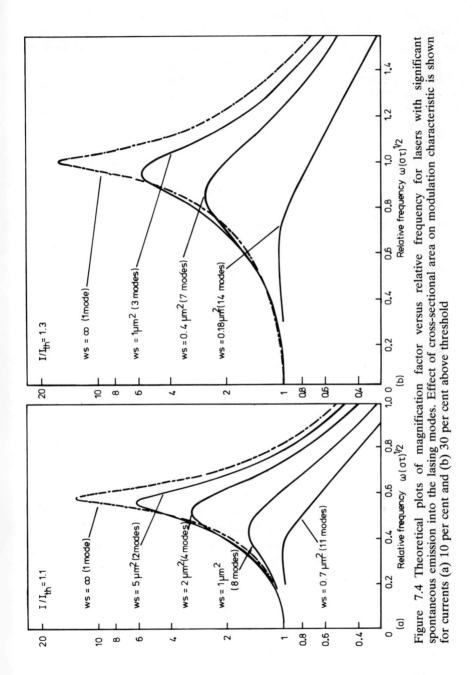

Figure 7.4 Theoretical plots of magnification factor versus relative frequency for lasers with significant spontaneous emission into the lasing modes. Effect of cross-sectional area on modulation characteristic is shown for currents (a) 10 per cent and (b) 30 per cent above threshold

We can make a rough estimate of the maximum lasing output that is obtainable with critically damped transient behaviour. We will assume that the output is confined to the zero-order transverse mode only (an increase in the number of transverse modes would increase the limiting output in approximate direct proportion). We take the criterion of critical damping as $\epsilon_0 > \sigma\omega$. (When $\epsilon_0 = \sigma\omega$ we have $\alpha = 1$, $A = 0.22$, and $B = 0.32$.) $\sigma\omega$ at the transient frequency is of the order of 10^{-2} at current 10 per cent above threshold and in this condition we therefore require $\epsilon_0 > 10^{-2}$. To obtain the total output per unit volume we use the integral of equation (7.18). [Also for total output, see equation (2.124), Section 2.8.3, which is expressed in terms of Γw_{spon} ($= \delta V$) the spontaneous emission rate per mode.] The total spontaneous emission rate per mode at threshold is proportional to the threshold current density J_{th} per unit volume (see Section 2.7.3) and for a typical value of J_{th} of 4000 A cm^{-2} μm is 0.5 μW per mode. This must be multiplied by $\pi M/\epsilon^{1/2}$ [see equation (2.124)] to obtain the total lasing output. M is proportional to laser length, being about 100 for a 300-μm long laser. Using $\epsilon^{1/2} = 10^{-1}$ we obtain a total output of 1.5 mW. Allowing for normal values of incremental efficiency this corresponds to less than 0.5 mW from one end of the laser. This value would drop, although not in direct proportion, for shorter lasers, but would increase with an increase in threshold current density, as, for example, in optically lossy narrow stripe lasers. The exact situation could be investigated, if necessary, in more detail using the treatment of Section 2.8.3.

7.3.4 Diffusion Damping of Laser Oscillations

In this section we consider the damping effect which transverse diffusion of carriers can exert on the modulation resonance in narrow lasers. When the optical filament is narrow a sharp dip is created in the injected carrier concentration at the centre of the laser stripe as a result of the stimulated recombination. This causes a considerable diffusion current of carriers to flow inwards. Under oscillatory conditions an alternating inwards and outwards diffusion current is superimposed on the direct diffusion current and this can exert a considerable damping effect on the oscillation. The diffusion current is proportional to the concentration gradient of the injected carriers, and this gradient tends to be greater when the optical filament is narrower. Under many circumstances the diffusion current can be taken to be inversely proportional to the filament width. Since the total laser current required to produce any given optical intensity is approximately directly proportional to the laser width the relative effect produced by diffusion tends to be approximately inversely proportional to the square of the laser width. However, the precise form of the boundary conditions for the injected carriers at the edge of the laser also plays a part. Different effects, for instance, can be expected depending on whether there is a large reservoir of injected carriers at the edges of the filament, as in a normal stipe laser, or whether there are confinement barriers at the edges, as in the buried heterostructure, across which no further carriers can be supplied. Ikegami[13] has given an approximate treatment of the former case and shown that the extent of the additional damping is proportional to $(l/s)^2$, where l is the lateral diffusion length and s is the width of the optical filament. Suematsu et al.[14] have treated the latter case for the buried heterostructure and shown that the diffusion response is somewhat different. As in the former unconfined case diffusion damping increases in the initial stage as the width of the device is decreased. However, the damping reaches a peak when the device is about one diffusion length wide and thereafter diminishes as the width is further reduced. When the width is small enough there is negligible damping because the diffusion processes are sufficient to impose a nearly constant injected carrier concentration across the whole width of the stripe and in this condition there is little damping.

We present a treatment of diffusion damping here which is similar to Suematsu's, but which is capable of dealing with the cases of both laterally confined and laterally unconfined structures. We use this treatment to derive the modulation efficiency, the damping constant of the transient oscillations, and the resonance frequency as a function of stripe width and current.

When the photon and electron populations are a function of the lateral position x the rate equations for the photon concentration $\phi(x)$ and the injected carrier concentration $\mathbf{n}(x)$ can be written, including a carrier diffusion term, as follows

$$\frac{d\mathbf{n}}{dt} = D\frac{d^2\mathbf{n}}{dx^2} - \frac{\mathbf{n}}{\tau} - \mathbf{J}_{st} + \mathbf{J} \tag{7.41}$$

$$\frac{d(\int\phi dx)}{dt} = \int\left[G'(\mathbf{n} - n_t) - \frac{1}{\sigma}\right]\phi \, dx \tag{7.42}$$

where $\mathbf{J}_{st}(x)$, the current density due to stimulated recombination, is given by

$$\mathbf{J}_{st}(x) = G'(\mathbf{n} - n_t)\phi \tag{7.43}$$

D is the diffusion constant and $\mathbf{J}(x)$ is the driving current density, τ is the carrier recombination time, and σ is the photon lifetime. Optical gain varies linearly with $\mathbf{n}$ with a coefficient of proportionality G' and with zero gain at $\mathbf{n} = n_t$. We obtain an approximate solution for the above equations for the case of a particular (and reasonably typical) optical distribution of arbitrary width in the x direction given by

$$\phi = \phi(1 + \cos ax), \qquad \text{for} - \frac{\pi}{a} < x < \frac{\pi}{a}$$

$$\phi = 0, \qquad \qquad \text{for } x < - \frac{\pi}{a} \text{ and } \frac{\pi}{a} < x \tag{7.44}$$

We consider devices both with and without lateral carrier confinement. The boundary condition for **n** with carrier confinement, taking the carrier confinement and optical confinement barriers to be effectively coincident, is

$$\frac{\mathbf{dn}}{\mathrm{d}x} = 0, \quad \text{at } x = \pm \frac{\pi}{a} \tag{7.45}$$

Without carrier confinement the boundary condition is $\mathbf{n} \to 0$ as $x \to \pm\infty$. The drive current **J** will be assumed to have a rectangular distribution of amplitude J and of width either equal to $2\pi/a$ in the case of lateral carrier confinement or equal to some appropriate width $2w$ ($>2\pi/a$) in the case of no carrier confinement. As an approximation which makes it much simpler to calculate the lateral distribution of **n** from equation (7.41) we will assume that $\mathbf{J}_{\mathrm{st}}(x)$ has a cosinusoidal distribution of the form

$$\mathbf{J}_{\mathrm{st}}(x) = J_{\mathrm{st}}(1 + \cos ax), \quad \text{for } \frac{-\pi}{a} < x < \frac{\pi}{a}$$

$$\mathbf{J}_{\mathrm{st}}(x) = 0, \qquad \qquad \text{for } x < \frac{-\pi}{a} \text{ and } \frac{\pi}{a} < x \tag{7.46}$$

where J_{st} is the average value of $\mathbf{J}_{\mathrm{st}}(x)$ over the interval where it is non-zero. This distribution will be found, at the end of the analysis, to be somewhat inconsistent with the x-variation given by equation (7.43) when the final value of **n** is re-inserted. We can, however, approximately reconcile the two expressions by making their integrals equal over the active width. This gives

$$J_{\mathrm{st}} \simeq \left(\frac{a}{2\pi}\right) \int G'(\mathbf{n} - n_{\mathrm{t}})\phi \, \mathrm{d}x \tag{7.47}$$

This approximation is also useful in that it allows us to combine equation (7.47) with (7.42) and (7.44) and obtain the following additional convenient relation

$$\left(\frac{\mathrm{d}}{\mathrm{d}t} + \frac{1}{\sigma}\right)\phi = \frac{a}{2\pi} \int G'(\mathbf{n} - n_{\mathrm{t}})\phi \, \mathrm{d}x \tag{7.48a}$$

$$= J_{\mathrm{st}} \tag{7.48b}$$

We consider the case of small oscillations and split the quantities up into d.c. and small r.f. components as follows

$$\mathbf{n} = \mathbf{n}_0 + \mathbf{n}_1; \qquad \mathbf{J} = \mathbf{J}_0 + \mathbf{J}_1$$
$$\boldsymbol{\phi} = \boldsymbol{\phi}_0 + \boldsymbol{\phi}_1; \qquad \mathbf{J}_{st} = \mathbf{J}_{st0} + \mathbf{J}_{st1}$$

(7.49)

with similar expressions for the coefficients ϕ, J, etc., where the d.c. components have subscript zero and r.f. components have subscript one. The r.f. components will be assumed to vary as $\exp(j\omega t)$, where ω is the angular frequency.

Equation (7.41) may be solved for $\mathbf{n}$ in terms of J and J_{st} for both the confined and unconfined boundary conditions by inserting the rectangular distribution for $\mathbf{J}$ and the cosinusoidal distribution for $\mathbf{J}_{st}$ as given in equation (7.46). Very similar solutions are obtained for both the r.f. and the d.c. components of $\mathbf{n}$. The solution for the r.f. component is

$$\mathbf{n}_1 = \frac{\tau}{1 + j\omega\tau}\left[J_1 - J_{st1}\left\{1 + \frac{\cos(ax)}{1 + a^2L^2}\right\} + J_{21}\cosh\left(\frac{x}{L}\right)\right]$$

(7.50)

where

$$J_{21} = J_{st1}\left\{\frac{a^2L^2}{1 + a^2L^2}\right\}\exp\left(\frac{-\pi}{La}\right) - J_1\exp\left(\frac{-w}{L}\right)$$

(7.51)

for no lateral carrier confinement and

$$J_{21} = 0$$

(7.52)

for the case of carrier confinement. The dynamic diffusion length L is given in terms of the d.c. diffusion length l by

$$L = \frac{l}{(1 + j\omega\tau)^{1/2}}$$

(7.53)

The solution for the d.c. component $\mathbf{n}_0$ differs only in that all subscripts one in equations (7.50) and (7.51) are replaced by subscript zero and $\omega = 0$ and $L = l$.

We use the relations between light, carrier concentration, and stimulated current in equation (7.48) in conjunction with equation (7.50) for carrier concentration in terms of stimulated current to eliminate the latter two quantities and obtain a relation between light and current. For d.c. components equation (7.48a) becomes

$$\frac{\phi_0}{\sigma} = \frac{a}{2\pi}\int G'(\mathbf{n}_0 - n_t)\,\phi_0\,dx$$

(7.54)

For r.f. components it becomes approximately:

$$\left(j\omega + \frac{1}{\sigma}\right)\phi_1 = \frac{a}{2\pi}\int\{G'\phi_0\mathbf{n}_1 + G'(\mathbf{n}_0 - n_t)\phi_1\}dx$$

(7.55)

which simplifies by analogy with (7.54) to

$$j\omega\phi_1 = \frac{a}{2\pi} \int G'\boldsymbol{\phi}_0\mathbf{n}_1 \; dx \tag{7.56}$$

Substituting in the above equation for $\boldsymbol{\phi}_0$ as in (7.44) and $\mathbf{n}_1$ from (7.50) and integrating gives

$$j\omega\phi_1 = \frac{\tau}{1 + j\omega\tau} G'\phi_0\left[J_1(1 - B_1) - J_{\text{st1}}\left\{1 + \frac{1}{2(1 + a^2L^2)} - A_1\right\}\right] \tag{7.57}$$

where

$$A_1 = 0; \qquad B_1 = 0 \tag{7.58}$$

for the case of lateral carrier confinement and where

$$A_1 = \frac{(aL)^5}{2\pi(1 + a^2L^2)^2}\left[1 - \exp\left\{-\frac{2\pi}{La}\right\}\right]$$

$$B_1 = \frac{aL}{\pi}\left\{1 - \frac{1}{1 + a^2L^2}\right\} \exp\left(-\frac{w}{L}\right) \sinh\left(\frac{\pi}{La}\right) \tag{7.59}$$

when there is no lateral confinement. Substituting the value of J_{st1} obtained from equation (7.48b) into equation (7.57) gives the following relation for ϕ_1 in terms of J_1

$$\phi_1 = \frac{G'\phi_0(1 - B_1)J_1}{-\omega^2 + j\omega\left[\dfrac{1}{\tau} + G'\phi_0\left\{1 + \dfrac{1}{2(1 + a^2L^2)} - A_1\right\}\right] + \dfrac{G'\phi_0}{\sigma}\left\{1 + \dfrac{1}{2(1 + a^2L^2)} - A_1\right\}} \tag{7.60}$$

We can find ϕ_0 in terms of J_0 by following the same procedure for the d.c. components. The distribution of the d.c. component $\mathbf{n}_0$ of the carrier concentration is given by the same relation as (7.50) but with zero subscripts throughout and with $\omega = 0$ both in (7.50) and in the expression for the diffusion length in (7.53). Then substituting for ϕ_0 from (7.44) and $\mathbf{n}_0$ from the equivalent of equation (7.50) in equation (7.54) gives

$$J_{\text{st0}} = \frac{J_0(1 - B_0) - (1/\sigma G' + n_t)/\tau}{1 + \dfrac{1}{2(1 + a^2l^2)} - A_0} \tag{7.61}$$

where $l = (D\tau)^{1/2}$ and where A_0 and B_0 are given by the same expressions as for A_1 and B_1 in (7.59) but with l substituted for L. Using (7.48b) with $d/dt = 0$ (steady state component) to eliminate J_{st0} we then find

$$\phi_0 = \frac{(J_0 - J_{\text{th}})(1 - B_0)\sigma}{1 + \dfrac{1}{2(1 + a^2l^2)} - A_0} \tag{7.62}$$

where J_{th} is the threshold current density and is given by

$$J_{th} = \frac{n_{th}}{\tau} = \frac{1/\sigma G' + n_t}{\tau(1 - B_0)} \tag{7.63}$$

n_{th} being the carrier concentration injected under uniform conditions by J_{th}.

Before examining the modulation behaviour described by equation (7.60) let us briefly consider the d.c. light/current characteristic given by equation (7.62). According to this equation the photon concentration depends linearly on the excess current density above threshold so that the slope efficiency is constant with current. (The precise linearity is a consequence of the approximation involved in assuming a cosinusoidal distribution of stimulated current.) For lasers with lateral carrier confinement ($A_0 = 0$) the slope efficiency varies between $\frac{2}{3}$ for wide lasers (al small) to unity for narrow lasers (al large). For lasers with no lateral confinement the slope efficiency measured with respect to the current supplied only over the width of the optical filament, increases beyond unity as the filament width is narrowed, corresponding to the term A_0 in the denominator of the right-hand side of equation (7.62) becoming larger. This behaviour is the result of the filament intercepting current over an area greater than its own width because of the inwards diffusion of injected carriers.

By substituting equation (7.62) for the d.c. photon concentration into equation (7.60) for the r.f. photon concentration and using equation (7.63) to substitute for G' in the form

$$G' = \frac{1}{\sigma(n_{th} - n_t)} = \frac{1}{\tau\sigma\beta J_{th}} \tag{7.64}$$

we obtain an expression for the small-signal modulation efficiency as a function of frequency which is similar in most respects to the original equation (7.22). It depends on the same known quantities, namely the recombination times of the photons and carriers and the excess current above threshold, but in addition there are terms depending on the width of the optical and current distributions which are also frequency sensitive. However, despite some additional complexity both the modulation and the transient characteristics can be deduced from this expression in a way similar to that used before.

Consider first the behaviour of lasers which have lateral confinement of injected carriers. The terms A_1, A_0, and B_0 are zero and equation (7.60) can be written to give the power output per unit volume, P_1 in terms of J_1 as follows, using (7.62),

$$P_1 = \frac{\omega_0^2 J_1\left[1 + \dfrac{1}{2(1 + a^2 l^2)}\right]^{-1}}{-\omega^2 + j\omega\dfrac{1}{\tau}\left\{1 + \left(\dfrac{c}{\beta}\right)\left(\dfrac{J}{J_{th}} - 1\right)\right\} + c\omega_0^2} \tag{7.65}$$

with ω_0 as in equation (7.23) and c given by

$$c + \frac{1 + \dfrac{1}{2}\left\{1 + \dfrac{a^2 l^2}{1 + j\omega\tau}\right\}^{-1}}{1 + \frac{1}{2}\{1 + a^2 l^2\}^{-1}} \qquad (7.66)$$

c tends to unity both for lasers wide compared with the d.c. diffusion length l ($al \ll 1$) and narrow compared with l ($al \gg 1$) and in both these cases equation (7.65) becomes identical with the original equation for uniform conditions. For lasers of intermediate width, c has a magnitude

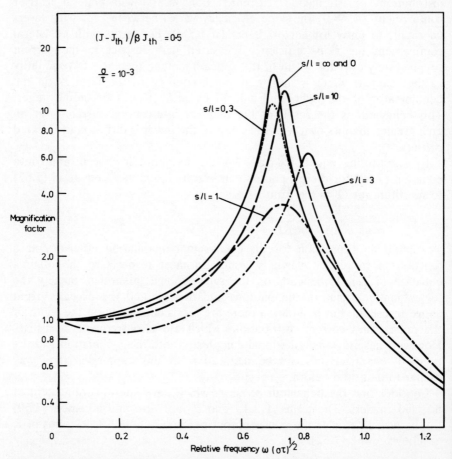

Figure 7.5 Effect of diffusion damping in semiconductor lasers on modulation response versus modulation frequency. Curves apply to lasers without lateral confinement of injected carriers. Variable parameters s/l is ratio of stripe width to diffusion length, σ/τ is ratio of photon to carrier lifetime

greater than unity and is complex with a positive imaginary part. As a result the modulation resonance frequency is slightly increased beyond its normal value of ω_0 and, more importantly, the damping is also considerably increased.

Figure 7.5 shows the range of modulation resonance curves obtained for a particular value of $(J/J_{th} - 1)/\beta$ as the effective width s $(=\pi/a)$ of the optical filament is varied by varying the total width w $(=2s)$ of the laterally confined laser. The resonance peak falls to a minimum for a value of s/l in the vicinity of unity and the resonance frequency rises to a maximum at a somewhat larger value of s/l.

Figure 7.6 shows the way s/l affects the decay time τ_{tr} of the transient. τ_{tr} is obtained from equation (7.65) by equating the denominator of the expression to zero and solving the resultant cubic equation for ω. τ_{tr} reaches a minimum value for approximately the same value of s/l that minimizes the resonance peak of the modulation. The resonance peak height and the transient decay constant for this value of s/l are smaller by about a factor of three in the instances shown than their values for wide

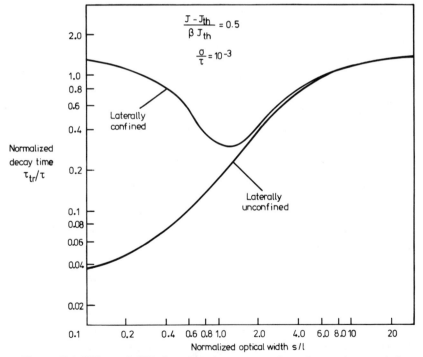

Figure 7.6 Effect of diffusion damping on transient decay characteristics of semiconductor lasers. Decay time plotted against optical filament width for lasers both with and without lateral confinement of injected carriers

lasers. Thus, diffusion exerts a considerably damping effect for this width of laser.

Consider now the behaviour of lasers with no lateral confinement of carriers. The effect of terms A_1 and A_0 in the equations must now be taken into account although unless the current distribution (as opposed to the optical distribution) is very narrow, B_1 and B_0 remain of little significance. As mentioned above, A_0 increases the slope efficiency of the laser when steady state diffusion becomes important at optical widths not much larger than a diffusion length. The increased intensity of the light raises the resonance frequency. Dynamic diffusion, associated with the term A_1, has little effect at this stage because of its shorter diffusion length. It only becomes significant for narrower filaments when it adds additional damping because of its appreciable imaginary contribution. The result of

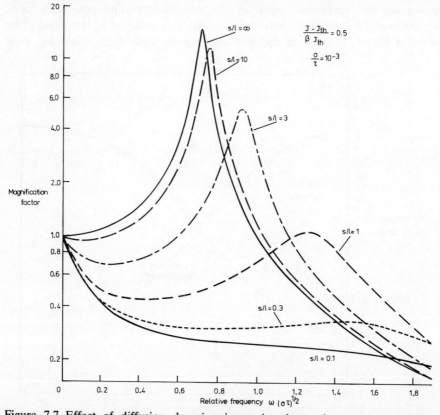

Figure 7.7 Effect of diffusion damping in semiconductor lasers on modulation response versus modulation frequency. Curves apply to lasers without lateral confinement of carriers. Variable parameter is ratio of stripe width to diffusion length

these effects is that there is no great difference in the way the damping increases with reduction in filament width between confined and unconfined lasers down to a width of around a diffusion length, although there is a more significant increase in the resonance frequency of the unconfined lasers over this range. However, when the filament width is narrowed further the unconfined lasers exhibit a continued increase in damping and a continued increase in resonance frequency rather than a reduction, as in the confined lasers. This behaviour is illustrated in Figure 7.7 which shows a series of modulation resonance curves for various filament widths in a laser with no lateral carrier confinement and in Figure 7.6 which shows how the envelope damping of the transient oscillation depends on filament width. There is a very considerable modification in the behaviour as the effective filament width is reduced below a diffusion length. In general, however, practical limitations prevent lasers being made in this range of filament width.

7.3.5 Typical Experimental Observations in Stripe Lasers

We now present some typical experimental meaurements of the dynamic response of an actual stripe laser to illustrate the various oscillatory effects that have been described in the previous sections of this chapter. Figure 7.8(a) shows oscillograph traces of the switch-on and ringing response of a good oxide insulated stripe laser at several different drive currents. The laser concerned was 20 μm wide and 500 μm long. The current pulses, which were superimposed on a d.c. bias 6 mA below threshold, were adjusted in five successive steps to give a total current between 1 and 7 per cent above threshold. They are shown in Figure 7.8(a) below each optical response so that the switch-on delay can be seen.

The ringing response in each optical output is clearly visible. The first spike in the light emission rises to a level that is between two and three times the final steady output. The first few cycles in the transient oscillation which follows are somewhat distorted as a result of the non-linear mechanism, having a sharp peak and a flattened trough. The ringing frequency f_r varies between the different traces, depending on the square root of the current excess over threshold. f_r^2 is plotted against I/I_{th} in Figure 7.8(b) and a straight line is obtained.

The envelope of the decaying transient is closely exponential, and its reciprocal time constant $1/\tau_{tr}$ is also plotted against I/I_{th} in Figure 7.8(b). There is a noticeable increase in $1/\tau_{tr}$ as the current is increased, in qualitative agreement with equations (7.24) and (7.30).

Measurement of the delay time t_d between the current pulse and the light output under conditions when the laser is switched from just below to just above threshold allows the incremental time constant at threshold to

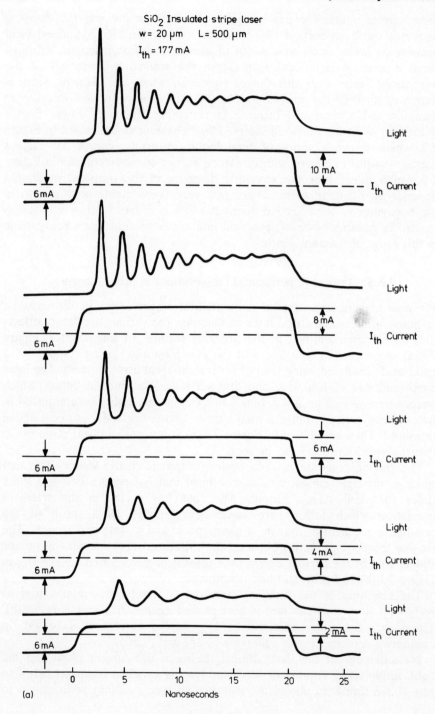

SiO$_2$ Insulated stripe laser
w = 20 μm   L = 500 μm
I$_{th}$ = 177 mA

Light

10 mA

6 mA

I$_{th}$ Current

Light

8 mA

6 mA

I$_{th}$ Current

Light

6 mA

6 mA

I$_{th}$ Current

Light

4 mA

6 mA

I$_{th}$ Current

Light

2 mA

6 mA

I$_{th}$ Current

(a)   Nanoseconds

0   5   10   15   20   25

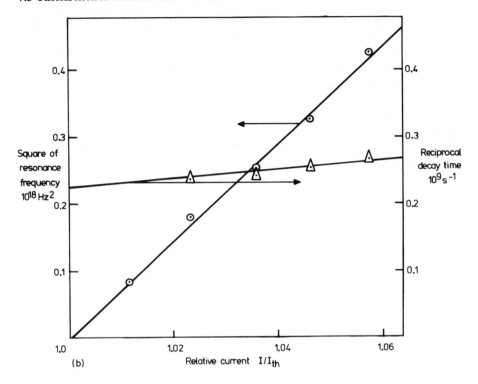

(b)

Relative current I/I_{th}

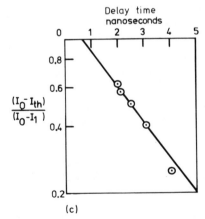

(c)

Figure 7.8 (a) Example of light pulses obtained from oxide insulated stripe laser with various amplitudes of current pulse, showing transient oscillation of varying intensity and frequency and switch-on delays of varying extent. (b) Plot of square of transient resonance frequency and of reciprocal time constant of decay of transient against current for laser light pulses illustrated in (a). (c) Plot of switch-on delay versus $\ln\{(I_0 - I_{th})/(I_0 - I_1)\}$ for laser light and current pulses in (a). I_1 = bias current, I_0 = current during pulse

be deduced using equation (7.3). This is the appropriate time constant to insert in the rate equations [equation (7.14)]. Figure 7.8(c) shows the method of using equation (7.3) to find the incremental time constant by plotting $\ln\{1 - I_{th}/I_0)/(1 - I_1/I_0)\}$ against t, I_1 being the bias current, I_{th} the threshold current, and I_0 the total drive current. A reasonable straight line is obtained the slope of which can be used to deduce a value of the incremental recombination time τ of 2.9 ns.

The photon lifetime σ can be deduced from the cavity length and the probable optical scattering and absorption losses according to equation (7.9). For a laser of length 500 μm with total losses of the order of 10 cm^{-1} this gives $\sigma = 3.6$ ps.

Knowledge of σ and τ can be used in conjunction with the measured slope of the f_r^2 versus the current characteristic of Figure 7.8(b) to deduce the value of β [see equation (7.23)]. In the present instance we find $\beta = 0.33$. Using this value we plot the variation of τ_{tr}, the time constant for envelope damping of the transient, against $I/I_{th} - 1$ with a gradient according to equations (7.30) and (7.24) which best matches the measured points in Figure 7.8(b). The gradient of the theoretical line gives a reasonable fit to the measured points and the value of τ_{tr} extrapolated to the threshold current is approximately 4.5 ns. In a wide laser we would expect this value to be twice the incremental carrier recombination of 2.9 ns. The discrepancy is about 22 per cent. This might be attributed to diffusion damping, as treated in Section 7.3.4. According to Figure 7.6 this extra degree of damping would occur for an effective filament width of approximately 3.5 diffusion lengths. The effective filament width in the laser concerned is of the order of 10 μm which would be compatible with the results if the diffusion length were of the order of 3 μm, a not unreasonable figure. In general, therefore, the behaviour of this laser is reasonably in agreement with the theoretical treatment which has been presented, although the accuracy of the measurements is not sufficient to confirm the theory in detail.

The response of a very narrow stripe laser to a rectangular current pulse, which illustrates the critical damping behaviour possible in these devices, has already been presented in Chapter 6, Figure 6.48(b). This shows the extreme damping which can be found when both diffusion damping and damping due to the presence of appreciable spontaneous emission in the lasing mode are combined.

7.4 EFFECT OF NON-UNIFORMITY OF INJECTION CURRENT ON TRANSIENTS

In this section we consider an effect on the modulation characteristics of stripe lasers which occurs when the injected carriers are tightly confined and the light spreads into regions where little injection current flows. In extreme circumstances the light may interact strongly with parts of the active layer which are not even pumped into the inverted state. Such a condition greatly affects the transient behaviour of the laser and can lead to instability and the emission of a continuous train of pulses. Variations in pumping level over the volume of the laser can occur in a variety of circumstances. In stripe lasers there are unpumped regions bordering the edge of the stripe. These can exert a considerable effect on the behaviour if, for any reason, the lasing light happens to be deflected into them to any appreciable extent. Crystalline defects in the active layer introduce recombination centres which locally reduce the degree of inversion. Their influence can become more marked as a result of effects which accompany the degradation process over the laser's operating life [15] Devices with non-uniform pumping may be deliberately made by dividing the laser into two or more sections with a separate current supply but with a continuous path for the light. Basov[16] and Lee and Roldan[17] have experimented with such tandem structures.

Sufficient non-uniformity in current density leads to a situation where certain parts of the active layer produce optical absorption rather than gain. Such regions are optically pumped by the light and, under appropriate circumstances, their optical losses may be reduced to a low level (bleached) as the laser is driven harder. This gives rise to a non-linear light/current characteristic and a range of current where the apparent internal incremental efficiency is greater than 100 per cent. The additional efficiency is obtained by drawing on part of the current originally required to reach threshold. Thus, as the total laser current is increased the 'holding' current required to overcome the optical losses and the output loading of the resonator drops and the difference, which increases more than the total, is supplied to the lasing output.

The bleaching action speeds up the response of the laser to a switch-on step in the current. Once the threshold 'barrier' has been exceeded the excess gain available for multiplying the photon population increases not only as a result of the continuing inflow of carriers but also because the overall optical loss diminishes when the lossy regions are bleached. This type of snap-on behaviour has been investigated by Basov[16] and others. A situation can arise in which the effect of the additional carriers created in the region of negative gain by the absorption of light from the lasing filament more than compensates for the effect of the carriers which are lost from the region of positive gain by stimulated recombination. In this case no inflowing carriers are required to switch the laser on and a condition of complete instability is produced.

In a non-linear situation of this type the small-signal modulation characteristics are very considerably modified both in their resonance frequency and in their damping coefficient. Small-signal modulation can of course only be analysed over the range of the parameters where the laser is stable. As the point of instability is approached so the Q of the small-signal oscillations increases, tending towards infinity at the point of instability.

The most straightforward non-uniform device is the tandem laser in which the contact on one of the sides is divided into two parts by a cross-ways cut, around which little current can flow. Both Basov[16] and Lee and Roldan[17] have fabricated and investigated such tanden structures, applying different current density to the two parts of the contact. Under certain conditions the devices become unstable and operate in a continuous self-pulsing regime. Basov derived the instability condition by analysing the small-signal behaviour and Lee and Roldan used a computer to model the complete self-pulsing sequence. They all assumed a uniform optical distribution along the length of the laser and showed that, by taking into account the saturation of the gain/carrier concentration characteristic with increasing current, they could explain the behaviour satisfactorily.

In the more general situation the current density varies continuously over the width or length of the device. The optical intensity also varies continuously over the region. Carroll et al.[19] have made a theoretical investigation of the resonance behaviour for any arbitrary but fixed distribution function for these two quantities. They obtained general criteria for stability and derived a simple general relation, irrespective of the particular light/current characteristic of the device, between the resonance frequency of the transient oscillation and the excess of the current over threshold. Below we present an analysis of the resonance, based on that of Carroll et al.

7.4.1 Analysis of Small Oscillations

First, we require expressions for the lateral distribution of light and current denisty. We let ϕ and J be peak values of the photon concentration and the current density, respectively, and multiply these by the respective appropriate distribution functions, say $f(x)$ and $\rho(x)$, that have maximum values of unity and whose effective widths, s and w respectively, are given by the total integrals of $f(x)$ and $\rho(x)$ over x. These distributions are illustrated in Figure 7.9. To cover the various types of pumping non-uniformity we may align the axis of x either along the transverse or the longitudinal axis of the laser. The injected carrier concentration n and the gain G are also functions of x. The rate equations, equivalent to (7.11) and (7.12) but assuming single mode operation and ignoring spontaneous emission and optical drive, are

$$\frac{dn}{dt} + \frac{n}{\tau} + f\phi G = \rho J \tag{7.67}$$

$$\frac{d\phi}{dt} = \phi\left(\int \frac{fG\,dx}{s} - \frac{1}{\sigma}\right) \tag{7.68}$$

Using subscripts zero and one as before to indicate the steady state and

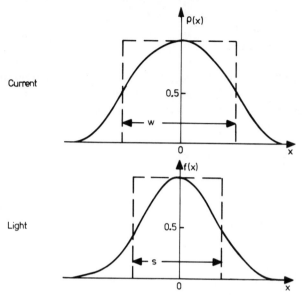

Figure 7.9 Diagram to show distribution functions $\rho(x)$ for current and $f(x)$ for light used in analysis of effect of non-uniform lateral distribution of these quantities on the light/current characteristics and modulation response of stripe lasers. Corresponding effective widths w and s also shown

small oscillatory components, respectively, we can write the following equations for the small oscillatory components

$$\frac{dn_1}{dt} + n_1\left(\frac{1}{\tau} + fG'\phi_0\right) + fG\phi_1 = \rho J_1 \tag{7.69}$$

$$\frac{d\phi_1}{dt} = \frac{\phi_0}{s}\int fG'n_1 \, dx \tag{7.70}$$

G' in these equations represent the derivative of G with respect to n; it is also a function of x.

We can derive an approximate solution for the frequency and the damping term of the transient oscillation, which is accurate close to threshold, as follows. We put the oscillatory component of drive current J_1 in equation (7.69) equal to zero. We put $d/dt = p$ and obtain an expression for the x-dependent oscillatory component n_1 of the carrier concentration in terms of ϕ_1, which we substitute into the integral of equation (7.70) to produce an equation for complex p, which we then solve to give the frequency and decay constant of the transient. Thus, from equation (7.69) we obtain

$$n_1 = \frac{\rho J_1 - fG\phi_1}{p + 1/\tau + fG'\phi_0} \tag{7.71}$$

To simplify the subsequent integration we split the denominator of this expression into a term $R(p)$ independent of x but dependent on p, and a term $\phi_0\delta$ dependent on x but independent of p which is small close to threshold, as follows

$$\left(p + \frac{1}{\tau} + fG'\phi_0\right) = R(p) + \delta\phi_0 \tag{7.72}$$

where

$$R(p) = p + \frac{1}{\tau} + \phi_0 G_2' \tag{7.73}$$

and

$$\delta = fG' - G_2' \tag{7.74}$$

and G_2', which is constant, remains to be chosen in the most appropriate way. Close to threshold, where ϕ_0 is small, equation (7.71) with the expression in (7.72) substituted in the denominator can now be written approximately

$$n_1 = \left\{1 - \frac{\delta\phi_0}{R(p)}\right\} \frac{\rho J_1 - fG\phi_1}{R(p)} \tag{7.75}$$

where no x-dependent terms appear in the denominator.

To consider the transient oscillation we put $J_1 = 0$ and substitute (7.75) into (7.70). This gives the following equation for p

$$p^2 + p\left(\frac{1}{\tau} + \phi_0 G_2'\right) + \frac{\phi_0}{s} \int f^2 GG' \left\{1 - \frac{\delta\phi_0}{R(p)}\right\} dx = 0 \tag{7.76}$$

Except for the term containing $R(p)$ in the integral this expression is a simple quadratic in p. The offending term can be made to disappear on integration if the constant G_2' in the expression for δ [see equation (7.74)] is chosen so that

$$G_2' = \frac{\int f^3 GG'^2 \, dx}{\int f^2 GG' \, dx} \tag{7.77}$$

Equation (7.76) then describes a transient with a damping time constant $2\tau_1$ given by

$$\frac{1}{\tau_1} = \frac{1}{\tau} + \phi_0 G_2' \tag{7.78}$$

[for comparison see equation (7.30) for the uniform case], and an angular frequency ω_{tr} which, for small damping, is given approximately by

$$\omega^2 \simeq \phi_0 K \tag{7.79}$$

where

$$K = \frac{1}{s} \int f^2 G G' \, dx \tag{7.80}$$

This equation can be compared with the similar relation in equation (7.23) for the resonance frequency in the uniform case. The equations only differ by the presence of f^2 in the above integral.

Let us consider the effect of the integral expressions G'_2 and K on the damping, according to equation (7.78), and the resonance frequency, according to equation (7.79). Circumstances can arise in which K and G'_2 are negative in which case there is a very drastic modification to the behaviour. To gauge when this may happen it is useful to compare the integrals for K and G'_2 with the integral expression for $1/\sigma$ which, according to equation (7.68), is given in the steady steady state by

$$\frac{1}{s} \int fG \, dx = \frac{1}{\sigma} \tag{7.81}$$

In various circumstances (narrow stripes, etc.) G in the above integral can assume negative values over an appreciable portion of the width of the distribution f for the photon density. The integral remains positive, of course, but it is composed of both negative and positive contributions (see curve for stimulated emission in Figure 7.10). The integrals in equations (7.77) and (7.80) that give G'_2 and K differ from the above integral by including further weighting factors, in addition to f, to multiply G, namely fG' and $(fG')^2$, respectively. If these weighting factors become relatively larger in the regions where G is negative then the overall integrals for G'_2 and K may themselves become small, or even negative. G'_2 is affected more by this than K. Negative values for G'_2 or for K lead to instability. Negative G'_2 reduces the damping constant and eventually turns it negative. Negative K produces an imaginary value for the resonance frequency which causes the system to move away from the bias point with an unstable exponential characteristic. Negative damping causes the system to oscillate with increasing amplitude about the bias point. Both effects combine to produce self-pulsing in the lasers after the lapse of an appropriate time to allow the oscillations to build up.

The natural variation to be expected from G' over the width of the gain profile makes a contribution to the weighting factor which tends to promote instability. Thus, G' increases as the gain G moves down to negative values as a direct result of the mechanism of the semiconductor gain process and

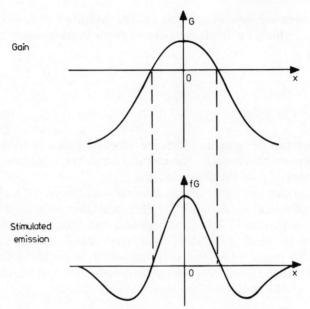

Figure 7.10 Example of transverse distribution of gain, and stimulated emission in narrow stripes

its dependence on the density of states distribution in the bands. The gain/carrier concentration characteristic derived as an example in Chapter 2, Section 2.6.3.1, equation (2.82) from the density of states in the conduction band tail illustrates this effect, showing that in this case G' varies approximately as the reciprocal of the injected carrier concentration. This would cause a marked increase in G' in the wings of the gain profile, and weight the integrals in the expressions for K and G_2' [equations (7.77) and (7.80)] more strongly to the region where G is negative.

The predominant factor which varies in the different possible laser geometries is the shape of the photon distribution function f and the amount this distribution extends into the lossy regions. In the case of the tandem lasers investigated by Basov[16] and Lee and Roldan[17] the same photon density interacts with both the amplifying and the lossy regions. The distribution of f in the longitudinal direction can therefore be regarded as retangular with f unity throughout. fG' therefore becomes equal to G'. Under these circumstances instabilities can be induced for a wide range of relative sizes of the lossy and amplifying regions if the relative proportions of loss and gain are suitably adjusted. Such a condition can, of course, arise inadvertently in a narrow laser if some portion of its length is subject to strong non-radiative recombination so that the injected carrier concentration is greatly reduced in that region.

In stripe lasers, where 'gain-guiding' is operative, the relevant distribution of f, now measured in the transverse direction, is determined by the gain distribution itself. As shown in Section 4.2, the light spreads furthest out of the gain region into the surrounding lossy region when the stripe is narrow. f then falls off least steeply away from the centre of the laser and counteracts the incipient instability produced by rising G' to the smallest extent. The analysis of the parabolic gain profile in Section 4.2.3 showed that for stripes less than about 10 μm wide f drops to a value of somewhat less than $e^{-1/2}$ at the point where the gain reaches zero. This relatively small drop probably allows the effect of increasing G' still to predominate in the factor fG'. Hence some modification of the resonance frequency and some decrease in damping are to be expected, although instability should not occur.

A situation which can produce much more serious consequences in stripe lasers occurs when the peak of the optical distribution does not coincide with the peak of the gain distribution. In such circumstances both f and G' contribute to the increase of the weighting factor fG' on the side to which light is deflected, and promote the tendency to instability. If the peak of the optical distribution is situated in a lossy region instability is virtually guaranteed. It seems highly probable that such effects can be produced as a result of slight curvature in the propagation path of the light between the two ends of the laser caused by defects or wedging of the heterostructure layers, or by the asymmetric gain-guiding described in Chapter 6, Section 6.6.2.4.

To evaluate the expressions for the transient frequency in equation (7.79) and the expression for the damping constant in equation (7.78) it is necessary to know the optical distribution f, the gain distribution $G(x)$, and the photon density ϕ_0. The gain distribution can be evaluated at currents close to threshold in terms of the distribution of injection current and the gain/current relation. However, at currents appreciably above threshold the gain and carrier distributions change, being reduced by stimulated emission in the region close to the peak of the optical intensity, and increased by optical pumping where the gain is negative. These effects can be calculated once the photon density is found.

In general, in the conditions considered the photon density is a non-linear function of the excess of current above threshold. It can be obtained in principle by solving for the steady state components in the rate equations (7.67) and (7.68). This is difficult in all but certain special cases. However, Carroll et al.[19] have shown that the factors which determine the resonance frequency are also directly concerned in determining the light output and some of the unknown quantities can be eliminated to give a simple result. The treatment is presented below.

At currents appreciably above threshold the steady state component of the carrier concentration n_0 can be considered to be the sum of its value n_{th}

at threshold and a small additional part n_δ. Similarly, the gain can be considered to have an additional component G_δ. Both quantities depend on x. Equations (7.67) and (7.68) can then be used to obtain the following expressions for the additional steady state components

$$\frac{n_\delta}{\tau} + f\phi_0 G = \rho(J_0 - J_{th}) \tag{7.82}$$

$$\frac{1}{s} \int fG_\delta \, dx = 0 \tag{7.83}$$

Over a reasonable range above threshold equation (7.83) may be written in terms of the derivative G' of G with respect to n as follows

$$\frac{1}{s} \int fG'n_\delta \, dx = 0 \tag{7.84}$$

Multiplying equation (7.82) by fG', integrating, and substituting (7.84) gives the following expression for the steady state photon density ϕ_0

$$\phi_0 = \frac{J_0 - J_{th}}{Ks} \int fG'\rho \, dx \tag{7.85}$$

where K is the integral included in the expression for the resonance frequency [equation (7.80)]. In the above expression $fG'\rho \, dx$ varies little with current over a considerable range above threshold since G' is always positive and is a smoothly varying function of n and the integral is not greatly affected by changes in the distribution of n. However, K may be a sensitive function of G and G'. Hence it is helpful to use (7.85) to substitute for ϕ_0 in equation (7.79) for the transient frequency (7.85). We obtain

$$\omega_{tr}^2 = G_1'(J_0 - J_{th}) \tag{7.86}$$

where

$$G_1' = \frac{1}{s} \int fG'\rho \, dx \tag{7.87}$$

The interesting point about relation (7.86) is that, because G_1' varies little, ω_{tr}^2 is still approximately the same linear function of current above threshold as it is in the case of the uniform laser. This applies despite the fact that the light/current characteristic may be very non-linear.

The information which we have presented on the behaviour of stripe lasers with gain-guiding in Chapter 6 is sufficient to enable us to evaluate the integral in equation (7.87), calculate the transient frequency for such lasers, and compare the result with the resonance frequency for broad contact lasers given in equation (7.23). In accordance with the gain-guide treatment we take the distribution function f of the light in equation (7.87) to be Gaussian, and we take the distribution ρ of the current to be an inverted parabola which is fitted to the diffusion profile of the injected carriers as described in Chapter 6, Section 6.5.1.1, in deriving equation (6.40). We take G' to be a constant (see, for example, Figure 6.30). The value of the integral, in the nomenclature of Chapter 6, is then

$$\int \frac{f\rho \, dx}{s} = \frac{n_{th}}{(1-A)n_0}$$

$$= \left(1 + \frac{8s_1^2}{s_{eff}^2}\right)^{-1} \tag{7.88}$$

Hence we obtain the following relation for ω_{tr}^2

$$\omega_{tr}^2 = \frac{J_0/J_{th} - 1}{\beta\sigma\tau(1 + 8s_1^2/s_{eff}^2)} \tag{7.89}$$

This is very similar to the expression for the resonance frequency of a broad contact laser in equation (7.23). It differs only in the final term in the denominator, which somewhat reduces its magnitude. For a typical value of s_1 of $2 \, \mu m$, as quoted in Section 6.5.2, and for a $10 \, \mu m$ stripe width ($s_{eff} \approx 15 \, \mu m$) the additional term reduces the transient frequency by a factor of only 0.9. In practice this may well be cancelled out by the increase in β which tends to accompany the increased gain at the centre of a narrow stripe. Hence little difference is to be expected as a result of the transverse distributions concerned between the transient frequency of stripe and broad contact lasers except, of course, when the stripe is so narrow that super-radiance and diffusion become important features (see Section 7.3.3 and 7.3.4).

7.4.2 Theoretical Model of Unstable Laser

To illustrate the way in which non-uniformity of gain can promote instability in a laser, as described for the general case in the previous section, we choose a specific model as an example and make a theoretical analysis of the transient frequency, the damping coefficient of the transient oscillations, and the light/current characteristics. For simplicity of evaluation the model we choose is analogous to the tandem laser evaluated by Basov[16] and Lee and Roldan.[17] This model can either be used to represent a device in which the gain varies along the length of the laser or across the width, the latter being more relevant to our previous discussion. We choose the general specification arbitrarily to provide an interesting range of characteristics for illustrative purposes. We take the two sections of the laser to have lengths, or widths, in a four to one ratio. In transverse section this might, for instance, represent a laser with high gain in a centre

446   **Dynamic response of lasers**

section 0.8 of the total width, flanked by low gain or lossy sections on the two sides each 0.1 of the total width (see Figure 7.11). Light is assumed to spread uniformly across the whole width. The current density applied to the lower and higher gain sections is taken to be in a ratio b lying between 1 and 0.1. Following Lee and Roldan the relation between gain g and injected carrier concentration n is taken as $g \propto \ln(n/n_0)$ and the threshold condition is taken as $n_1^{0.8} n_2^{0.2} = n_0 e$, where subscripts 1 and 2 refer to the larger and smaller sections of the laser, respectively, and n_0 is the carrier concentration which gives zero gain at the wavelength concerned. The threshold condition applies to a situation in which the quasi-Fermi level lies in the conduction band tail. It is related to that given for a uniform laser in a similar situation in equation (2.82), Chapter 2. The threshold condition corresponds, in fact, to low temperature operation $(kT < E_v,$

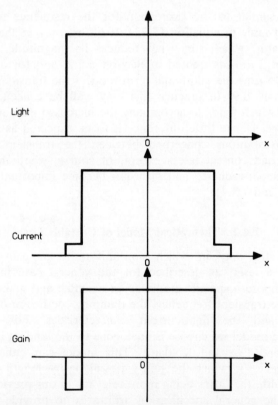

Figure 7.11 Distribution of light and typical distributions of current density and gain in theoretical model of laser with tendency to instability

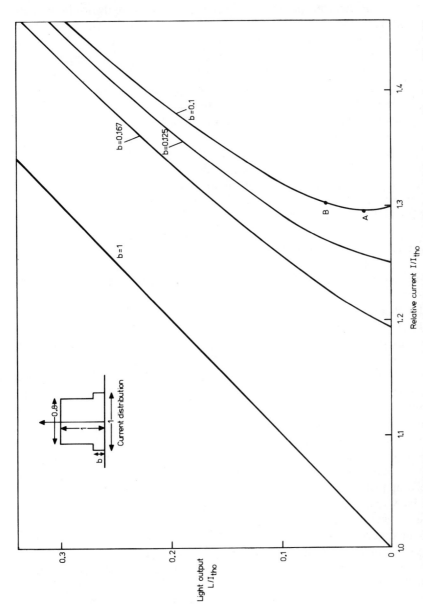

Figure 7.12 Non-linear light/current characteristics derived for theoretical model of unstable laser. Variable parameter is the proportion in which current is divided between high and low regions. Widths of high and low gain regions are in the ration 4 : 1

where E_t is the tail depth) but no particular significance should be attached to this. It is only a means of simplifying the calculations, and the values chosen for the relevant parameters in fact apply more realistically at room temperature.

The ratio of the carrier recombination time τ to the photon lifetime σ has been taken as 10^3. The laser is analysed by solving rate equations of the type given in equations (7.11) and (7.12), but with (7.12) duplicated for the two sections of the tandem configuration. The steady state light/current characteristic is obtained by iterative solution of the three simultaneous equations, and the frequency and damping of the small-signal transient is evaluated by the solution of a cubic equation in complex ω.

The light/current characteristics obtained for this model are illustrated in Figure 7.12 and plotted as functions of the ratio of the actual current I to the threshold current I_{th0} in an equivalent uniform laser. The characteristics are in general curved, with a region of enhanced efficiency close to threshold. The total threshold current increases when the proportion of current fed to the short end section of the laser is reduced, and the curvature of the characteristic also increases until, for a current density ratio of $1:10$, the characteristic has an initial negative slope and has a region below threshold which is dual valued in light output for a given current.

The damping constant for small-signal oscillations is plotted in Figure 7.13 as a function of the light level alongside the light/current characteristics. In the uniform laser the damping constant increases with light level as a result of the additional stimulated recombination. In the non-uniform lasers the damping constant initially falls and then subsequently rises as the current is increased beyond threshold. In the most extreme case of non-uniformity (current density ratio of $1:10$) the dual valued region of the light/current characteristic exhibits negative damping. In the region of negative slope, up to the point A, the system is non-oscillatory and exhibits exponential instability. From point A to point B the system is oscillatory, with negative damping. Point B corresponds to a current just greater than threshold. From point B onwards the system is positively damped but initially has a high Q.

The square of the transient frequency is also plotted as a function of I/I_{th0} in Figure 7.13. As predicted by equation (7.86) the relation is very close to being a linear function of $(I - I_{th})$, where I_{th} is the threshold current, except for the most non-uniform laser. In the latter case some curvature is evident and also the intercept on the current axis is no longer at I_{th} but lies close to the minimum current associated with the point A. The curve of ω_{tr}^2 corresponds to the upper branch of the light/current characteristic.

The typical features that can be seen clearly on these curves are that there are both regions of negative slope on the light/current characteristics

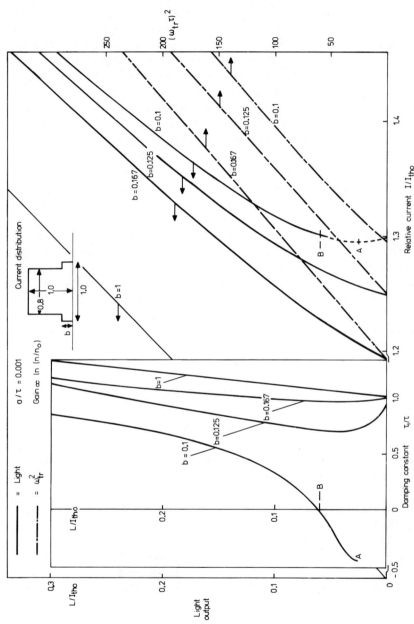

Figure 7.13 Comparison of all results obtained from theoretical model of unstable laser. Includes light versus current characteristics, square of resonance frequency versus current, and damping constant versus light output. Other conditions as for Figure 7.12

with exponential instability and regions of positive slope with reduced damping, or indeed negative damping. The occurrence of negative values of both quantities is generally, but not necessarily, associated in the theoretical treatment. Negative slope and exponential instability corresponds to negative values of $\int f^2 GG' dx/s$ $(=K)$ at threshold [according to equations (7.76) and (7.80)]. Negative values of the damping corresponds, according to equation (7.78), to $\phi_0 G_2' < -1/\tau$. Negative values of G_2' can occur for light/current characteristics with positive slope. They exert a stronger influence on the overall damping as the photon density ϕ_0 increases, as can be seen in Figure 7.13 by the tendency for the damping to decrease in the initial stages as the light output is increased.

Biasing lasers at points on the characteristic which give negative damping cause self-pulsing with substantially 100 per cent modulation as shown both theoretically and experimentally by Lee and Roldan[17] on lasers with characteristics very similar to those illustrated in Figure 7.13.

The theory of the transient characteristics of non-uniform lasers that we have presented gives a good qualitative explanation of the behaviour which has been observed in a variety of devices, both stripe geometry or tandem configurations, and where defects have caused the non-uniformity, and appears to be well founded. However, up to the present only in a few cases and to a limited extent have the quantitative predictions of the theory been investigated. These results have been reasonably in accord with experiment.[17,19]

7.5 SWITCH-ON OF LASING EMISSION

In this section we consider the processes that are involved in switching-on a laser after the injected carrier concentration in the active layer has been raised to the threshold level. We analyse the way in which the various modes grow from the spontaneous emission level. We investigate the relative rate of growth of the different modes, and hence show how the linewidth of the spectrum narrows. We determine the time that elapses before the first peak of the transient is produced and evaluate the intensity of the peak relative to the steady state output. We show that there is a class of so-called lasers with a very different type of switch-on behaviour. This class includes devices with very small crosssections or with many transverse modes per unit crosssection. These operate in a super-radiant mode, even at currents appreciably beyond nominal threshold, and exhibit no distinct switch-on period and no oscillatory transient.

In the process of setting a laser into operation the optical gain in the active layer must be raised to a level where it significantly exceeds the optical losses. The excess gain then provides the source of photons for building up the population in the resonator. Some starting supply of photons is required and this is provided by spontaneous emission. The input current to the laser causes an initial linear rise of gain with time and the rate of increase is determined by the rate of accumulation of injected carriers. The photon population experiences a steadily increasing gain and therefore the photon concentration grows at a greater than exponential rate. The build-up terminates relatively abruptly when the rate of stimulated recombination exceeds the injection rate of carriers. A transient oscillation then ensues. Even though the laser may finally become single mode a number of modes are taken temporarily above threshold during the switch-on operation, and the process of selecting out one of these takes considerably longer than the process of raising the total emission to its final level.

7.5.1 Dynamic Spectrum of Longitudinal Modes

In treating the evolution of the mode spectrum during the period of laser switch-on we consider first the relative values of the optical intensity among the different modes. Taking the relative rather than the absolute values allows the analysis to be carried out in a simple way as originally presented by Ikegami.[13] The analysis is based only on the rate equations for the photon population densities ϕ_{mq} in the different longitudinal and transverse modes, as given in equation (7.11). We consider one set of longitudinal modes, all with transverse number q, and take as reference level the photon density of the central spectral member of this set which we label ϕ_{0q}. We number the longitudinal modes using m measured positively and negatively with respect to the central mode. Taking the expressions for $d\phi_{mq}/\phi_{mq}$ and $d\phi_{0q}/\phi_{0q}$ from equation (7.11), subtracting then and ignoring the small differences in the spontaneous emission terms gives

$$\frac{d\phi_{mq}}{\phi_{mq}} - \frac{d\phi_{0q}}{\phi_{0q}} = -(G_{0q} - G_{mq})dt \tag{7.90}$$

Integrating gives

$$\frac{\phi_{mq}}{\phi_{0q}} = \rho_{mq}(0) \exp\{-(G_{0q} - G_{mq})t\} \tag{7.91}$$

where $\rho_{mq}(0)$ is the ratio of the photon density of the mth longitudinal mode to the zeroth mode at zero time. Although G_{0q} and G_{mq} in the exponent each vary individually with time in the process, say, of switching on the laser, they vary only to a relatively small extent and in proportion to one another. Hence to the first order their difference remains constant. Equation (7.91) therefore states that modes away from the centre of the gain spectrum diminish with time relative to the central mode in an exponential way at a rate which is determined by their relative position in the gain spectrum.

We can represent this condition quantitatively by introducing a time independent shape factor for the modal gain spectrum, represented as a function of longitudinal mode number m by $r(m)$. Then $G_{mq} = G_{0q}r(m)$. Since G_{0q} does not greatly exceed the loss rate $1/\sigma$ during switch-on, the exponent of the exponential in equation (7.91) becomes approximately $(1 - r(m))t/\sigma_q$. Hence to a reasonable approximation the shape factor, in conjunction with σ_q, uniquely determines the evolution of the lasing spectrum.

As a suitable approximation we take the shape factor to be an inverted parabola with the gain being positive over, say, $2M$ longitudinal modes between $+M$ and $-M$, so that $r(m)$ is given by

$$r(m) \simeq 1 - \left(\frac{m}{M}\right)^2 \tag{7.92}$$

This approximation is very adequate over the important part of the spectrum where $m/M < 0.1$. Inserting (7.92) into (7.91) gives a Gaussian spectrum the width of which diminishes with time. If the initial spectrum described by ρ_{mq} is also Gaussian and independent of q then the envelope linewidth $\delta\lambda$ at time t measured to the $1/e$ points (assuming the spectrum is still multimode) can be expressed in the form

$$\delta\lambda = \Delta\lambda_0 \left\{\frac{\sigma}{t - t_0}\right\}^{1/2} \tag{7.93}$$

where $\Delta\lambda_0$ is the spectral width of the gain. t_0 must be chosen to have a negative value so that the spectral width $\Delta\lambda_0/(-\sigma_a/t_0)^{1/2}$ at $t = 0$ corresponds to the initial distribution ρ_{mq} (t_0 is defined as negative for later convenience). The spectral width of the envelope of the individual modes therefore diminishes approximately as the reciprocal square root of time.

As the spectral width diminishes a time comes when the output of the laser is predominantly restricted to a single mode. This occurs in a laser of average length when $\delta\lambda/\Delta\lambda$ is of the order of 10^{-2}. Equation (7.93) shows that this condition applies at a time about 40 ns after switch-on for a typical value of τ of 4 ps and of $\Delta\lambda_0$ of 250 Å. At a time of about 1 ns after switch-on such a laser would have about 7–10 significant longitudinal modes.

To eliminate the arbitrary constant t_0 we need to specify the starting condition of the system. In practice it is more useful to relate the time variation of the modes to a datum measured with respect to the first peak of the lasing emission (see Figure 7.1) than to a rather arbitrary moment of switch-on. To find this datum point we must solve equation (7.11) for the absolute magnitude of the modes as a function of time.

7.5.2 Magnitude of Multimode Output verses Time

To find the way the total output of the laser increases with time after switch-on we must first consider the intensity in the individual modes, and then sum all the contributions. Equation (7.11) gives the rate of change of photon density for each mode, once the gain G_{mq} and the photon lifetime σ appropriate to each mode are known.

To describe the variation of the gain G_{mq} with the longitudinal mode number m we use the parabolic shape factor as given in equation (7.92).

The variation of gain with transverse mode number cannot be so simply treated. When there are many transverse sets of modes, as in a wide laser, it is probably adequate to ignore spatial variations of gain over the width of the laser and take the effective value of G_{mq} as being independent of the transverse mode number q. This, however, is certainly not justified in the case of a stripe laser where there are only a very limited number of sets of transverse modes. In practice these transverse mode sets are frequently found to be so independent of one another that they can be ragarded as being driven by different and independent regions of the active layer. The higher order transverse modes couple more strongly to the part of the active layer nearer the edge of the stripe. The injected carrier concentration at the edge responds more slowly to a step in current as a result of the additional loss of carriers due to edge diffusion.[19] Hence higher order transverse modes, when they exist, tend to be delayed compared with the zero-order mode by an appreciable fraction of the injected carrier recombination time. We will not consider them further in this treatment, which will therefore deal with the behaviour of stripe lasers either with only a single transverse mode or in the period before the higher order transverse modes are significant.

The start of the switch-on is taken as occurring when the injected carrier concentration is a certain small amount below threshold. Although later we will find the exact starting point to be of little importance we now specify it precisely by letting the proportional amount by which the initial gain G_0 for the central longitudinal mode falls short of equalling the end losses be given by the small quantity ϵ_0. The initial photon population is obtained by inserting this relation into equation (7.11). The carrier concentration additional to the starting value, injected during switch-on, will be denoted by n_1. The net gain for the central longitudinal mode is then given in terms of n_1 and ϵ_0 and the losses $1/\sigma$ by

$$G_0 - \frac{1}{\sigma} = G'n_1 - \frac{\epsilon_0}{\sigma} \tag{7.94}$$

where $G' = dG_0/dn$. The corresponding quantity for an arbitrary longitudinal mode m is given approximately, for m/M small, by

$$G_m - \frac{1}{\sigma} = G'n_1 - \left(\frac{1}{\sigma}\right)\left\{\epsilon_0 + \left(\frac{m}{M}\right)^2\right\} \tag{7.95}$$

where we have dropped the subscript q. Hence the photon rate equation (7.11) for mode m becomes

$$\frac{d\phi_m}{dt} - \phi_m\left[G'n_1 - \left(\frac{1}{\sigma}\right)\left\{\epsilon_0 + \left(\frac{m}{M}\right)^2\right\}\right] - \delta_m = 0 \tag{7.96}$$

where we have not, of course, included the photon drive term.

To proceed further we need to know how the carrier concentration n_1, and correspondingly how the gain, varies with time. This is derived from equation (7.12). Over the majority of the switch-on period up to the time of the first intensity maximum we can ignore both the spontaneous and the stimulated recombination of the additional electrons and, following Boers et al.,[11] approximate to equation (7.12) using the following linear rate of increase of carriers with time

$$\frac{dn_1}{dt} = \Delta J \quad \text{and} \quad n_1 = \Delta J\, t \tag{7.97}$$

where ΔJ is the amount by which the current density is switched above threshold. It will be apparent below that only in the very last stages of switch-on does the additional carrier recombination, which has been neglected here, become significant.

We can now obtain the rate equation for the photon density ϕ_m of any individual mode as a function of time by inserting equation (7.97) into equation (7.96) using equation (7.21) to express G' in terms of σ, τ, and J_{th}. This gives

$$\frac{d\phi_m}{dt} = \phi_m\left\{\omega_0^2 t - \frac{\epsilon}{\sigma}\right\} + \delta_m \tag{7.98}$$

where

$$\omega_0^2 = \frac{\Delta J}{J_{th}\sigma\tau\beta}$$

and

$$\epsilon = \epsilon_0 + \left(\frac{m}{M}\right)^2$$

ω_0 lies very close to the small-signal resonance frequency given in equation (7.23) except in the case where the amount ΔJ by which the current is switched up is not much greater than the amount by which the laser was initially below threshold.

Equation (7.98) may be integrated to obtain the following expression for the optical output per unit volume $P_m(=\phi_m/\sigma)$ for mode m as a function of time

$$P_m = \frac{\delta_m}{\sigma\omega_0}\exp\left\{\frac{(\omega_0 t - \epsilon/\sigma\omega_0)^2}{2}\right\}\left\{\left(\frac{\pi}{2}\right)^{1/2}\left[\operatorname{erf}\left\{\frac{\omega_0 t - \epsilon/\sigma\omega_0}{\sqrt{2}}\right\} + \operatorname{erf}\left\{\frac{\epsilon/\sigma\omega_0}{\sqrt{2}}\right\}\right]\right.$$

$$\left. + \frac{\sigma\omega_0}{\epsilon}\exp\left\{\frac{-1}{2}\left(\frac{\epsilon}{\sigma\omega_0}\right)^2\right\}\right\} \tag{7.99}$$

This expression satisfies the starting condition $P_m = \delta_m/\epsilon$ at $t = 0$ corresponding to the steady state solution of equation (7.98).

To find the variation of P_m with mode number m we must substitute the m-dependent value of ϵ given in equation (7.98) into equation (7.99). The resulting expression is complicated, but after a sufficient elapse of time from switch-on it tends to a much simpler form, as follows

$$P_m \simeq (2\pi)^{1/2}\left(\frac{\delta}{\sigma\omega_0}\right)\exp\left[\frac{\{\omega_0(t-t_0)\}^2}{2}\right]\exp\left[\frac{-(m/M)^2(t-t_0)}{\sigma}\right] \tag{7.100}$$

where $t_0 = \epsilon_0/\sigma\omega_0^2$ and where we have ignored terms in ϵ^2 and also any variation of δ with m. This equation is a good approximation at an elapsed time for which $\omega_0(t - t_0) > 2$ and provided that the initial condition before switching is sufficiently below threshold such that $\epsilon_0 > \sigma\omega_0$.

An approximation for P_m which is adequate at $t = t_0$ provided $\epsilon_0 > \sigma\omega_0$ is

$$P_m(t = t_0) = \left(\frac{\delta_m}{\sigma\omega_0}\right)\left[\left(\frac{\pi}{2}\right)^{1/2} - \frac{(m/M)^2}{\sigma\omega_0}\right] \tag{7.101}$$

Equation (7.100) indicates that the developing spectrum of longitudinal modes (as regards both spectral width and amplitude) appears to originate from a uniform spectrum at $t = t_0$ with output $\delta/\sigma\omega_0$ per mode (compared with δ/ϵ at $t = 0$ for the real spectrum). t_0 is the time required to raise the carrier concentration from its initial below-threshold value up to nominal threshold, where the optical losses are just compensated by the gain at the centre of the spectrum. t_0 can hence be regarded as part of the delay time as evaluted in Section 7.2.

The only way in which conditions before $t = t_0$ affect the behaviour is in determining the intensity $\delta/\sigma\omega_0$ per mode of the virtual starting spectrum. This intensity is proportional to $(J/J_{th} - 1)^{-1/2}$ which is a somewhat paradoxical inverse relation with current. It arises because the smaller the margin by which the final current exceeds threshold the longer it takes for the carrier concentration to reach its nominal threshold value and the longer is the interval in which only spontaneous emission is contributing to raising the photon population in the resonator under near lossless conditions.

To obtain the total light output per unit volume P as a function of time we must sum the outputs P_m per unit volume of all the individual modes. Starting from equation (7.100) we can express the sum in the form

$$P = (2\pi)^{1/2}\left(\frac{\delta}{\sigma\omega_0}\right)M_{\text{eff}}\exp\left[\frac{\{\omega_0(t-t_0)\}^2}{2}\right] \tag{7.102}$$

where M_{eff} is the effective number of longitudinal modes at time t, given by

$$M_{\text{eff}} = \sum_m \exp\left\{-\left(\frac{m}{M}\right)^2\frac{(t-t_0)}{\sigma}\right\} \tag{7.103}$$

Over the period where the output is still divided between a reasonable number of modes we can replace the sum in equation (7.103) by an infinite integral over m and obtain

$$M_{\text{eff}} \simeq M\left\{\frac{\pi\sigma}{(t-t_0)}\right\}^{1/2} \tag{7.104}$$

provided that M_{eff} is greater than one and $(t-t_0) > 1/\omega_0$. The total output per unit volume as a function of time can then be expressed as

$$P = \left\{\frac{2^{1/2}\pi M\delta}{\sigma^{1/2}\omega_0(t-t_0)^{1/2}}\right\}\exp\left[\frac{\{\omega_0(t-t_0)\}^2}{2}\right] \tag{7.105}$$

for $\omega_0(t-t_0) > 2$. An approximate expression for the total output at $t = t_0$, obtained by integrating expression (7.101) over the region of m where it is positive, is

$$P(t = t_0) \simeq \frac{\delta M_{\text{eff}}}{\sigma\omega_0} \tag{7.106}$$

where

$$M_{\text{eff}}(t = t_0) = \frac{4}{3}\left(\frac{\pi}{2}\right)^{3/4}M(\sigma\omega_0)^{1/2} \tag{7.107}$$

7.5.2.1   Switch-on Time

Equation (7.105) is useful for calculating the switch-on time of the laser. It describes the increase of light output with time satisfactorily between the light level that applies at $t = t_0 + 2/\omega_0$ and the level that the laser would produce in the steady state, which is first attained at $t = t_0 + t_a$ (see Figure 7.1, point A). Beyond this time the stimulated recombination of carriers, which was neglected in equation (7.98), becomes important and the treatment is no longer appropriate. The effect of the stimulated recombination puts an end to the increase in injected carrier concentration with time, as indicated in Figure 7.1 at point X.

To evaluate $(t_0 + t_a)$ we therefore start by setting P in equation (7.105) equal to the output the laser produces in the steady state, i.e. $P = J - J_{th}$. We may also insert into the equation a suitable value for the spontaneous output δ per mode per unit volume by setting it equal to $\eta_s J_{th}/N$, where η_s is the spontaneous efficiency and N is the total number of modes in the laser resonator over the bandwidth of the spontaneous emission. N can be obtained from equation (2.5) in Chapter 2. For convenience in solving the equation we introduce a normalized time given by $x_a = \omega_0 t_a$ and obtain the following implicit equation for x_a

$$\frac{\exp(x_a^2/2)}{x_a^{1/2}} = \left(\frac{J}{J_{th} - 1}\right)^{5/4} \left(\frac{\sigma}{\beta\tau}\right)^{1/4} \frac{N}{2^{1/2}\pi M \eta_s} \tag{7.108}$$

which is in a convenient form for solving numerically for x_a in terms of the other parameters.

For the evaluation of x_a it remains to assign reasonable values to the quantities on the right-hand side of the above equation. In Chapter 2, equation (2.140) we showed that N/M is given in terms of the cross-sectional area ws of the laser by

$$\frac{N}{M} = \frac{8\pi\mu^2 ws}{B\lambda^2} \tag{7.109}$$

where B is the ratio of the gain to the spontaneous bandwidth and μ is the refractive index. The normalized switch-on time x_a in equation (7.108) therefore depends on the cross section of the laser in addition to the current and the time constants.

Consider first a normal single-transverse-mode stripe laser of cross section say $15\ \mu m \times 0.5\ \mu m$. To obtain a reasonable estimate of x_a we take $\eta_s/B \simeq 1$, $\sigma/\beta\tau \simeq 0.003$, $\lambda = 0.85\ \mu m$, and $\mu^2 = 12.5$. For a current of twice threshold we find $x_a \simeq 3.6$ and for a current 10 per cent above threshold we find $x_a \simeq 2.5$. Both these results lie within the range where the approximations in equation (7.105) are valied. However, for small values of $(J/J_{th} - 1)$ and for smaller values of the cross-sectional area the treatment becomes less exact.

We can extend our investigation below the limit of $x_a = 2$ that applies to equation (7.105) by considering the conditions necessary to make x_a zero, as given approximately by equation (7.106). Substituting for δ and ω_0 in equation (7.106) in the same way as in the derivation of equation (7.108) and also using (7.109) gives the following condition to be satisfied between $(J/J_{th} - 1)$ and the laser cross section to give nominal zero switch-on time

$$\left(\frac{J}{J_{th}} - 1\right)_{t_d = 0} = \left[\frac{\eta_s(2\beta\tau/\pi\sigma)^{1/4}B\lambda^2}{12\mu^2 ws}\right]^{0.8}$$

$$= (55ws)^{-0.8} \tag{7.110}$$

for $\beta\tau/\sigma = 330$, $\lambda = 0.85~\mu\text{m}$, $\mu^2 = 12.5$, $\eta_s = 1$, and $B = 1$ with w and s being measured in microns. For the value of ws of $7.5~\mu\text{m}^2$ used in the previous example, and for values of the other parameters as listed above, equation (7.110) gives zero switch-on time for a current about 0.75 per cent above threshold. For a laser with a cross section of say $1~\mu\text{m}^2$, i.e. almost an order of magnitude smaller, the current concerned is 4 per cent above threshold. In the latter case the behaviour associated with zero switch-on time starts to encroach on the operating range of the device and becomes of some practical consequence.

7.5.2.2 Damping

Zero switch-on time has no particular significance in itself since it arises simply from the definition of what constitutes delay time and what constitutes switch-on time. However, it does mean, according to equation (7.98), that the carrier concentration injected during switch-on never rises to a value which gives more than unit round trip gain in the resonator. This would suggest that the switch-on process is likely to be highly damped and no transient oscillations should occur. In Section 7.3.3, on the effect of spontaneous emission on transient oscillations, we introduced the parameter α to measure the extent of the damping with $\alpha < 2$ corresponding to suppression of the oscillations. α is defined in equation (7.35) and in our present nomenclature it is given by

$$\alpha = \sigma\omega_0\left(\frac{P}{\pi M~\delta}\right)^2 \tag{7.111}$$

where P in this instance is the steady state output. Using equations (7.105) and (7.106) for P at different times we find the following expression for α in terms of x_a

$$\alpha \simeq \frac{2\exp(x_a^2)}{x_a}, \quad \text{for } x_a > 2$$

$$\simeq 0.355, \qquad \text{for } x_a = 0 \tag{7.112}$$

For a laser with nominal zero switch-on time $(x_a = 0)$ the damping is therefore very strong. Interpolation between the two expressions in (7.112) suggests that a value of x_a of 0.8 is required to give critical damping $(\alpha = 2)$, and that the corresponding value of $(J/J_{th} - 1)$ is twice that which gives zero switch-on time, as given in equation (7.110). In the case, for instance, of the laser previously considered with a cross section of $1~\mu\text{m}^2$, critical damping corresponds to a current about 8 per cent above threshold and no transient oscillations would be seen for current less than this. In practice the additional effect of diffusion damping in such a small laser (see Section 7.3.4) would suppress oscillation at even higher current.

We see from the above examples that it is possible, with lasers of small cross sectional area, to step the current up to a value that will give a considerable output of stimulated emission while still. barely driving the device into a condition of net gain. The associated switch-on process has predominantly the characteristics associated with carrier injection, as in a spontaneous emitter. Ten or twenty longitudinal modes are excited during switch-on and their number diminishes only to a relatively small extent as equilibrium is achieved so that a multimode output persists. Equilibrium is attained without the generation of any appreciable transient oscillations.

With lasers of cross-sectional area greater than about 3 μm^2—the precise value depending on current and the amount of diffusion damping—there is a definite and distinguishable period of switch-on. The associated value of $\omega_0 t_a$ measured between the end of the delay period and the point at which the light first reaches its final level lies in the range 2.5–3.5. The first peak of the optical transient, point B in Figure 7.1, follows after a further interval in ωt of about $\pi/2$, corresponding to an additional quarter period in the transient. For convenience in evaluating the mode spectrum in the next section we define the elapsed time between the start of switch-on and the first transient peak as t_b and the associated phase angle as x_b so that

$$x_b = \omega_0 t_b = x_a + \frac{\pi}{2} \tag{7.113}$$

To a first approximation the relative height of the first peak in the transient is also determined by the angular delay period x_a. Using the small-signal theory of Section 7.3, which of course is not fully justified when the first peak is large, we can obtain an approximate relation between the additional injected carrier concentration n_a at time t_a and the additional upward swing δP at the first peak of the transient. The equation for n_a is

$$n_a \simeq (J - J_{th}) t_a \tag{7.114}$$
$$\simeq P t_a$$

Let the light output at the first peak be P_b $(= P + \delta P)$. The oscillatory photon density ϕ_{m1} in one mode is given in terms of n_1 $(=n_a)$ by equation (7.14) with subscripts q suppressed. Neglecting the term containing ϵ in this equation, setting $F_{m1} = 0$, summing over m and putting $\Sigma \phi_{m1} = \delta P \sigma$, $\Sigma G'_m \phi_{m0} = \omega_0^2 \sigma P$ and $d/dt = \omega_0$, we obtain the following estimate for P_b

$$P_b \simeq P(1 + x_a) \tag{7.115}$$

This is an under-estimate when $x_a > 2$. Applying equation (7.115) to the laser of 15 $\mu m \times 0.5$ μm cross section gives a peak output which is 4.6 times the equilibrium level when switching up to twice threshold and 3.5 times the equilibrium level when switching up to 1.1 times threshold.

Let us compare the theoretical results for the laser of larger cross section with the typical transient observed in practice and illustrated in Figure 7.8. The general trend evident in this figure is in good agreement with the theoretical treatment and the relative height of the first peak of the transient increases as the current is increased. Measurements on lasers of smaller cross section (narrow stripe lasers[21] and buried heterostructure lasers[22]) indicate that the relative amplitude of the transient oscillation at comparable excess currents is greatly reduces, as expected (see, for instance, Figure 6.48(b)).

7.5.3 Mode Distribution during Transient Oscillations

The expression derived in Section 7.5.1, equation (7.93), to describe the evolution of the spectral width of the mode spectrum is referred to the moment of first switch-on. Now that we have established in Section 7.5.2 the time t_b that elapses between the moment of first switch-on and the occurrence of the peak of the first transient oscillation, we can relate the mode distribution to events in the more significant part of the switch-on period where the output has reached a substantial level.

The phase angle x_b $(=\omega_0 t_b)$ associated with the switch-on time t_b has been shown in the previous section to lie in the range 4–5 rad for average stripe lasers operated at sufficiently high current to give (ideally) a single longitudinal mode in c.w. operation [see equations (7.108) and (7.113)]. Taking equation (7.93) for the linewidth of the laser and inserting x_b we obtain the following relations for the linewidth $\delta\lambda$ and the effective number of longitudinal modes $2m$ with more than half the intensity of the central mode at a time Δt after the peak of the first transient

$$
\begin{aligned}
\delta\lambda &= \Delta\lambda_0 \left\{ \frac{\sigma}{(\Delta t + x_b/\omega_0)} \right\}^{1/2} \\
2m &= (2M + 1) \left\{ \frac{\sigma}{(\Delta t + x_b/\omega_0)} \right\}^{1/2}
\end{aligned}
\tag{7.116}
$$

where ω_0 is the resonance frequency given by equation (7.23), $\Delta\lambda_0$ is the spectral width of the gain, and $(2M + 1)$ is the total number of longitudinal modes in the spectral width of the gain.

Ikegami[13] has made measurements on the time variation of the spectral width of stripe lasers after switch-on. He obtained good confirmation of the functional form of equation (7.116) and reasonable agreement with the absolute values. His results are illustrated in Figure 7.14.

7.5.4 Mode Spectrum during Switching from Low to High Level

A much narrower mode spectrum is produced by switching a laser from a low level of lasing to a high level rather than from below threshold to

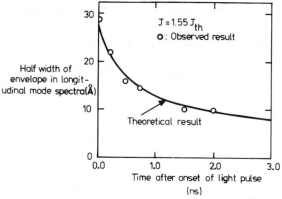

Figure 7.14 Reduction of spectral width of laser emission with time after switch-on. Curve shows measured half width of spectral envelope of longitudinal modes versus elapsed time after initial peak in amplitude of optical transient (after Ikegami[13])

above threshold. Under these circumstances the starting spectrum may be made much narrower than the amplified spontaneous emission spectrum given in equation (7.100), and if a moderately high output can be tolerated can be made single mode. The minimum theoretical power output for single mode operation is derived in Section 2.8.3, equation (2.126), and is of the order of 0.5–2 mW from each end of the laser, depending on its length.

Provided that the gain spectrum continues to coincide with the starting spectrum during the switching process the mode spectrum will continue to narrow if it is multimode at the start, or will remain single mode if it is single mode at the start. This behaviour is described by equation (7.93).

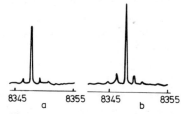

Figure 7.15 Time resolved spectra of a laser (a) before and (b) after switching from a lower level to a higher level of lasing emission (after Selway and Goodwin[23])

Heating effects may cause a slow shift in the dominant mode, which leaves a transient trail of 'ghosts' as it moves.

Figure 7.15 shows the observed behaviour of a 20-μm wide stripe laser being switched from a low level with output 1 mW to a high level with output 3 mW. The spectrum is predominantly single mode throughout.[23]

7.6   ANOMALOUS SWITCH-ON DELAYS AND Q-SWITCHING

In treating switch-on delays we have so far only been concerned with the time required to raise the injected carrier concentration to some given value, stipulated as the threshold level. However, there are certain situations where the threshold level is itself dependent on time. In some cases the resonator losses decrease after switch-on tending to a lower level with a time constant which may be considerably greater than the time constants associated with the carrier injection process. The threshold level of injected carrier concentration will, of course, follow such a variation. If such a laser is switched on with a current which lies between the initial and final threshold levels then the delay is mainly determined by the time constant with which the threshold is reduced, rather than the time constant of the injected carriers.

Time dependent optical losses with a relatively long time constant (e.g. $\geqslant$5 ns) may arise from deep level absorption processes. These can slowly be bleached by spontaneous emission or slowly saturated by injected carriers. Time dependent losses may also arise from localized heating effects which can alter the waveguiding properties of the laser structure. The heating, which is most strongly concentrated in the neighbourhood of the eventual lasing filament, can raise the refractive index of the semiconductor and provide a type of self-focusing waveguide effect. The guiding changes are relatively small but are probably sufficient to exert an appreciable effect on narrow stripe lasers in the plane of the junction. In such lasers both anomalous delay effects and an increase in laser output with time have been observed,[24] which may be attributed to the effect of localized heating.

The anomalous delays and various associated effects which occur in single heterojunction lasers close to the critical temperature may also be attributed to heating effects.[25] As described in Section 5.2.3 such lasers suffer a discontinuous rise in threshold versus temperature at some critical temperature, a characteristic which can be ascribed to the effect of additional injected carriers in destroying the heterostructure waveguide. At this temperature any changes in the guiding arising from, say, temperature differences, have a very large effect on the threshold. Any changes in optical losses also have a large effect as a result of the positive feedback operating via the heterostructure waveguide on the injected carrier concentration.

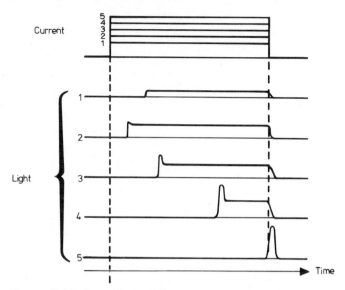

Figure 7.16 Anomalous delays and Q-switching in single heterostructure lasers. Schematic representation of the effect of an increasing current pulse on the delay and shape of the light pulse

Typically a single heterostructure laser in the critical temperature region exhibits a lasing delay that decreases to a small extent as the current is first increased beyond threshold, but then increases again to greater than several hundred nanoseconds, until a current is reached at which the laser will no longer oscillate at all. This sequence of events is illustrated schematically in Figure 7.16. In the current range where the delay increases with current the point of switch-on is frequently characterized by a large initial spike. In the current range where the current is high enough to quench lasing althogether a spike of lasing is normally observed at switch-off.

All three aspects of the above behaviour can be explained along the lines of the treatment given in Section 5.2.3. The analysis is carried out in terms of the balance between the intrinsic gain available in the active layer and the variable loading imposed on it by the resonator, the latter being a function of both carrier concentration and time.[26] Figure 7.17 shows schematically a plot of the available intrinsic gain g_i of the active layer as a function of injected carrier concentration. It also shows the gain required to reach threshold as it is affected by changes in the waveguiding produced by changes in the injected carrier concentration. Two curves are given, one applying at zero time and one applying at infinite time. At infinite time the optical loading is reduced as a result of either improved guiding or reduced optical losses. With the curves disposed as shown there is no point where

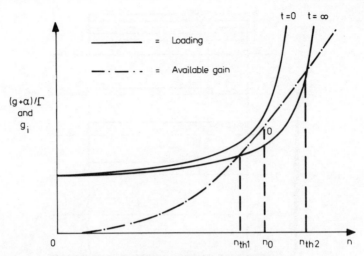

Figure 7.17 Curves to show conditions necessary for Q-switching and anomalous delays in laser switch-on. A curve of the intrinsic gain versus the injected carrier concentration is compared with curves of loss versus injected carrier concentration. Loss curves are time dependent and examples are given at $t = 0$ and $t = \infty$. Lasing takes place at values of the injected carrier concentration where the gain curve lies above the appropriate loss curve

the curve for available gain intersects the loading curve at zero time and so there is no current at which the switch-on delay is determined only by the speed of injection of carriers. Lasing is eventually attained for any injected carrier concentration (and for equivalent current drive) lying in the range n_{th1} to n_{th2}, and it occurs when the moving loading characteristic intercepts the gain curve at the point concerned. Minimum delay applies to the operating point zero which lies closest to the $t = 0$ loading curve and which corresponds to the injected carrier concentration n_0. Maximum delay applies to the normal threshold concentration n_{th1} and also to the 'quench' threshold n_{th2}. The upper of the two intercept points between the available gain and loading curves is unstable and when lasing starts at such a point the system relaxes to the lower point with the emission of an additional optical output. This explains the spike of emission which frequently accompanies the switch-on of the anomalously delayed higher current pulses. Current which gives an injected carrier concentration higher than n_{th2} gives no lasing, but on switch-off a spike of lasing is produced as the carrier concentration decays through the point n_{th2}. This so-called Q switched pulse is almost invariable observed experimentally after the laser has been driven into a quenched condition.

The above treatment gives an excellent qualitative explanation of all the experimentally observed delay effects in single heterostructure lasers. However, the evidence to decide which time dependent effect is actually responsible for the delays, whether it is, for instance, heating or deep level optical absorption or some other process, is at present only circumstantial. From the point of view of economy of hypothesis the heating theory is the most attractive.

7.7 NOISE FLUCTUATIONS IN LASER OUTPUT

Noise fluctuations which are greater than the natural quantum noise of the photon stream are present in the output of all lasers, semiconductor or otherwise. They arise as a result of amplification of the quantum fluctuations in the electron and photon population in the optical resonator. These occur because of the discrete and random nature of the emission and recombination processes. In the case of the photons in the laser mode, both the stimulated and spontaneous emission processes and the absorption and loss processes are discrete and cause fluctuations in the population. In the case of the injected carriers all spontaneous emission at other wavelengths, or by non-radiative mechanisms, are discrete and cause fluctuations. The effect of the fluctuations in the photon and carrier populations on the output of the laser is similar to that which would be produced by deliberate modulation of the two populations. Fluctuations produced by the complementary processes of photon emission or absorption and electron recombination or generation are, of course, correlated in time and this must also be taken into account in assessing the overall effect.

The way in which the laser responds to the fluctuations depends, in the same way as for modulation, on the pumping current, and there is a similar resonant interaction which magnifies the noise over a certain band of frequencies. The noise behaviour can be analysed using the same rate equations as used for small-signal modulation, e.g. equations (7.11) and (7.12) in Section 7.3, once appropriate levels of quantum shot noise are specified for the photons in the laser mode and for the injected carriers.

7.7.1 Observed Behaviour

Measurements of the noise performance of good semiconductor stripe lasers confirm the main points of the above picture.[27-29] As the laser current is increased through threshold the frequency components of the relative output noise below 100 MHz or so increase to a maximum around threshold and then decrease with a further increase in current. The size of the initial relative increase is of the order of 10 dB in electrical power from the detector. Noise centred at frequencies higher than a few hundred megahertz is additionally affected by the resonant enhancement. This resonance behaves in the same way as the modulation resonance. Its centre frequency increases with current as the square root of the excess current over threshold, moving into the gigahertz region for currents greater than about 10 per cent above threshold. The noise magnification at resonance corresponds to an increase of between 10 and 15 dB in the detector noise output power at the resonance frequency.

The above results apply to a single mode laser, or to the total output power of a multimode laser. If the individual modes of a multimode laser are spectrally resolved and detected separately a different behaviour is observed. As the current is increased beyond threshold the noise in the individual modes in the lower frequency range, e.g. 100 MHz and below, does not diminish like the summed output of all the modes. Instead it increases, and can rise to a level which is 30 dB greater than that of the summed output at the current concerned. It appears in certain cases[29] to continue to increase with increasing current as long as the intensity of the individual modes increases (as opposed to the number of modes). This noise consists of partition noise between the different modes and is most marked when the average characteristics of the modes are most similar. For instance, in a laser which is predominantly single mode but where mode hopping occurs with increasing current as the centre of the gain spectrum moves through the resonances of the longitudinal modes, a particularly noisy situation recurs whenever the centre of the spectrum passes through points equidistant between two modes.[30] The laser seems uncertain in which of the two modes to oscillate and the division of power fluctuates randomly between them. There is a negative correlation between the fluctuations in each of the modes so that the total output is relatively noise free. Also the combined effect of the two photon populations on the injected carrier concentration is almost zero. Increased stimulated recombination induced by one mode is compensated by reduced stimulated recombination from the other. At high output levels in a single mode the important stabilizing factor is gain saturation which acts by balancing the input current against the optical output via the injected carrier concentration. This is absent for partition noise between modes, leaving only the small amount of cavity damping which results from a round trip gain of just less than unity to limit the fluctutations. As the total optical intensity is raised so the active Q of the cavity increases, with the result that the upwards and downwards drifts in the output of adjacent modes can persist for steadily lengthening periods. This in particular explains why the partition noise is concentrated towards the lower frequencies.

7.7.2 Theory

Various theoretical analyses have been made of laser noise[31-35] two of which include the effect of partition noise between different laser modes.[31-35] The first two treatments are based predominantly on the characteristics of lasers with four-level systems rather than on the characteristics of semiconductor lasers. Although the conclusions are in general adaptable to semiconductor lasers the initial assumption normally used in four-level systems that the lower lasing level is completely unpopulated gives results which need some modifying.

The important first point which must be established in the theoretical analysis is the appropriate magnitude of the quantum shot noise sources necessary to represent the fluctuations in the carrier and photon population of the laser. The noise power spectrum of these sources is then inserted in the carrier and photon rate equations [equations (7.14) and (7.15)]. The solution that is obtained gives the noise power emitted by the laser and is analogous to that for the modulated power output in equation (7.22). In practice it is the electrical noise power generated by the laser light in an optical detector that is the quantity of interest. This quantity is equivalent to the mean square of the modulus of the optical noise power, and the latter will be discussed in the following treatment.

Let the mean square photon noise input rate per unit bandwidth into the laser be $\Delta_{\phi\phi}(\omega)$, let the mean square injected carrier noise input rate per unit bandwidth be $\Delta_{nn}(\omega)$, and let the mean cross product of the two sources be $\Delta_{\phi n}(\omega)$. Various estimates for the values of these quantities have been obtained by several authors.[31-34] Using equation (7.22) for the modulation efficiency of the laser, but with a more exact version of the damping term in the denominator to give greater accuracy near threshold, and inserting the above three noise sources, we obtain the following expression for the mean square output noise spectrum $\langle |N(\omega)|^2 \rangle$

$$\langle |N(\omega)|^2 \rangle \simeq \frac{\sigma^{-2}(1/\tau^2 + \omega^2)\Delta_{\phi\phi} + \omega_0^4\Delta_{nn} + 2(\omega_0^2/\tau_1\sigma)\Delta_{\phi n}}{(\omega_0^2 + 1/\sigma_1\tau_1 - \omega^2)^2 + \omega^2(1/\sigma_1 + 1/\tau_1)^2} \qquad (7.117)$$

where τ_1 and ω_0^2 are the quantities already defined in equations (7.21) and (7.22), although to give them validity over an extended range around threshold we will re-define them specifically in terms of the average photon concentration ϕ_0 in all modes as

$$\omega_0^2 = \frac{1}{\sigma\tau}\left(\frac{\phi_0}{J_{th}\sigma\beta}\right) \qquad (7.118)$$

$$\frac{1}{\tau_1} = \frac{1}{\tau}\left(1 + \frac{\phi_0}{J_{th}\sigma\beta}\right) \qquad (7.119)$$

σ_1 is the effective time constant of the cavity in the presence of gain and is given in terms of the photon concentration ϕ_0 by

$$\frac{1}{\sigma_1} = \left(\frac{1}{\sigma} - G\right) = \frac{mC J_{th}}{\phi_0} \tag{7.120}$$

where CJ_{th} is the current density per unit volume involved in supplying spontaneous emission to each lasing mode at threshold and m is the number of equivalent modes. C is of the order of 10^{-5} in a stripe laser. ϕ_0, which with ω is the independent variable in these equations, can be related approximately to the current density J both below and above threshold by

$$J \simeq J_{th} + \frac{\phi_0}{\sigma} \left\{ 1 - \beta C m \left(\frac{J_{th}\sigma}{\phi_0}\right)^2 \right\} \tag{7.121}$$

which can be obtained from equations (7.11) and (7.12) for m identical modes when δ_{mq} is set equal to CJ.

Authors concerned with four level laser systems set the mean square shot current noise per unit bandwidth, both for photons and injected carriers, equal to the sum of the generation and loss rates, i.e. to twice the total particle current involved.[32] Thus

$$\Delta_{\phi\phi} = \frac{2\phi_0 V}{\sigma} = 2P$$

$$\Delta_{nn} = 2\left(J_{th} + \frac{\phi_0}{\sigma}\right) V = 2(I_{th} + P) \tag{7.122}$$

and

$$2\Delta_{\phi n} = \frac{-2\phi_0 V}{\sigma} = -2P$$

where V is the volume of the active region of the laser, I_{th} is the threshold current in carriers per second, and P is the total output in photons per second. McCumber,[31] however, uses $\Delta_{nn} = 0$. Haug[33] and Morgan and Adams,[34] whose analyses are specifically applied to a semiconductor laser, add an additional term to each expression to take account of the many photon emission processes which, in a partially inverted system, are directly followed by absorption processes generating optical noise but no net light, and of the corresponding number of carrier recombination processes which are directly followed by optical excitation processes causing shot noise but no net loss of carriers. These each represent an additional shot noise of $2(\gamma - 1)P$, where $1/\gamma$ represents the degree of inversion which is defined in equation (2.72), Chapter 2, and is given in terms of the quasi-Fermi level separation $(F_c - F_v)$ and the frequency, by equation (2.27). γ may have a value considerably greater than unity (e.g. 5–10) and hence may be of appreciable significance.

If we insert the values for the noise sources as given in equation (7.122), but including the additional facor γ, into equation (7.117) we obtain the following expression for the overall mean square noise $\langle |N(\omega)|^2 \rangle$ per unit bandwidth in photons^2 per second.

$$\langle |N(\omega)|^2 \rangle = \frac{2\gamma P[\sigma^{-2}(1/\tau_0^2 + \omega^2) + \omega_0^2(1 - \beta)/\beta\sigma\tau]}{(\omega_0^2 + 1/\sigma_1\tau_1 - \omega^2)^2 + \omega^2(1/\sigma_1 + 1/\tau_1)^2} \tag{7.123}$$

McCumber[31] shows that when partition noise between m similar modes is taken into account additional noise is produced. If n of the m modes are detected then the total value of $\langle |N(\omega)|^2 \rangle$ is given in terms of the total photon output rate P from all the modes by

$$\frac{\left(\dfrac{2nP}{m}\right)\left\{ \left[\sigma^{-2}\left(\dfrac{1}{\tau_1^2} + \omega^2\right) + \dfrac{\omega_0^2(1 - \beta)}{\beta\sigma\tau} \right] + \left(1 - \dfrac{n}{m}\right)\sigma^{-2}\left[2\omega_0^2\left(\dfrac{1}{\sigma_1\tau_1} - \omega^2\right) + \omega_0^4\right]\left(\omega^2 + \dfrac{1}{\sigma_1^2}\right)^{-1} \right\}}{\left(\omega_0^2 + \dfrac{1}{\sigma_1\tau_1} - \omega^2\right)^2 + \omega^2\left(\dfrac{1}{\sigma_1} + \dfrac{1}{\tau_1}\right)} \tag{7.124}$$

For semiconductor lasers an additional factor γ is required.

In fact modes are subject to the gain spectrum and are not exactly similar. Arnold and Petermann[35] allow for this and find that, except for chance pairs of equal modes, partition noise is less than indicated by (7.124), particularly when there are more than about five to ten modes.

The photon fluctuation term $\Delta_{\phi\phi}$ provides the predominant contribution to the overall noise output of the laser. The carrier fluctuation terms Δ_{nn} and $\Delta_{\phi n}$ have an insignificant effect except for low frequency noise in high current operation. This can be seen by comparing the relative magnitude of the various terms in the numerator of equation (7.117), also taking into account the relative magnitude of the respective noise sources. It is not an account the relative magnitude of the respective noise sources. It is the result of the high optical gain in the device.

Because the mean square noise power depends on the linear rather than the squared output power of the laser, there is some difficulty in choosing a way of representing the theoretical results in a general form for lasers of varying power output. It would be convenient to describe the mean square noise power as a proportion of the square of the total output power P of the laser, i.e. $\langle |N(\omega)|^2 \rangle / P^2$, particularly for transmission applications since this ratio remains constant, despite attenuation, down to the level at which the quantum nature of the signal again becomes dominant. However, such a ratio depends inversely on the laser power. In order to compare drive levels in a given laser we express the output power P in terms of total current in electrons per second at threshold, say I_{et}. Let us consider the quantity $I_{et}\langle |N(\omega)|^2 \rangle / P^2$ which we will denote by M. This quantity, which we call the mean square normalised relative noise power per unit bandwidth, depends only on the proportion by which the laser is driven above threshold and is independent of the absolute power output. M can be obtained by dividing the expressions on the right hand side of equations (7.123) and (7.124) by $P(J/J_{th} - 1)$ or $P\omega_0^2\sigma\tau/\beta$. The ratio of the mean square noise power per unit bandwidth to the total output power is M/I_{et} Hz^{-1}. The absolute value of the mean square noise power per unit

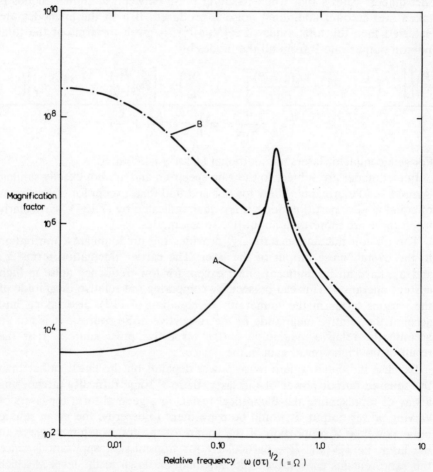

Figure 7.18 Theoretical curves for intensity of noise fluctuations in laser output as a function of frequency of noise for typical laser operating at a current around 3 per cent above threshold. Quantity plotted is ratio of mean square optical noise power per unit bandwidth as a proportion of square of total laser output power divided by electron current at threshold. Typical value of latter is 6×10^{17} electrons s^{-1} (see text). Curve A, noise power in all modes. Curve B, noise power in one out of total of two modes

bandwidth is $MI_{et}(J/J_{th} - 1)^2$ photons^{2}s^{-2} or $MI_t e V_g^2 (J/J_{th} - 1)^2$ w^{2}Hz^{-1}, where I_t is the threshold current in amps, e is the electronic charge and V_g is the photon energy in eV. To put the figures in perspective for a laser with a typical threshold current of 100 mA and a photon energy of 1.5 eV I_{et} is 6×10^{17} electrons s^{-1} and $I_t e V_g^2$ is 3.5×10^{-20} w^{2}Hz^{-1}.

Figure 7.18 shows a typical plot, according to equation (7.124), of the mean square normalized relative noise power M per unit bandwidth as defined above against the normalized noise frequency Ω $(= 2\pi f(\sigma\tau)^{1/2})$ for a laser operating around 3 per cent above threshold. $\Omega = 1$ corresponds to a frequency of around 1.25 GHz in a typical laser. Curve A shows the relative mean square noise power that is obtained if the laser operates in a single mode or if it is multimode and all the output power is detected. In these circumstances the laser mean square noise at low frequencies is not more than about two orders of magnitude greater than the pure photon mean square shot noise associated with the output concerned. However, this increases to a factor of about 3×10^5 at the centre of the resonance. To obtain the total relative noise power we will assume that most of the power is contained within the spectral width of the resonance which, in this instance, is about 80 MHz. This gives a total relative noise power of about 0.5 per cent at the current concerned, i.e. around 25 μW for a 5-mW output.

Curve B shows the additional effect of partition noise. This curve gives the spectral distribution of the relative noise in one mode under conditions where two modes can operate with identical characteristics. There is a very obvious difference in the noise in the low frequency range compared with the previous curve. Instead of approaching a low value with decreasing frequency curve B rises as the inverse square of frequency over a considerable range before levelling off at a saturation value which, in this instance, is greater by a factor of about 10^7 than the noise in the combined outputs of both modes. This value even surpasses the level at the resonance peak by an order of magnitude. The effect of increasing current is to increase the saturation value of the noise in direct proportion to the optical output but to reduce the frequency at which it is attained in inverse proportion. Taking account of the bandwidth of the partition noise in the curves shown one finds that a further 2 per cent of relative noise is added on to the 0.5 per cent associated with the resonance peak. The noise in the vicinity of the resonance peak differs little between the single and double mode cases.

Figure 7.19 shows the effect of laser current on the spectral distribution of noise in the total output of a typical laser as derived from equation (7.124). The laser is assumed to have a constant product of number of modes times output up to a current about 2 per cent above threshold and to be single mode thereafter. C/β is taken as 3×10^{-5}, corresponding to a

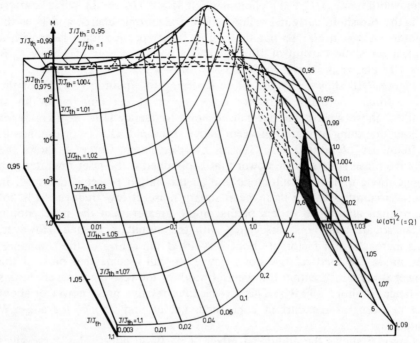

Figure 7.19 Theoretical curves for intensity of noise fluctuations in laser output as function of both noise frequency and laser current for a typical laser when the output of all modes is combined. Same quantity plotted as in previous figure

stripe laser of average size. The relative noise centred on a particular frequency peaks at a current close to the nominal threshold up to an angular frequency of around $0.1/(\sigma\tau)^{1/2}$, i.e. about 125 MHz. Beyond this frequency peak noise occurs at the current which gives resonance although a small subsidiary peak around threshold continues to exist up to considerably higher frequencies.

These results apply reasonably to all stable c.w. semiconductor stripe lasers, although the resonance linewidths observed in practice are normally wider than those illustrated in Figure 7.18, particularly in the case of very narrow stripes. This can be ascribed both to values of C/β larger than that taken above and also to the same diffusion damping which broadens the resonance of the modulation efficiency, as described in Section 7.3.4. On the other hand, lasers which suffer from enhanced ringing and from instability, as described in Section 7.4.1, can exhibit narrower and more peaky resonances in the noise spectrum than those illustrated, and harmonics of the resonance frequency may be present in extreme cases. When more than one transverse mode is present in a stripe laser the noise characteristics of the second mode are normally reasonably independent of those in the first, being mainly determined by the relative threshold values and the relative outputs of the two modes.

REFERENCES

1. T. Ikegami and Y. Suematsu, 'Direct modulation of semiconductor junction lasers', *Electron. Commun. (Japan)*, **51-B**, 1968, 51.
2. M. Chown, A. R. Goodwin, D. F. Lovelace, G. H. B. Thompson, and P. R. Selway, 'Direct modulation of double-heterostructure lasers at rates up to 1 Gbit/s', *Electron. Lett.*, **9**, 1973, 34.
3. P. Russen and S. Schultz, 'Direct modulation of a double heterostructure laser with a bit-rate of 2.5 Gbit/s', *Anchiv fur Electronik und Unertragungstechnik,* **27**, 1973, 193.
4. K. Konnerth, 'Delay between current pulse and light emission of a gallium arsenide injection laser', *Appl. Phys. Lett.,* **4**, 1964, 120.
5. N. Chinone, R. Ito, and O. Nakada, 'Measurement of minority carrier lifetime during gradual degradation of GaAs–GaAlAs DH lasers', *J. Quantum Electron.,* **JQE-10**, 1974, 81.
6. J. E. Ripper, 'Measurement of spontaneous carrier lifetime from stimulated emission delays in semiconductor lasers', *J. Appl. Phys.,* **43**, 1972, 1762.
7. H. Namizaki, H. Kan, M. Ishi, and A. Ito, 'Current dependence of spontaneous carrier lifetime in GaAs–Ga$_{1-x}$Al$_x$As double heterostructure lasers', *Appl. Phys. Lett.,* **24**, 1974, 486.
8. T. Ikegami and Y. Suematsu, 'Resonance-like characteristics of the direct modulation of a junction laser', *Proc. IEEE,* **55**, 1967, 122.
9. T. Ikegami and Y. Suematsu, 'Large signal characteristics of directly modulated semiconductor injection lasers', *Electron. Commun. (Japan)*, **53-B**, 1970, 69.
10. M. J. Adams, 'Rate equations and transient phenomena in semiconductor lasers', *Opto-electronics,* **5**, 1973, 201.
11. P. M. Boers, M. T. Vlaardingerbroek, and M. Danielsen, 'Dynamic behaviour of semiconductor lasers', *Electron. Lett.,* **11**, 1975, 206.
12. W. Harth, 'Large signal direct modulation of injection lasers', *Electron. Lett.,* **9**, 1973, 532.
13. T. Ikegami, 'Spectrum broadening and tailing effect in directly modulated injection lasers', First European Conference on Optical Fibre Communication, IEE London, September 1975.
14. K. Furuya, Y. Suematsu, and T. Hong, 'Reduction of resonance-like peak in direct-modulation due to carrier diffusion in injection lasers', *Applied Optics,* **17**, 1978, 1949.
15. E. S. Yang, P. G. McMullin, A. W. Smith, J. Blum, and K. K. Shih, 'Degradation induced microwave oscillations in double heterostructure injection laser', *Appl. Phys. Lett.,* **24**, 1974, 324.
16. N. G. Basov, '0-1-Dynamics of injection lasers', *J. Quantum Electron,* **JQE-4**, 1968, 855.
17. T. P. Lee and R. H. R. Rolden, 'Repetitively Q-switched light pulses from GaAs injection lasers with tandem double section stripe geometry', *J. Quantum Electron.,* **JQE-6**, 1970, 359.
18. T. Ohmi and S. Yamazaki, 'A limitation on the repetition rate of pulsations of

junction lasers due to the repetitively Q-switched mechanism', *J. Quantum Electron.,* **JQE-9**, 1973, 366.

19. J. E. Carroll, S. G. Eldon, and G. H. B. Thompson, 'Incremental efficiency enhancement and r.f. response of GaAs–GaAlAs double heterostructure stripe lasers', *Electron. Lett.,* **12**, 1976, 564.

20. J. Buus and M. Danielsen, 'Carrier diffusion and higher order transversal modes in spectral dynamics of the semiconductor laser', *J. Quantum Electron.,* **JQE-13**, 1977, 669.

21. T. Kobyashi, H. Kawaguchi, and Y. Furukawa, 'Lasing characteristics of very narrow planar stripe lasers', *Jap. J. Appl. Phys.,* **16**, 1977, 601.

22. K. Nogaro, M. Maeda, M. Tana, I. Saito, and R. Ito, *Papers of Tech. Group on OQE Japan,* **OQE77**, 1977, 19.

23. P. R. Selway and A. R. Goodwin, 'Effect of DC bias level on the spectrum of GaAs lasers operated with short pulses', *Electron. Lett.,* **12**, 1976, 25.

24. D. F. Lovelace, unpublished.

25. F. D. Nunes, N. B. Patel, and J. E. Ripper, 'A theory on long time delays and internal Q-switching in GaAs junction lasers', *J. Quantum Electron.,* **QE-13**, 1977, 675.

26. G. H. B. Thompson, P. R. Selway, G. D. Henshall, and J. E. A. Whiteaway, 'Role of optical guiding in critical temperature behaviour, delays and Q-switching in single heterostructure GaAs/(GaAl)As lasers', *Electron. Lett.,* **10**, 1974, 354.

27. T. L. Paoli, 'Noise characteristics of stripe-geometry double-heterostructure junction lasers operating continuously—1 Intensity noise at room temperature', *J. Quantum Electron.,* **QE-11**, 1975, 276.

28. H. Jackel and G. Guekos, 'High frequency intensity noise spectra of axial mode groups in the radiation from CW GaAlAs diode lasers', *Optical and Quantum Electronics,* **9**, 1977, 233.

29. T. Ito, S. Machida, K. Nawata, and T. Ikegami, 'Intensity fluctuations in each longitudinal mode of a multimode AlGaAs laser', *J. Quantum Electron.,* **QE-13**, 1977, 574.

30. P. R. Selway, Private communication.

31. D. E. McCumber, 'Intensity fluctuations in the output of CW laser oscillators I', *Phys. Rev.,* **141**, 1966, 306.

32. M. Lax, 'Quantum noise VII: The rate equations and amplitude noise in lasers', *J. Quantum Electron.,* **QE-3**, 1967, 37.

33. H. Haug, 'Quantum-mechanical rate equations for semiconductor lasers', *Phys. Rev.,* **184**, 1969.

34. D. J. Morgan and M. J. Adams, 'Quantum noise in semiconductor lasers', *Phys. Stat. Sol. (a),* **11**, 1972, 243.

35. G. Arnold and K. Petermann, 'Intrinsic noise of semiconductor lasers in optical communication systems', *Optical and Quantum Electron.,* **12**, 1980, 207.

CHAPTER 8

Lasers with Distributed Feedback and Bragg Reflectors

8.1 INTRODUCTION

Up to this point we have only considered lasers with a Fabry–Perot type of optical resonator, where the feedback is provided by reflection at the end-faces. Such a resonator has many equivalent longitudinal resonances equally spaced over the optical frequency band. As we have described the only longitudinal mode discrimination present in such a structure is that provided by the gain spectrum itself which, being much wider than the spacing between resonances, is not very selective. Single mode oscillation can be achieved during c.w. operation, but any disturbances such as occur, for instance, during switch-on, etc. easily excite many additional longitudinal modes. Various methods have been suggested for improving the mode discrimination, including the use of externally coupled optical cavities[1,2] and integrated twin-guide stripe lasers.[3,4] However, a particularly interesting and original form of construction which is capable of fulfilling this function suggested by Kogelnik and Shank,[5] uses an optical grating that is incorporated into the heterostructure waveguide. When the periodicity is correctly chosen this structure produces a very significant effect on the guided waves. It may be applied over the whole active length of the laser, when it provides what has come to be known as distributed feedback, and eliminates the need for end-mirrors. Alternatively the grating may be located at the end of a normal active layer, in which case it exactly reproduces the effect of a mirror and is called a distributed Bragg reflector. In addition to being frequency selective this form of laser resonator is particularly adapted to the construction of integrated optical assemblies in which the laser and other optical components are fabricated together on a single semiconductor chip. In appropriate circumstances the grating may also be designed to emit a radiated beam which emerges at an angle to the plane of the structure.

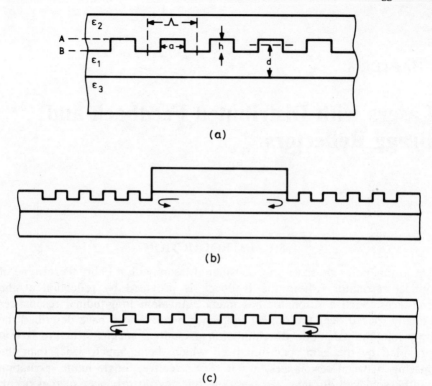

Figure 8.1 Corrugated dielectric waveguides and their application in laser resonators. (a) Longitudinal section of corrugated dielectric waveguide with dimensions indicated, (b) schematic diagram of laser resonator comprising uniform waveguide terminated at each end with distributed Bragg reflectors, (c) schematic diagram of distributed feedback laser terminated at each end with uniform dielectric waveguide

Figure 8.1(a) illustrates a possible longitudinal section of the grating structure. In this example the central layer of the laser which forms the optical waveguide is corrugated with a period very close to either 1/2 or 3/2 of the internal wavelength of the lasing mode. The individual corrugations have negligible effect on the wave, but a large number of appropriately spaced corrugations can produce a very considerable cumulative effect.

Figure 8.1(b) illustrates the use of the corrugated section as a distributed Bragg reflecting mirror when placed at the end of a laser resonator. Here it performs the same function as a multilayer dielectric mirror, but because of the small variation of properties over the length of a single corrugation a much larger number of corrugations must be used than the number of layers in a normal dielectric mirror. Such a large number of corrugations are only effective when the lasing wavelength is accurately centred on the relatively narrow stop band of the corrugated waveguide and when the optical losses are low. The losses must be low enough so that the optical dissipation between corrugations is small compared with the reflection from individual corrugations. In practice the overall reflection from the corrugated section can provide at least as much feedback as a cleaved laser end-face. The reflection coefficient tends to a limiting value as the length of the corrugated section is increased.

The alternative application as used in the distributed feedback laser is illustrated in Figure 8.1(c). Here the corrugated section forms the main part of the laser resonator and is used to support propagating waves in the distributed feedback mode. This is a more subtle form of operation than is employed in the Bragg reflector since the wave-length must in general lie outside the stop band of the structure to enable the waves to propagate. Just outside the stop band, both at lower and higher frequencies, there is a range of operation where the waves may propagate but where they still interact very strongly with the corrugations. Nearly normal standing waves build up in this region but they have superimposed on them a beat wavelength which arises from the interference between the closely related periodicity of the standing waves and the corrugations. As a result of this effect any particular length of corrugated waveguide exhibits a natural resonance at the optical frequency that creates a beat wavelength to match the total length of the section, or some sub-multiple of that length.

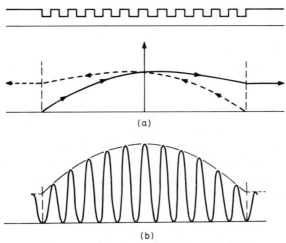

(a)

(b)

Figure 8.2 Resonance condition in distributed feedback laser. (a) Typical distribution of forward and backward propagating waves along length of resonator, (b) schematic diagram of distribution of standing waves along length of resonator

This behaviour is illustrated in Figure 8.2. The amplitude of the standing waves may be said to build up steadily from the end to the centre of the corrugated section as if there were a reflector at each end whose effect was spread out over half the length of the resonator. As the corrugated section is lengthened, so the amplitude of the standing wave pattern at its centre increases compared with that at its ends. This corresponds to a larger effective reflection coefficient, a greater energy storage, and a higher Q. A corrugated section of appropriate length therefore serves as a reasonably satisfactory resonator without the need for additional mirrors. It becomes more effective as its length is increased, and with reasonable dimensions its Q does not fall greatly below that of a Fabry–Perot resonator using cleaved end-faces.

8.2 THEORY

In order to understand the behaviour of distributed feedback and distributed Bragg reflection lasers it is necessary first to consider how waves propagate in periodic structures, and how different boundary conditions at the ends of the laser can be used to create the equivalent of a cavity resonance. The theory of the propagation of coupled modes in a periodic structure has been treated generally by Yariv[5] and has been applied to lasers in somewhat different ways by Kogelnik and Shank[7] and by Wang.[8] Kogelnik and Shank emphasize the coupling between the forward and backward waves, whereas Wang defines eigen combinations of forward and backward waves that propagate unchanged through the periodic structure. The two treatments give the same results where they overlap, but the use of eigen functions provides a more powerful tool for analysing a wider range of situations. We give here a simplified treatment incorporating elements from both the above approaches. We use characteristic eigen functions to describe the solutions in a form that may be simply applied to analysing a variety of structures. We will, however, derive these from coupled mode equations.

The two principal properties which may be varied periodically to create periodic wave guide structures are the dielectric constant and the gain. Only the former property is at present employed in making semiconductor periodic structures, and we limit our consideration accordingly.

A simplification can be introduced into the treatment of a periodic dielectric waveguide structure by describing the interaction between the structure and a propagating wave only in terms of the periodic variation produced in the propagation characteristics of the wave. This description is entirely adequate if the periodic variation of the dielectric constant extends over the whole cross section of the wave. This is not, of course, true in the corrugated waveguide, where the non-uniformity in the dielectric constant can be considered to be limited to a relatively small cross section of the wave. Thus, only the portion of the material lying between planes A and B in Figure 8.1(a) exhibits a periodic variation with an abrupt change between ϵ_1 and ϵ_2 at the vertical interfaces of the corrugation. The problem of finding the interaction in such circumstances can be solved by using an appropriate two-dimensional wave equation[9], but the treatment is too lengthy to be presented here. Instead, we adopt a simpler method that illustrates the fundamental principles clearly and at the same time gives satisfactory quantitative results. In this treatment we regard the corrugated waveguide as a succession of dielectric guides of alternating thickness. The variation in thickness creates a variation in propagation coefficient, an accompanying variation in the impedance (E_x/H_y), of the guided wave, the two being directly related, and also a variation in the transverse field distribution. The variation in impedance is the main factor that determines the reflection and transmission characteristics of the corrugation and hence the periodic interaction. The variation in the field distribution causes some radiation into the surrounding medium and its main effect is to introduce loss into the propagation characteristics of the structure. Otherwise its effects can be largely ignored. In respects other than the direct calculation of the emitted radiation from the corrugated structure an effective treatment of wave interactions can therefore be carried out in terms of the variation of the propagation constant only.

The analysis of guides with a periodic variation of the propagation constant starts with a wave equation of the following form[8]

$$\frac{d^2E}{dz^2} + \{\beta_z(z)\}^2E = 0 \tag{8.1}$$

where z is the propagation direction and where the propagation constant $\beta_z(z)$ is a periodic function of z. There is a general form for the solution of this equation, according to Floquet's theorem, which depends predominantly on the periodic length of $\beta_z(z)$ and not particularly on the precise form of its periodic variation. This means that the general behaviour of a periodic guide is determined mainly by the period of the corrugations and much less by their shape.

To solve equation (8.1) for a specific form of corrugation we need to express the periodic part of $\{\beta_z(z)\}^2$ in a Fourier series, the fundamental periodicity being that of the corrugation period which we will represent by the wave vector K_0. The solution becomes interesting when the optical frequency is chosen so that the unperturbed propagation constant of the guided wave (without corrugations) approaches $nK_0/2$, where n is an integer. The field E of the guided wave may then usefully be expanded in a Fourier series with wave vectors of $(n/2 + m)K_0$ (where m takes integral values from zero upwards), multiplied by a term with phase and amplitude slowly varying with z. Substituting both sets of Fourier series into (8.1) and equating terms with the same z dependence gives an infinite set of equations for the Fourier coefficients of E. However, when the periodic part of $\{\beta_z(z)\}^2$ is small, only the fundamental forward and backward components of E have appreciable value ($m = 0$ or $-n$). Then a pair of coupled equations are obtained that relate the slowly varying coefficients of these forward and backward waves and determine the relatively long distance amplitude variation and additional phase change of the waves.

The above treatment is very effective in providing approximate solutions for a variety of periodic structures. However, it is possible to obtain a somewhat clearer physical picture of the general principles involved and derive the same pair of coupled equations by adopting a slightly different approach and considering the effect on the guided wave of the reflection at each individual corrugation. This method is most conveniently adapted to rectangular corrugations.

Let us consider the magnitude of the reflection produced by a rectangular corrugation when a guided wave is incident on it. This situation is illustrated in Figure 8.3, where A_1 and A_2 represent waves incident on

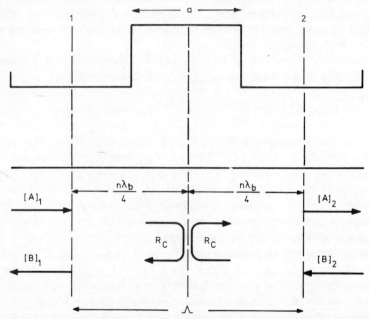

Figure 8.3 Transmitted and reflected waves associated with individual corrugation. Reference planes 1 and 2 sited at centres of minima in corrugation pattern. Reflection coefficient referred to centre of maximum of corrugation pattern. Corrugation period $= n\lambda_b/2$

the corrugation from both directions and B_1 and B_2 represent the respective reflected waves. The total reflection in each direction is composed of two individual components, one produced at the upward and one at the downward step, of equal and opposite magnitudes. As mentioned above these reflections are predominantly determined by the difference in impedance between the thicker and thinner sections of the guide and are approximately given by

$$R \simeq \frac{z_1 - z_2}{z_1 + z_2}$$
$$\simeq \delta z / 2z, \quad \text{for } z_1 - z_2 \text{ small} \tag{8.2}$$

where z_1 is the impedance of the input guide, z_2 is the impedance of the output guide, δz is the difference, and z is the average value. In an E wave (electric field parallel to the plane of the junction) of the type with which we are mainly concerned the impedance is inversely proportional to the propagation constant β_z.

Let us derive the total reflection coefficient R_c of the corrugation as observed in the thinner guide, with its phase defined as if it were originating from the centre of the corrugation. Appropriate vector addition of the contributions from the two sides gives the following relation between R_c and the step-up $\delta\beta_z$ of the propagation constant in the thicker region

$$R_c = j\left(\frac{\delta\beta_z}{\beta_z}\right)\sin(\beta_z a) \tag{8.3}$$

where a is the width of the corrugation. The reflection is a maximum when the width of the corrugation is one-quarter of a guide wavelength (or any odd multiple) and is zero when it is half a guide wavelength or any multiple.

The transmission coefficient of the corrugation in the absence of gain has a modulus of $(1 - |R_c|^2)^{1/2}$. In the cases we will consider, R_c is small and therefore it is sufficiently accurate to take the modulus of the transmission coefficient as approximately unity, and the phase change as corresponding to the width of the corrugation.

We will use the above expressions for the reflection and transmission coefficients for the derivation of the coupled wave equations in the next section.

8.3   WAVE PROPAGATION IN THE PERIODIC GUIDE

In this section we use the example of the periodic guide with rectangular corrugations to derive the general coupled wave equations for propagation in a periodic system.

Let the corrugation length of the guide be Λ, giving a corrugation wave vector K_0 of $2\pi/\Lambda$. We consider guided waves of an optical frequency such that their propagation constant β_z lies close $nK_0/2$, where n is an integer. We also assume that optical gain (positive or negative) is present in the system. Representing $nK_0/2$ by β_b (the Bragg wave vector) or $2\pi/\lambda_b$ (λ_b = Bragg wavelength) we can then write β_z in the form

$$\beta_z = \beta_b + (\delta + jg) \tag{8.4}$$

where

$$\beta_b = \frac{2\pi}{\Lambda_b} = \frac{nK_0}{2}$$

and where δ is the small error in phase per unit length by which the propagation constant differs from $nK_0/2$ and g is the amplitude gain per unit length (*not* the intensity gain as previously). The sign of jg is the result of taking the expression for the t and z dependence of the wave in the form $\exp(j\Omega t - \beta z)$. The phase error per corrugation is $\delta\Lambda$ and the gain per corrugation is $g\Lambda$, both of which will be small in the cases that we treat.

We consider the case where both a forward wave of amplitude, say A, and a backward wave of amplitude, say B, propagate past the corrugation. Let us investigate how the relationship between A and B changes with position along the corrugated guide. This comparison must be made at reference planes located appropriately with respect to the corrugation pattern, and for convenience we choose reference planes centred on each minimum of the pattern (marked 1 and 2 in Figure 8.3).

To eliminate the inversion of phase for waves of wave vector β_b which occurs between such planes when n is odd we extract the wave vector β_b from the propagation constant of the general wave and deal with the quantities $A \exp(-j\beta_b z)$ and $B \exp(j\beta_b z)$, which we will represent respectively by $[A]$ and $[B]$. If the zero of z is chosen coincident with one of the reference planes then $[A]$ and $[B]$ at any of the reference planes are either equal to A and B (n even) or change sign alternately with respect to A and B (n odd).

Consider first how the reflection coefficient R_c of an individual corrugation, as given in equation (8.3), is affected by changing the reference planes from the maximum to the minimum of the corrugations. For waves of a wavelength close to twice that of the corrugation length or any sub-multiple, the phase of R_c transforms by approximately 180° or 360°; 360° for corrugation lengths of even numbers of half wavelengths and 180° for odd numbers. Since R_c is purely imaginary the reflection at the new reference planes is therefore still purely imaginary and, in the cases with which we shall deal, also small. We set it equal to $jk\Lambda$, where the new quantity k may be regarded as the in-phase sum of the reflections of all the corrugations per unit length. It will be called the coupling coefficient. With the above choice of reference planes k is real, negative for n odd in equation (8.4) and positive for n even. It is equal for both forward and backward waves. If the reference planes were not taken centrally then k would be complex and would have complex conjugate values for the forward and backward waves.

Consider the forward and backward waves, respectively $[A_1]$ and $[B_1]$, at the input reference plane 1 in Figure 8.3 and the forward and backward waves, respectively $[A_2]$ and $[B_2]$, at the output reference plane 2. We may write the following approximate relations between them

$$[A_2] = \{1 + (g - j\delta)\Lambda\}[A_1] + jk\Lambda[B_2]$$
$$[B_1] = \{1 + (g - j\delta)\Lambda\}[B_2] + jk^*\Lambda[A_1] \tag{8.5}$$

where we have introduced the complex conjugate k^* for generality in the second equation. We assume that $g\Lambda$, $\delta\Lambda$, $k\Lambda$ and hence $[A_2] - [A_1]$ and $[B_2] - [B_1]$ are small. We may then rewrite the above relations, taking z as the propagation direction, in the form

$$\frac{d[A]}{dz} = (g - j\delta)[A] + jk[B]$$

$$\frac{d[B]}{dz} = -(g - j\delta)[B] - jk^*[A] \tag{8.6}$$

where $[A]$ and $[B]$ are only defined at the reference planes. These expressions represent a pair of coupled wave equations where the coupling coefficient k causes a mutual perturbation of the phase and amplitude of waves $[A]$ and $[B]$ and affects the way they depend on z.

Coupled equations of the same general type as (8.6) can be obtained by the method described in connection with equation (8.1) for any shape of corrugation. They only vary in respect of how k is related to the corrugation depth.

The difference between Kogelnik and Shank's treatment[7] and Wang's treatment[8] of corrugated structures consists essentially in the method used for the solution of the pair of equations in (8.6). Kogelnik and Shank solve the equations for specific boundary conditions taking the forward waves $[A]$ and the backward wave $[B]$ to be zero at opposite ends of the laser. These boundary conditions apply to the type of laser where the central corrugated section is terminated at both ends by non-corrugated sections, and where there are no additional sources of reflection. Wang takes a more fundamental approach in his treatment. He obtains eigen solutions for the particular combinations of forward and backward waves which will propagate unchanged over unlimited lengths of corrugated guide and evaluates their combined propagation coefficients. There are two eigen solutions consisting respectively of overall forward and overall backward propagating waves. However, each eigen wave comprises the combination of a main component propagating in the direction of the overall wave and a subsidiary backward-scattered Bragg component propagating in the opposite direction. To analyse the behaviour of resonators incorporating a corrugated structure it is then necessary to evaluate the effective reflection coefficient for the eigen combinations at the boundaries. Such a treatment is more general than Kogelnik and Shank's and it can be applied, for instance, without special treatment to Bragg reflecting lasers (with corrugated sections outside the main pumped region) and to corrugated guides which are only pumped over a portion of their length, as well as to the case where the laser is defined by the length of a central corrugated region. We follow Wang's eigen function treatment.

Let the two eigen solutions for the coupled wave equations in (8.6) consist respectively of a forward wave component A associated with a smaller Bragg scattered backward component, say B_b, and a backward wave component B associated with a smaller Bragg scattered forward component, say A_b, with the ratio of the Bragg scattered component to the main component having a value s which is in general complex. s can be obtained by putting $[B] = s[A]$ in the pair of equations in (8.6) and finding the condition necessary to make them identical. Since B/A and $[B]/[A]$ are equal at the reference planes this gives

$$\frac{[B]}{[A]} = \frac{B_b}{A} = s_+ = \frac{(\delta + jg) \pm \{(\delta + jg)^2 - |k|^2\}^{1/2}}{k}$$

$$\frac{[A]}{[B]} = \frac{A_b}{B} = s_- = \frac{(\delta + jg) \pm \{(\delta + jg)^2 - |k|^2\}^{1/2}}{k^*}$$

(8.7)

where we must take the sign of the alternative pair to be opposite to that of δ, so that $|s| < 1$. s_+ and s_- are equal when the reference plane is taken at the mid-point of the corrugation. (Note that Wang[8] substitutes jk for k and so obtains a slightly different expression for s that is referred to a plane $\lambda/8$ away from the minimum of the corrugations.) Integration of the equation which results from inserting (8.7) into (8.6) gives the propagation constant $\pm\beta_e$ of the two eigen waves. β_e is given by

$$\beta_e = \{(\delta + jg)^2 - |k|^2\}^{1/2}$$

(8.8)

The complete expressions for the two eigen modes are then

$$A\{\exp(-j\beta_b z) + s_+ \exp(j\beta_b z)\}\exp(-j\beta_e z) \quad \text{forward}$$

and

$$B\{\exp(j\beta_b z) + s_- \exp(-j\beta_b z)\}\exp(j\beta_e z) \quad \text{backward}$$

(8.9)

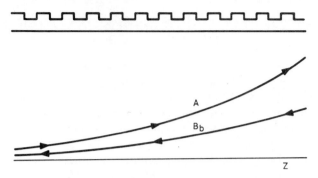

Figure 8.4 Diagrammatic representation of amplitudes of forward and back scattered components of forward (left-to-right) propagating eigen wave combination in corrugated dielectric waveguide

whilst the expressions for the forward and backward components of the local waves are:

$$\{A \exp(-j\beta_e z) + s_- B \exp(j\beta_e z)\}\exp(-j\beta_b z) \quad \text{forward}$$
$$\{B \exp(j\beta_e z) + s_+ A \exp(-j\beta_e z)\}\exp(j\beta_b z) \quad \text{backward} \qquad (8.10)$$

Equations (8.9) and (8.10) above deserve careful examination. Each individual expression in equation (8.9) describes an eigen combination of forward and backward waves which, over long distances, may be considered to propagate with wave vector β_e in only one direction in the sense that its combined amplitude and its combined phase relationship changes steadily in that direction. For instance, in a gain situation the amplitude of the backward-scattered component of the wave increases in the direction of propagation of the main forward wave. Paradoxically, therefore, as shown in Figure 8.4, the backward component gives the impression of an attenuating wave. When the two oppositely propagating eigen waves, corresponding to the two expressions in equation (8.9), are combined the individual forward and individual reverse waves from each eigen wave both interfere. Since the slowly changing components of their phase characteristics are oppositely directed this interference, over long distances, is periodically constructive and destructive. Equation (8.10) illustrates this effect. The expressions within the curly brackets represent the local amplitude of the forward and backward waves, and these vary slowly with position according to the wave vector β_e. The local waves, however, effectively propagate with a wave vector β_b, which is equal to the Bragg vector, and which is not greatly different from the unperturbed propagation constant of the waves.

8.4   REFLECTION AND TRANSMISSION COEFFICIENTS
OF EIGEN WAVES

A periodic structure can only operate as a resonant cavity if it has a termination at each end which reflects the eigen modes. Such reflections can be produced in a variety of ways and can result from relatively small changes in the periodic structure. For instance, a change only in the gain properties of the medium, which would have negligible effect in a normal waveguide, can be sufficient to produce a considerable reflection in a periodic guide close to the Bragg condition. To analyse the behaviour it is necessary to evaluate the effective reflection coefficients for the various possible terminations. The values obtained from the reflection coefficients can then be used, in conjunction with the propagation coefficients of the eigen waves, to write down the threshold condition for the resonator in the same way as for a conventional laser. The transmission properties of the termination also need investigation. The output path in most lasers with periodic structures occupies an extended region and so, to obtain the magnitude of the net output, the effect of the transmission coefficient between the regions needs to be combined with the effect of the propagation characteristics along the output region. The incremental efficiency of the device can then be calculated.

Let the proportional reflected component of the eigen waves at any point in the structure be R_{eff}. R_{eff} will be defined in terms of the quantities A and B in equation (8.9) at reference plane $z = 0$ as follows

$$R_{eff} = \left(\frac{B}{A}\right) \exp(-2j\beta_e z) \tag{8.11}$$

We consider below the magnitude of the reflection R_{eff} created at different boundaries.

To investigate the transmission of eigen waves across a boundary let us treat the junction between two periodic regions of different characteristics, say region 1 on the input side and region 2 on the output side. The proportional transmission from region 1 to region 2, say T_{12}, will be defined as follows

$$T_{12} = \frac{A_2}{A_1} \tag{8.12}$$

where A_1 and A_2 apply to regions 1 and 2, respectively. It should be noted that $|T_{12}|^2$ does not give the proportional power transfer across the boundary, unlike most transmission coefficients. The net power transfer is affected by the backward waves associated with A_1 and A_2 (see equation (8.10)) and is dependent upon the associated values of s. Also, in cases where s is complex (e.g. when gain or loss is present) the forward and backward eigen waves are not orthogonal and their power flows cannot be treated independently. The first inconvenience can be overcome by redefining the A's and B's in terms of the s's but the second inconvenience cannot be simply removed. Therefore it is probably simpler to retain the original definitions of A and B, since their interpretation is straightforward.

We now proceed to evaluate the reflection coefficient R_{eff} at various boundaries between different corrugated sections. The boundaries may comprise a change in the depth, or the period, or the phase or the gain, of the corrugations. As a simplifying assumption we take the local transmitted and reflected waves to be unaffected by the boundary and therefore to be continuous across it. This is a satisfactory assumption when the reflections from an individual corrugation or part of a corrugation are negligible compared with the longer distance effects associated with the change in the periodic characteristics at the boundary. Consider two different corrugated regions adjacent to one another, region 1 on the input side and region 2 on the output side. Let R be the proportional reflected component of the local (conventional) wave at the boundary. Let A_2 and B_2 be the amplitudes of the forward and reflected eigen waves in region 2 (B_2 resulting, say, from a second discontinuity beyond region 2). Close to $z = 0$ (the point of reference for the phases of A and B at a minimum in the corrugated pattern), where $\beta_e z$ can be ignored, R is given in terms of A_2 and B_2, according to equation (8.10), by

$$R = \frac{B_2 + s_2 A_2}{A_2 + s_2 B_2} \exp(-j\theta_2) \tag{8.13}$$

where $\theta_2 = 2\beta_b z_2$ and z_2 is the (small) distance between the reference point for the reflection and the minimum in the corrugation pattern. Expressed in terms of the effective reflection coefficient of the eigen wave in region 2, say R_{e2}, this becomes

$$R = \frac{R_{e2} + s_2}{1 + R_{e2} s_2} \exp(-j\theta_2) \tag{8.14}$$

Conversely, when the local wave has a reflection coefficient R the effective reflection coefficient, say R_{e1}, for the eigen wave in region 1, where s has the value, say s_1, is given by

$$R_{e1} = \frac{R \exp(j\theta_1) - s_1}{1 - s_1 R \exp(j\theta_1)} \tag{8.15}$$

where $\theta_1 = 2\beta_b z$ and z_1 is the (small) distance equivalent to z_2 but on the input side of the junction. Substituting R from (8.14) into (8.15) gives the effective reflection coefficient of the eigen wave in region 1 in terms of that in region 2 as follows

$$R_{e1} = \frac{s_2 \exp(j\theta) - s_1 + R_{e2}(\exp(j\theta) - s_1 s_2)}{1 - s_1 s_2 \exp(j\theta) + R_{e2}(s_2 - s_1 \exp(j\theta))} \tag{8.16}$$

where $\theta = \theta_2 - \theta_1$ takes account of a possible phase discontinuity in the corrugations at the boundary between the two regions. The presence of the term R_{e2} in the right-hand side of (8.16) is convenient for analysis of the behaviour when further reflections occur beyond the boundary concerned. The normally understood reflection coefficient at the boundary is obtained by setting R_{e2} equal to zero.

To evaluate the proportional transmission across the boundary [equation (8.12)] we first obtain a relation between A_1 and A_2 across the boundary by equating the expressions for the local forward wave on the input and output sides obtained from equation (8.7). This gives

$$A_1(1 + s_1 R_{e1})\exp\left(\frac{j\theta_1}{2}\right) = A_2(1 + s_2 R_{e2})\exp\left(\frac{j\theta_2}{2}\right) \tag{8.17}$$

Substituting the expression for R_{e1} given in equation (8.16) into (8.17) and then substituting the value for A_2/A_1 into (8.12) gives the following expression for T_{12} in terms of R_{e2}, s_1, and s_2

$$T_{12} = \frac{(1 - s_1^2)\exp(j\theta/2)}{1 - s_1 s_2 \exp(j\theta) + R_{e2}(s_2 - s_1 \exp(j\theta))} \tag{8.18}$$

In the same way as for equation (8.16), equation (8.18) can be used for the analysis of the behaviour when further reflections occur beyond the boundary concerned. The normally understood transmission coefficient of the boundary [with the provisos mentioned in connection with equation (8.12)] is obtained by setting R_{e2} equal to zero.

The above general expressions for the reflection and transmission coefficients will be evaluated in the next section for the various terminations appropriate for resonators in the periodic guide and used for deriving the laser threshold conditions and the output coupling efficiency.

8.5 THRESHOLD CONDITIONS AND OUTPUT COUPLING OF PERIODIC STRUCTURES

Let us consider the condition that determines laser threshold. The requirement to be satisfied is that the eigen wave, in a periodic structure, in its roundtrip propagation within the laser resonator, involving a forward and backward pass and a reflection at each end, should be transformed precisely back to its initial state. The equation that describes this condition is

$$(R_{eff})_1 (R_{eff})_2 \exp(-2j\beta_e L) = 1 \tag{8.19}$$

where L is the length of the resonator and where subscripts 1 and 2 on R_{eff}, respectively, represent reflections at opposite ends of the resonator.

In the sub-sections that follow we use equation (8.19) in conjunction with the expression for the reflection coefficients of the eigen modes given in the previous section to derive the threshold for three different periodic laser structures. In certain cases we also use the transmission coefficients from the previous section to derive the output coupling efficiency.

8.5.1 Partially pumped DFB Laser

Let us first consider a laser structure in which the gain is applied only over a central portion of the length of the corrugated section, with the remainder being left in a lossy condition. The inner and outer portions then have different values for s which we denote respectively by s_1 and s_2. In this case we assume that the outer sections are sufficiently long such that any component of the eigen wave which is reflected at the far end of the outer section is attenuated to a negligible value when it returns to the point of transition between the inner and outer sections. The reflection coefficient observed at the boundary to the outer section from within the centre section is then obtained from equation (8.16) by setting R_{e2} and θ equal to zero, giving

$$R_{e1} = \frac{s_2 - s_1}{1 - s_1 s_2} \tag{8.20}$$

The imaginary parts of s_1 and s_2 are of opposite sign [see equation (8.7)] whereas the real parts are of the same sign. Hence R_{e1} in the above expression is largely imaginary, of negative sign, and it can have a considerable amplitude. This result shows that a change from gain to loss, which is a normal waveguide would introduce a negligible discontinuity, can create a considerable reflection coefficient for the eigen waves in a corrugated guide. Provided that the change is reasonably abrupt it can form a satisfactory termination to a resonant cavity and provide as much feedback under appropriate circumstances as a normal end-face in a laser cavity.

8.5.2 Distributed Bragg Reflection Laser

Secondly we treat the case of a laser where a pair of distributed Bragg reflectors enclose between them a length of uniform guide. We analyse this case in more detail than in the previous instance and consider how the length of the Bragg reflectors as well as their periodicity influences the behaviour. It is assumed that each Bragg reflector feeds, at its output end, into further uniform guides. The reflection originating from this second discontinuity will also be taken into account.

To obtain the reflection coefficient for the eigen wave at the output end of the Bragg reflector, say R_{e3}, we use an equation of the type of (8.15), with R, the reflected wave in the uniform output line, taken to be zero and s_1 set equal to s, the value appropriate to the distributed Bragg reflecting sections. This gives

$$R_{e3} = -s \tag{8.21}$$

Transforming this reflection back over the length L of the Bragg reflector to a point just on the output side of its input end produces a different reflection coefficient R_{e2} with smaller amplitude (if lossy) and altered phase, given by

$$R_{e2} = -s \exp(-2j\beta_e L) \tag{8.22}$$

where β_e is the propagation coefficient of the eigen wave [see equation (8.8)]. To find the reflection in the uniform guide just on the input side of the boundary to the Bragg reflector we use equation (8.14) with $s_2 = s$ and $\theta_2 = 0$ [or equation (8.16) with $s_2 = s$, $\theta_2 = 0$, and $s_1 = 0$] and R_{e2} as given above obtaining

$$R_{e1} = \frac{s\{1 - \exp(-2j\beta_e L)\}}{1 - s^2 \exp(-2j\beta_e L)} \left\{ = \frac{k \sin(\beta_e L)}{(\delta + jg)\sin(\beta_e L) + \beta_e \cos(\beta_e L)} \right\} \tag{8.23}$$

The overall transmission coefficient, say T, between the uniform guide at the input of the Bragg reflector and the uniform guide at its output is equal to the product of three terms, namely the transmission coefficient at the input boundary, say T_{12}, the transformation produced by propagation along the Bragg section, i.e. $\exp(-j\beta_e L)$, and the transmission coefficient at the output boundary, say T_{23}. T_{23} is obtained from equation (8.18) by setting $s_1 = s$, $s_2 = 0$, $\theta = 0$, and $R_{e2} = 0$. T_{12} is obtained from the same equation setting $s_1 = 0$, $s_2 = s$, $\theta = 0$, and R_{e2} equal to the value given by equation (8.22). Hence

$$T = \frac{(1 - s^2)\exp(-j\beta_e L)}{1 - s^2 \exp(-2j\beta_e L)} \left\{ = \frac{\beta_e}{(\delta + jg)\sin(\beta_e L) + j\beta_e \cos(\beta_e L)} \right\} \tag{8.24}$$

The above transmission coefficient relates the magnitude of a conventional wave in a normal guide at the input to the reflector to a similar wave at the output, and therefore $|T|^2$ represents the real proportional power transfer.

First let us consider the behaviour of a Bragg reflector which is sufficiently long such that the naturally occurring loss effectively isolates the far end. As a result the overall transmission coefficient becomes small; we consider later how we must compromise on reflector length to prevent it becoming too small. The input reflection coefficient R_{e2}, however, tends in these conditions to a specific value which, according to equation (8.23), is simply equal to s.

Let us investigate how this value is affected by the other parameters. From equation (8.7) it can be seen that s depends on the normalized quantity $\delta/|k|$, which represents the relative amount by which the optical frequency is mistuned from the exact Bragg condition, and on the relative gain (or loss) $g/|k|$. The curves in Figure 8.5 illustrate this relation. The amplitude $|s|$ of the reflection is plotted in Figure 8.5(a) as a function of $\delta/|k|$ in a series of curves with the parameter $g/|k|$ taking various values in the range $0 > g/|k| > -0.5$. The phase ϕ of s is plotted in a similar way in Figure 8.5(b).

The curves in Figure 8.5(a) show that the amplitude of the reflection coefficient is in general relatively large and close to unity over the stop-band of the Bragg reflector $(-1 < \delta/|k| < 1)$ although it becomes appreciably less when the loss exceeds a value corresponding approximately to $g/|k| < -0.2$. The curves in Figure 8.5(b) show that the phase of the reflection changes by approximately π rad as the optical frequency moves through the stop-band. Such a tuning range is sufficient to bring all cavities into resonance whatever their precise length, except perhaps the very shortest, somewhere within the stop-band. The threshold condition depends on the exact length of the cavity and on how close the optical frequency is to that which gives the maximum value of $|s|$. Under optimum conditions threshold occurs for a value of g given by

$$g = \ln\left(\frac{1}{|s_{\max}|}\right) \tag{8.25}$$

This expression is of the same form as that in a conventional laser, but of course can be satisfied for only one longitudinal mode.

Let us now consider the reflection and transmission properties of a Bragg reflector of shorter length. We will take the (coupling × length) product $|k|L$ as a convenient measure of the reflector length since this parameter can be used in conjunction with the other parameters $\delta/|k|$ and $g/|k|$ to obtain the total phase change $\beta_e L$ of the eigen wave from equation (8.8). $\beta_e L$ may then be inserted into equations (8.23) for R_{e1} and (8.24) for T. As an example of the results that may be obtained we show in Figures 8.6(a) and (b) and 8.7 how the phase and amplitude of R_{e2} and the amplitude of T vary with $\delta/|k|$ for the particular case $|k|L = 1$ and for various negative values of $g/|k|$. Comparison of these curves with those of Figure 8.5 for a long Bragg reflector shows a behaviour which is in general similar, but where the peak value of the reflection coefficient at the centre of the frequency band is reduced and where the frequency response is broadened [see Figure 8.6(a)]. In the region outside the stop-band the

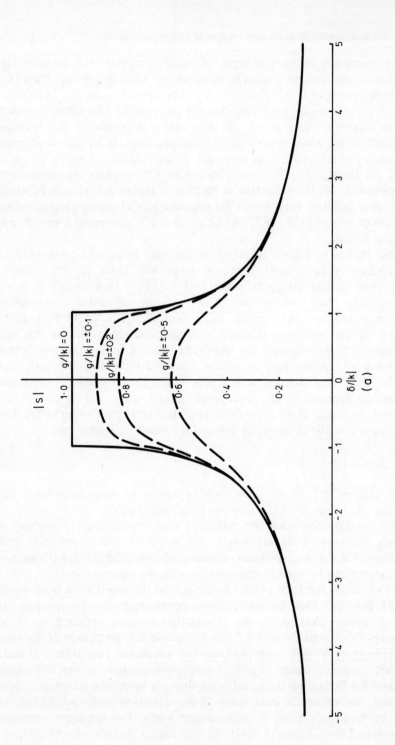

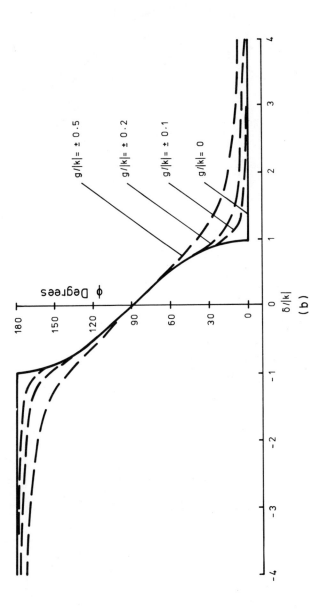

Figure 8.5 Amplitude and phase of back scattered components of eigen wave in corrugated waveguide. Also represents amplitude and phase of reflection coefficient between uniform and corrugated waveguide. (a) Amplitude $|s|$ as a function of normalized offset frequency $\delta/|k|$ for various values of normalized gain (or loss) $g/|k|$, (b) phase ϕ of s as a function of normalized offset frequency $\delta/|k|$ for various values of normalized gain (or loss) $g/|k|$

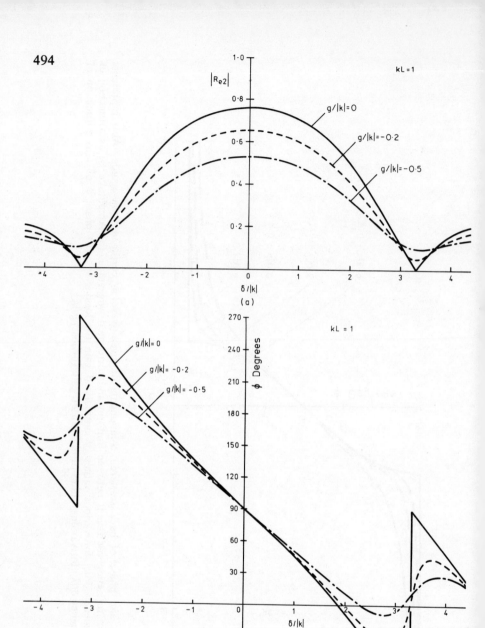

Figure 8.6 Reflection coefficient produced by a distributed Bragg reflector of limited length ($|k|L = 1$). (a) Modulus of reflection coefficient as a function of normalized frequency offset $\delta/|k|$ for various negative values of normalized gain $g/|k|$, (b) phase of reflection coefficient as a function of normalized frequency offset $\delta/|k|$ for various negative values of normalized gain $g/|k|$

reflection coefficient varies periodically with the optical frequency as a result of interference between the reflections from opposite ends of the Bragg reflector, and when the loss is small ($g/|k| < 0.2$), the two reflections almost cancel at certain values thereby giving very deep minima. These minima become less pronounced as the losses increase. The phase ϕ of the reflection coefficient [see Figure 8.6(b)] varies somewhat more strongly with frequency within the stop-band than for the long reflector, particularly for low losses, and also shows a periodic behaviour outside the stop-band. The transmission coefficient (see Figure 8.7) shows a complementary dependence on the optical frequency to the reflection coefficient, although only when losses are zero does the sum of the transmitted and incident power equal that of the reflected power. As the losses increase the transmitted power naturally becomes relatively smaller.

To illustrate the combined effect of the length of the Bragg reflector and the size of the optical losses on the transmission and reflection coefficients, and to show how the length should be chosen in terms of the losses for optimum performance, we illustrate in Figure 8.8 the relation between the reflection coefficient of the Bragg section and its transmission loss, as measured at the centre optical frequency, for various values of $|k|L$ and $g/|k|$. The curves show the relation between the power reflection $|R_{e1}|^2$ and the proportion of non-reflected power which is transmitted through the

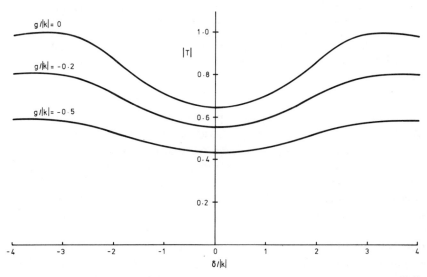

Figure 8.7 Transmission coefficient between input and output of distributed Bragg reflector of limited length ($|k|L = 1$). Modulus $|T|$ plotted against normalized offset frequency $\delta/|k|$ for various negative values of normalized gain $g/|k|$

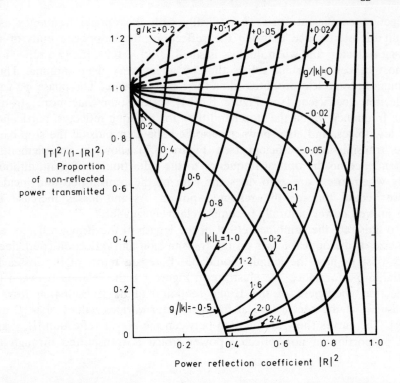

Figure 8.8 Relation between input power reflection coefficient $|R|^2$ of distributed Bragg reflector and fractional transmission of non-reflected power between input and output ($|T|^2/(1 - |R|^2)$) at Bragg frequency Curves shown for constant gain (or loss) and variation of normalized length $|k|L$, and also for constant length and variation of normalized gain $g/|k|$

Bragg reflector, i.e. $|T|^2/(1 - |R_{e1}|^2)$, plotted either for $g/|k|$ constant and $|k|L$ varied or for $|k|L$ constant and $g/|k|$ varied. As an example, for an optical loss corresponding to $g/|k| = -0.5$, we see that if we wish to retain at least 50 per cent of the optical power transmitted into the input of the Bragg reflector we cannot increase the power reflection coefficient of the reflector, by increasing its length, above about 18 per cent. The length concerned corresponds to $|k|L = 0.6$. If these losses are reduced so that $g/|k| = -0.1$ then the corresponding figures are 66 per cent power reflection for 50 per cent transmission in the section and a value of $|k|L$ of around 1.5. The maximum value of $|k|$ that can be easily achieved, as is described in a later section, is around 100 cm^{-1} and hence losses need to be kept well below 50 cm^{-1} in order to combine a good reflection (e.g. 30 per cent in power) coupled with reasonable transmission.

The longitudinal mode discrimination of the distributed Bragg reflection laser depends on the frequency spacing between the longitudinal modes in the cavity and the frequency spectrum of the reflection coefficient R of the periodic Bragg reflectors. The discrimination increases in proportion to the amount by which $\ln(1/R)$ for the subsidiary modes exceeds that for the dominant modes. This depends on a variety of factors including the value of $\ln(1/R_{max})$ at the Bragg frequency, the length L_c of the centre section of the resonator, the coupling coefficient k, the length L, and the amount of loss $-g$ associated with the Bragg reflector, and requires evaluation for any particular situation. However, in the normal practical cases where R_{max} does not approach unity an adequate criterion of satisfactory mode discrimination is that the mode spacing of the cavity should be greater than about one-third of the nominal width of the stop-band, so that subsidiary resonances are displaced to points where the reflection coefficient has normally dropped by at least 10 per cent. The proportional width of the stop-band is $|k|/\epsilon^{1/2}\beta_0$. The proportional spacing between longitudinal modes in a normal cavity length L_c is $\lambda/2\bar{\mu}_{eff}L_c$ (see Chapter 2, Section 2.8.1), where $\bar{\mu}_{eff} \simeq 4.5$, but the frequency dependence of the phase of the reflection from the periodic sections reduces this spacing by about 20 per cent in a Bragg reflection laser. Taking the criterion of a mode spacing of one-third of the stop-band and putting $\epsilon^{1/2} = 3.6$ gives $|k|L_c < 3$. This is a relatively demanding requirement and indicates that perfect longitudinal mode control is not necessarily obtained automatically in lasers with distributed Bragg reflectors, but must be carefully taking into account in the design.

8.5.3   Distributed Feedback Laser with Uniform Output Guides

Thirdly, let us consider the threshold condition for a conventional distributed feedback laser. Here the corrugated central section is pumped over its whole length and is terminated at both ends by uncorrugated sections. There is no reflected component of the output wave in these terminating sections, and therefore the local reflection coefficient R at the boundary with the central section is zero (ignoring any small effects produced by incomplete corrugations at the interface). By inserting $R = 0$ in equation (8.15) we find that the effective reflection coefficient R_{eff} for the eigen wave combination in the central section is $-s$. The threshold condition for oscillation given in equation (8.19) for a laser of length L therefore becomes

$$s_+ s_- \exp(-2j\beta_e L) = 1$$

or   (8.26)

$$s \exp(-j\beta_e L) = \pm 1 \text{ for } s_+ = s_-$$

This is a more demanding condition than that in equation (8.25) for the Bragg reflection laser because of the close interdependence between s and β_e. Using equations (8.7) and (8.8) to eliminate s (note $s - 1/s = -\beta_e/|k|$) gives the following equation for determining the possible values of β_e

$$\frac{\sin(\beta_e L)}{\beta_e} = \pm \frac{j}{|k|} \tag{8.27}$$

[obtained from (8.26), (8.7), and (8.8) by subtracting s from its reciprocal]. The quantities of more practical interest which control threshold current and wavelength are δ and g. These are related to β_e by

$$(\delta + jg) = \pm|k|\cos(\beta_e L) = j\beta_e \cot(\beta_e L) \tag{8.28}$$

Before discussing the detailed solution of equation (8.27) for threshold let us consider qualitatively the interaction between the reflection coefficient $-s$ and the propagation coefficient β_e. As the optical frequency is made to approach the stop-band from (say) above [$(\delta/|k|)$ correspondingly being decreased in magnitude towards unity] by suitable variation of the length of the corrugated section (see below) so both the reflection coefficient of the eigen waves at the output termination rises [as illustrated in Figure 8.5(a)] and the amplification becomes larger [imaginary component of β_e in equation (8.8)]. The threshold condition of equation (8.26) is satisfied with steadily decreasing values of the gain g of the local wave, until at the point that the stop-band is entered g becomes zero. Beyond this point a solution to equation (8.26) is impossible, and no lasing occurs within the stop-band (here defined as $-|k| < \delta < |k|$), the mathematical reason being a combination of excessive gain and excessive reflection coefficient for the eigen modes.

The amount by which the lasing frequency in the fundamental resonance lies outside the stop-band is determined by the length of the corrugated section. Examination of equation (8.7) for s shows that the reflection coefficient for the eigen modes at the output termination of the corrugated section lies in the fourth quadrant of the complex plane. It therefore provides a degree of phase delay to the reflected eigen wave and this decreases as the gain g of the local wave is reduced. Because of this phase delay the total phase change of the eigen modes in the fundamental resonance corresponds to somewhat less than π rad between the two ends of the resonator, or a multiple of π for the higher order modes. As the length of the resonator is increased so, therefore, the propagation constant of the eigen waves must decrease in approximate inverse proportion. This decrease can only be realized by the optical frequency approaching the stop-band. In the process the reflection coefficient for the eigen waves at the output termination approaches unity. Also, the gain coefficient for the eigen waves becomes increasingly magnified with respect to that of the plane waves. Hence increasing the length of the corrugated section reduces the threshold gain coefficient not only in the conventional way directly because of the greater length but also beause of the increased reflection coefficient and because of the greater relative magnification of the gain. The amount of backward coupling k is important in this process. Increasing the coupling causes the increase in reflection and the enhancement of the gain to set in for shorter lengths of the corrugated section and hence reduces the total threshold current.

A more precise illustration of the above behaviour is given in the threshold curves in Figures 8.9, 8.10, and 8.11, which are obtained by numerical solution of equations (8.27) and (8.28). These equations can conveniently be normalized with respect to L. Thus, dividing equations (8.27) by L gives an equation for $\beta_e L$ with $|k|L$ as the only variable parameter. Similarly, multiplying equation (8.28) by L shows that δL and gL depend via $\beta_e L$ on $|k|L$. Hence $|k|L$ may be regarded as the only independent variable.

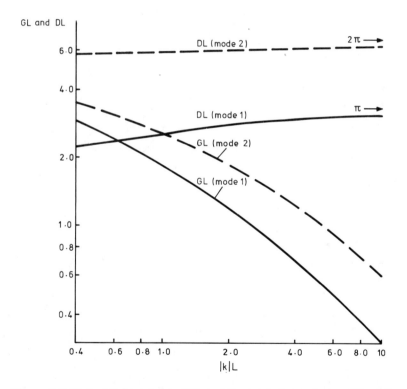

Figure 8.9 Plot of the total gain GL and the total phase change DL of the eigen waves of the first two longitudinal modes in a distributed feedback laser as a function of normalized length $|k|L$

Figure 8.9 shows how the values of the real (phase component) and imaginary (gain component) parts of $\beta_e L$, labelled as DL and GL, respectively, vary as a function of $|k|L$ for the first-order and second-order longitudinal modes. DL tends towards $n\pi$, where n is the mode number, as $|k|L$ becomes large. The total gain GL of the eigen mode decreases as $|k|L$ is increased, indicating that the reflection coefficient for these modes increases as the length of the resonator is increased. The proportional difference in gain between adjacent modes also increases with the length of the resonator, tending to a gain ratio of 2 for large $|k|L$.

Figure 8.10 shows how the total threshold gain gL, as conventionally defined for normal waves, varies with $|k|L$. Curves are given for a series of different modes. Beyond a certain value of $|k|L$, gL decreases more rapidly

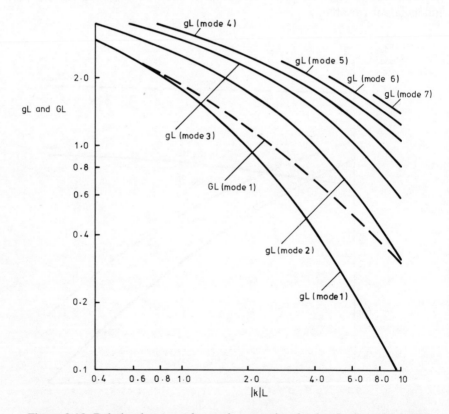

Figure 8.10 Relation between the total conventional gain gL along the length of the resonator and the normalized length $|k|L$ of a distributed feedback laser for various longitudinal modes. A curve of GL for the first mode also given for comparison

with increase of $|k|L$ than does GL and for the first-order mode this is true for values of $|k|L$ greater than unity, as is illustrated in the figure. As a result of the steeper characteristics the discrimination between the modes is greater as measured in terms of the intrinsic gain g than in terms of the eigen mode gain G. Discrimination relative to g is what determines the mode distribution in practice. For values of $|k|L$ greater than about 5 the important threshold gain ratio between the first- and second-order modes approaches a value of around 4. This is more than sufficient to suppress all except the first-order mode in all practical circumstances.

Figure 8.11 shows how $\delta/|k|$ for the various modes varies with $|k|L$. $\delta/|k|$

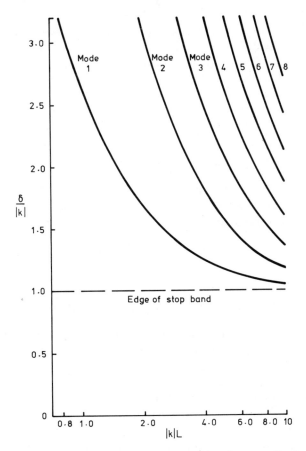

Figure 8.11 Plot of deviation $\delta/|k|$ of normalized resonance frequency of distributed feedback laser from Bragg condition for different longitudinal modes as a function of normalized length $|k|L$

measures the relative displacement of the optical resonance frequency for the different modes from the central Bragg frequency. All the resonances occur outside the stop-band. They close up as $|k|L$ is increased and the lowest order modes bunch closely just outside the stop-band. In addition to the curves shown in the figure a set of mirror-image curves occur for negative values of $\delta/|k|$. As mentioned above, in all normal circumstances only the first-order mode is excited but in principle there are two such modes equally spaced on either side of the stop-band.

From the curves for threshold gain gL in Figure 8.10 we can find what value of the coupling $|k|L$ is required in a distributed feedback laser to make the threshold current density comparable to that in a Fabry–Perot laser whilst obtaining satisfactory performance in other respects. To operate at the same gain in a Fabry–Perot laser of the same length ($gL \simeq 0.57$–0.3) $|k|L$ for the distributed feedback laser should lie in the range 3–5. The value of $|k|$ is then between 5 and 15 times the net gain g per unit length. For efficient operation the net gain should be at least equal to the radiation losses, and preferably considerably greater. However, the amount of radiation depends on the depth of the corrugations (see Section 8.8) and therefore increases as $|k|$ is increased. Hence for performance comparable to a Fabry–Perot laser we must demand that the backward coupling $|k|$ should be at least an order of magnitude greater than the associated radiation loss. Only then can the device be operated efficiently with a value of $|k|L$ large enough to give comparable feedback to that in a Fabry–Perot laser. As an example it is likely that radiation losses will have a value of at least 10 cm^{-1} equivalent to 20 cm^{-1} when measured in terms of power. Hence k should be 100 cm^{-1} or greater. With this value the laser length L can be chosen to be 300 μm and upwards, and the performance and convenience approach that in a Fabry–Perot laser.

8.6   INCREMENTAL EFFICIENCY

The incremental efficiency of a laser incorporating a corrugated guide is determined by considerations similar to those for a normal laser and depends on the optical losses in the resonator.

Let us first consider a laser with distributed Bragg reflectors. Here we assume that the gain is only applied to the uniform centre section and treat the losses in the uniform centre section and the two outer Bragg reflecting sections separately.

The behaviour in the uniform centre section of the DBR laser is precisely the same as that in a conventional laser. The standard equation for the incremental efficiency [see Chapter 2, equation (2.91)], with the length L_c and the loss coefficient α of the centre section and the power reflection coefficient $|R_{el}|^2$ of the Bragg reflecting sections incorporated [see equation (8.23) for R_{el}], becomes

$$\eta_c = \eta_0 \left\{ 1 + \frac{\alpha L_c}{2} \ln \left(\frac{1}{|R_{el}|} \right) \right\}^{-1} \tag{8.29}$$

This equation gives the efficiency η_c with which optical power is fed to the input ends of the Bragg reflectors.

The transmission characteristics of Bragg reflectors are treated in Section 8.5.2. In terms of the quantities defined in that section the proportion of non-reflected optical power which is transmitted through the Bragg reflector is given by $|T|^2/(1 - |R_{el}|^2)$. Hence the overall efficiency η of the Bragg reflecting laser is given by

$$\eta = \frac{\eta_0 |T|^2}{(1 - |R_{el}|^2)\{1 + \alpha L_c/2 \ln(1/|R_{el}|)\}} \tag{8.30}$$

The value of $|T|^2/(1 - |R_{el}|^2)$ at the Bragg frequency can be obtained from the curves in Figure 8.8 in terms of the length and loss of the Bragg reflector.

Let us now consider the incremental efficiency of the distributed feedback laser. We may apply the same treatment as given for the conventional laser in Section 2.7.2. This treatment derives the efficiency by comparing the power being supplied to the growing wave with the power being dissipated in optical losses. The analysis shows that, for limited power output, whatever the longitudinal distribution of optical field may be, the power supplied to the growing wave and the power dissipated in optical losses are related to one another at all points in the fixed ratio of the gain to the loss coefficient. Because of this independence to the particular longitudinal distribution of field the equation (2.90) that was previously obtained for the efficiency is still valid in the present instance. However, we must be careful to define our present gain in the same way as for the above equation. The gain in equation (2.90) is related to optical power and includes the gain necessary to counteract optical loss. We now denote this gain by **g**. **g** is related to the amplitude gain g in the present instance by

$$\mathbf{g} = \alpha + 2g \tag{8.31}$$

Equation (2.90) for the incremental efficiency η in terms of the internal efficiency η_0 therefore becomes

$$\eta = \frac{\eta_0 g}{g + \alpha/2} \tag{8.32}$$

where g is obtained for any particular value of $|k|L$ and L from the curves in Figure 8.10.

In principle the incremental efficiency of a distributed feedback laser should be very similar to that of a conventional laser of similar general properties. However, it is probable that, in practice, radiation loss arising from the corrugations, particularly scattering loss due to random irregularities, would be greater than in a conventional laser, and hence the incremental efficiency would be lower.

8.7 MAGNITUDE OF THE COUPLING COEFFICIENT

In this section we derive the magnitude of the coupling coefficient k for a periodic structure with a rectangular corrugation as a function of the height and width of the corrugation. We compare this with the theoretical results obtained for other corrugation patterns.

The coupling coefficient k for a corrugated waveguide was shown in Section 8.2 to be equal to $R_c/j\Lambda$, where R_c is the effective reflection coefficient of a single corrugation. An expression was given for R_c, appropriate to a rectangular corrugation pattern, in equation (8.3) in terms of the change in propagation constant β_z between the thick and thin sections of the dielectric guide. We now wish to re-express this result directly in terms of the height of the corrugation. The necessary background treatment is given in Chapter 4, Section 4.1.2, where β_z is derived in terms of the normalized transverse wave vector Q and relations are given between Q and the thickness of the guide. The relation for β_z is

$$\beta_z^2 = \beta_0^2(\epsilon_1 - Q^2\delta\epsilon) \tag{8.33}$$

where $\delta\epsilon$ is the dielectric step between the centre and outer regions of the guide, $\beta_0 = 2\pi/\lambda$, and Q is expressed in terms of the actual transverse wave vector q as $q/\delta\epsilon^{1/2}\beta_0$. Differentiating (8.33) with respect to Q and β_z to obtain the term $\delta\beta_z/\beta_z$ that appears in equation (8.3) for R_c gives

$$\frac{\delta\beta_z}{\beta_z} = -\left(\frac{\beta_0}{\beta_z}\right)^2 \delta\epsilon Q \delta Q$$

$$\simeq -\frac{Q\delta Q\delta\epsilon}{\epsilon_1} \tag{8.34}$$

According to Chapter 4, Section 4.1.2, Q, for a symmetrical dielectric waveguide, is given in terms of the normalized thickness D of the guiding layer $(= d\delta\epsilon^{1/2}\beta_0$, where d is the actual thickness) by

$$\cos\left(\frac{QD}{2}\right) = Q \tag{8.35}$$

Differentiating with respect to Q and D gives

$$\delta Q = \frac{-Q\delta D}{2/P + D} \tag{8.36}$$

(where $P^2 = 1 - Q^2$). Substituting (8.36) into (8.34) and then into (8.3) to obtain R_c, and then using $k = 2R_c/jn\lambda_b$ to find k, gives

$$k = \left[\frac{1}{n\lambda_b}\right]\left[\frac{\delta\epsilon}{\epsilon_1^{1/2}}\right][\sin(\beta_z a)]\left[\frac{Q^2}{s}\right]\delta d \qquad (8.37)$$

where $\beta_z \simeq \epsilon_1^{1/2}\beta_0$ and where s is given by

$$s = \frac{S}{\beta_0\delta\epsilon^{1/2}}$$

with

$$S = \left(\frac{1}{P} + \frac{D}{2}\right) \qquad (8.38)$$

s is the effective width of the optical distribution and S is its normalized value (see Chapter 4, Section 4.1.3).

The expression for k in equation (8.37) divides up, as indicated by the brackets, into five terms, the first dependent on the wavelength and the order of the grating, the second on the dielectric step $\delta\epsilon$, the third depending on the width of the corrugations, the fourth depending on the normalized thickness of the centre layer, and the fifth depending on the height of the corrugations. The corrugation width that gives a maximum effect is one-quarter of a guide wavelength plus any integral number of half wavelengths. In most practical cases third-order diffraction is used ($n = 3$). A typical value of $\delta\epsilon/\epsilon^{1/2}$ is 1/3. Hence the product of the first three terms in (8.37) typically lies close to $1/9\lambda_b$. The fourth term needs more careful consideration, and we investigate its effect below.

To simplify the treatment of the fourth term we slightly alter equation (8.37). The equation remains valid if S [see (8.38)] is substituted for s and δD is substituted for δd. It is then easier to handle because it is expressed entirely in terms of normalized quantities. In treating the fourth term we therefore consider the value of Q^2/S which is a function only of the normalized thickness D.

Figure 8.12(a) shows how Q^2/S varies with D and also, on subsidiary scales, how the linear relation between the coupling k and the step height δd depends on d for the particular values $\lambda = 0.88$ μm, $\delta\epsilon = 1.3$, and the value of $1/9\lambda_b$ suggested above for the product of the first three terms on the right-hand side of equation (8.37). The normalized curve shows that Q^2/S rises rapidly from zero as D increases, reaching a peak value of around 0.3 close to $D = 1$ and then dropping rapidly away and falling below 0.05 at $D \simeq 5$. For the particular values of the parameters mentioned above, which are reasonably typical of a GaAs/(GaAl)As heterostructure, the coupling coefficient depends on the thickness of the centre layer as follows. The largest value of coupling coefficient for a given corrugation depth is

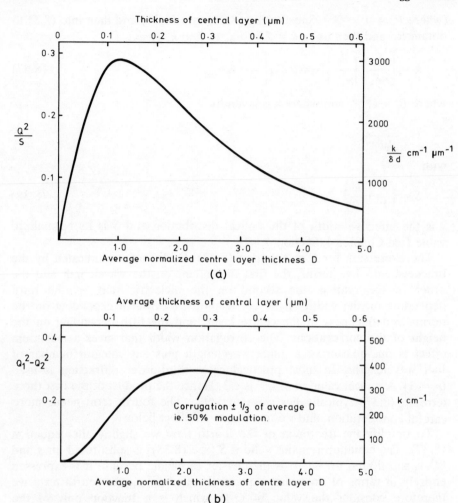

Figure 8.12 Relation between coupling coefficient k and thickness of centre layer for corrugated dielectric waveguide. Normalized curves given and also specific scales for $\delta\epsilon = 1.3$, $\lambda = 0.85$ μm, and Bragg order $n = 3$. (a) coupling coefficient per unit tooth height as a function of thickness of centre layer, (b) coupling coefficient of teeth with 50 per cent modulation depth as a function of thickness of centre layer

produced for a value of d of around 0.1 μm, the value concerned being about 3000 cm^{-1} per μm of corrugation depth. As d is increased beyond this value k decreases rapidly, falling to a value of about 1000 cm^{-1} per μm of corrugation depth at $d = 0.5$ μm.

The maximum depth of corrugations which can be used in obviously limited by the thickness of the centre layer. The thickness which gives maximum sensitivity to corrugation depth is relatively small and does not allow particularly deep corrugations to be used. To give an idea of the maximum value of k that can be achieved we consider instead the case where the corrugations penetrate through the thickness of the active layer by a fixed proportion, say 50 per cent. The curve given in Figure 8.12(b) shows how the associated value of k depends on the average thickness of the centre layer. This curve gives the difference between the value of Q^2 for the thinner and thicker sections of the guide, i.e. $Q_1^2 - Q_2^2$, as a function of D. $Q_1^2 - Q_2^2$ replaces the term $(Q^2/S)\delta D$ in equation (8.37) (normalized) when δD is no longer small, and can be used in the present instance for obtaining a more accurate value of k. Subsidiary scales are provided in the figure which give k in terms of d for the same typical values of the parameters as are used for Figure 8.12(a). The normalized curve has a fairly broad maximum over the range of normalized thickness between $D = 1.5$ and 3. This corresponds, for the special case considered, to k having a value which barely drops below its maximum value of 350 cm^{-1} between points corresponding to a thickness of the central layer of 0.2 and 0.4 μm. In practice it is not often possible, particularly in distributed feedback as opposed to passive Bragg reflecting lasers, to use layers as thin as this or to apply a 50 per cent modulation of the corrugation depth. Hence the values of k actually achieved are considerably less than the maximum figure given above.

A general expression for the coupling constant for a corrugation of arbitrary shape can be obtained using the treatment described in Section 8.2 and described in more detail in reference (10). It is closely related to that given for the rectangular corrugation in equation (8.37) and has the form

$$k = F_n \left[\frac{\pi}{2\lambda_b} \right] \left[\frac{\delta\epsilon}{\epsilon^{1/2}} \right] \left[\frac{Q^2}{S} \right] \delta d \tag{8.39}$$

where F_n is the Fourier component of the corrugation profile with period $\lambda_b/2$. This expression depends on the parameters $\delta\epsilon$ and D in exactly the same way as the previous expression and only differs according to the overall factor F_n. Hence, as stated previously, the exact shape of the corrugation in a periodic structure is normally not important to the operation of the device. However, under certain circumstances the relevant Fourier components can become small, in which case the coupling constant k is similarly affected. A particular case of great importance arises when the peaks and valleys of the corrugations have identical shape. All the even Fourier components are then zero, and the coupling constant for waves of the corresponding optical frequencies vanishes. This is the general reason for avoiding corrugation periods whose lengths are one guide wavelength or any multiple of it. Although such structures are not satisfactory for distributed feedback or Bragg reflecting devices they have interesting radiation properties, as will be described in the next section.

8.8   RADIATION FROM PERIODIC STRUCTURES

The regular grating formed at the dielectric interface in a corrugated dielectric waveguide can cause the guided wave to be radiated into the surrounding dielectric medium to an extent which depends strongly on the depth of the corrugations. The radiation is highly directional and the angle at which it is emitted depends on the period of the grating relative to the wavelength of the guided mode. This behaviour is illustrated schematically in Figure 8.13. When a wave propagates down the dielectric guide the grating can be considered to be illuminated by the component plane waves that compose the guided wave and are directed at a small angle to the guide axis (θ in the figure). In addition to the normal internal reflection which such waves undergo at the dielectric interface they are also diffracted by the grating into positive and negative first and higher orders which may be reflected respectively at greater and lesser angles than the main beam or, when the grating period is short, instead of being reflected at lesser angles, they may be transmitted into the outer dielectric medium.

Figure 8.13 shows the first-order beam being transmitted at angle ϕ into the second dielectric medium and gives the relation between θ, ϕ, the TEM wavelengths λ_1 and λ_2 in the two media, and the grating period Λ. The general form of this relation for any order m may be alternatively expressed in terms of the propagation constant β_z of the guided wave and

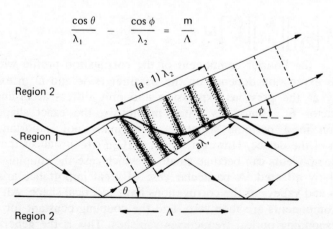

$$\frac{\cos \theta}{\lambda_1} - \frac{\cos \phi}{\lambda_2} = \frac{m}{\Lambda}$$

Figure 8.13 Schematic diagram to show how a wave is radiated from the corrugated interface of a dielectric slab waveguide

the TEM propagation constant in region 2, say β_{02} $(= \epsilon_2^{1/2}\beta_0)$, as follows

$$\beta_{02} \cos \phi = \beta_z - mK_0 \tag{8.40}$$

where $K_0 = 2\pi/\Lambda$. It should be noted that $\beta_{02} < \beta_z$ since in the absence of the grating the wave is perfectly guided, ie the equation has no solution for real ϕ for the zero-order beam and there is therefore no direction in the zero order into which power is radiated in region 2. Power is however radiated at different angles ϕ into region 2 for all values of m for which

$$\beta_{02} > \beta_m > - \beta_{02} \tag{8.41}$$

where

$$\beta_m = \beta_z - mK_0$$

Let us investigate the radiation behaviour of the different orders close to the various Bragg frequencies were $\beta_z \simeq nK_0/2$. The quantity β_m therefore becomes approximately $(n/2 - m)K_0$. Consider the case of the lowest Bragg frequency with $n = 1$. We see that the value β_1 in the first order $(m = 1)$ is approximately $-K_0/2$, i.e. $-\beta_z$. This lies outside the radiation range given in equation (8.41) and, instead of radiating, the first order couples to the backward guided wave. The behaviour of this order therefore constitutes the distributed feedback interaction with which we have been concerned in our previous treatment. As the frequency is increased so β_1 becomes less negative and when it passes the value of $-\beta_{02}$ a radiated wave becomes possible, backwardly directed at a glancing emergent angle from the centre layer.

At the second Bragg frequency $(n = 2)$ it is the second-order value of β_m that supplies the backward coupling. The first-order value is zero which corresponds to a wave being radiated at right angles to the plane of the guide. At the third Bragg frequency both first and second order radiate, equally spaced in angle both forwards and backwards from the normal to the guide and the third order provides the backward coupling.

To obtain the actual amount of radiation it is necessary to solve the appropriate two-dimensional wave equation for all the appropriate orders m of the partial waves. This has been described by Streiffer et al.[9,11,12] who have obtained numerical solutions for various particular cases. We have only space here to give a brief indication of the method.

The necessary analysis is very similar to that sketched out in Section 8.3 for deriving the propagation characteristics of the periodic guide. In fact, for a rigorous analysis of the latter problem the radiation analysis needs to be carried out to obtain the correct solution. In both analyses the approximation is made that the effect of the corrugations need only be taken into account in considering the interaction between the different partial waves, i.e. the waves with different values of m [see equation

(8.41)]. In determining the behaviour of the individual partial waves, including the fundamental forward wave ($m = 0$) and (if present) the fundamental backward wave ($m = n$) the corrugations may be regarded as smeared out and only the longitudinal average of the dielectric constant need be considered in their vicinity. Each partial wave therefore appears to propagate along or obliquely across a normal uniform waveguide. However, in the region that spans the corrugations there are present driving and driven fields that couple power from or to the other partial modes. To carry out the analysis the appropriate two-dimentsional wave equations must be solved for the partial modes and a sufficient number must be taken into account to give a satisfactory overall approximation. For greater detail the reader is recommended to refer to Streiffer *et al.*[11]

Figures 8.14 and 8.15 show some of the results of such a treatment. Figure 8.14 gives the radiated power in a particular rectangularly corrugated structure as a function of the thickness of the centre guiding layer. The dielectric step has a value of 1.4, reasonably typical of a (GaA1)As/GaAs heterostructure and the tooth height is 0.2 μm. The corrugation period of 0.21 μm is chosen to be somewhat less than needed to give a second order Bragg resonance at the specified wavelength. The radi-

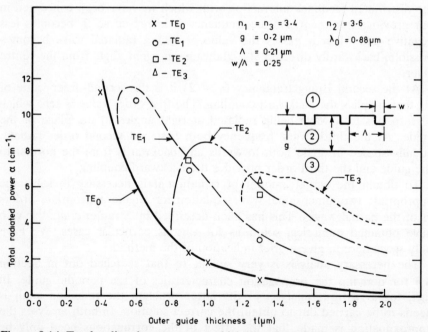

Figure 8.14 Total radiated power versus thickness of centre layer for a corrugated dielectric waveguide with rectangular grating. Curves shown for various transverse modes. (After Streifer *et al.*[11])

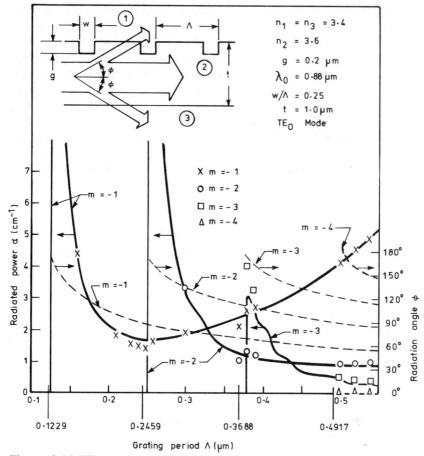

Figure 8.15 TE_0 mode radiated power (continuous curves) and radiated angle (dashed curves) in corrugated dielectric waveguide versus period of grating for each partial wave. (After Streifer *et al.*[11])

ated power is expressed in terms of the loss in cm^{-1} it imposes on the propagating wave. It can be seen that the radiation of the various transverse modes that can propagate in the structure depends inversely on the thickness of the guide, roughly as the inverse square, and that the radiation loss can rise to between 5 and 10 cm^{-1} . Other results show that the loss depends more than linearly on the dielectric constant difference between the layers of the heterostructure. It depends approximately linearly on the tooth height although superimposed on this is an oscillatory effect which gives maxima for odd numbers of half wavelengths tooth height (in the dielectric medium) and minima for even numbers.

Figure 8.15 shows the radiated power in the various orders as a function of grating period for the zero-order transverse mode at a wavelength of 0.88 μm in a waveguide with the same properties as quoted above and with a relatively thick guiding layer of 1 μm. Figure 8.15 also shows the angle ϕ of the radiated beams. The various Bragg resonances are indicated. No radiation occurs until the period just exceeds half the wavelength of the guided wave when significant power starts to be radiated in the backward direction. The power drops to a minimum at the second-order Bragg wavelength, and just beyond this point the second partial mode starts to radiate with considerable intensity. The same procedure is repeated as each new radiating order appears after each successive Bragg resonance. The total radiation at the various Bragg resonances increases with their order as a result of the larger number of radiating modes.

Let us now consider the conditions necessary for the emission of radiation through region 2 and out into external space. Let θ be the angle of the emitted beam to the normal—see Figure 8.16. Then making allowance for the refraction of the beam as it emerges from region 2 and using equation (8.40) we find for a free space wavelength of λ_0

$$\sin \theta = \epsilon_{\text{eff}}^{1/2} - \frac{m\lambda_0}{\Lambda} \tag{8.42}$$

where Λ is the grating period and $\epsilon_{\text{eff}} [= (\beta_z/\beta_0)^2]$ is the effective dielectric constant that applies to the guided wave.

At the Bragg condition

$$\frac{\lambda_0}{\Lambda_n} = \frac{2\epsilon_{\text{eff}}^{1/2}}{n} \tag{8.43}$$

where n is the Bragg order and Λ_n is the Bragg period for order n. For

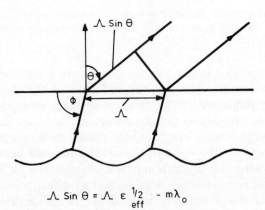

$$\Lambda \sin \theta = \Lambda \; \epsilon_{\text{eff}}^{1/2} - m\lambda_0$$

Figure 8.16 Angles associated with radiation emitted from top face of laser

even values of n we find from (8.42) that $\theta = 0$ for $m = n/2$. For odd values of m the smallest value of θ is equal to $\sin^{-1} (\epsilon_{\text{eff}}^{1/2}/n)$ which for normal values of $\epsilon_{\text{eff}}^{1/2}$ has no solution below $n = 5$ (i.e. the wave is internally reflected). For $n = 5$, $\theta \simeq \pm 45°$. These results apply reasonably accurately to distributed feedback and Bragg reflection lasers, both of which operate with wave-vectors very close to the Bragg values.

For a grating periodicity which is mistuned with respect to the Bragg value at the laser operating wavelength λ_0 we can express the radiation angle θ in terms of the ratio of the actual grating period Λ to the Bragg period Λ_n of the closest even order n as follows

$$\sin \theta = \epsilon_{\text{eff}}^{1/2}(1 - \Lambda_n/\Lambda) \qquad (8.44)$$

For normal values of ϵ_{eff}, Λ must lie within about ± 20 per cent of Λ_n in order to obtain radiation at an angle less than, say, $45°$ to the normal. Lasers radiating in this way are called grating-coupled lasers and the two directions of wave propagation within the laser emit beams inclined at opposite angles to the normal. Such lasers require external mirrors since there is no effective internal feedback from the periodic guide.

8.9   DESIGN AND PERFORMANCE OF LASERS WITH PERIODIC STRUCTURES

The construction of a satisfactory periodic waveguide for distributed feedback and Bragg-reflecting lasers is a highly demanding task and sophisticated techniques have had to be developed to give satisfactory results. Although the methods used for fabricating the corrugated structures and embedding them in further semiconductor material have now been sufficiently refined to achieve a high standard of optical performance, it is still difficult to avoid degrading the electro-luminescent characteristics of the semiconductor during the course of the various operations involved. As a result it has been found necessary to adapt the layout of the heterostructure particularly to conserve good laser performance and this has to be done at some expense to the properties of the periodic waveguide. The complete range of behaviour that is theoretically possible cannot therefore be fully exploited at present.

In the sections that follow we describe the actual performance that has been achieved in both distributed feedback and Bragg-reflecting lasers and give some indications of where the main practical difficulties lie.

8.9.1   Distributed Feedback Lasers

In the early work on distributed feedback lasers corrugations were applied directly to the active layer, either in a single heterostructure layout,[13,14] as

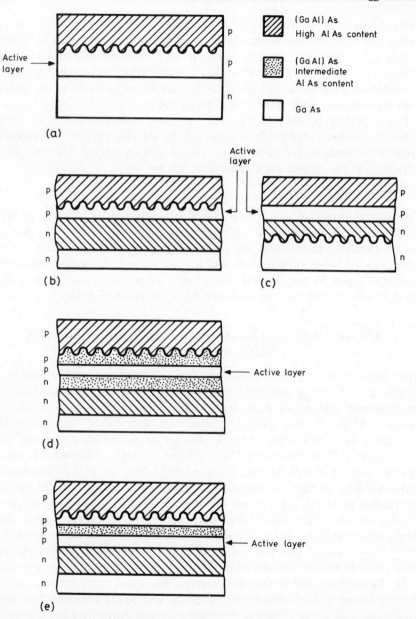

Figure 8.17 Schematic longitudinal section of various designs of distributed feedback laser. (a) single heterostructure, (b) double heterostructure, (c) double heterostructure with thin remotely corrugated lower passive layer, (d) separate confinement (GaAl)As heterostructure designed for MBE growth of final passive layer, (e) separate confinement (GaAl)As heterostructure designed for LPE growth throughout

illustrated in Figure 8.17(a) or in a double heterostructure layout,[15] as illustrated in Figure 8.17(b). Such devices were made to operate satisfactorily as injection lasers at 80 K but their performance deteriorated rapidly as the temperature was raised above this value. It is now believed that the processes involved in the formation of the corrugations, particularly ion milling, introduce non-radiative recombination centres which, when in contact with the active layer, cause a large increase in threshold current density. This occurs particularly at the higher operating temperatures when the centres become more accessible because of the greater mobility of the carriers.

To overcome this problem the corrugations may be separated from the active layer but still be made to couple strongly to the light by incorporating them in a separate confinement heterostructure. Examples of such structures, as developed respectively by Casey et al.[16] and Nakamura et al.[17,18] are illustrated in Figures 8.17(d) and (e).

Figure 8.17(d) shows a conventional five-layer separate confinement heterostructure in which the corrugations are made in the intermediate band-gap $Ga_{0.12}Al_{0.88}As$ layer on the p-side of the junction. The relatively thin GaAs active layer in this structure (0.13 μm) allows the light to spread sufficiently sideways into the adjacent layers such that a considerable light intensity reaches the corrugated region and a satisfactory coupling constant can be achieved. However, such a structure, particularly as a result of its Al content, is very difficult to grow by conventional liquid phase epitaxy (LPE) since, in the second growth stage after processing the corrugations, a (GaAl)As surface which has inevitably been somewhat oxidized by the treatment that it has previously received is presented to the growth melt, and poor nucleation results. Casey et al. avoided this difficulty by using molecular beam epitaxy (MBE) in the second growth stage. LPE was retained for the first growth stage since this provides a superior active layer with better luminescent properties.

Nakamura et al. overcame the problem by modifying the design of the separate confinement (GaAl)As heterostructure so that LPE growth could be used throughout. Basically they divide the p-type intermediate band-gap layer into two parts, the lower one having sufficient AlAs content to form an effective carrier confinement barrier at the junction with the active layer (e.g. 17 per cent AlAs) and the upper one having sufficiently low AlAs content to allow satisfactory subsequent LPE re-growth after processing for corrugations (e.g. 7 per cent AlAs). The intermediate band-gap layer on the n-side is omitted. Typical layer thicknesses are 0.2 μm for the active layer, 0.1 μm for the adjacent layer, and 0.15 μm for the corrugated layer, with the corrugations occupying the major part of this thickness. This structure provides a satisfactory degree of coupling between the corrugations and the optical field but suffers from the possible disadvantage that, because of the twin-guide layout, the discrimination against the first-order transverse mode is reduced.

Both of the above types of separate confinement distributed feedback lasers were shown to give good performance in most respects. Both use third-order Bragg corrugation periods. The devices produced by Casey *et al.* had an active length of 1760 μm (i.e. considerably longer than a normal laser) with an additional unpumped section of 100 μm to suppress Fabry–Perot modes, and a width of 160 μm. Threshold current density in pulsed operation was 2.2 kA cm^{-2} (100 ns pulses), little greater than in

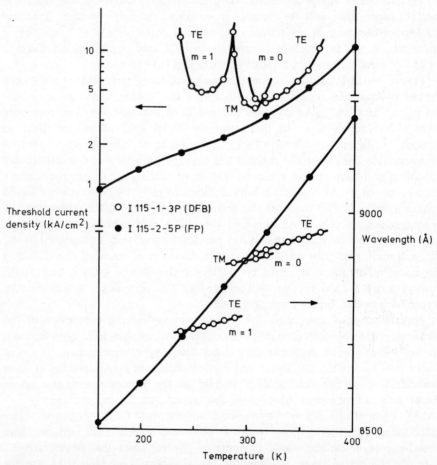

Figure 8.18 Threshold current density and lasing wavelength of a distributed feedback separate confinement laser as a function of temperature. Curves for a Fabry–Perot laser of similar construction also shown for comparison. (After Nakamura *et al.*[18])

conventional lasers made in the same material. The spectrum was limited to one or two identifiable modes and the relative insensitivity of wavelength to temperature (0.5 Å deg^{-1}) showed that the Bragg resonance was the determining factor in selecting the modes. However, various features of the spectrum, i.e. the mode spacing and the relatively broad linewidth, were difficult to explain and may have been associated with imperfections in the grating.

The devices produced by Nakamura *et al.* were designed for c.w. operation. They had a width of 50 μm using a shallow mesa construction to limit contact area and an active length of 730 μm. Again a certain additional length in the device adjacent to a cleaved end was left unpumped to suppress Fabry–Perot modes. Figure 8.18 shows the measured threshold current density and wavelength as a function of temperature and compares these with the results obtained from a Fabry–Perot cleaved laser made from the same material. Either the zero- or the first-order transverse modes were excited in the DFB laser at somewhat different wavelengths. Selection between the modes depends on temperature according to the spectral position of the peak gain with respect to the mode resonances. Between 300 and 350 K oscillation is in the zero-order mode with a threshold current density about 20 per cent higher than that of the Fabry–Perot laser. The DFB laser operated in a single longitudinal mode. The spectrum either had sub-peaks (180 K) or was somewhat broadened (320 K) giving a total width of around 0.3 Å, probably as a result of lateral modes in the junction plane. The behaviour remained consistent up to currents of twice threshold. Even during transient operation the output was restricted to a single longitudinal mode.

The above results show that, with suitable adaptation, periodic structures can be made to the necessary standard to exploit most of the desirable properties of the distributed feedback laser. However, the problems of manufacturing such devices in any quantity are still formidable, one particular difficulty being the matching of the corrugation period to the guide wavelength of the propagating wave at an optical frequency which lies close to the centre of the gain spectrum at the desired operating temperature. This requires very accurate control of the thicknesses of the heterostructure layers as well as a good technology for grating fabrication.

8.9.2   Lasers with Bragg Reflectors

The laser with Bragg reflectors has the basic advantage over the distributed feedback laser that the reflecting regions of the passive end sections are separated from the generation region of the active layer. There is no longer the necessity of combining good electro-luminescence with the good optical properties of the corrugated section and since in principle no current need be supplied no further semiconductor need be re-grown on top of the corrugations. However, as we have described in Section 8.5.2, the optical losses over the necessary length of the Bragg reflector must be kept small in order to avoid degrading its performance. Unfortunately this condition is not very satisfactorily met by using the material of the active layer to form the grating since in the absence of a pumping current its optical losses are normally comparable with or greater than the optical gain that is available when current is supplied. Although some devices have been made in this fashion[19] good performance at room temperature has not been achieved.

Reinhart and Logan[20] have produced an ingenious structure, schematically illustrated in Figure 8.19, which overcomes these problems. The active portion of the device is basically composed of a four-layer

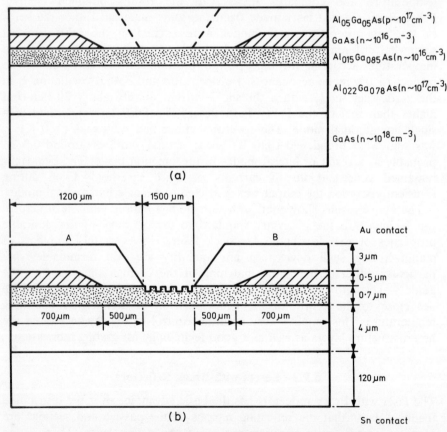

Figure 8.19 Schematic longitudinal sections of laser with distributed Bragg reflector and taper coupling. (After Reinhart *et al.*[20]) (a) Layer compositions and doping levels, (b) final device with typical dimensions

separate confinement heterostructure with a 0.7-μm thick n-type (GaAl)As layer of intermediate dielectric constant (15 per cent AlAs) lying adjacent to the 0.5-μm thick GaAs active layer. In the grating section of the device the GaAs layer is omitted and the light is mainly confined to the $Ga_{0.85}Al_{0.15}As$ layer. The corrugations are formed directly in this layer, after selective removal of the covering layer, and a single heterostructure periodic waveguide is created. A taper coupler is interposed between the two sections to smoothly transfer the light from the GaAs to the $Ga_{0.85}Al_{0.15}As$ layer without appreciable reflection or loss. The taper is introduced by appropriate masking during the LPE growth.

Broad contact lasers of this type were made and operated in the pulsed mode (100 ns) by applying current to section A only. The resonant cavity then consists of a composite section 1200-μm long terminated by the grating at one end and a cleaved face at the other. The devices lased at a satisfactory threshold current density of 5.5 kA cm^{-2}, but the incremental efficiency was rather low (<1%) with a somewhat filamentary output. The output spectrum consisted of several modes contained within the 1.5 Å bandwidth of the Bragg reflector, with polarization both parallel and perpendicular to the junction plane. Four longitudinal modes are to be expected theoretically for such a structure, two of each polarization.

A simplified version of Reinhart's structure has been developed by Namizaki et al.[21] In this modified structure the active layer taper is omitted, for ease of fabrication, and instead the active layer is terminated abruptly at the point where the corrugated section starts. To reduce the discontinuity presented to the guided wave at this point the guide in the lasing region is designed with a relatively wide intermediate passive layer (2.1 μm) so that only a small proportion of the light is confined to the active layer. These large dimensions allow several transverse modes to propagate and tend to raise the threshold current. The higher of the possible transverse modes are favoured because of their greater coupling to the grating. Thus, the TE$_3$ mode was observed in the temperature range 230–255 K and the TE$_2$ mode in the range 255–300 K, the selection being determined by the location of the centre of the gain spectrum relative to the wavelength of Bragg resonance for the mode concerned. Threshold current density at room temperature lay around 6.5 kA cm^{-2} for shallow mesa devices of 100 μm width. The incremental efficiency was the highest yet measured for a Bragg-reflecting laser at around 30 per cent from the two ends.[22]

Kawanashi et al.[23] have reported on a somewhat similar structure using an integrated twin-guide laser (double-decker guide), also with an abrupt termination for the active layer. Good performance was obtained.

The above results are very promising and indicate the general feasibility of lasers with relatively low loss Bragg reflectors. However, work still remains to be done on methods of stabilizing the lateral modes and obtaining single longitudinal-mode operation with narrow bandwidth.

8.9.3   Lasers with a Grating-Coupled Output Beam

Various experimental lasers have been constructed to demonstrate the possibility of using the periodic structure of distributed feedback and other lasers to generate output beams that emerge in the plane perpendicular to the p–n junction. This construction has the possible advantages of providing an output beam which has a very small divergence in the longitudinal plane, and of allowing a considerably greater total optical power to be radiated from the device than is possible with end-fire without incurring damaging levels of optical electric field at the emitting surface of the semiconductor. The construction has the disadvantage of interfering with the normal position of the heat sink for c.w. operation and of making it difficult to couple the light to thin optical fibres.

The radiation properties of periodic lasers have been studied both with gratings incorporated in or adjacent to the active layer and also with passive gratings either forming part of the transmission path of the resonator or constituting a terminating Bragg reflector. The first experiments with uniformly incorporated gratings were performed with single heterostructure lasers at 80 K using the fourth Bragg order.[13] Output radiation was observed at 90° to the junction plane, indicating the presence of locking by distributed feedback, with a half power beamwidth normal to the corrugations of 0.35°, mainly determined by the finite 7 Å line width. The beam was polarized with its electric field parallel to the corrugations indicating the presence of TE modes only. Room temperature studies have since been carried out on double heterostructure lasers incorporating either fourth-order gratings at the substrate interface[24] [see Figure 8.17(c)] or second-order gratings at the top surface[25], in both cases with thin passive layers adjacent to the grating to allow interaction between the grating and the evanescent tail of the optical distribution. Also, a twin-guide heterostructure has been investigated [see Figure 8.17(e)], where a 0.5-μm thick $Ga_{0.7}Al_{0.3}As$ layer separates a corrugated GaAs layer from the GaAs active layer.[26] All these devices were found to operate at reasonable values of threshold current density (2–4 kA cm^{-2}) and their beam divergence in the plane perpendicular to the corrugations was around 0.65° to the half power points. In most cases the angle of emission indicated that the Bragg condition was not satisfied although in one case[24] adjustment of temperature brough about Bragg locking, in which case emission was normal to the device.

Alferov et al.[27] have investigated a device where a window was etched down to the active layer of a double heterostructure, on which a 0.22-μm period grating was then formed. This device emitted beams at $\pm 20°$ to the normal with a beam divergence perpendicular to the grating of 0.5°. The threshold current density was reported to be little increased by the presence of the window and it was suggested that the narrowing of the width of the forbidden gap by injected carriers in the undoped active layer resulted in sufficient lengthening of the laser wavelength for the light to be little absorbed by the unpumped grating region. Reinhart *et al.*[20] investigated the radiation from the third-order grating in their distributed Bragg-reflector laser (see Figure 8.19) extracting the light which would normally be totally internally reflected using a glass prism and oil immersion. The divergence at the half power points was $0.3° \times 6°$.

These results indicate that the radiation pattern of grating-coupled lasers can be controlled and that output beams which are highly parallel in one dimension can be created. However, at present the efficiency of emission is poor and the output power is divided between both the upward and downward directions. Further work is required on optimization of the grating profile before the devices will have much practical application.

REFERENCES

1. A. P. Bogatov, P. G. Eliseev, L. P. Ivanov, A. S. Logginov, M. A. Manko, and K. Ya. Senatorov, 'Study of the single-mode injection laser', *IEEE J. Quantum Electron.*, **JQE-9**, 1973, 392.
2. J. A. Rossi, S. R. Chinn, and H. Heckscher, 'High-power narrow-linewidth operation of GaAs diode lasers', *Appl. Phys. Lett.*, **23**, 1973, 25.
3. Y. Suematsu, M. Yamoda, and K. Hayashi, 'A multi-hetero AlGaAs laser with integrated twin guide', *Proc. IEEE*, **63**, 1975, 208.
4. Y. Suematsu, K. Hishino, and T. Kambayashi, 'Axial-mode selectivities for various types of integrated twin-guide laser', *IEEE J. Quantum Electron.*, **QE-13**, 1977, 619.
5. H. Kogelnik and C. V. Shank, 'Stimulated emission in a periodic structure', *Appl. Phys. Lett.*, **18**, 1971, 152.
6. A. Yariv, 'Coupled-mode theory for guided-wave optics', *IEEE J. Quantum Electron.*, **QE-9**, 1973, 919.
7. H. Kogelnik and C. V. Shank, 'Coupled-wave theory of distributed feedback lasers', *J. Appl. Phys.*, **43**, 1972, 2327.
8. S. Wang, 'Principles of distributed feedback and distributed Bragg-reflector lasers', *IEEE J. Quantum Electron.*, **QE-10**, 1973, 413.
9. W. Streifer, D. R. Scifres, and R. D. Burnham, 'Coupled wave analysis of DFB and DBR lasers', *IEEE J. Quantum Electron.*, **QE-13**, 1977, 134.
10. S. Wang, 'Design considerations for the DBR injection laser and the waveguiding structure for integrated optics', *IEEE J. Quantum Electron.*, **QE-13**, 1977, 176.
11. W. Streifer, D. R. Scifres, and R. D. Burnham, 'Analysis of grating-coupled radiation in GaAs:GaAlAs lasers and waveguides', *IEEE J. Quantum Electron.*, **QE-12**, 1976, 422.
12. W. Streifer, R. D. Burnham, and D. R. Scifres, 'Analysis of grating-coupled

radiation in GaAs:GaAlAs lasers and waveguides — II Blazing effects', *IEEE J. Quantum Electron.*, **QE-12**, 1976, 494.

13. D. R. Scifres, R. D. Burnham, and W. Streifer, 'Distributed feedback single heterojunction diode laser', *Appl. Phys. Lett.*, **25**, 1974, 203.

14. R. D. Burnham, D. R. Scifres, and W. Streifer, 'Single heterostructure distributed feedback diode lasers', *IEEE J. Quantum Electron.*, **QE-11**, 1975, 439.

15. M. Nakamura, K. Aiki, J. Umeda, A. Yariv, H. W. Yen, and T. Morikawa, 'GaAs–Ga$_{1-x}$Al$_x$As double heterostructure distributed feedback diode lasers', *Appl. Phys. Lett.*, **25**, 1974, 487.

16. H. C. Casey, Jr, S. Somekh, and M. Ilegems, 'Room temperature operation of low-threshold separate-confinement heterostructure injection laser with distributed feedback', *Appl. Phys. Lett.*, **27**, 1975, 142.

17. K. Aiki, M. Nakamura, J. Umeda, A. Yariv, A. Katzin, and H. W. Yen, 'GaAs–GaAlAs distributed feedback diode lasers with separate optical and carrier confinement', *Appl. Phys. Lett.*, **27**, 1975, 145.

18. M. Nakamura, K. Aiki, J. Umeda, and A. Yariv, 'CW operation of distributed feedback GaAs–GaAlAs diode lasers at temperatures up to 300 K', *Appl. Phys. Lett.*, **27**, 1975, 403.

19. W. Tsang and S. Wang, 'GaAs–Ga$_{1-x}$Al$_x$As double heterostructure injection lasers with distributed Bragg reflectors', *Appl. Phys. Lett.*, **28**, 1976, 596.

20. F. K. Reinhart, R. A. Logan, and C. V. Shank, 'GaAs–Al$_x$Ga$_{1-x}$As injection lasers with distributed Bragg reflectors', *Appl. Phys. Lett.*, **27**, 1975, 45.

21. H. Namizaki, M. K. Shams, and Shyh Wang, 'Large-optical cavity GaAs–(GaAl)As injection laser with low-loss distributed Bragg reflectors', *Appl. Phys. Lett.*, **31**, 1977, 122.

22. M. Shams and Shyh Wang, 'GaAs–(GaAl)As LOC-DBR laser with high differential quantum efficiency', *Appl. Phys. Lett.*, **33**, 1978, 170.

23. H. Kawanishi, Y. Suematsu, and K. Kishino, 'GaAs–GaAlAs integrated twin-guide laser with distributed Bragg reflectors', *IEEE J. Quantum Electron.*, **QE-13**, 1977, 64.

24. D. R. Scifres, R. D. Burnham, and W. Streifer, 'Output coupling and distributed feedback utilizing substrate corrugation in double heterostructure GaAs lasers', *Appl. Phys. Lett.*, **27**, 1975, 295.

25. P. Zory, 'Grating coupled double heterostructure AlGaAs diode lasers', *IEEE J. Quantum Electron.*, **QE-11**, 1975, 451.

26. R. D. Burnham, D. R. Scifres, and W. Streifer, 'Low divergence beams from grating-coupled composite guide heterostructure GaAlAs diode lasers', *Appl. Phys. Lett.*, **26**, 1975, 644.

27. Zh. I. Alferov, V. M. Andreyev, S. A. Gurevich, R. F. Kazarinov, V. R. Larionov, M. N. Mizerov, and E. L. Portnoi, 'Semiconductor lasers with the light output through the diffraction grating on the surface of the waveguide layer', *IEEE J. Quantum Electron.*, **QE-11**, 1975, 449.

APPENDIX 1

Thermal Dissipation of Laser Structures

Even in double heterostructure stripe lasers the heat generation per unit area at threshold is sufficient for it to be necessary to pay careful attention to heat sinking to obtain c.w. operation. The most important source of heat is that generated by non-radiative recombination within the thickness of the active layer. Laser dice are normally bonded on the p-side to bring the heat sink as close as possible to the active layer. To reach the bulk of the heat sink the heat has to flow through a thin passive layer of the heterostructure, a thin semiconductor contacting layer, a layer of metal associated with the bonding, and a portion of the heat sink material itself (see Figure 1.1 Chapter 1). In (GaAl)As/GaAs devices, for instance, the (GaAl)As passive layer has the lowest thermal conductivity of all the materials involved (about 0.13 W cm^{-1} deg^{-1} compared with 0.5 W cm^{-1} deg^{-1} for GaAs) and provides about half of the total thermal resistance between the active layer and the heat sink when the heat sink is made of Cu. The top GaAs layer and the bonding metal, normally In, provide most of the remainder. A typical theoretical value for the total thermal resistance for a stripe of, say 13 × 400 μm, is 30°C W^{-1}

Two additional sources of heat generation are present in the stripe laser. The first is the Joule heat generated across the resistance of the contacts. In most lasers this accounts for less than 20 per cent of the heat generated. The thermal resistance for this source is lower than that quoted above for the active layer because the heat is mainly generated at the p-contact which lies close to the heat sink. The second additional source of heat generation arises because the injected carriers in the active layer lose their recombination energy not only by non-radiative processes but also by spontaneous emission of photons. The spontaneous photons generate heat when they are re-absorbed, which takes place either in the substrate or the contact layers, if they are absorbing as in (GaAl)As/GaAs lasers, or in the unpumped parts of the active layer, as in (InGa)(AsP) lasers. In either case the energy is spread over a greater volume than that from which it originated and the thermal resistance is again lower than that for the heat generated directly in the active layer.

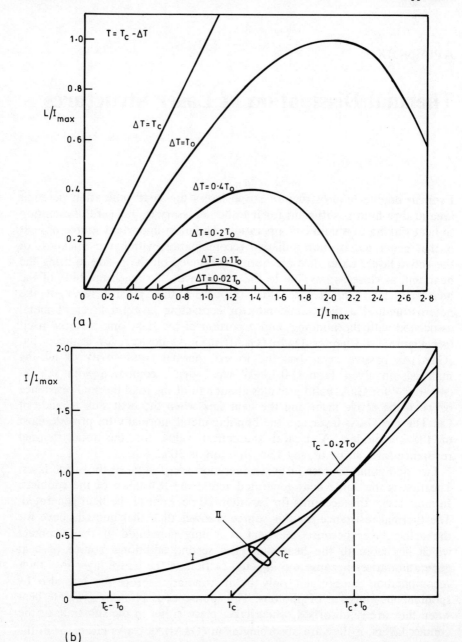

Figure A1.1. Effect of thermal dissipation on c.w. light output of laser. (a) Normalized light/current characteristics of laser over a range of values for the amount ΔT by which the heat sink temperature lies below the critical value T_c. Threshold current taken as varying with temperature according to exp

As a result of these additional processes, and possibly because of approximations in the theoretical analysis, measured figures for thermal resistance for (GaAl)As/GaAs devices tend to lie somewhat lower than 30°C W^{-1} as mentioned above, approaching 20°C W^{-1} in some cases.

The threshold current density of a semiconductor laser increases with temperature as is described in Chapter 5, Sections 5.1.1 and 5.2.2. The thermal dissipation in the active layer at threshold therefore also rises with temperature and the temperature difference between the active layer and the heat sink becomes correspondingly greater. At high enough heat sink temperature a run-away process is initiated whereby the temperature rise caused by turning the current up raises the threshold current by more than the increase in the current supplied, and c.w. threshold becomes unattainable, however much the current is increased.

The condition at the limiting temperature for laser operation is illustrated by the theoretical curves in Figure A1.1. Although somewhat idealized these curves give a good indication of the behaviour of the light/current characteristic close to the maximum operating temperature and show the reason for this behaviour. A series of light/current characteristics for several different heat sink temperatures close to the maximum operating temperature are shown in Figure A1.1(a). For each of these characteristics there is a certain value of current I_{max} beyond which the light output starts to diminish. As the temperature is increased so the threshold current I_{th} rises and the current I_{max} for maximum output diminishes until the two merge at the maximum temperature for laser operation.

The reason for the optical saturation is illustrated by the threshold and heating curves of Figure A1.1(b). Curve I in this figure is a typical plot of threshold current I_{th} against active layer temperature (normalized for convenience to the current I_{max} at which the laser finally ceases to operate with increasing temperature). The pair of curves labelled II are plots of laser current versus the temperature in the active region created by the current, for two different values of the heat sink temperature. The graphs show a linear relation between current and temperature as applies if the laser voltage does not increase with current but the relation may also be quadratic if resistive heating is appreciable. Lasing occurs for each value of heat sink temperature over the range where the current I for the appropriate curve of type II is greater than the threshold current I_{th} on

---

(T/T_o). (b) Current/temperature plot for obtaining the maximum c.w. operating current I_{max} of the laser and the maximum heat sink temperature T_c. Curve I gives the threshold current as a function of junction temperature. The pair of curves II gives the junction temperature due to heating as a function of the current for two different heat sink temperatures. Lasing occurs where curve I lies below the appropriate curve II

curve I at the temperature concerned. The intensity of the lasing emission is then proportional to $I - I_{th}$. At the critical heat sink temperature T_c above which lasing is impossible the heating curve just touches the threshold curve so that $I - I_{th}$ never becomes positive, and no lasing emission is produced at any current.

By using a suitable approximate relation for the threshold current versus temperature characteristic we can calculate the limiting temperature T_c for any particular temperature/current characteristic. As an example we use the frequently found empirical relationship for threshold current I_{th}

$$I_{th} = I_0 \exp\left(\frac{T}{T_0}\right) \tag{A1.1}$$

where T_0 is an adjustable parameter to fit the measured results, and we take the case where the contact heating can be ignored so that the temperature T of the active layer is given by

$$T = T_s + RVI \tag{A1.2}$$

where R is the thermal impedance, eV is the band gap energy, and T_s is the heat sink temperature.

Choosing T_s so that the curve for the rise in temperature touches the threshold curve in Figure A1.1(b) gives the following relation for the critical threshold current I_{max} at which c.w. lasing ceases

$$I_{max} = \frac{T_0}{RV} \tag{A1.3}$$

at which point the active layer temperature is greater than that of the heat sink by the amount T_0. The maximum heat sink temperature T_c at which c.w. lasing is possible can be expressed in terms of the pulsed threshold versus temperature characteristic and corresponds to the value where the pulsed threshold is equal to I_{max}/e (e here represents the base of the common logarithm). In practice the above relationships are found to give incorrect results if one inserts the value of the thermal impedance R measured at temperatures well below the critical temperature. A larger value of R must be used instead. The reason is not fully understood but it is possible that R changes with temperature as a result of a change in the way the input energy is divided between radiative and non-radiative processes.

To find the value of the thermal resistance in any particular laser and investigate its temperature dependence an appropriate means must be employed for estimating the temperature rise of the active layer. Some investigators have successfully used a thermal probe applied directly to the laser cross section.[1] A more convenient method, however, is to make use of some temperature dependent property of the active layer that can be calibrated. Lasing and light-emitting properties can themselves be used provided they are calibrated in low-duty-cycle pulsed operation where the temperature can be taken as uniform. Two suitable characteristics are (a) the intensity of the lasing emission at a fixed current and (b) the optical wavelength of a given Fabry–Perot mode of the laser cavity at a fixed current,[2] preferably below lasing threshold. (The Fabry–Perot resonant wavelength depends on the effective refractive index of the heterostructure waveguide which in turn depends on temperature. It also depends on the injected carrier concentration. The latter is possibly more sensitive to small changes associated with temperature gradients, etc. under lasing compared with non-lasing conditions, and hence greater accuracy can be obtained in the null reading when the laser is below threshold.) Calibration of the temperature dependence in both cases is best achieved by the following null method. The laser is first operated c.w. with a certain heat sink temperature and the property concerned is measured. The laser is then operated pulsed with low duty cycle and the heat sink temperature is adjusted until the same value of the particular property is obtained, when time resolved to a point not long after the beginning of the pulse. The amount the heat sink temperature has to be raised gives the rise in temperature of the active layer in c.w. operation. Care has to be taken, however, to ensure that the temperature gradients set up in c.w. operation do not interfere with the property concerned. Failure to be certain about this may account for the difficulty in obtaining precise agreement between the two different methods.

REFERENCE

1. T. Kobayashi and Y. Furukawa, 'Temperature distributions in the GaAs–AlGaAs double-heterostructure laser below and above threshold', *Jap. J. Appl. Phys.*, **14**, 1975, 1981.
2. T. L. Paoli, 'A new technique for measuring the thermal impedance of junction lasers', *IEEE J. Quantum Electron.*, **QE-11**, 1975, 498.

APPENDIX 2

Approximate Analysis of Two-dimensional Waveguide in Stripe Lasers

We wish to solve the differential waveguide equations [(4.48) in Chapter 4, Section 4.2.2] for the E mode in a slab waveguide in which there is a small variation of the dielectric constant ϵ across the plane of the structure (the x direction) in the centre layer. This variation is therefore added to the abrupt variations of dielectric constant in the dielectric slab guide in the y direction, perpendicular to the plane of the structure. Under such conditions we may simplify equation (4.48) by neglecting the term in grad ϵ, an approximation that is justified provided the variation of ϵ in the x direction is sufficiently small.

We try a solution for H_y of the form

$$H_y = A(x)B(x,y) \exp(\pm j\beta_z z) \tag{A2.1}$$

The predominant x variation occurs in the term A, which is taken to be independent of y. The term B describes the y variation. For generality it must also depend on x, but this dependence will be very weak in the cases with which we shall deal. The z variation is taken as that of a propagating wave with wave-vector β_z. Equation (4.48) then becomes

$$\frac{\partial^2 A}{A \partial x^2} + \frac{2}{AB}\frac{\partial A}{\partial x}\frac{\partial B}{\partial x} + \frac{\partial^2 B}{B \partial x^2} + \frac{\partial^2 B}{B \partial y^2} - \beta_z^2 + \beta_0^2 \epsilon(x, y) = 0 \tag{A2.2}$$

We ignore the terms containing $\partial B/\partial x$ and $\partial^2 B/\partial x^2$ on the basis that the x variation of B is small. Because $\partial^2 A/A \partial x^2$ does not depend on y we set it equal to a quantity $k(x)$ which we will expect to depend only weakly on x. Equation (A2.2) can then be written to give the y variation of B in the form

$$\frac{\partial^2 B}{B \partial y^2} + \beta_0^2 \epsilon(x, y) = \beta_z^2 - k(x) \tag{A2.3}$$

Equation (A2.3) can be solved in the normal way for a slab waveguide for

528

any value x and the eigen value of the left hand side found, which we will denote by $\beta_0^2 \epsilon_{\text{eff}}(x)$, giving

$$k(x) = \beta_z^2 - \beta_0^2 \epsilon_{\text{eff}}(x) \tag{A2.4}$$

We may then write the following differential equation for the x variation of A

$$\frac{\partial^2 A}{A \, \partial x^2} - \beta_z^2 + \beta_0^2 \epsilon_{\text{eff}}(x) = 0 \tag{A2.5}$$

This equation provides an approximate solution to the x variation of H_y. It has the same form as equation (4.49) which described the condition where the fields do not change with y (infinitely thick slab), except that $\epsilon_{\text{eff}}(x)$ is substituted for $\epsilon(x)$.

Let us find how small variations in the dielectric constant ϵ_1 of the centre layer of a symmetrical double heterostructure affect the value of the effective dielectric constant ϵ_{eff}. According to equation (4.18) in Chapter 4, Section 4.12, ϵ_{eff} is given by

$$\epsilon_{\text{eff}} = \epsilon_2 + P^2 \delta \epsilon \tag{A2.6}$$

Differentiating this expression with respect to ϵ_1 (equivalent to differentiating with respect to $\delta \epsilon$) and remembering that P also depends on ϵ_1 gives

$$d\epsilon_{\text{eff}} = \left(P^2 + 2\delta \epsilon P \frac{dP}{d\epsilon_1} \right) d\epsilon_1 \tag{A2.7}$$

It is convenient to evaluate $dP/d\epsilon_1$ in the form $(dP/dD)(dD/d\epsilon_1)$. Inserting the value of $dD/d\epsilon_1$ obtained by differentiating equation (4.14) gives

$$\frac{dP}{d\epsilon_1} = \left(\frac{D}{2\delta \epsilon} \right) \left(\frac{dP}{dD} \right) \tag{A2.8}$$

so that (A2.7) becomes

$$d\epsilon_{\text{eff}} = \left(P^2 + PD \frac{dP}{dD} \right) d\epsilon_1 \tag{A2.9}$$

According to the relation between P and Q in equation (4.15) this may alternatively be written

$$d\epsilon_{\text{eff}} = \left(P^2 - QD \frac{dQ}{dD} \right) d\epsilon_1 \tag{A2.10}$$

In order to find dQ/dD we use the characteristic equation (4.16), which for a symmetrical heterostructure becomes

$$\cos \frac{QD}{2} = Q \tag{A2.11}$$

Differentiating and using sin $QD/2 = P$ gives

$$\frac{dQ}{dD} = \frac{-PQ}{(PD + 2)} \tag{A2.12}$$

Inserting (A2.12) into (A2.10) gives

$$d\epsilon_{eff} = \left[\frac{2P + D}{2/P + D}\right] d\epsilon_1$$

$$= \Gamma\, d\epsilon_1 \tag{A2.13}$$

where Γ is the confinement or loading factor for gain defined in equation (4.23) and evaluated in equation (4.28). This shows that the loading factor for small changes in the real part of the dielectric constant of the centre layer is identical to the loading factor for gain. Such a result is to be expected since gain also represents a small perturbation on the dielectric constant although with an imaginary rather than a real value.

Guiding of optical modes in parabolic guides with spatial offset between real and imaginary profiles of the dielectric constant

A.3.1 GENERAL DESCRIPTION

We present here a description of the properties of an optical waveguide with a parabolic variation of the dielectric constant but in which the contributions of the real and imaginary components, the latter referring to gain, are offset in a lateral direction with respect to one another. The detailed analysis is given in Section A3.2 of this Appendix. Mathematically the shift of the two distributions is equivalent to a pair of coincident distributions with a linear gradient added to one of them, say the real component. This additional linear variation can be neatly incorporated into the standard Hermite Gaussian formulation of Maxwell's equations for parabolic complex profiles of the dielectric constant by shifting the origin of the position coordinate by a complex quantity. The analysis otherwise follows that for the simple quadratic distribution presented in Chapter 4, Section 4.2.3.

The results of the analysis show that in general the offset twin parabolic structure provides a satisfactory waveguide. The guided mode still has a Gaussian (or Hermite–Gaussian) transverse distribution of intensity but in general not centred on either the real or the imaginary distributions of dielectric constant, [see equation (A3.3) in Section A3.2 of this Appendix], and the wavefront is tilted so that it no longer lies at right angles to the axis along the centre line of the waveguide. The position which the mid-point of the guided mode occupies with respect to the mid-points of the real and imaginary profiles of the dielectric constant is very important in determining the overall behaviour when the light and carriers interact in the self-focusing process. According to Section A3.2 of this Appendix, equations (A3.8) and (A3.9), certain simple rules apply for finding the sense of displacement of the filament with respect to the real part of the waveguide, which are given below.

A3.1.1 Location of Filament

A peak in the dielectric constant distribution and both a peak and trough in the gain distribution exert guiding effects which tend to centralize the optical mode on the distributions concerned. The trough in the gain creates its guiding action by advancing the phase of the wave at the edges compared with that at the centre, hence creating a convergent beam. In contrast a trough in the dielectric constant creates an anti-guide with a divergent beam. When guiding profiles due to both gain and dielectric constant are simultaneously present and separated in position then the mid-point of the optical mode lies somewhere between the mid-points of the two respective profiles, in general being more influenced by the real dielectric profile than the gain profile. When a gain-guiding profile of either type is combined with a dielectric anti-guiding profile then the mode is repelled to the side of the gain-guiding profile opposite to that of the mid-point of the anti-guiding profile.

Two special cases occur where one or other of the profiles loses its curvature and becomes a sloping straight line. If the gain has a linear slope then the optical mode is located at the mid-point of the dielectric profile, provided that it is a guiding profile. If the dielectric profile is anti-guiding then the combination is also anti-guiding. If the dielectric constant has a linear slope then the optical filament is displaced to the side of the gain-guide where the dielectric constant is higher. (This latter rule is general even when the dielectric profile is curved.)

A3.1.2 Tilt of Wavefront

Different rules are required to determine the direction of tilt of the wavefront. The analysis shows that in all cases the normal to the wavefront is deflected from the axis to the side of the optical distribution where the gain is lower [see equation (A3.4) and (A3.5)]. Using this rule in combination with the previous rules it is useful to compare the direction in which the wavefront is tilted with the direction in which the optical intensity profile is offset with respect to the mid-point of the gain distribution. The combined rules show that if the gain distribution has the normal shape with a peak at the centre then the wavefront is tilted in the same direction as the offset of the optical intensity distribution from the mid-point of the gain distribution, whereas if the gain distribution has the inverted shape with a minimum at the centre then the wavefront is tilted in the opposite direction to the offset of the intensity distribution.

A.3.2   MATHEMATICAL FORMULATION OF ANALYSIS

We wish to obtain the transverse optical distribution in a waveguide where the real and imaginary parts of the dielectric constant both vary in a parabolic way over the lateral direction but where the stationary values of the two parts are not coincident in position.

According to equations (4.51) and (4.52) in Chapter 4, Section 4.2.2, on guiding by complex parabolic profile of the dielectric constant, a Gaussian solution of the optical distribution can be obtained if the lateral x variation of effective dielectric constant $\epsilon_{\text{eff}}(x)$ can be written in the form

$$\beta_0^2 \epsilon_{\text{eff}}(x) - \beta_z^2 = a - a^2 x^2 \tag{A3.1}$$

where $a = a_1 + ja_2$. The distribution of the optical field A is then given by

$$A = A_0 \exp\left(\frac{-ax^2}{2}\right) \tag{A3.2}$$

We may shift the origin of x by adding a constant complex quantity, without changing the form of the original differential equation or affecting the solutions. If we substitute say, $x - jX/(a_1 + ja_2)$ for x then we do not shift the peak of the optical distribution in equation (A3.2), although we introduce an overall tilt to the original cylindrical wavefront. The field distribution is then given by

$$A = A_0 \exp\left\{\frac{-(a_1 + ja_2)x^2}{2} + jXx\right\} \tag{A3.3}$$

The term jXx in the exponent causes an angular tilt θ to be superimposed on the Gaussian beam emitted by the laser, given by

$$\sin\theta = \frac{\lambda X}{2\pi} \tag{A3.4}$$

With the above substitution equation (A3.1) becomes

$$\beta_0^2 \epsilon_{\text{eff}}(x) - \beta_z^2 = X^2 + a_1 + ja_2 - \{(a_1^2 - a_2^2 + 2ja_1a_2)x^2 + 2(a_2 - ja_1)Xx\} \tag{A3.5}$$

This expression represents a pair of parabolic distributions of the real and imaginary components of $\epsilon_{\text{eff}}(x)$ which, as we require, have stationary values at non-coincident values of x. For instance let x_g and x_m be the positions of the stationary values of the imaginary and the real components of the dielectric constant respectively. Then according to equation (A3.5)

$$x_g = \frac{X}{2a_2} \tag{A3.6}$$

and

$$x_\mu = \frac{-Xa_2}{a_1^2 - a_2^2} \tag{A3.7}$$

$$= \frac{-2x_g}{a_1^2/a_2^2 - 1}$$

Expression (A3.5) may be used to match any arbitrary pair of non-coincident parabolic distributions of real and imaginary dielectric constant by selecting appropriate values of a_1, a_2 and X, together with an appropriate origin for x. The transverse distribution of field in the guided wave, which constitutes the solution to the wave equation, can then be obtained by inserting these values into equation (A3.3).

APPENDIX 4

Effect of injected carriers on dielectric constant of semiconductor

The perturbation produced by injected carriers on the dielectric constant of the semiconductor has been invoked in Chapter 4, Section 4.2 as an additional factor to the gain in determining the lateral spread of light in stripe lasers, and in Chapter 6, Sections 6.4 and 6.6, also in conjunction with the gain, it has been invoked as the factor in determining self-focusing and filament shift. In this Appendix we make quantitative estimation of the magnitude of the perturbation.

Direct interaction between the optical field of the electromagnetic wave and the free carriers produces a reduction in the dielectric constant by the plasma effect. The change $\delta\epsilon$ is given in terms of the concentration n of the carriers, their effective mass m_{eff}, and the angular frequency ω of the wave by

$$\delta\epsilon = \frac{-ne^2\epsilon_0}{m_{\text{eff}}\omega^2} \tag{A4.1}$$

where e is the electronic charge and ϵ_0 is the permittivity of free space. For GaAs the sum of the effect of the injection of equal concentrations of electrons and holes gives a constant of proportionality between $\delta\epsilon$ and n of -1.23×10^{-20} cm^3 at a wavelength of 0.88 μm. Hence the reduction in dielectric constant at the carrier concentration appropriate to room temperature threshold in GaAs is of the order of -0.02. This varies in other III–V materials mainly as a result of the change in wavelength and, for instance, in (InGa)(AsP) at 1.3 μm is of the order of -0.03.

The injected carriers also perturb the dielectric constant as a result of the change they produce in the spectral distribution of the absorption coefficient including, of course, the region where the absorption is converted to gain. The fundamental relationship derived by Kramers and Kroenig[1] demonstrates that any electrical interaction in a material which gives rise to a uniform gain or loss in a propagating wave must necessarily

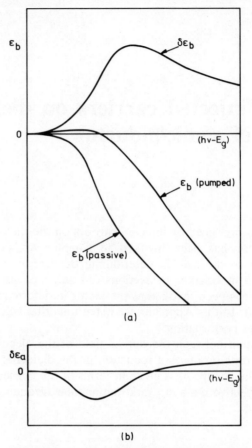

Figure A4.1 Relation between the real and imaginary parts of the dielectric constant spectra (schematic). (a) Spectrum of the imaginary part ϵ_b of the dielectric constant of a semiconductor in pumped and unpumped conditions and spectrum of the difference $\delta\epsilon_b$. (b) Spectrum of the change $\delta\epsilon_a$ in the real part of the dielectric constant derived by the Kramers–Kroenig relations from the spectrum of $\delta\epsilon_b$

affect the dielectric constant of the material. The gain or loss may be represented by an imaginary contribution to the dielectric constant (see Chapter 4, Section 4.2.1). The real part of the dielectric constant $\epsilon_a(\omega)$ at some particular angular frequency ω may then be related to the integral over the whole spectrum of an expression containing the imaginary part

$\epsilon_b(\omega)$ as follows

$$\epsilon_a(\omega) - 1 = \frac{2}{\pi} \int_0^\infty \frac{x\,\epsilon_b(x)\,dx}{(x^2 - \omega^2)} \tag{A4.2}$$

If there is a change $\delta\epsilon_b(x)$ in ϵ_b over a limited part of the spectrum caused by the injection of carriers then the change $\delta\epsilon_a(\omega)$ in $\delta\epsilon_a$ at frequency ω is given approximately by

$$\delta\epsilon_a(\omega) \simeq -\frac{1}{\pi} \int_{\omega - x_0}^{\omega + x_0} \frac{\{\delta\epsilon_b(x) - \delta\epsilon_b(\omega)\}\,dx}{x - \omega} \tag{A4.3}$$

where the limits to the integration are taken equidistantly on the positive and negative sides of $x = \omega$, sufficiently apart such that $\delta\epsilon_b(x)$ is approximately zero at both ends.

Figure A4.1(a) gives a schematic illustration of the spectrum of the imaginary part ϵ_b of the dielectric constant in the pumped and unpumped condition and the resulting spectrum of $\delta\epsilon_b$. Figure A4.1(b) shows the spectrum of the change in the real part $\delta\epsilon_a$ of the dielectric constant derived according to equation (A4.3) from the spectrum of $\delta\epsilon_b$. $\delta\epsilon_a$ has its largest negative value close to the point where the gradient of $\delta\epsilon_b$ is a maximum and its magnitude is of the order of $\delta\epsilon_b/\pi$. The magnitude of $\delta\epsilon_a$ throughout the spectrum is independent of the photon energy at which the gain is centered. Hence the gain related perturbation of the dielectric constant, in contrast to the plasma interaction, is not affected by wavelength. In GaAs the coefficient relating the dielectric constant change, due to gain effects at the centre of the gain spectrum, to the injected carrier concentration for low doped material is of the order of -3×10^{-20} cm^3, about twice that associated with the plasma interaction.[2,3]

REFERENCES

1. L. D. Landau and E. M. Lifshitz, *Electrodynamics of Continuous Media*, Pergamon Press, 1960, p. 256 *et seq*.
2. G. H. B. Thompson, 'A theory for filamentation in semiconductor lasers including the dependence of dielectric constant on injected carrier density', *Opto-electronics*, **4**, 1972, 257.
3. P. R. Selway, G. H. B. Thompson, G. D. Henshall, and J. E. A. Whiteaway, 'Measurement of the effect of injected carriers on the p–n refractive index step in single heterostructure diode lasers', *Electron. Lett.*, **10**, 1974, 453.

Index